TELE · TUNES

COMPILED BY

MIKE PRESTON

TELEVISION FILM & SHOW MUSIC

ON CD, CASSETTE & VINYL

WITHDRAWN

PRESTON MUSIC 1994

T E L E - T U N E S   1 9 9 4

Television Film and Show Music on
Compact Disc, Cassette and Vinyl

12th Edition Completely Revised

Compiled & Edited by Mike Preston
Assisted by Pru and Robb Preston

Published in Great Britain 1994

Copyright © Mike Preston 1994

ISBN 0 906655 11 0

Published in England 1994 by
Mike Preston Music
The Glengarry
Thornton Grove
Morecambe
Lancashire
LA4 5PU
England

Orig Copyright Regs. Stationers Hall
London England 1979, 1986 and 1994
Registration Number B8 / 744 / 32640

Printed and Bound in England by
Airey and Stephenson Limited
Penrith, Cumbria CA11 7AJ

Tele-Tunes 1994 © Mike Preston Music 1

TELE-TUNES: Updated Quarterly Supplements
Published in April July and October under
ISSN 0266-6944 Subscription Details p.249

TELE-TUNES 1994 : The Reference Book Of Television Film And Show Music On Compact Disc, Cassette and Vinyl

WELCOME TO THE LATEST EDITION OF TELE-TUNES 1994. FOR NEW READERS HERE IS A BRIEF EXPLANATION OF THE TEXT.

TELEVISION COMMERCIALS:

An Alphabetical Listing By Product Name Of Television Commercials. Title Of Music Followed By The Composer The Artist The Record Label And Distributor And Finally The Catalogue Number And Format.
NOTE: The Artist Is Not Always The Performer On The Actual Advert (Information Given If Known). TV Commercials With Specially Commissioned Music Are Generally Marked 'not available' And Listed For Reference Only.

TELEVISION PROGRAMME INDEX:

An Alphabetical Listing Of Television Programmes With Details Of Theme Music Generally Used Over The Credits Title Of Programme Followed By The Production Channel The Original Transmission Date (If Known), Theme Music Title And Composer Followed By Artist, Record Label, Catalogue Number And Format. *NOTE: Entries Marked* **NA** *= NOT AVAILABLE i.e. Music Specially Commissioned For The Series And Currently Unavailable. Listed For Reference.*

FILMS AND SHOWS:

An Alphabetical Listing Of Motion Picture Soundtracks And Musical Stage Shows (Broadway-London) The Title Is Followed By The Year Of Release, The Composer (Film) Orig Cast Details (Show), Label, Distributor & Format *NOTE: Any Deleted Items Are Listed For Reference Only.*

COLLECTIONS:

An Alphabetical Listing Of Television And Film Collections.Title And Artist Followed By Record Label Catalogue Number Format,Year Of Issue And Complete Track Listing.

AWARDS:

1992-1993 Awards For The Film And Television Industry: BAFTA / BRITISH COMEDY AWARDS / EVENING STANDARD FILM AND DRAMA / IVOR NOVELLO / LAURENCE OLIVIER / OSCARS 93 SONG FOR EUROPE / EUROVISION SONG CONTEST /VARIETY CLUB

ABBEY NATIONAL (1)"Happy Endings Give Yourself A Pinch"
    (L.Bart) LIONEL BART *EMI:(CD)(TC)(12)EMI121 deleted*
ABBEY NATIONAL (2) "Be Young Be Foolish Be Happy" (A.J.
    Gibber-R.Whiteley-J.Cobb) SONIA: *IQ (BMG): ZD 44936*
    (CDs) ZT 44936 (12"s) ZB 44935 (7") ZK 44935 (Cass)
    TAMS: *Old Gold (Pinn): OG 9219 (7s)*
ABBEY NATIONAL (3) "Wide Awake" (John Altman) p.Jeff Wa
    yne Music *(not available)*
ACCESS (1)"Is You Is Or Is You Ain't My Baby" (L.Jordan
    B.Austin) film 'Follow The Boys' (44)- LOUIS JORDAN
    'Five Guys Named Moe' *MCA (BMG): MCLD(MCLC) 19048*
ACCESS (2) based on "Teacher's Pet" (Joe Lubin) origina
    lly from 1958 film 'Teacher's Pet' with DORIS DAY
    on 'Best Of' *Columbia: CD31825 (CD) 40-31825 (Cass)*
ACCURIST WATCHES "Give Me Just A Little More Time" (Ron
    Dunbar-Edith Wayne) TV ver: KYLIE MINOGUE on 'Let's
    Get To It' *PWL (WEA): HF(C)(CD) 21 (LP/Cas/CD)* also
    PWL(T) 212 (7"/12"s) PWMC 212 (Cass) PWCD 212 (CDs)
    orig CHAIRMAN OF THE BOARD *HDH (Pin):HDH(CD)(LP)001*
ADT (Sponsor for 91 London Marathon) "Keep On Running"
    (Jackie Edwards) SPENCER DAVIS GROUP on 'The Island
    Story' *Island (Poly): ISL(C) 25 (LP/CS) CID 25 (CD)*
AEG "Morning" from 'Peer Gynt Suite No.1 op.46' (Grieg)
    Ulster Orchestra (Vernon Handley) *Chandos (Chandos)*
    CHAN 8524 (CD) ABTD 1234 (Cass)
AER LINGUS "Andante" - 'Piano Concerto No.21' (Mozart)
    see under FILMS title 'Elvira Madigan'
AERO (92) "The Umbrella Man" ('Any Umbrellas') from
    'Underneath The Arches'(V.Rose-L.Stock-J.Cavanaugh)
    TER (Conifer): ZCTER 1015 (Cass) TER 1015 (LP)
AIR CANADA "Breath Of Fresh Air" (Gary Bell) p.Jeff Way
    ne Music *not available*
AIRTOURS "Let's Work Together" (Wilbert Harrison) by
    CANNED HEAT 'Best Of Canned Heat' *Liberty (EMI):*
    CZ 226 (CD) TCGO 2026 (Cass) GO 2026 (LP)
AKAI PRODUCTS "China" (Vangelis) from 'China' Vangelis
    Polydor: 813 653-2 (CD) SPELP 19 (LP) SPEMC 19 (CS)
ALBERTO PURE & CLEAR "Polegnala E Todata" (p.Momentum)
    BULGARIAN VOICES on 'Les Mystere Des Voix' Vol.1 on
    4AD (Pinn):CAD 603CD(CD) CADC 603(Cass) CAD 603(LP)
ALL GOLD Terry's "True Love Ways" (Norman Petty & Buddy
    Holly) - BUDDY HOLLY - *MCA (Poly): MCA 1302 (7"s)*
    also by PETER and GORDON - *C5 (Pinn): C5-502 (LP)*
ALLIED DUNBAR (1) "Chanson De Martin No.2" Op.15(Elgar)
    London PO - *EMI EX 290617-3 (2LP) EX 290617-5 (Cas)*
ALLIED DUNBAR (2) "You Can't Always Get What You Want"
    (M.Jagger-K.Richards) THE ROLLING STONES from 'Let
    It Bleed' - *Decca (Poly): 820 052-2 (CD)*
ALPEN MUESLI "Sun Rising" (Jon Marsh) by The Beloved on
    'Happiness' *WEA Int (WEA): WX 299(C)(CD)=LP/Cass/CD*
ALTON TOWERS (92) "In The Hall Of The Mountain King"
    from 'Peer Gynt Suite' (Grieg) *many recordings*
AMBRA COMPUTERS (ICPI) "NDH Lamine" (unknown) THE BACA
    TRIBE (South Africa) p.Gallo Music *not available*

AMBRE SOLAIRE "Relax" FRANKIE GOES TO HOLLYWOOD - *ZTT-Island: ZTTIQ 1 (Dbl LP) ZCIQ 1 (C) ZCIDQ 101 (CD)*
AMIGA GAMES "Sunshine On A Rainy Day" (Glover-Pollock) ZOE - *M&G (Poly): MAGS(MAGX)(MAGCD) 14 (7"/12"/CDs)*
ANAIS-ANAIS PERFUME "Andante Maggiore" 'Concerto for 2 Mandolins in G.Minor" (Vivaldi) *many versions*
ANCHOR BUTTER (1) "Day Trip To Bangor" (Fiddlers Dram) FIDDLERS DRAM - *Dingles (Spartan): SID 211 (7"s)*
ANCHOR BUTTER (2) "In The Mood"(Andy Razaf-Joe Garland) GLENN MILLER ORCHESTRA - *Old Gold: OG 9602 (7")* *RCA (BMG): PD 89260 (CD) / see* 'GLENN MILLER STORY'
ANDREX "Real Wild Child" (O'Keefe-Greenham-Owens) TV version (Tim Whitnall *unavailable*) IGGY POP on "Bl ah Blah Blah" *A.& M.: CDA 5145 (CD) AMA(AMC)5145*
ANDREX "The Wanderer" (Ernie Marseca) DION 'Runaround Sue' *Ace (Pinn): CDCHM 148 (CD) & Old Gold: OG 6112*
ANDREX (Products) "Itchycoo Park"(Steve Marriott-Ronnie Lane) SMALL FACES on 'The Collection' *Castle (BMG): CCSCD 108 (CD) CCSLP 108 (2LP) CCSMC 108 (2Cass)*
ANDREX (Puppies) Mus (Christopher Gunning) *unavailable*
ANDREX (Shaggy Dog) "Forgotten Dreams" (Leroy Anderson) RUSS CONWAY on 'The EMI Years' *EMI: 792 587-2 (CD)*
ANTI DRINK DRIVING CAMPAIGN "In The Sumertime" (Ray Dor set) *Saraja (TBD): MJCDS 1 (CD single) also avail:* orig 1970 by MUNGO JERRY *available on* '70s Pop Number Ones' *Old Gold (Pickwick): OG 3505 (CD)*
AQUA LIBRA "Cico Buff" from 'Bluebell Knoll' by COCTEAU TWINS *4AD (R.Trade): CAD(CADC)CADT 807 (LP/CD/Cass)*
ARCHER'S PEACH COUNTY SCHNAPPS "Assignation" (Magnus Fi ennes-David Watson) *not available*
ARIEL LIQUID arrangement of music from 'The Barber Of Seville' (Rossini) *TV version unavailable*
ARIEL ULTRA 'Overture to The Thieving Magpie' Opera 'La Gazza Ladra' (Rossini) *many recordings available*
ARISTON "Da Da Da" (TRIO) on Coll 'A Kick Up The 80's' *Old Gold: OG 3523 (CD) OG 2523 (Cass) OG 1523 (LP)*
ARRID EXTRA DRY "Love Theme from "Lawrence Of Arabia" (Maurice Jarre) Philharmonia Orchest (Tony Bremner) *Silva Screen (Conifer): FILMC(CD) 036 (Cass/CD)*
ARTHUR'S CAT FOOD - *see under* 'SPILLERS ARTHUR'S'
ASDA (1) "Perfect" (Mark E.Nevin) FAIRGROUND ATTRACTION 'First Of A Million Kisses' *RCA: 74321 13439-2 (CD)*
ASDA (2) (Pat-Pat ads) composed by Roger Greenaway and arranged by Graham Preskett *not available*
ASILONE LIQUID Music taken from the Pastoral Symphony No.6 In F.(Op.68) (Beethoven) *many recordings*
ATS "S.O.S."(Alex Hamilton-Richard Morris-Charles Hatch er) orig by EDWIN STARR (69) '20 Greatest Hits' on *Motown (pol): WD 72429 (CD) WK 72429 (Cass) WL (LP)*
AUDI (Hospital Ad) "Nick Of Time" (Anthony and Gaynor Sadler) Logorythm Music - *unavailable*
AUDI COUPE "Ain't No Pity (In The Naked City)" (Jackie Wilson) JACKIE WILSON - *Ace (Pinn): CDCH 913 (CD) SMP: JAK 101 (Double LP) ZCJAK 101 (Cassette)*

AUSTIN MAESTRO 1.3 "You Ain't Seen Nothin' Yet" BACHMAN
    TURNER OVERDRIVE - *Mercury (Poly): 830 839-2 (CD)*
AUSTIN METRO (1) "Batman" (Neal Hefti) original version
    Silva Screen (BMG): FILM(C)(CD) 024D (Dbl LP/CS/CD)
AUSTIN METRO (2) "Stayed Awake All Night" (Bachman-Tur
    ner) KROKUS 'Alive & Screaming' *Arista (BMG) 208025
    (LP) 408025 (CS)*- BTO version current|y *DELETED*
AUSTRALIA (Seen To Be Believed) "Epic" (John Altman)
    p.Jeff Wayne Music *(not available)*
AUTUMN GOLD CIDER (1) "The Ying Tong Song" (T.Milligan)
    The GOONS *Decca Go! Discs (Poly) GOONCD 1 (CDs)* and
    820 646-2 (CD) 820 908-4 (Cass)

B.& Q. (1) "Nobody Does It Better"(Carol B.Sager/Marvin
    Hamlisch) CARLY SIMON - *Elektra (WEA): K 12261 (7")*
    see also 'JAMES BOND FILM INDEX' (Spy Who Loved Me)
B.& Q. (2) (Pots Of Paint) "Coronation Scot" (V.Ellis)
    on 'FAMOUS THEMES' *Grasmere (Taylors): GRCD 10 (CD)*
BABYBEL MINI CHEESE based on "Barbara Ann" (F.Fassert)
    orig BEACH BOYS (65) *Capitol-EMI: CDP 746738-2 (CD)*
BABYCHAM (1) "Tiger Feet" (Mike Chapman-Nicky Chinn) by
    MUD - *Rak (EMI): CZ 280 (CD) TCEMS 1356 (Cass)*
BABYCHAM (2) "Softly Whispering I Love You" (Roger Cook
    Roger Greenaway) PAUL YOUNG from 'Other Voices' *CBS
    017-2(CD) -1(LP) -4(Cas)* Orig (71) THE CONGREGATION
    '20 One-Hit Wonders' *C5-SFM (Pinn): C5 CD607 (CD)*
BABYCHAM (3) "Big Spender" (Cy Coleman-Dorothy Fields)
    from 'Sweet Charity' *(TV vers.unavailable)* SHIRLEY
    BASSEY on 'Diamonds The Best Of' *EMI: CDP 790469-2
    (CD)* also on *Dino (Pinn): DIN(CD)(MC) 49 (CD/Cass)*
BACI CHOCOLATES (1) "Overture Cavalleria Rusticana" (Ma
    scagni) (2) "Nessun Dorma" (Puccini) *many versions*
BAILEYS IRISH CREAM "Barcarolle" Tales Of Hoffmann (Off
    enbach) Elizabeth Schwarzkopft-Jeanine Collard 'CLA
    SSIC EXPERIENCE' *EMI (CD)(TC)EMTVD 45 (2CD/Cass/LP)*
BALKAN HOLIDAYS "Sunny Afternoon" (Ray Davies) - KINKS
    Old Gold: OG 9577 (7"s) OG 1007 (LP) OG 2007 (Cas)
    PRT (BMG) PYL 4001 (LP) PYM 4001 (CS) PYC 4001 (CD)
BARCLAYS BANK (1) "Road Runner" JUNIOR WALKER ALL STARS
    Motown (Polyg): 530 033-2 (CD) 530 033-4 (Cass)
BARCLAYS BANK (2) "Imagination"(B.Some) BELOUIS SOME on
    'Some People' *MFP-Fame (EMI): TCFA 3197 (Cass)*
BARCLAYS BANK (3) "Pathetique" Symphony No.6 in B.min
    Op.74 (Tchaikovsky) - *many versions available*
BARCLAYS BANK (4)"Under Pressure" (D.Bowie/Queen) David
    Bowie & Queen *EMI: (TC)EMA 797 (CS/LP) CDP 746215-2*
BARCLAYS BANK (5) "Pride" (Geoff MacCormack) p.Paradi
    se Music *not available*
BATCHELOR'S (HARVEST) SOUPS Music (Rick Wentworth) P.Da
    vid Dundas Music *not available*
BATCHELOR'S SLIMMER SOUPS "The Little Swans" from 'Swan
    Lake' Ballet Op.20 (Tchaikovsky) *many recordings*
BATCHELOR'S SOUP "Andante" (2nd movement) from 'Eine Kl
    eine Nachtmusik' (Mozart) *many recordings available*

BAXTER'S VEGETARIAN SOUPS Music composer (Barry Kirsch)
P.Candle Music - *not available*

BEAMISH STOUT (Courage) "Karla With A K" by THE HOOTERS
on 'One Way Home' *Sony: 465564-2 (CD) 4 (Cass)*

BEECHAM HOT LEMON "Everybody Loves Somebody Sometime"
(K.Lane-I.Taylor) - DEAN MARTIN '20 Original Hits'
MCS Bridge (Target): 105 001 (CD) FRANK SINATRA etc

BEJAM "Chick Chick Chicken Lay A Little Egg For Me" (T.
McGhee-F.Holt-I.King) - TED WEEMS & HIS ORCHESTRA -
ASV (Koch): AJA 5029 (LP) ZCAJA 5029 (Cass)

BIO SPEED WEED "Can-Can" from Orpheus In The Underworld
(Jacques Offenbach) *many recordings on all formats*

BIOTEX "You Make Me Feel Brand New" (Linda Creed-Thom
Bell) THE STYLISTICS - *Mercury (Poly): 512 985-2 CD*

BIRDS-EYE CRISPY CHICKEN "Chicken Rhythm" (Slim Gaill
ard) SLIM GAILLARD on 'The Legendary McVouty" on
Hep-New Note (Pinn): HEPCD 6 (CD)

BIRDS-EYE MENU MASTER "Just The Two Of Us" (B.Withers-
W.Salter-R.McDonald) GROVER WASHINGTON with Bill
Withers on 'Winelight' *Elektra: K2-52262 (CD)*

BIRMINGHAM MID-SHIRES BUILDING SOCIETY "Reach Out I'll
Be There" (Holland-Dozier-Holand) FOUR TOPS 'Great.
Hits' *Motown (Poly):530 016-2 (CD) -4 (Cass) -1(LP)*

BIRMINGHAM POST "Love Theme" from 'Romeo and Juliet'
(Prokofiev) - *recordings available in all formats*

BISTO (1) "Save The Best For Last" by VANESSA WILLIAMS
'The Comfort Zone' *Polydor: 511267-2 (CD) -4(Cass)*

BISTO (2) "Black Eyes" or"Dark Eyes" Russian Folk based
melody "Otschi Tchornyie" (Niklas Krotsch)instrumen
tal vers.by PALM COURT THEATRE ORCHESTRA on 'Picnic
Party' on *Chandos: CHAN 8437 (CD)*

BLACK & DECKER DUSTBUSTER "Blockbuster" (Mike Chapman-
Nicki Chinn) orig The SWEET *RCA (BMG): ND(NK) 74313*

BLACK & DECKER PAINT STRIPPER "Flight Of The Bumblebee"
from 'Tsar Sultan' (Rimsky-Korsakov) *many versions*

BLACK MAGIC (It's The Black Magic) 'The Stranger' Theme
(Christopher Gunning) *not available*

BLACK MAGIC "Love Is The Sweetest Thing" (Ray Noble) AL
BOWLLY & RAY NOBLE ORCH-*EMI Cedar:CDP 794341-2 (CD)*

BLUE BAND MARGARINE "Pastoral-Shepherds Thanksgiving Af
ter The Storm" 'Symph No.6 in F.Major' (Beethoven)

BMW (1) "Cantilena" from 'Bachianas Brasileiras No.5'
(Villa-Lobos) *many recordings available all formats*

BMW (2) "It Seems To Be A Dream" by FRANK DUVAL from
'When You Were Mine' *Teldec (ASV-Koch): 8.26555(CD)*

BODDINGTONS (Smoke Rings ad) "Smoke Rings" (Roger Webb)
not available

BODDINGTONS (Gondola ad) "O Sole Mio" (Di Capua)sung by
ENRICO CARUSO on '18 Favourite Arias and Songs' on
Deja Vu Reference (TBD): DCRECD(DVREMC) 61 (CD/Cas)

BOLD WASHING POWDER "Ebben-Ne Andro Lontana" Aria from
'La Wally' (A.Catalini) *see coll* 'Essential Opera'

BOOTS (A Better Buy At) "Jelly Babies" (Rod Bowkett)
p.Final Touch Music *(not available)*

BOOTS **(Natural Collection)** "Tahiti" arr.and composed by John Altman (p.Jeff Wayne Music) *(not available)*
BOOTS OPTICIANS WINTER SALE "Surprise" by PETER HAMMILL and GUY EVANS on 'Spur Of The Moment' *Red Hot/RTM (Pinn): CDR 102 (CD) ZCRH 102 (Cass)*
BOOTS SKIN CARE NO.6 "I Say A Little Prayer" (Burt Bach arach-Hal David) TV instrumental vers.*not available* ORIG ARETHA FRANKLIN (1968) *Old Gold: OG 9102 (7"s)*
BOOTS SKIN CARE NO.7 "You Wear It Well" (Rod Stewart & Martin Quintetton)ROD STEWART 'Best Of Rod Stewart' on *WEA: 926034-2 (CD) WX 314C (Cass)*
BOUNTY BAR "Try A Little Tenderness" (Woods-Campbell-Co nnelly) FRANK SINATRA *Capitol: ED 260142-4(CS)* OTIS REDDING *Atl:K41118-2(CD)-4(Cas)* TV vers.*unavailable*
BOURSIN CHEESE "Claire De Lune" (Debussy) *various rec.*
BOVRIL "The Wonder Of You" (Baker Knight) ELVIS PRESLEY *Old Gold: OG 9761 (7"s) / RCA: PD 90100-2(2CD)*
BP (For All Our Tomorrows)"Loveliest Night Of The Year" (Juventino Rosas-Paul Francis Webster) from 'The Gr eat Caruso' (Film 50) - *see FILMS & SHOWS*
BRITANNIA BUILDING SOCIETY "Ain't No Stopping Us Now" (Gene McFadden-John Whitehead-Jim Cohn) McFADDEN & WHITEHEAD 'Gr.Hits' *Kenwest (TBD): KWEST 5406 9CD)*
BRITISH AIRWAYS (1) "Flower Duet" from 'Lakme'(Delibes) by MADY MESPLE on *EMI: CDS 749430-2 (2CD's)*
BRITISH AIRWAYS (2) "Superman" Theme (John Williams)
BRITISH AIRWAYS (3) "Va Pensiero" (Chorus Of Hebrew Sl aves") from Act 3 'Nabucco' (Verdi) - *many versions*
BRITISH AIRWAYS (4) (Beach Formation) "Aria On Air" arr of 'Flower Duet' from 'Lakme' (Delibes) by MALCOLM McLAREN on 'Round The Outside' *Virgin: CDV 2646 and OVEDC 409 (Cass) / VS(T)(C)(CDT) 1273 (singles)*
BRITISH AIRWAYS (5) "Nessun Dorma" 'Turandot' (Puccini)
BRITISH AIRWAYS (6) arrangement of "Flower Duet"'Lakme' (Delibes) with African Mix titled "VIVA" by CRAZY FAN TUTTI on *Oval (WEA): OVAL 109CD (CD) OVAL 109T (12") OVAL 109C (Cass) OVAL 109 (7")*
BRITISH AIRWAYS (7) NEW CLUB WORLD "Up On The Roof" (G. Goffin-Carole King) DRIFTERS (62) 'Best Of'*Pickwick PWKS 589(CD) Atlantic (WEA): 241122-2(CD)* and KENNY LYNCH *THC (Total-BMG): CDMBE 1(CDs) CAMBE 1 (Cass)*
BRITISH BEEF (1) "You Are My Sunshine" (Jimmy Davis-Cha rles Mitchell)TV version by Linda Hayes *unavailable* orig (Tex Ritter 1940) / *many contemporary versions*
BRITISH BEEF (2) "Can't Help Lovin'Dat Man" (Show Boat) (Kern-Hammerstein) SHIRLEY BASSEY 'Sophisticated La dies Vol.3' *Connoisseur (Pinn): VSOP(CD)(MC)(LP)145*
BRITISH COAL (1) "Fever" (John Davenport-Eddie Cooley) from 'Hey Boy Hey Girl' (Film 59) PEGGY LEE on 'Fev er' *EMI: CDFEVER 1 (CD) TCFEVER 1 (Cass)*
BRITISH COAL (2) "In The Heat Of The Night" (Quincy Jon es-Alan & Marilyn Bergman) *see under FILMS & SHOWS*
BRITISH COAL (3) "In The Hall OfThe Mountain King" from 'Peer Gynt' (Grieg) *many recordings available*

BRITISH GAS (1) "All Right Now" (Andy Fraser-P.Rodgers) FREE 'Island Story' *Isl: (CID)ISL(C) 25 (CD/LP/Cas)*

BRITISH GAS (2) "Mission Impossible" (Lalo Schifrin) - see 'Mission Impossible' *TV THEMES section*

BRITISH GAS (3) "Shame Shame Shame" (Sylvia Robinson) SHIRLEY & CO.*Chess: CXMP 2001 (LP) ZCCXP (Cass)*

BRITISH GAS (4) "Crazy Weather" BILLY COTTON BAND 'Crazy Weather' *Happy Days (Conif): (M)CHD 125(Cas/LP)*

BRITISH GAS (5) "The Sun HasGot His Hat On" (Noel Gay) NEMO *Music Club (TBD): MCCD 108 (CD) MCTC 108 Cas*

BRITISH GAS (6) "The Birdie Song" by THE TWEETS (1981) on *Old Gold (Pinn): OG 9891 (7"s)*

BRITISH GAS (7) "I Want It All" (QUEEN) from 'Miracle' *EMI: (12)QUEEN 10 (s) (CD)(TC)PCSD 107 (CD/Cas/CD)*

BRITISH GAS (8) "Them There Eyes" (Maceo Pinkard-Doris Tauber-William Tracey)TV version sung by ALMA COGAN

BRITISH GAS (9) "Now Is The Time" (Biddu) orig 1976 by JIMMY JAMES & THE VAGABONDS *-Old Gold: OG 9137 (7")*

BRITISH GAS (10) "Let's Put It All Together" (Luigi Creatore-Hugo Peretti-George D.Weiss) *ORIG:* STYLISTICS (74) on 'Great Love Songs' *Pickwick: PWK 139 (CD)*

BRITISH GAS (11) "Whatever You Want" (Richard Parfitt-Andrew Brown) STATUS QUO (79) on '12 Gold Bars' on *Vertigo (Poly): 800 062-2 (CD) QUOMC2 (Cass)*

BRITISH GAS (12)"Canon In D" (Pachelbel)*many recordings*

BRITISH GAS (13) "Goodbye-ee" (PETER COOK-DUDLEY MOORE) on The Clean Tapes' *RIO (AMT): RDC 1206 (Cass)*

BRITISH GAS (14)"More More More" (Gregg Diamond) by the ANDREA TRUE CONNECTION on 'Get On Up!' *Music Club Int. (TBD/Mus.Coll): MCCD 063 (CD) MCTC 063 (Cass)*

BRITISH GAS (15) "Lazybones" (Hoagy Carmichael-Johnny Mercer)orig by HOAGY CARMICHAEL on 'Stardust & Much More' on *RCA Bluebird (BMG): ND/NK 88333 (CD/Cass)*

BRITISH GAS (16) "What's New Pussycat" TOM JONES'What's New Pussycat' *Decca (Poly): 820 523-2 (CD) -4(Cass)*

BRITISH HEART FOUNDATION "Stop In The Name Of Love" (B. Holland-L.Dozier-E.Holland) DIANA ROSS AND SUPREMES *Motown (Poly): 530 013-2 (CD) 530 013-4 (Cass)*

BRITISH KNIGHTS FOOTWEAR "U Can't Touch This" (James-Miller) - MC HAMMER on 'Please Hammer Don't Hurt 'em' *Capitol (EMI):CDEST 2120 (CD) (TC)EST 2120 (Cas/LP)*

BRITISH PARALYMPIC ASSOCIATION music specially composed & orchestrated by HOWARD BLAKE *not available*

BRITISH RAIL (Poem by Sir John Betjeman) *not available*

BRITISH RAIL: INTERCITY - *see under* 'INTERCITY'

BRITISH RAIL: REGIONAL RAILWAYS based on "I'll Take You There" (Alvertis Isbell) STAPLE SINGERS on'Best Of' *Stax/Ace (Pinn): CDSXE 006 (CD)*

BRITISH STEEL "Andante" from 'Symph No.1 in A.flat' Op. 55 (E.Elgar) *many recordings available*

BRITISH TELECOM (1) "Daybreak" from 'Daphnis et Chloe' Ballet (Ravel) *many recordings available*

BRITISH TELECOM (2) "Are You Lonesome Tonight"(Roy Turk Lou Handman) ELVIS PRESLEY *RCA: NL(NK) 89168 (LP/C)*

BRITISH TELECOM (3) "Call Me" (Go West) GO WEST - *Chrys alis: CHR 1495 (LP) ZCHR 1495 (Cass) CD 1495 (CD)*
BRITISH TELECOM (4) "Say You Say Me" (L.Richie) LIONEL RICHIE) *Motown (Poly): 530 024 (CD) 530 024-4(Cass)*
BRITISH TELECOM (5) (In Paris) "April In Paris" (V.Duke Yip-Harburg) sung:Joe Campbell-Paul Hart-Val Stokes Nick Curtis-Tracy Miller-Kate Bott *not available*
BRITISH TELECOM Chargecard ad "Private Investigations" (Mark Knopfler) DIRE STRAITS on 'Money For Nothing' *Vertigo (Poly): 836 419-2 (CD) VERHC 64 (Cass)*
BRITISH TELECOM Stephen Hawking ad "Stephen's Theme" (A.Badalamenti) ANGELO BADALAMENTI *not available*
BRUT "On The Road" from film soundtrack of 'Rain Man' -S/T- *Capitol (EMI): CZ 4567 (CD) TCATAK 180 (Cass)*
BRYLCREEM Wear It "Principles Of Lust"(Curly-Fairstein) ENIGMA on 'Principles Of Lust' *Virgin: DINS(T) 110 (7"/12") DINSD 110 (CDs) DINSC 110 (Cass)*
B.T.3 SHARE OFFER (1) "Sugar Baby Love" (Bickerton-Wadd ington) The RUBETTES *Dice (Total-BMG): RUBCD 9(CDs) RUBMC 9 (Cass)* also on 'Singles Collection' on *Dice (Total/BMG):RUBCD 2(CD) RUBMC 2(Cass)*
B.T.3 SHARE OFFER (2) "Chirpy Chirpy Cheep Cheep" (Clau dio Fabi-Harold Stott) MIDDLE OF THE ROAD (1971) on *Old Gold: OG 9632 (7")* also on 'Middle Of The Road' *Ariola Expr.(Taylors): 295 594 (CD) 495 294 (Cass)*
BUDWEISER (1)"Got The Money In My Pocket" (Ronnie Bond-Nigel Jenkins) R.Bond Music - *not available*
BUDWEISER (2) "Ain't Too Proud To Beg" (Holland-Whitfie ld) TEMPTATIONS *Motown 530 015-2 (CD) -4 (Cass)*
BUDWEISER (3) "Tracks Of My Tears" (S.Robinson) SMOKEY ROBINSON & MIRACLES *Motown (Poly): 530 121-2 (CD)*
BUDWEISER (4) (piano ad) "Piano Player Theme" (Pinetop Perkins) PINETOP PERKINS boogie woogie examples on *Black & Blue (Koch Int): BLE 59520-2 (CD)*
BUDWEISER (5) (slide guitar ad) "Les Paul" (Mark Huke Zalic-Rik Shurman) Canadian recording *not available*
BUPA "Body" (Joe Campbell) p.Joe & Co. *not available*
BURGER KING based on "That's The Way I Like It" (Harry Casey-Robert Finch) KC & THE SUNSHINE BAND (75) on 'Best Of' *Roulette (EMI): CD(TC)ROU 5007 (CD/Cass)*
BUXTON SPRING WATER "Concerto For Cello & Orch In E.Min Op.85" (Elgar) Royal Philh Orch (YEHUDI MENUHIN) & JULIAN LLOYD WEBBER - *Philips (Poly): 416354-2 (CD)*
BUITONI ITALIAN FOODS (original music composed by Dario Balden Bembow) *not available*

CADBURY'S - *see under brand name e.g. 'Cream Eggs'*
CAFE HAG "Luna Rossa" (Antonio Vian-Vincenzo De Crescen zo) sung by Nicole Tobbles - *not available*
CAMPBELLS SOUPS TASTES OF THE WORLD "Madam Butterfly" (Puccini) Complete Opera *EMI: CMS 769654-2 (2 CD's)*
CANON PHOTO-COPIERS "T'ain't What You Do" (Sy Oliver-J. Young) - BANANARAMA WITH FUN BOY 3 on *London (Poly) 828 146-2 (CD) KRAMR 5 (Cass) RAMR 5 (LP)*

CARACTERE PERFUME "On The Sunny Side Of The Street" (Jimmy McHugh-Dorothy Fields) - FRANK SINATRA 'Come Swing With Me' *Capitol (EMI): CZ 391 (CD)*

CARLING BLACK LABEL (1) "When You Wish Upon A Star"from 'Pinocchio' -S/T- *see WALT DISNEY FILM INDEX*

CARLING BLACK LABEL (2) "I Heard It Through The Grapevine" (N.Whitfield-B.Strong) MARVIN GAYE *Motown (pol)*

CARLING BLACK LABEL (3) (squirrel) "Mission Impossible" (Lalo Schifrin) *see TV Section*

CARLING BLACK LABEL (4) "Dam Busters March" (E.Coates) RAF CENTRAL BAND "Hello Children Everywhere V2" *EMI*

CARLING BLACK LABEL (5) (Synchro-Swimmers) "Excaliber" (Rachel Portman) p.Jeff Wayne Music *(not available)*

CARLSBERG (Antique Chair) "Wooden Heart" (B.Kaempfert-Kay Twomey-Fred Wise-Ben Weisman) ELVIS PRESLEY on *Old Gold: OG 9702 (7"s)* JOE DOWELL *YDG 45734 (Cass)*

CARLSBERG (Guitars) "Duelling Guitars" (Dan Simmons-Joe Glasman) *not available* note: similar to "Duelling Banjos" from film 'Deliverance' *WB (WEA) K.16223 7"*

CARMEN 1500 PROFESS.HAIR DRY "Only You" (Buck Ram) -The PLATTERS - *Old Gold (Pinn): OG 9485 (7"s)*

CARNATION COFFEE-MATE "Boramei" (Steve Barker & Carmen Day) *not available*

CASTROL OIL "2nd m/m Symph.No.7 in B.Minor" (G.Mahler)

CATHAY PACIFIC Part of 'Symph No.4 in A Op.90 Italian' (Mendelssohn) - *recordings available in all formats*

CELLNET "Busy Line" (Murray Semos-Frank Stanton) - ROSE MURPHY on *RCA (BMG): PB 44087 (7"s) PK 44087 (Cass) PD 44088 (CDs)* also contains PETER SKELLERN version from 'A String of Pearls' *Ariola (BMG) 260342 (CD)*

C'EST LA VIE (Christian Lacroix) "Chili Poum" composed and played by MANITAS DE PLATA - *CBS (deleted)*

CHANEL "L'EGOISTE" "Dance Of The Knights" from Act.1 of 'Romeo & Juliet' Op.64 (Prokofiev) *many recordings*

CHANEL NO.5 (1) "Sea Of Love" (George Khoury-Phil Baptiste) (1959) MARTY WILDE on *Old Gold: OG 9241 (7"s)*

CHANEL NO.5 (2) "My Baby Just Cares For Me" (Donaldson-Kahn) NINA SIMONE on *Charly: CYZ (7)112 (7"s/12"s)*

CHANEL NO.19 (1) "Spring"'Four Seasons Suite No.1 in E' (Vivaldi) *many recordings available on all formats*

CHANEL NO.19 (2) "Arrival Of The Queen Of Sheba" 'Solomon' Oratorio (Handel) *many recordings available*

CHAT MAGAZINE "Yakety Yak" (Jerry Leiber-Mike Stoller) COASTERS *Old Gold: OG 9089 (7")* & 'Stand By Me' S/T

CHESHIRE WHOLE FOODS MUESLI "After The Storm" from 'Pastoral Symphony' No.6 In F.Major (Op.68) (Beethoven)

CHOCOLATE BREAK "Kinderszenen" Op.15 No.7 'Traumerei" (Schumann) *played by* HOWARD SHELLEY (piano) on *Chandos (Chandos): CHAN 8814 (CD) /also by* VLADIMIR HOROWITZ *RCA Vict (BMG): GD(GK) 87755 (CD/Cass)*

CITIZEN WATCHES "Kyrie" from 'Misa Criolla' Mass (Ariel Ramirez) JOSE CARRERAS + A.Ramirez, Laredo Choral Salve and Bilbao Choral Society on *Philips (Polyg): 420 955-2PH (CD) 420 955-4PH (Cas) 420 955-1PH (LP)*

CITROEN AX "Cupid" (Sam Cooke) JOHNNY NASH 'Greatest Hi
ts' *Epic: 465306-2 (CD) -4 (Cass) Old Gold: OG 9196*
CITROEN AX GT/MIAMI "Keep On Running" (Jackie Edwards)
SPENCER DAVIS GROUP on 'The Island Story 62-87' -
Island: CID 25 (CD) ISL(C) 25 (LP/Cass)
CITROEN AX SALSA/JIVE Special Editions "Dancing In The
Street" (William Stevenson-Marvin Gaye) MARTHA REEV
ES & THE VANDELLAS *Motown (Poly): TMG(CD)(CS) 1418
(CDs/Cass)* also on "24 Greatest Hits" on *Motown
(Poly): 530 040-2 (CD) 530 040-4 (Cass)*
CITROEN BX CAR "Winter" from 'The Four Seasons Suite'
(Vivaldi) *many recordings available on all formats*
CITROEN XANTIA "Chariots Of Fire" (Vangelis) VANGELIS
on "Themes" *Polydor: 839 518-2 (CD) VGTVC 1 (Cass)*
CITROEN ZX "The Bridge" specially composed by Geoff
MacCormack *(not available)*
CITROEN ZX 16 Valve "Marriage Of Figaro" (Mozart) *many
recordings available on all formats*
CLAIROL "I Got You (I Feel Good)"(James Brown) by JAMES
BROWN on 'Sex Machine The Very Best' *Polydor (Poly)
845 828-2 (CD) 845 828-4 (Cass)*
CLAIROL LOVING CARE "You're Sixteen" (Richard & Robert
Sherman) JOHNNY BURNETTE 'Best Of' *EMI:CDP 792924-2
(CD)* also RINGO STARR 'Ringo' *EMI: CDEMS 1386 (CD)*
CLARK'S SHOES TIK TOK RANGE "Soul Sisters" (Rick Fenn)
(not available)
CLARK'S SHOES FOR CHILDREN "Overture" from 'Peter & The
Wolf' (Prokofiev) *many versions available*
CLEARASIL "You Sexy Thing" (E.Brown-T.Wilson) by HOT
CHOCOLATE - *EMI: (TC)EMTV 42 & CDP 746375-2 (CD)*
CLERICAL MEDICAL "Clerical Medical" (Rod Bowkett) Final
Touch Productions *not available*
COCA-COLA (TV Ad-UK) "The First Time" (Spencer-Anthony-
Boyle) ROBIN BECK *Mercury: MER(X) 270 (7"/12") del*
COCA-COLA "Always Coca-Cola" (Terry Coffey-John Nettles
by) *orig commission - not available (USA produced)*
COLMAN'S MELLO & MILD "Walk On The Wild Side"(Lou Reed)
LOU REED - *Old Gold: OG 9635 (7"s)*
COMFORT FABRIC SOFTENER "What Is Life Without Thee"from
'Orpheus and Eurydice' (Gluck) GEOFF LOVE CONCERT
ORCHESTRA on 'Opera Without Words' *EMI: CZ 23 (CD)*
COMFORT PURE SILK SOFTENER "(Wrap Me In Your) Warm and
Tender Love" (B.Robinson-Ida Berger) - ELKIE BROOKS
'Pearls' *A&M CDA 20116 (CD) ELK(CLK) 1981 (LP/Cass)*
PERCY SLEDGE - *Old Gold: OG 9496 (7"s)*
COMMODORE AMIGA "Sunshine On A Rainy Day" (Glover-Polla
ck) ZOE on *M.& G.(Poly) MAGS(X)(CD)(CS)14 (singles)*
CONCORDE WINE "(He Was) Really Saying Something" (Eddie
Holland-Norman Whitfield-William Steveson) sung by
BANANARAMA with FUN BOY 3 (1982) on 'Greatest Hits'
*London (Poly): 828 106-2 (CD) -5 (DCC) KRAMC 005
(Cass)* note: orig 60's version by The VELVELETTES
CONTRAST "Concerto No.2 in F.Major for Piano and Orch
estra" Op.102 2nd movement (Shostakovich)

COOK ELECTRIC - see under ELECTRICTY COUNCIL (various
advertising campaigns)
COTY FATALE "T'Ain't What You Do" (Sy Oliver-J.Young)
BANANARAMA WITH FUN BOY 3 - *London (Poly): RAMR 5
(LP) KRAMR 5 (Cass) 828 146-2 (CD)*
COURTS FURNISHING "Galaxy Song" (Eric Idle-John DuPrez)
'Monty Python Sings' *VIRGIN: MONT(C)(D) 1 (Cass/CD)*
COVER GIRL MASCARA "Hidden Camera" (Simon Alexander &
David Moore) *not available*
COW & GATE OLIVARIT BABY FOOD "Nut Rocker" (arr.by Kim
Fowley) B.BUMBLE & THE STINGERS on coll. 'Wipe Out'
Ocean (BMG): OCN(WD)(WK)(WL) 2005 (CD/Cass/LP)
COX'S ENGLISH APPLES "In The Summertime" (Ray Dorset)
MUNGO JERRY *PRT (BMG): PYL 6026 (LP) PYM 6026 (Cas)*
CREAM EGGS (1)"Float On" (W.Willis-A.Ingram-J.Mitchell)
THE FLOATERS *Old Gold: OG 9218 (7"s)*
CREAM EGGS (2) "Intro & Outro" (Viv Stanshall) original
by THE BONZO DOG BAND - *Liberty (EMI): CZ 499 (CD)*
CREAM LIQUEUR "The Way You Look Tonight" (Jerome Kern-
Dorothy Fields) orig from 'Swing Time'(36) featuri
ng Fred Astaire *TV version unavailable*
CROSSE & BLACKWELL FOUR SEASONS SOUP "Spring" 'Four Sea
sons Suite' (Vivaldi) *many recorded versions*
CROWN LIVING TEXTURE PAINT "Reach Out& Touch Somebody's
Hand" (N.Ashford-V.Simpson) DIANA ROSS *Motown (Pol)*
CROWN PAINTS "Shades" (David Mindel) United Kingdom Sym
Phony Orch - *Food For Thought: YUM 108 (7") deleted*
CROWN PLUS TWO ROLLER PAINTS "Good Golly Miss Molly"
(Robert Blackwell-John Marascalo) - LITTLE RICHARD
Old Gold: OG 9492 (7"s) Sonet: SNTF 5000 (LP)
CROWN SOLO PAINT "Rewriting The Rule Book" composed by
Ken Freeman *(not available)*
CRUNCHIE (Cadbury) "I'm So Excited" (Pointer-Lawrence)
ORIG (82) POINTER SISTERS on 'Break Out' *Planet-RCA
(BMG): FD 89450 (CD) FK 89450 (Cass) FL 89450 (LP)*
CUSSONS IMPERIAL LEATHER "Timezone" composed and perfor
med by Clannad - *(not available)*
CUSSONS IMPERIAL LEATHER (Julie Walters Ad) song compos
ed by Craig Pruess *(recording unavailable)*
CUSSONS IMPERIAL LEATHER SHOWER GEL "Tired Of Waiting
For You" (Ray Davies) The KINKS *BMG: PYC 7002 (CD)*
CUSSONS PEARL (1) "Venus" (Ed Marshall) FRANKIE AVALON
1959 hit on Coll 'The Fabulous Frankie Avalon' on
Ace (Pinn): CDFAB 007 (CD) FABC 007 (Cass)
CUSSONS PEARL (2) "One Fine Day" from 'Madam Butterfly"
(Puccini) *many recordings available on all formats*

DAIHATSU CHARADE "Built To Survive Japan" Paul Mottram
orig commission - not available
DAILY EXPRESS "How Will I Know" (N.M.Walden-G.Merill-S.
Rubican) orig (86) WHITNEY HOUSTON *Arista (BMG):
610359 (CD) 406978 (Cass) 206978 (LP)*
DAILY MIRROR "You Ain't See Nothin' Yet" (orig 74) by
BACHMAN TURNER OVERDRIVE *Old Gold: OG 9764 (7s)*

DAILY STAR "Got My Mind Set On You" (Rudy Clark) GEORGE
   HARRISON 'Cloud Nine' *WEA: WX 123(C)(CD)*
DAIRY BOX (Nestle) (1) "Just An Old Fashioned Girl" by
   Eartha Kitt - *MCA: MCL 1702 (LP) MCLC 1702 (Cass)*
DAIRY BOX (Nestle) (2) "Too Busy Thinkin' bout My Baby"
   (N.Whitfield-Janie Bradford) ELKIE BROOKS 'Pearls'
   A&M (Poly): CDA 20116 (CD) ELK(CLK) 1981 (LP/Cass)
   MARVIN GAYE 'Motown's Greatest hits' *Motown (Poly):
   530 012-2 (CD) 530 012-4 (Cass)*
DAIRY MILK Cadbury (1) "Thinkin'About Your Body" (Bob
   McFerrin) B.McFERRIN *Blue Note (EMI):CDP 746298-2CD*
DAIRY MILK Cadbury (2) (Town Square) performed by THE
   LADYSMITH BLACK MAMBAZO GROUP *not available*
DATAPOST "Timing" (Geoff MacCormack) *not available*
DE BEERS - *see under* 'DIAMONDS'
DE KUYPER CHERRY BRANDY (1) "Sherry" (Bob Gaudio) FOUR
   SEASONS - *Telstar (BMG) STAR(STAC)(TCD) 2320*
DE KUYPER CHERRY BRANDY (2) "What Is Life"from 'Orfeo &
   Eurydice' (Gluck) instrum.version on 'Opera Without
   Words' on *EMI: CZ 23 (CD) (TC)EMS 1261 (Cass/LP)*
DE KUYPER CHERRY BRANDY (3) "O Mio Babbino Caro" from
   'Gianni Schicchi' (Puccini)sung by FELICIA WEATHERS
   'Puccini Operatic Arias' *Decca: 417 686-4DC (Cass)*
DECRA LED WINDOWS "Look Through Any Window" (Graham Gou
   ldman-Charles Silverman) HOLLIES (65)'All The Hits'
   EMI: CDEM 1301 (CD) TCEM 1301 (Cass) EM 1301 (LP)
DEEP FRESH based on "Deeply Dippy" (Fred & Richard Fair
   brass-Rob Manzoli) orig RIGHT SAID FRED (92) on *TUG
   (BMG): CD(CAS)SNOG 3 (CDs/Cass) also on* "UP" *Tug
   (BMG): SNOGCD 1 (CD) SNOGMC 1 (Cass) SNOGLP 1 (LP)*
DEL MONTE "Humming Chorus" from 'Madame Butterfly' (Puc
   cini) *many recordings available in all formats*
DEL MONTE FRUIT COOLERS" Island In The Sun"(H.Belafonte
   Irv.Burgess) HARRY BELAFONTE *Old Gold: OG 9640 (7")*
DELIGHT SPREAD "La Vie En Rose" (E.Piaf-R.Louiguy-F.Eyt
   on) EDITH PIAF *EMI: CZ 132 (CD) (TC)EN 5008 (CS/LP)*
DETTOL "Clouds" (Joe and Co) TV Ad sung by MAE McKENNA
   not available
DETTOX CLEANSER (1)"Good bye-ee" (R.P.Weston-Bert Lee)
   'Oh What A Lovely War' (Show 63) *TER: (ZC)TER 1043*
DETTOX CLEANSER (2) "Liberty Bell March" (John Philip
   Sousa) *various recordings available all formats*
DHL WORLDWIDE EXPRESS "Ain't No Mountain High Enough"
   (Nick Ashford-Val Simpson) - DIANA ROSS 'Anthology'
   Motown (Pol): WD 72532 (2CD) 'G.Hits' *WD 72478 (CD)*
DIAMONDS (A Diamond Is Forever) (Karl Jenkins-Mike Ratl
   edge) *not available*
DIET COKE "Taste It All" (USA produced recording) *under
   negotiation for release in the USA*
DIXEL KITTEN SOFT (1) (How Much Is That) "Doggie In The
   Window" (Bob Merrill) PATRTI PAGE *Old Gold: OG 9482*
DIXEL KITTEN SOFT (2) "I Wanna Be Loved By You" (Kalmar
   Ruby-Stothart) MARILYN MONROE 'Complete Recordings'
   Rare (TBD): RARECD 06/07 (2CD) RARELP 06/07 (2LP)

DIXCEL KITTEN SOFT (3) "Let It Snow Let It Snow" (Sammy
Cahn-Jule Styne) *TV vers.*(LINDA TAYLOR *unavailable*)
MANHATTAN TRANSFER *Columb (Sony): 472 412-2 (CD) -4*
DO-IT-ALL "Strangers In The Night" (Charles Singleton-
Eddie Snyder-Bert Kaempfert) BERT KAEMPFERT ORCH on
'Greatest Hits' *Polydor: 827 516-2 (CD)*
DOLLAND AND AITCHISON "I Can See Clearly Now" (J.Nash)
(TV version by SHEILA GOTT *unavailable)* JOHNNY NASH
'Greatest Hits' *Epic (Sony): 465306-2(CD) -4(Cass)*
DOMESTOS (1) "Summer Holiday" (Bruce Welch & B.Bennett)
CLIFF RICHARD - *Columbia: DB 4977 (7"s)* & Film S/T
DOMESTOS (2) "Big Bad John" (Jimmy Dean) - JIMMY DEAN
Old Gold (Pinn): OG 9399 (7"s)
DOUBLE DECKER (Cadbury) "Love & Marriage" (Sammy Cahn-
Jimmy Van Huessen) from 'Our Town' - FRANK SINATRA
Capitol (EMI): CZ 228 (CD)   792 160-4 (Cass)
DRAMBUIE (Dinner Party) "45 Revolution" (Martin Swan)
MOUTH MUSIC on 'Blue Door Green Sea' *Triple Earth
(Sterns): TERRACDEP 209 (CD)*
DRIFTER BAR (Nestle) "Drift Away" (Dobie Gray) - DOBIE
GRAY *Cottage (TBD): CDCOT 106 (CD) TCCOT 106 (Cass)*
DULUX "Starman Leaves" (Jack Nitzsche) from the -S/T-
'Starman' *TER (Conif): (CD)(ZC)TER 1097 (CD/Cas/LP)*
DULUX ONCE "Thus Spake Zarathrusta" (Richard Strauss)on
-S/T- '2001-A Space Odyssey' *EMI-MGM: CDMGM 6 (CD)*
DULUX PAINTS "My Way" (Claude Francois-Jacques Revaux-
Paul Anka) TV Dog Version sung by DARRYL KNOCK *not
available / original by* FRANK SINATRA *(WEA)*
DULUX PAINTS "Nights In White Satin" (Justin Hayward)
THE MOODY BLUES - *Old Gold (Pinn): OG 9349 (7"s)*
DULUX PEACH COLLECTION "Over The Rainbow" from 'Wizard
Of Oz' (S/T) (H.Arlen-Y.Harburg) *SEE FILMS & SHOWS*
DULUX SOFT WHITE "You Do Something To Me" (Cole Porter)
(TV vers.unavailable) MARLENE DIETRICH '20 Golden
Greats' *Deja Vu (TBD): DVCD(DVMC) 2098 (CD/Cass)*
DULUX VINYL SILK PAINTS "A Whiter Shade Of Pale" (Reid-
Brooker) - PROCUL HARUM: *Old Gold: OG 9225 (7"s)*
DULUX VINYL SOFT SHEEN "Orinoco Flow" (Enya)from 'Water
mark' produced by Nicky Ryan & Enya - ENYA *WEA Int
(WEA): 243875-2 (CD) 243875-4 (Cass) 243875-1 (LP)*
DULUX WEATHERSHIELD "Jupiter" 'Planets Suite' (G.Holst)
DUNLOP TYRES (1) "You're So Vain" (C.Simon) CARLY SIMON
Elektra (WEA): EKR 123(CD)(T)(C) (7"/CD/12"/Cass)
DUNLOP TYRES (2) "He's Misstra Know It All" (S.Wonder)
STEVIE WONDER from 'Innervisions' *Motown (Pol): WD
72606 (CD) ZK 72012 (Cass) ZL 72012 (LP)*
DUNLOP TYRES (3) "Venus In Furs" (Lou Reed) VELVET UNDE
RGROUND on 'Velvet Underground With Nico' *Polydor
(Poly): 823 290-2 (CD) 823 290-4 or SPEMC 20 (Cass)*
DURACELL BATTERIES "The Chain" (FLEETWOOD MAC)'Rumours'
Reprise: K 56344 (LP) K4 56344 (CS) K2 56344 (CD)
DUREX "The Power Of Love" FRANKIE GOES TO HOLLYWOOD -
ZTT-Island ZTTIQ 1 (LP) ZCIQ 1 (C) ZCIDQ 1 (C.Disc)
DUSTBUSTER *see* 'BLACK & DECKER DUSTBUSTER'

EAGLE STAR INSURANCE "Reflections" (Raf Ravenscroft)
  (not available)
EASY JEANS "Easy Snappin'"(Theopholus Beckford) by THEO
  BECKFORD *Metronome (Tel: 081 203 4378) MR 001 (7"s)*
EDWARDIAN HOTELS "O Mio Babbino Caro" (Oh My Beloved Fa
  ther) from 'Gianni Schicchi' (Puccini) / on 'Opera
  Without Words' (G.Love) - *EMI: CDP 746 931-2 (CD)*
ELECTRIC : LONDON/MANWEB/NORWEB/SEEBOARD etc. see below
ELECTRICITY COUNCIL (1) 'Eroica' Symph No.3 E.flat Op55
  1st m/m (Beethoven) *many recordings available*
ELECTRICITY COUNCIL (2) "Let's Work Together" (Wilbert
  Harrison) CANNED HEAT - EMI: 'Best Of Canned Heat'
  Liberty (EMI): CZ 226 (CD) and (TC)GO 2026 (Cas/LP)
ELECTRICITY COUNCIL (3) (Cook Electric) "It's Magic"(S.
  Cahn-J.Styne) from film 'Romance On The High Seas'
  'A Portait Of DORIS DAY' *Stylus: SMD 984 (CD)+LP/CS*
ELECTRICITY COUNCIL (4) (Dry Electric) "Funeral For A
  Marionette" *see TV Themes 'ALFRED HITCHCOCK PRES..'*
ELECTRICITY COUNCIL (5) "You Make Me Feel So Young" (M.
  Gordon-J.Myrow) 'A Portrait Of Doris Day' see *(3)*
ELECTRICITY COUNCIL (6) "When You're Smiling" (Goodwin-
  Fisher-Shay) TV ver.by JEROME MURRAY *(unavailable)*
ELECTRICITY COUNCIL (7) 'Time On Your Hands' solo piano
  "Gnossiennes" (Erik Satie) ANNE QUEFFELEC *Virgin:*
  VC 790754-2 (CD) VC 790754-4 (Cass) -1 (LP)
ELECTRICITY COUNCIL (8) "You Can Do Magic" (S.Linzer)
  (73) LIMMIE & FAMILY COOKING *Old Gold: OG 9477 (7")*
ELECTRICITY COUNCIL (9)(Dishwash Electric) "Gnossiennes
  No.1-3" (Erik Satie) ANGELA BROWNRIDGE - *EMI: CDEMX*
  9507 (CD) TCEMX 2071 (Cass) / ANNE QUEFFELEC on
  Virgin: VC 709754-2 (CD) -4 (Cass) -1 (LP)
ELECTRICITY COUNCIL NATIONAL POWER see 'NATIONAL POWER'
ERNEST AND JULIO GALLO WINE "Harp Concerto In C.Major"
  (Adrien Boieldieu) - The Paris Chamber Orchestra on
  Turnabout (Conif): TV 334 148 (LP) KC 334 148 (Cas)
ESSO COLLECTION "Eye Of The Tiger" from Film 'Rocky 3'
  also on 'Classic Rock' *Telstar (BMG): STAR(C) 6005*
ESSO UNLEADED PETROL "I Want To Break Free" (Brian May-
  Freddie Mercury) - QUEEN on 'Live Magic' - *EMI: CDP*
  746 413-2 (CD) TCEMC 3519 (Cass) EMC 3519 (LP)
ESTEE LAUDER WHITE LINEN "Tristesse" Etude No.3 Op.10
  (Chopin) *Many recordings available in all formats*
EUROPEAN NEWSPAPER "European" (John Altman)p.Jeff Wayne
  Music *not available*
EVER READY BATTERIES "Blueberry Hill"(Lewis-Stock-Rose)
  FATS DOMINO *MFP: CDMFP 6026 (CD) MFP 415747-1/-4*
EVO STIK "Stuck On You" (Aaron Schroeder-Leslie MacFarl
  and) ELVIS PRESLEY - *RCA (BMG) PB 49595 (7") NL 827*
  65 (LP) NK 82765 (Cas) ('Gold Records Vol.3')

FADS HOMESTYLE "Dream Baby" (Cindy Walker) ROY ORBISON
  'The Hits' *Pickwick: PWKS 576 (CD) SHM 3303 (LP)+CS*
FAIRY DISHWASHER "Overture To The Thieving Magpie" (Ros
  sini) *many recordings available in all formats*

FAMILY CIRCLE MAGAZINE "We Are Family" (Bernard Edwards
    Nile Rodgers) SISTER SLEDGE on 'Disco Years 74-79'
    Atlantic (WEA): 241678-2 (CD) 241678-4 (Cass)
FARLEY'S RUSKS (1) "Be Bop A-Lula" (G.V.Craddock) GENE
    VINCENT - *Capitol: EG 260760-1 (LP) 260760-4 (Cas)*
FARLEY'S RUSKS (2) "Chantilly Lace"(J.P.Richardson) The
    BIG BOPPER - *Old Gold (Pinn): OG 9483 (7"s)*
FELIX CAT FOOD "The Entertainer" (Scott Joplin) 'The St
    ing' *see under Films & Shows for -S/T- details*
FERRERO ROCHER CHOCOLATE (Ambassadors Reception ad)
    orig music (Graham De Wilde) *not available*
FIAT CINQUENCENTO "But I Do" (Paul Gayten-Rob Guidry)
    CLARENCE FROGMAN HENRY *MCA (BMG): MCSTD(MCSC) 1797
    (CDs/Cass)* 'But I Do' *Chess (Charly): CDRED 13 (CD)*
FIAT LA STRADA "Largo Al Factotem" from 'Barber Of Sevi
    lle' (G.Rossini) *many recorded versions available*
FIAT MIRAFIORI (1) "Legend Of The Glass Mountain" (Nino
    Rota) *see* FILMS & SHOWS section
FIAT MIRAFIORI (2) "La Donna E Mobile" from 'Rigoletto'
    Act 3 (Verdi) *many versions available all formats*
FIAT REGATA "An American Hymn" (Leonard Rosenman) from
    'East of Eden' (Film 55) sung by PLACIDO DOMINGO on
    'Perhaps Love' - *CBS: CBS 73592 (LP) 40-73592 (Cas)*
FIAT TEMPRA "Only You" (Simon Goldenberg and Geoff McCo
    rmack) sung by PRAISE feat Miriam Stockley - *Epic:
    469 048-2 (CD) 469 048-4 (Cass)* 'COMMERIAL BREAKS'
FIAT UNO (1) "The In-Crowd" (Billy Page)- ROXY MUSIC *EG
    (Poly): EGTV 2 (LP) EGMTV 2 (Cas) EGCTV 2 (C.Disc)*
    also by DOBIE GRAY - *Kent (Pinn): KENT 071 (LP)*
FIAT UNO (2) "The Race" (D.Meyer-B.Blank) YELLO 'Flag'
    Mercury (Poly): 836 426-2 (CD) -4 (Cass) -1 (LP)
FIESTA KITCHEN TOWEL (Elephant Ad) "The Sorcerer's Appr
    entice" (Paul Dukas) - *many recordings available*
FINDUS DINNER SUPREME "O Mio Babbino Caro" from 'Gian
    ni Schicchi' (Puccini) *various available versions*
    MONSERRAT CABALLE *HMV: (TC)SXLP 30562 (Cass/LP) CDC
    747841-2 (CD)* MARIA CALLAS *HMV: CDC 747966-2 (CD)*
FINISH ULTRA "Singing In The Rain" *see* Films & Shows
FINNIGANS HAMMERITE/SMOOTHRITE "Any Old Iron" (Collins-
    Terry-Shephard) 'EastEnders Sing-A-Long' *MFP (EMI):
    MFP 5779 (LP) TC-MFP 5779 (Cass) DELETED*
FISONS LEVINGTONS COMPOST "Turkish Finale" from 'The Ab
    duction From The Seraglio' ('Entfuhrung Aus Dem Ser
    ail') Music (Mozart) Libretto (C.F.Bretzner) / ASMF
    (Colin Davis) *Philips (Poly): 416 479-2PH2 (2 CD's)*
FLAKE (Cadbury) "Only The Love" (Ronnie Bond-Craig Lin
    dsay) GRAHAM STOKES on 'All By Myself' *Dover (Chrys
    alis-EMI): CCD 12 (CD)*
FLAKE (Cadbury) (Hotel Ad) "Hotel" (Ronnie Bond) P.Ronn
    ie Bond Music *(recording unavailable)*
FLASH (92) "Waltz Of The Flowers" from 'The Nutcracker
    Suite' (Tchaikovsky) *many recordings available*
FLAVEL EMBERGLOW FIRES "Concerto For Piano & Orch No.5
    In E.Flat" ('Emperor') (Beethoven) *many recordings*

FLEX BY REVLON "90 Dawn Workout" (Anne Dudley)   pub.by
    Buffal Music *(not available)*
FLORA "If I Love Ya Then I Need Ya" (Merrill) by EARTHA
    KITT 'Best Of' *MCA (BMG):MCLD(MCLC) 19120 (CD/Cass)*
FLYMO SPRINTMASTER "Devil's Gallop" 'Dick Barton' theme
    (Charles Williams) - CHARLES WILLIAMS ORCHESTRA on
    Grasmere (Taylors): GRALP 10 (LP) GRTC 10 (Cass)
FORD "Driven By You" (Brian May) BRIAN MAY *Parlophone:*
    CDPCSD 123 (CD) TCPCSD 123 (Cass) PCSD 12D 123 (LP)
    CDR 6304 (CDs) (12)R 6304 (12"/7") TCR 6304 (Cass)
FORD (The Champion Is Back) "Gonna Fly Now" (The Rocky
    Theme) (Bill Conti) *see* FILMS & SHOWS section
FORD (Skating Cars) "Bolero" (Ravel) *many recordings*
FORD (Various) "Mony Mony" TOMMY JAMES & The SHONDELLS
    (1968) on 'Anthology' *EMI Roulette: CDROU 5004 (CD)*
FORD ESCORT CABROLET "Temptation" (Glenn Gregory-Ian Ma
    rsh-Martyn Ware) by HEAVEN 17 on 'Best Of' *Virgin-*
    Pickwick: VVIPD 108 (CD) VVIMC 108 (Cass)
FORD ESCORT 16 VALVE (Athletes) "Split Second" (Daniel
    Donovan) *not available*
FORD ESCORT 91 (1) "I Can" (Scarlett Antaloczy) sung
    by Scarlett *not available*
FORD ESCORT 91 (2) "Lovely Day"(B.Withers) BILL WITHERS
    Columbia: 469048-2(CD) -4(Cass) 'Commercial Breaks'
FORD FIESTA (1) Best Small Car "Straight No Chaser" (T.
    Monk) THELONIOUS MONK 'Genius Of Modern Music Vol2'
    Bluenote (EMI): BST 81511 (LP)
FORD FIESTA (2) "Fun Fun Fun" (B.Wilson-M.Love) - BEACH
    BOYS - *Capitol: CDEMTV 1 (CD) TCEMTV 1 (Cass)*
FORD ORION "Take 5" (Paul Desmond) GEORGE BENSON 'Best
    Of' - *Polydor: 813 659-2 (CD)* DAVE BRUBECK on *Old*
    Gold: OG 9300 (7"s) also on 'COMMERCIAL BREAKS'
FORD ORION (Around The World) "World 2" (John Altman)
    P.Jeff Wayne Music *not available*
FORD RS 2000 - see 'FORD (The Champion Is Back)' above
FORD SCORPIO "Piano Concerto No.21 In C.Major" (Mozart)
    on 'Essential Classics' *DG (Poly): 431 541-2 (2CDs)*
    431 541-4 (Cass) 431 541-1 (2LP)
FORD SIERRA (1) "Rocking Stone" (Darras-Leroux) p.Ampho
    nic music / Tape Gallery *not available*
FORD SIERRA (2) "Don't Worry'bout A Thing" (Bob Marley)
    'Exodus' BOB MARLEY AND THE WAILERS - *Island (Poly)*
    CID 9498 (CD) ILPM 9498 (LP) ICM 9498 (Cass)
FORD THAMES "Move On Up" (Mayfield) CURTIS MAYFIELD on
    'A Man Like Curtis, The Best Of Curtis Mayfield' on
    Music Club Int (VCI/TBD): MUS(CD)(MC) 007(CD/Cass)
FORTE (TRUSTHOUSE) "Le Lac De Come" (Galas) *(TV version*
    unavailable) vers.on 'Classics' by FRANCK POURCEL &
    HIS ORCHESTRA on *EMI: CZ 22(CD) TCEMS 1263 (Cass)*
FOSTER'S LAGER (1) "Yuppie" (John Altman) p.Jeff Wayne
    not available
FOSTER'S LAGER (2) (Urban Survival) "This Is Hip" (John
    Lee Hooker) JOHN LEE HOOKER on 'The Boogie Man' on
    Charly (Charly): CDCHARLY 4 (CD)

FOX'S CLASSIC BISCUITS "Light Cavalry Overture" (Franz
   Von Suppe) NEW YORK P.O. (L.Bernstein) -*CBSCD 44719
   (CD)* BERLIN P.O. (Karajan) *DG (Poly): 415377-2 (CD)*
FOX'S ROCKY BAR - *see under* **'ROCKY BAR'**
FRISPS "I Heard" (Don Redman) versions by PASADENA ROOF
   ORCHESTRA on 'Fifteen Years On' - *Trax (Pinn): ARC
   1018 (LP) ARCT 1018 (Cas)* / CARROLL GIBBONS & SAVOY
   ORPHEANS with AL BOWLLY on 'I Saw Stars' - *Saville
   (Conifer): SVLD 001 (2LP) CSVLD 001 (Dplay Cass)*
FRUIT & NUT (Cadbury) "Dance Of The Mirlitons" from The
   'Nutcracker Suite' (Tchaikovsky) *many versions incl*
   'The Classic Experience' *EMI: CDEMTVD 45 (2 CD's)*
FRUIT-TELLA "I'm Too Sexy" (Fred/Richard Fairbrass-Rob
   Manzoli) RIGHT SAID FRED *TUG (BMG): CDSNOG 1 (CDs)
   CASNOG 1 (Cass) 12SNOG 1 (12"s) SNOG 1 (7"s)*
FURNESS BUILDING SOCIETY "Anitra's Dance" from 'Peer Gy
   nt Suite No.1' Op.46 (Grieg) recordings inc: Berlin
   P.O. (H.Von Karajan) - *DG: 423 208-2 (CD) -4 (Cass)*

G.A. (GEN.ACCIDENT) HELPLINE "I Can Help" (Billy Swan)
   BILLY SWAN on 'Country Gold' *Knight: KNCD 13012(CD)*
   ELVIS PRESLEY on 'Today' *RCA (BMG): ND(NK) 90660*
GALAXY "Rhapsody In Blue" (Gershwin) LEONARD BERNSTEIN
   'Bernstein's America' *DG (Poly): 427 088-2 (CD)*
GALES HONEY based on "Toast" by The STREETBAND featur:
   Paul Young on 'Paul Young The Early Years' *Connoiss
   eur Collect (Pinn): VSOPCD(VSOPMC) 160 (CD/Cass)*
GAS - *see under heading BRITISH GAS*
GAYMER'S OLDE ENGLISH CYDER (1)"How Long"(Paul Carrack)
   ACE on *Old Gold (Pinn): OG 9731 (7"s)* also on 'Best
   Of Ace' - *See For Miles (Pinn): SEE(CD) 214 (LP/CD)*
GAYMER'S OLDE ENGLISH CYDER (2) "Ivories" and "New Hous
   es" composed/performed by TOM BLADES *not available*
GENERAL ACCIDENT HELPLINE - see under G.A.
GILLETTE / GILLETTE CONTOUR PLUS "Looking Sharp" (Jake
   Holmes) and "The Best A Man Can Do" *not available*
GINSTERS CORNISH PASTIES "The Watermill" (Ronald Binge)
   on 'Music For A Country Cottage' *EMI: CD(TC)GO 2039*
GIVENCHY AMARIGE "Mon Manege A Moi" (Constantin-Glanzbe
   rg) EDITH PIAF 'Piaf Album' *EMI: TCEMS 172789-4 Cas*
GOLDEN LADY STOCKINGS "Summer Kisses Winter Tears" (J.C
   ruise) JULEE CRUISE on *WB (WEA): 0095(T)(C)(CD)*
GOLDEN VALLEY POPCORN "Popcorn" (Gershon Kingsley) by
   HOT BUTTER - *Old Gold (Pinn): OG 9394 (7"s)*
GOLDEN WONDER POT TV "Ace Of Spades" by MOTORHEAD on
   'Anthology' *Raw Power/Castle (BMG): RAWCD 011 (CD)*
GRAHAM & BROWN'S SUPER FRESCO based on "Spinning Wheel"
   (David Clayton Thomas) orig 1969 by BLOOD SWEAT AND
   TEARS on *BGO (Pinn): BGOCD 28 (CD) BGOLP 28 (LP)*
GUARDIAN NEWSPAPER "Symphony No.10 In D.Maj" (J.Haydn)
GUINNESS PURE GENIUS (1) "Wipeout" THE SURFARIS - *MCA:
   (Poly): MCA 1170 (7"s)* and Old Gold: OG 9171 (7"s)*
GUINNESS PURE GENIUS (2) "Hawaii Five-O" (Mort Stevens)
   Silva Screen (Con): FILM 024 (Dbl LP) also Cass/CD

HALIFAX (1) "Our House"(Jenkins-Nash) CROSBY STILLS
NASH & YOUNG on 'Deja Vu' *Atlantic: K.250001 (CD)*
HALIFAX (2) "I Only Want To Be With You" (Mike Hawker-
Ivor Raymonde) DUSTY SPRINGFIELD on 'Sounds Of The
60s' *Pickwick: PWK 104 (CD)*
HALIFAX (3) "Let's Do It(Let's Fall In Love)"(C.Porter)
EARTHA KITT 'Best Of' *MCA (BMG): MCLD(MCLC 19120*
HALIFAX CASH CARD (1) "Easy" (Lionel Richie) COMMODORES
Motown (Poly): 530 051-2 (CD) -4 (Cass)
HALIFAX CARD CASH (2) "Money" (B.Gordy-J.Bradford) FLYI
NG LIZARDS - *Statik-Virgin: VS 276 (7"s)* / BEATLES
Parlophone: PCS 3045 (LP) TC-(Cas) CDP 746436-2 (CD)
HALIFAX CARD CASH (3) (Nightime) "Ghost" (Mike Ratledge
Carl Jenkins) sung by Lance Ellington *unavailable*
HALIFAX FINANCIAL SERV. (1) "Sentinel" (Mike Oldfield)
from 'Tubular Bells II' MIKE OLDFIELD on *WEA (WEA)
4509 90618-2 (CD) -5 (DCC) WX 2002(C) (LP/Cass)*
HALIFAX FINANCIAL SERV. (2) "Moon River" (Henry Mancini
Johnny Mercer) *TV vers.unavailable* / Version by The
Cincinnati Pops Orch (Erich Kunzel) on 'MANCINI'S
GREATEST HITS' *Telarc (Conifer): CD 80183 (CD)* also
various other recordings available
HALIFAX INSTANT EXTRA "We're In The Money"(Harry Warren
-Al Dubin) from 'Gold Diggers Of 1933' orig Ginger
Rogers & Studio Orch on 'Hollywood Musicals' *Milan
(Silva Screen): ACH 023 (LP) CCH 023 (Cass)*
HALIFAX MAXIM A/C "The Walker" (Don Gould) P. Mingles
Music - *not available*
HALLS MENTHOLYPTUS "Coronation Scott" (Vivian Ellis) by
QUEENS HALL LIGHT ORCH (V.Ellis) Coll: 'On The Air'
HAMLET CIGARS "Air On A G.String" from Suite No.3 in D
(Bach) JACQUES LOUSSIER TRIO *Start:SMCD 19 (CD)*
HARMONY HAIR SPRAY "Photograph" (David Dundas) P.David
Dundas Music *(not available)*
HARPIC (1)"Pilgrim's Chorus"/'Tannhauser' (Rich.Wagner)
HARPIC (2) "If I Didn't Care" (Jack Lawrence) orig THE
INK SPOTS (39) on 'Best Of The Ink Spots' *MFP (EMI)
CDMFP 6064 (CD) TCMFP 50529 (Cass)*
HARPIC (3) "You're The One That I Want" (John Farrar)
from 'GREASE' -S/T- see under 'FILMS & SHOWS'
HEINEKEN (1) "Don't Laugh At Me" (Norman Wisdom) NORMAN
WISDOM from the 1953 film 'Trouble In Store'
HEINEKEN (2) "Clog Dance" from Ballet 'La Fille Mal Gar
dee' (Herold) *HMV: ASD 107770-1 (LP) -4 (Cass)*
HEINEKEN (3) "Raining In My Heart" (B.Holly-N.Petty)
BUDDY HOLLY *MCA: BH 7 (7") & Old Gold OG 9325 (7")*
HEINEKEN (4) "Great Pretender" (Buck Ram) THE PLATTERS
Old Gold (Pinn): OG 9485 (7"s)
HEINEKEN (5) "From A Jack To A King" (Ned Miller) NED
MILLER - *Old Gold (Pinn): OG 9340 (7"s)*
HEINEKEN (6) "Goldfinger" (J.Barry-L.Bricusse-A.Newley)
SHIRLEY BASSEY - (S/T) *see James Bond Film Section*
HEINEKEN (7) "Cupid" (Sam Cooke) SAM COOKE 'The Man and
His Music' *RCA (BMG): PD 87127 (CD)*

HEINEKEN (8) "Adagio in G.Minor" (Albinoni) *many record
    ings available in all formats*
HEINEKEN (9) "The Entertainer" (Scott Joplin) from 'The
    Sting' -S/T- MARVIN HAMLISCH - *MCA CMCAD 31034 (CD)
    MCLC 1735 (Cass)* also JOSHUA RIFKIN *(Nonesuch-WEA)*
HEINEKEN (10) "Donna" (Godley/Creme) 10CC on 'Changing
    Faces' *Polydor: 816355-2 (CD) TGCLP(MC) 1 (LP/Cass)*
HEINEKEN (11) (THE BLUES AD) "The Blues" (Paul Hart)
    performed   by LONNIE BROOKS *not available*
HEINEKEN (12) "Big Spender" (Sweet Charity) (Cy Coleman
    Dorothy Fields) SHIRLEY BASSEY *EMI:CDP 790469-2(CD)*
HEINEKEN (13) (Nigel Short Chess) "William Tell Overt."
    (Rossini) *many recorded versions on all formats*
HEINEKEN (14) "Alabatross" (Peter Green) by FLEETWOOD
    MAC on 'Albatross' *CBS (Sony):CD31569(CD) 40-(Cass)*
HEINEKEN (15) (Yacht Race) "Down The Hatch" (Simon Davi
    dson) *not available*
HEINEKEN EXPORT "Non Je Ne Regrette Rien" (No Regrets)
    (Charles Dumont-Michel Vocaire-H.David) EDITH PIAF
    '20 G.Hits' *Deja Vu (TBD):DVCD(DVMC) 2062 (CD/Cass)*
HEINZ BAKED BEANS (Heinz Builds Brits) "Diddle'um Song"
    by CHAS & DAVE 'All The Best' album *EMI deleted*
HEINZ SPOONABLE SALAD CREAM "Devil's Gallop"Dick Barton
    theme (Charles Williams) CHARLES WILLIAMS ORCHESTRA
    'Famous Themes' *Grasmere (Taylors): GRCD 10 (CD)*
HEINZ WEIGHT WATCHERS "Ying Tong Song" (Spike Milligan)
    The GOONS on 'World Of The Goons' *Decca (Polyg):
    820 646-2 (CD) 820 908-4 (Cass) GOONCD 1 (CDsingle)*
HELLMANNS MAYONAISSE (1) "Only You" (Buck Ram) orig by
    The Platters on *Old Gold: OG 9485 (7"s)*
HELLMANNS MAYONAISSE (2) Part of Symphony No.4 Brahms)
    LONDON SYMPHONY ORCH *various recordings available*
HENARA SHAMPOO "Modern Fairy Tale" (David Tattersall)
    recording not available
HERMESETAS (1) "Escape" (Peter Lawlor) *not available*
HERMESETAS (2) "Java Jive" (Milton Drake-Ben Oakland)
    INK SPOTS 'The Singing Detective' *Conn (Pinn):
    POTTCD 200 (2CD) POTTMC 200 (Cass)*
HERO AFTERSHAVE (Boots) "Holding Out For A Hero" (Jim
    Steinman) BONNIE TYLER from 'Footloose' -S/T- CBS:
    CBS 463000-2 (CD) CBS 463000-4 (Cass) -1 (LP) also
    Total (BMG): (CD)(12)(CA)TYLER 10 (CDs/12"/Cas/7")
HERTA FRANKFURTERS "The Continental" (Herb Magison-Con
    Conrad) TONY BAKER ORCH *Pickwick: PWKS 655 (CD)*
    PETER SKELLERN 'Astaire' *Ariola (BMG): 260341 (CD)*
HITACHI TELEVISION (1) "Baby Elephant Walk" (H.Mancini)
    H.MANCINI ORCH *see* Collections 'Henry Mancini'
HITACHI TELEVISION (2) "Non Je Ne Regrette Rien" (No Re
    grets) (Charles Dumont-Michel Vacaire-Hal David) by
    EDITH PIAF *Odeon (EMI): CZ 132 (CD) TCEN 5008 (Cas)*
HONDA ACCORD (1) "Butterflies" (Jeff McCormack-Simon Go
    ldenberg) *not available*
HONDA ACCORD (2) "Lawyer" (Tony & Gaynor Sadler) publis
    hed by Logorhythm Music *not available*

HONDA ACCORD (3) "Flashdance What A Feeling" (G.Moroder
-K.Forsey-I.Cara) *orig* 1983 by IRENE CARA on -S/T-
FLASHDANCE *Casablanca (Poly): 811 492-2 (CD)*
HORIZON PERFUME (Guy Laroche) "Storms Over Africa" ENYA
on 'Watermark' *WEA Int: 243 875-2 (CD) -4 (Cass)*
HORLICKS "You Sexy Thing" (Tony Wilson-Errol Brown) by
HOT CHOCOLATE '20 Hottest Hits' *EMI: CZ 213 (CD)*
HORLICKS LOW-FAT INSTANT "Blue Danube Op.314" (Strauss)
Vienna Phil Orc (C.Abbado) *DG (Poly): 423662-2 (CD)*
HOSEASONS HOLIDAYS "Messing About On The River" by JOSH
McRAE 'Hello Children Everywhere V2'*see collections*
HOTPOINT AQUARIUS "Whole Picture" (Paul Hart-Joe Campbe
ll) p.Joe & Co *not available*
HOVIS BREAD "Largo" from Symphony No.9 in E.Minor Op.95
'New World' (Dvorak) *many recordings available*
HULA-HOOPS (1) "Boog It" (C.Calloway-B.Ram-Jack Palmer)
CAB CALLOWAY ORCHESTRA *currently unavailable*
HULA-HOOPS (2) (Catfish) "The Cat Came Back" (Miller)
HUSH PUPPIES (1) "Walkin'The Dog"(Rufus Thomas) ROLLING
STONES - *Decca: LK 4605 (LP) KSKC 4605 (Cass)*
HUSH PUPPIES (2) "Puppy Love" (Paul Anka) PAUL ANKA *RCA
(BMG): PD 82691 (CD)* Donny Osmond version *deleted*

IBM COMPUTERS (1) "Fur Elise" Bagatelle No.25 in A.Min
(Beethoven) *many recordings available*
IBM COMPUTERS (2) "Pink Panther theme" (Henry Mancini)
see TELEVISION and FILMS & SHOWS sections
ICI (A Million People's Heartbeats) "Heartbeat" (compos
ed & performed by JOHN LEE HOOKER) *(not available)*
ICI GRASSHOPPER "The Walk" JIMMY McCRACKLIN on *Charly*
'Everybody Rock' *(TC)REDLP 10 (CS/LP) CDRED 10 (CD)*
ICI WORLD CLASS (Skeleton) "It Don't Mean A Thing If It
Ain't Got That Swing" (Duke Ellington-Irving Mills)
PASADENA ROOF ORCH *Transatlantic (Wynd-Up): TRA(C)
314 (LP/CS)* / GENE KRUPA/B.RICH *Poly: 835314-2 (CD)*
ICL COMPUTERS "Falls" from 'The Mission' (Ennio Morrico
ne) -S/T- on *Virgin: CDV 2402 (CD) TCV 2402 (Cass)*
IMMAC (1) "I Get The Sweetest Feeling" (Van McCoy-Alic
cia Evelyn) orig (68) JACKIE WILSON 'Very Best Of
Jackie Wilson on *Ace (Pinn): CDCH 913 (CD)*
IMMAC (2) Special lyrics and arrangement set to music
from ballet 'Coppelia' (Delibes) *not available*
IMPERIAL LEATHER - *see under* CUSSONS IMPERIAL LEATHER
IMPULSE DYNAMIQUE "Venus" (Robert De Leeuwen) orig by
SHOCKING BLUE (1970) on 'Golden Years 1970 Vol.2'
Connosseur Collect.(Pinn): RRT(CD)(MC) 70 (CD/Cass)
IMPULSE FREE SPIRIT "Fever" (John Davenport-Edd Cooley)
PEGGY LEE on 'Best Of The Capitol Years' *EMI:CZ 108
(CD) TCEMS 1294 (Cass) EMS 1294 (LP)*
IMPULSE PERFUME (1) "Black Eyes" *see TV Themes section
under 'Blackeyes' for version details*
IMPULSE PERFUME (2) "Hello Mary Lou" (Gene Pitney) ORIG
RICK(Y) NELSON (61) on 'Legendary Masters-Best Of
Rick Nelson Vol.2' on *Liberty (EMI): CZ 420 (CD)*

INDEPENDENT The "Music For A Found Harmonium" PENGUIN
CAFE ORCH *EG (Poly): EEGCD 38 (CD) OVEDC 430 (Cass)*
INDESIT "Harry Lime Theme" (from 'The Third Man' 1949)
(Anton Karas) ANTON KARAS on 'Third Man & Others'
on *Decca (Polyg): 421 264-2 (CD)*
INSETTE HAIR PRODUCTS "At The Hop" (A.Singer-J.Medora-
D.White) DANNY & THE JUNIORS 'Rock'n'Roll Years '56
59' *BBC: (ZCN)REN 631 (Cass/LP) /* Old Gold: OG 9215
INSIGNIA BODY SPRAY "It's All Over Now"(Shirley & Bobby
Womack) *TV Version unavailable* ORIG- ROLLING STONES
INSPIRATIONS (Cadbury) (1) "Girl Talk" (Neal Hefti-Bob
Troupe) 'Hits Of VINCE HILL' *MFP: HR 418106-4 (Cas)*
INSPIRATIONS (Cadbury) (2) "Sentimental Journey" (L.Bro
Brown-B.Green-B.Homer) 'A Portrait Of DORIS DAY' on
Stylus: SMD 984 (CD) SMR 984 (LP) SMC 984 (Cass)
INSPIRATIONS (Cadbury) (3)(Telescope Ad) music (Richard
G.Mitchell) *not available*
INTERCITY (89-91) "Relax" (Leon Redbone) - LEON REDBONE
Private (BMG): 662 885 (CD single also contains
'Intercity' 90 Ad "Untwist"* ('Let's Twist Again')
'Relax' on 'Sugar' *(BMG): 260555 (CD) 410555 (Cass)*
INTERCITY (92) "Mishima" (Philip Glass) PHILIP GLASS on
-S/T- 'Mishima' *WEA Elektra/Nonesuch: 979113-2 (CD)
EKTC 23 (Cass) EKT 23 (LP)*
IRN-BRU based on "You Don't Love Me Any More" (A.Yankov
ich) *Mick Mullans (unavailable)* WEIRD AL YANKOVICH
on 'Off The Deep End' *Polyd: 512 506-2(CD) -4Cass)*

JACOBS CLUB BISCUITS "Barbara Ann" (M.Love-B.Wilson)
BEACH BOYS - *Capitol: EMTV 1 (LP) TC-EMTV 1 (Cass)*
JACOB'S CLUB CLASSICS "Dance Of The Little Swans" from
Act 2 of 'Swan Lake Ballet' Op.20 (Tchaikovsky)
JACOBS CREAM CRACKERS "Release Me" (Miller-Stevenson-Ha
rris) ENGELBERT HUMPERDINCK *Old Gold: OG 9338 (7"s)*
JAMAICAN TOURIST BOARD "Dreaming Of A Little Island" by
JUDY BOUCHER - *Orbitone (Jetstar): OR 12-21 (12"s)*
JAMMIE DODGERS "Dance Of The Hours" from 'La Gioconda'
(Amilcare Poncielli) *many available versions*
JANET FRASER CATALOGUE "Memphis Tennessee" (C.Berry)
CHUCK BERRY (63) on '20 Great Tracks' on *MFP (EMI)
CDMFP 5936 (CD) TCMFP 5936 (Cass)*
JERSEY HOLIDAYS "Bergerac" theme (George Fenton) GEORGE
FENTON - *Food For Thought: YUM 110 (7"s) see TV sec*
JERSEY ROYAL POTATOES "Ma Vlast"'My Country' (Smetana)
Concertgebouw Orch (Antal Dorati) *Philips (Polyg):
420 607-2 (CD) 420 607-1 (2LP) 420 607-4 (Cass)*
JEWELLERS GUILD "Solid" (N.Ashford-V.Simpson) ASHFORD &
SIMPSON *Capitol: CDP 746466-2 (CD)EJ 240250-4 (Cas)*
JIF (1) "Dance Of The Hours" from Act 3 'La Gioconda'
(Amilcare Ponchielli) *many recordings available*
JIF (2) "Flower Duet" from 'Lakme' Opera (Delibes)
'Opera Spectacular' *IMP (Pickwick): MCD 15 (CD)*
complete 'Lakme' Opera - MADY MESPLE & PARIS OPERA
COMIQUE ORCH (A.Lombard) *EMI: CDST 749430-2 (2CDs)*

JOHN SMITH'S BITTER (Ladybirds Ad) "Je T'aime Moi Non
Plus" (S.Gainsbourg) JANE BIRKIN-SERGE GAINSBOURG
(69) on 'Amoreuse' coll *Pickwick: PWKS 539 (CD)*
JOHN SMITH'S BITTER (The Bubble Ad) "James Bond Theme
(Monty Norman) - *see Collections 'BOND & BEYOND'*
JOHN SMITH'S BITTER "Stop The Cavalry" (Jona Lewie)
JONA LEWIE *EMI NOX 1 (LP) TC-NOX 1 (C) CDNOX 1 (CD)*
JOHN SMITH'S MILLER LITE - see under 'Miller Lite'
JOHN SMITH'S YORKSHIRE BITTER "A Man and A Woman" (Fran
cis Lai) - *see under FILMS & SHOWS section*
JOHNSONS BABY BATH "Yes Sir That's My Baby" (Gus Kahn-
Walter Donaldson) *various recordings available*
JOHNSON'S BABY LOTION "Baby Face" (Harry Akst-Benny Dav
is) - JULIE ANDREWS from 'Thoroughly Modern Millie'
JOHNSON'S BABY LOTION "Moonlight Sonata" (Beethoven)
JOHNSON'S BABY POWDER "Twist and Shout" (R & O Isley)
BEATLES - *Parlophone (EMI): GEP 8882 (7"EP)*
JOHNSON'S PLEDGE (1) "These Foolish Things" (J.Strachey
H.Link-H.Marvell) NAT KING COLE *Capitol: CDEMTV 35*
JOHNSON'S PLEDGE (2) "Wooden Heart" (Bert Kaempfert and
others) ELVIS PRESLEY *Telstar STAR(C) 2264 (LP/CS)*
JOHNSON'S SPARKLE "This Ole House" (Stuart Hamblen)
vers: SHAKIN'STEVENS *Epic: 466993-2 (CD) -4 (Cass)*
ROSEMARY CLOONEY *Bridge (Target): 100 006-2 (CD)*
JUS-ROL "Valse" from the ballet 'Coppelia' (Delibes)
many recordings available in all formats

KATTOMEAT (Skateboard Cat Ad) "You Gotta Fight For Your
Right To Party" BEASTIE BOYS (87) from 'Licenced To
Ill' on *Def Jam (Sony):450062-2(CD) -4(Cass) -1(LP)*
KELLOGG'S CORN POPS "Popcorn" (Gershon Kingsley) by HOT
BUTTER on 'Sounds Of The 70's In The Summertime' on
Old Gold (Pickwick): OG 3714 (CD) OG 2714 (Cass)
KELLOGG'S FROSTIES (92) "Eye Of The Tiger" from 'ROCKY
3' (1982) SURVIVOR *see Rocky 3 -S/T- TT 1992 p.217*
KELLOGG'S POP TARTS "Pop Muzik" (Robin Scott) original
by M (1979) Originally on *MCA (deleted)*
KELLOG'S RICE CRISPIES "Sorcerer's Apprentice" (Dukas)
KELLOGG'S SPECIAL K(1)(Joe Campbell-Paul Hart) JOE & CO
orig commission - not available
KELLOGG'S SPECIAL K(2) "Itsy Bitsy Teeny Weeny Yellow
Polka Dot Bikini" (Lee Pockriss-Paul Vance) *orig*
BRIAN HYLAND (60) on *Old Gold: OG 9598 (7")* also by
BOMBALURINA (90) on *Polydor: 847 648-1 (LP)*
KELLOGG'S START "Let's Stick Together" Bryan Ferry
EG-Poly: 2302 045 (LP) 3100 345 (C) 821 561-2 (CD)
KELLOGG'S TEAM CEREAL "Les Patineurs" (Skaters Waltz)
(Emil Waldteufel) - GEOFF LOVE ORCH - *MFP (EMI): DL
1098 (Dbl LP) TC-DL 1098 (Cass)* / PHILHARMONIA PROM
ENADE ORCH (H.Kripps) - *MFP (EMI): HR 8132 (D.Cass)*
KENCO COFFEE "Bailero" from 'Songs Of The Auvergne' by
(Canteloube) - ENGLISH CHAMBER ORCHESTRA on *Virgin:
VC 7907-14-2 (CD)* / LAMOUREUX CONCERT ORCHEST with
Victoria De Los Angeles - *EMI: CDC 747970-2 (CD)*

KENTUCKY FRIED CHICKEN (1) "Jake The Peg" (Harris) ROLF
   HARRIS *EMI IDEAL: CDIDL 103 (CD) TCIDL 103 (Cass)*
KENTUCKY FRIED CHICKEN (2) "Canteloupe Island" (Herbie
   Hancock) *TV version unavailable* orig vers. on 'Best
   Of Herbie Hancock' *Bluenote (EMI): BNZ 143 (CD)*
KFC POPCORN CHICKEN (Alan Freeman Ad) "At The Sign Of
   The Swinging Cymbal" (Brian Fahey) BRIAN FAHEY ORCH
   (EMI deleted) and BRASS INCORPORATED *(PYE deleted)*
KINGSMILL BREAD "Spring"'Four Seasons Suite' (Vivaldi)
   see TV Themes section under 'Nigel Kennedy'
KIT-KAT (Andy Capp Ad) "Stand By Your Man" (Billy Sherr
   ill-Tammy Wynette) ORIG (68) by TAMMY WYNETTE- *Epic
   (Sony) 656953-7 (7") 656953-2 (CDs) 656953-4 (Cass)*
KIT-KAT (Skating Pandas) "Gimme A Break" (Paul Hart) p.
   Joe and Co. *(not available)*
KLEENEX Bathroom (and other campaigns) "Comfort" origin
   al composition by (Rachel Portman) *unavailable*
KLEENEX TISSUES "Overture to Cavalleria Rusticana" (Mas
   cagni) GHEORGHE ZAMFIR *Philips: PHH 5 (LP) PHHC 5
   (CS) 830627-2 (CD)* - also on The Classic Experience
   EMI: CDEMTVD 45 (2CDs) EMTVD 45 (2LPs) TC- (2Cass)
KNORR MINCE MAT:S "Roses From The South" (J.Strauss) VI
   ENNA S.ORCH (R.Stoltz)- *RCA Red Seal: VD 87742 (CD)*
KNORR SOUPS (1) "In Re Don Giovani" (Michael Nyman) by
   MICHAEL NYMAN - *Sheet: SHEET 1 (LP-82 deleted)*
KNORR SOUPS (2) "Bachianas Brasileiras No.5" (H.Villa-
   Lobos) National Philharmonic Orchestra (C.Gerhardt)
   with JAMES GALWAY - *RCA (BMG): RCD 25163 (C.Disc)*
   PLEETH CELLO OCTET with JILL GOMEZ (sop) - *Hyperion
   (Taylors) A.66257 (LP) KA 66257 (CS) CDA 66257 (CD)*
KNORR SOUPS (3) "Singin' In The Rain" from 1952 film mu
   sical (Nacio Herb Brown-Arthur Freed) - GENE KELLY
   CBS: CBS 70282 (LP) 40-70282 (Cas) CDCBS 70282 (CD)
KODAK GOLD "They Can't Take That Away From Me" (G.& I.
   Gershwin) TV version sung by SAM BROWN *unavailable*
   from 'Shall We Dance' (37) - Fred Astaire see Coll
   'Starring Fred Astaire' *TT.91 p.307*
KONICA FILM (1) "Greyhounds" (Tony Cox and Mike Wood)
   (2) "Cameras" (Charles Spenser) *(both unavailable)*
KP CRISPS "They're Coming To Take Me Away Aha" orig by
   NAPOLEON XIV - *Old Gold (Pinn): OG 9551 (7"s)*
KP DISCOS (1) "Stayin' Alive" (Gibb Brothers) BEE GEES
   83 Film -S/T- on *RSO Polydor: 813 269-2 (CD only)*
KP DISCOS (2) "Jealousy" (Jacob Gade-Winif.May-V.Bloom)
   originally from 'Anchors Aweigh' (45) 'Painting The
   Clouds With Sunshine' (Film 51) *versions available*
   GERALDO *Joy (Presid) JOYD 276 (LP) TC-JOY276 (Cass)*
   BILLY FURY *Castle Coll (BMG): CCSLP 160 (LP) CCSMC*
KP LOWER FAT CRISPS "It Started With A Kiss" (E.Brown)
   HOT CHOCOLATE *RAK EMI:TCEMTV 42(Cas) CDP 746375-2CD*
KP SALTED PEANUTS (1) "Rebel Yell" (B.Idol) BILLY IDOL
   Chrysalis: IDOL 6 (7"s) IDOLX 6 (12"s)
KP SALTED PEANUTS (2) "The Stripper" (David Rose) DAVID
   ROSE & HIS ORCHESTRA on *Old Gold: OG 9451 (7"s)*

KRAFT CHEESE SLICES "Puffin' Billy" (Edward White) on
'Famous Themes' *GRASMERE (Tayl): GRCD 10 (CD)*
KRAFT DAIRY LEA "Young Ballerina" p.Chappell *not avail.*
KRAFT FREE CHOICE "You're Sixteen" (R.& R.Sherman) orig
JOHNNY BURNETTE (1961) *MFP (EMI): CDMFP 6019 (CD)*
KRAFT MELLO "Mellow Yellow" (Donovan Leitch) by DONOVAN
EMI: CZ 193 (CD) EMS 133 (LP) TC-EMS 133 (Cass)
KRONENBERG LAGER "Goal" & "Saxophone" (Steve Parsons)
performed by STEVE PARSONS - *(not available)*
KYOMI DEODORANT music (K.Jenkins-M.Ratledge)*unavailable*

L.A.GEAR "The Way You Make Me Feel" (M.Jackson) from
'Bad' MICHAEL JACKSON *CBS: 450290-2/1/4 (CD-LP-Cas)*
LABATTS "Serenade" (Paul Hart-Joe Campbell) *unavailable*
LADYBIRD (WOOLWORTHS) "Busy Doing Nothin'"(Johnny Burke
Jimmy Van Huesen)from 1949 film 'A Connecticut Yank
ee In The Court Of King Arthur' sung by BING CROSBY
WILLIAM BENDIX-CEDRIC HARDWICKE *currently deleted*
LAMOT PILS "Albatross" (Peter Green) FLEETWOOD MAC on
'G.Hits' *CBSCD 69011 (CD) 40- (Cass)* / THE SHADOWS
on 'Shadows Collection' *Pickwick: PWKS 559 (CD)*
LANCASTRIAN BUILDING SOC "Narcissus" (Ethel Nevin) TED
HEATH MUSIC 'Thanks For The Memory' *President Everg
reen: PLE 529 (LP) TC-(Cas)* / JOYCE GRENFELL-NORMAN
WISDOM 'British Comedy Classics' *EMI: ECC 7 (2Cass)*
LAND ROVER (Discovery Ad) "Antarcticar" (Geoff McCorma
ck-Simon Goldenberg) - *(not available)*
LAND ROVER (2) "Dambusters March" (Eric Coates) - GEOFF
LOVE ORCH 'Big War Themes' *MFP: HR 8140 (Cass only)*
LAND ROVER (4) "Hippopotamus Song" orig by FLANDERS and
SWANN on *EMI: CDEM 1340 (CD)* also by IAN WALLACE on
'All Aboard' *EMI: CDEMS 1479 (CD)*
LAUGHING COW CHEESE SPREAD "Magic Roundabout Theme" (Al
ain Legrand) *see Coll* 'Themes From Children's BBC'
L'EGOISTE AFTERSHAVE Chanel "Dance Of The Knights" from
Act.1 of 'Romeo And Juliet' Op.64 (Prokofiev)
LE BOX Terry's "It Had To Be You"(Isham Jones-Gus Kahn)
Vers: TONY BENNETT 'Portrait Of A Song Stylist' *Har
mony (BMG): HAR(CD)(MC) 105 (CD/Cass)* / RAY ANTHONY
ORCH 'Dream Dancing' *Capitol: ED 260431-4 (Cass)*
LE JARDIN (Max Factor) "(Wrap Me In Your) Warm & Tender
Love" (Bobby Robinson-Ida Iral Berger) PERCY SLEDGE
'Soul' on *Knight-Castle (BMG): KNCD(KNMC) 12061*
LEA & PERRINS WORCESTER SAUCE "Sorcerer's Apprentice"
(Paul Dukas) *many recordings available all formats*
LEA & PERRINS WORCESTER SAUCE "Shake Rattle & Roll" (C.
Calhoun) BILL HALEY & COMETS *Old Gold: OG 9221 (7")*
LEE JEANS (1) "Homely Girl" UB 40 on 'Labour Of Love 2'
DEP/Virgin (EMI): DEPCD 14 (CD) CADEP 14 (Cass
LEE JEANS (2) "Vedi! Le Fosche" (The Anvil Chorus) from
'Il Trovatore' (Verdi) *many recordings available*
LEE JEANS (3) "Boom Boom" (J.L.Hooker) JOHN LEE HOOKER
Pointblank/Virgin: POBD3(CDs) POB3(Cass) POB3(7"s)
'Boom Boom' *Pb/Virgin: VPBCD12 (CD) VPBMC12 (Cass)*

LEEDS BUILDING SOCIETY (George Cole Ads) "Liquid Gold"
(John Altman)P.Jeff Wayne Music *(not available)*
LEGACY TIGHTS - *see under* 'PRETTY POLLY LEGACY'
LEGAL & GENERAL "Bring Me Sunshine" (Sylvia Dee-Arthur
Kent) version by PHIL KELSALL on 'At The Wurlitzer
Blackpool' *EMI: CDIDL 111 (CD) TCIDL 111 (Cass)*
LEGAL & GENERAL (Plant It With L&G) "Chanson Du Matin"
Op.15/2 (Elgar) Bournemouth Sinfonietta (Norman Del
Mar) on *Chandos (Taylors): CHAN 8371 (CD)*
LEMSIP (1) "Goodnight Sweetheart Well It's Time To Go"
(Calvin Carter-James Hudson) by The SPANIELS on
'Play It Cool' *CHARLY R&B: CDCHARLY 222 (CD)*
LEMSIP (2) "Moon River" (H.Mancini-J.Mercer) HENRY MANC
INI *see Collections under* 'Henry Mancini'
LEVI JEANS 501 Ads:-
LEVI 501 (1) "I Heard It Through The Grapevine"
(Norman Whitfield-Barrett Strong) orig MARVIN GAYE
LEVI 501 (2) "Wonderful World" (Sam Cooke-Lou Adl
er-Herb Alpert) SAM COOKE *RCA: PD 87127 (CD)*
LEVI 501 (3) "Stand By Me" (B.E.King-Mike Stoller
Jerry Leiber) BEN E.KING - *Atlantic: A.9361 (7"s) &
Old Gold OG 9101 (7"s)* also on film 'Stand By Me'
LEVI 501 (4) "When A Man Loves A Woman" (C.Lewis-A.Wrig
ht) PERCY SLEDGE *Old Gold (Pinn): OG 9496 (7"s)*
LEVI 501 (5) "C'mon Everybody" (Eddie Cochran-Jerry Cap
ehart) EDDIE COCHRAN *Liberty (EMI): (CD)(TC)ECR 1*
LEVI 501 (6) "Mannish Boy" (Morganfield-McDaniel-
London) MUDDY WATERS - *Epic (CBS): MUD 1 (7"s) MUDT
1 (12"s)* also incl "Hootchie Cootchie Man" *DELETED*
LEVI 501 (7) "Be My Baby"(Phil Spector-E.Greenwich-Jeff
Barry) - RONETTES available on'Dirty Dancing' S/T
RCA (BMG) BL 86408 (LP) BK 86408 (CS) BD 86408 (CD)
LEVI 501 (8) "Ain't Nobody Home" B.B.KING.on 'Best Of'
MCA: MCL 1612 (LP) MCLC 1612 (Cas) CMCAD 31040 (CD)
LEVI 501 (9) "Can't Get Enough" by BAD COMPANY on
'10 From 6' *Atlantic (WEA): 781625-2 (CD)* also 'Bad
Company' *Island: ILPS(ICT) 9279 (LP/Cass)*
LEVI 501 (10) "The Joker" (S.Miller) STEVE MILLER BAND
on *'The Joker' Fame-MFP (EMI): CDFA 3250 (CD) TCFA
3250 (CS) FA 3250 (LP)* & 'Best Of Steve Miller 1968
-73' *Capitol (EMI): (CD)(TC)EST 2133 (CD/Cass/LP)*
LEVI 501 (11) "Should I Stay Or Should I Go" CLASH *CBS
(Sony):'Story Of The Clash' 460244-2 (CD) -4 (Cass)*
LEVI 501 (12) "20th Century Boy" (Marc Bolan) by T.REX
'Ultimate Collection' *Telstar (BMG): TCD(STAC) 2539*
LEVI 501 (13) "Mad About The Boy" from 'Words & Music'
(Noel Coward) DINAH WASHINGTON on 'Best Of Dinah
Washington' *Mercury: 512214-2(CD) -4(Cass) -1(LP)*
also by KEN MACKINTOSH & HIS ORCH on 'Mac's Back'
President (Prism-Target): PLCD 532 (CD)
LEVI 501 (14) "Piece Of My Heart" (Bert Berns-Jerry Rag
avoy) sung by ERMA FRANKLIN *Epic (Sony M): 472413-2
(CD) -4 (Cass) 658384-2 (CDs) -4(Cass sing) -7(7"s)*
JANIS JOPLIN *CBS: CBS 32190-2 (CD) 40-32190 (Cass)*

LEVI 501 (15) "Heart Attack And Vine" by SCREAMING JAY
  HAWKINS *Epic (Sony): 659 109-2 (CDs) -4 (Cass) -7
  (7") -6 (12")* and on 'Black Music For White People'
  Demon (Pinn) FIEND(CD)(CASS) 211 (LP/CD/Cass)
  SEE ALSO COLLECTIONS 'ORIGINALS' (Various Artists)
LEVI 501 (16) "Ring Of Fire"(Merle Kilgore-June Carter)
  JOHNNY CASH 'Biggest Hits' Coll *CBS (Sony Music):
  CD 32304 (CD) 40.32304 (Cass)* also *Columbia (Sony):
  CDS 659 785-2 (CDsingle) -7 (7"s)*
LEVI 501 (16a) "Tackle" (Chris Blackwell) *not available*
LIBRA BODYFORM Music composed by Nick Glennie-Smith
  (not available)
LION BAR (Nestle) 'Urban Jungle Ad' original music by
  (Nigel Corsbie) *not available*
LITTLE CHEF "Bread and Butter" THE NEWBEATS - *WEA INT.
  (WEA): YZ 140 (7"s) YZ 140T (12"s)*
LLOYDS BANK "Zion Hears The Watchmen Singing" from 'Wac
  het Auf,Ruft Uns Die Stimme' (Sleepers Awake The Vo
  ice Is Calling) "Cantata No.BWV 140" (J.S.Bach)
  TV arrangement: Christopher Gunning *(not available)*
  MUNCHENER BACH-CHOIR & ORCH (KARL RICHTER)and Edith
  Mathis-Peter Schreier-Dietrich Fischer-Dieskau on
  DG (Poly): 419 466-2 (CD) 419 466-4 (Cass)
LONDON DOCKLANDS "Go With The Flow" (Philip Swain-Tracy
  Johnson) p.Humdrum Music *not available*
LOU-LOU "Pavane" (Faure) *(many recorded versions)*
LOWENBRAU LAGER (1) "Entrance OfThe Gods Into Valhalla"
  from 'Das Rheingold' (Wagner) *many recordings*
LOWENBRAU LAGER (2) "Overture"- 'Royal Fireworks Suite'
  (Handel) *various recordings available*
LUCOZADE (Daley Thompson) "Phantom Of The Opera" (Steve
  Harris-Phil Maloney) From 'Iron Maiden' IRON MAIDEN
  Fame-MFP (EMI): CDFA 3121 (CD) TCFA 3121 (Cass)
LUCOZADE (1) "I Believe" (J.Atkin-I.Dench-Zack Foley)
  EMF from album 'Schubert Dip' *EMI-Parlophone (EMI)
  CDPCS 7353 (CD) TCPCS 7353 (Cass) PCS 7353 (LP)*
LUCOZADE (2) "Soul Power" (J.Brown) JAMES BROWN on 'Sex
  Machine & Other Soul Classics' *Poly: 825 714-2 (CD)*
LUFT-HANSA "Symphony No.40 in G.Minor" K.550 (Mozart)
LUNN-POLY (1) Holiday Shop "Yellow Bird" (No.Luboff-Mar
  ilyn Keith-Alan Bergman) MANUEL *EMI:CDP 746932-2 CD*
LUNN-POLY (2) Winter "Will You Still Love Me Tomorrow"
  (Carole King-G.Goffin) SHIRELLES *Old Gold: OG 9286*
LUNN-POLY (3) "Animals Came In Two By Two" also "When
  Johnny Comes Marching Home" version by ADAM FAITH
  EMI: CZ 260 (CD) TCEMS 1350 (Cass)
LURPAK (1) "Leader Of The Pack" (E.Greenwich-J.Barry-
  G.Morton) SHANGRI-LAS on *Old Gold: OG 9085 (7"s)*
LURPAK (2) "Spread A Little Happiness" from the Musical
  'Mr.Cinders' (V.Ellis-R.Myers-G.Newman) - STING on
  A.& M.: AMS 8242 (7"s) see also 'Mr.Cinders' SHOWS
LURPAK CHEESE SPREAD "Flight Of The Bumblebee" (Rimsky-
  Korsakov) and part of "Requiem" (Faure) *many record
  ings available all formats*

LUX BEAUTY SOAP "Pavane" Op.50 (Faure) *many recordings*
LYCRA (DUPONT) "20 Years After" (Astor Pia Zzolo)
    (not available)
LYCRA SENSATION "Wind Surfing"(Tolga Kashif-Mark Sayer)
    recorded by Music Sculptors *(not available)*
LYNX SHOWER GEL "Samba Pa Ti" (Santana) SANTANA - *Old G
    old OG 9730 (7"s)* also *CBS CD32032 (CD)* 40- *(Cass)*
LYONS CAKES "Tales From The Vienna Woods" (J.Strauss)
LYONS MAID FAVOURITE CENTRES "Love Theme" from 'Romeo &
    Juliet' Op.64 (Prokofiev) *many recordings available*
LYONS ORIGINAL BLEND COFFEE "Blue Danube Waltz" (J.Stra
    uss) *many recordings available*

McCAINS MICRO CHIPS (1) "Yakety Yak" (Jerry Leiber-Mike
    Stoller) orig COASTERS (58) *Old Gold: OG 9089 (7")*
McCAINS MICRO CHIPS (2) "Rip It Up" (Robert Blackwell-
    John Marascalo) orig LITTLE RICHARD on 'Little Rich
    ard' on *Deja-Vu DVCD 2083 (CD) DVMC 2083 (Cass)*
McCAINS OVEN READY CHIPS (1) "Feed Me" (Alan Menken-How
    ard Ashman) from 'Little Shop Of Horrors' *see* FILMS
McCAINS OVEN READY CHIPS (2) "Superman" by BLACK LACE
    on *Telstar: STAR 2250 (LP) STAC 2250 (Cass)*
McCAINS PIZZA SLICES "Shaddap You Face" (Dolce) - JOE
    DOLCE MUSIC THEATRE - *Epic: EPC 9518 (7"s)(deleted)*
McCOYS CRACKER SNAPS "Two-Step Farouche" by JOHN DELAF
    OSE and The Eunice Playboys from 'Per Et Garcon' on
    Rounder (Celtic Music): ROUNDER CD 2116 (CD)
McEWANS LAGER (Boulders) "You've Got The Power" by WIN
    'Uh Tears Baby' *London: 828047-2 (CD) LON(C)(LP) 31
    (Cass/LP) all formats currently deleted*
McEWANS LAGER (Chinheads)"Something So Real"(Robin Gow)
    LOVE DECREE *Ariola (BMG):(6)112642 (12"/7") deleted*
McEWANS LAGER (Iceberg) "Souareba" (SALIF KEITA) 'Soro'
    Sterns (Poly): STCD 1020 (CD) STC 1020 (Cass)
McEWANS LAGER (Walkin') "Walkin'In A Straight Line" by
    RICK FENN *not available*
McEWANS LAGER (5) (92) "Difference" by D JUM D JUM on
    Rhythm King (RTM): 7"s/12"s
McVITIES BOASTERS "String Quartet Impressions" (Dominic
    Sands) p.Cavendish Music *(not available)*
McVITIES FRUIT JASPERS "Genius Of Love" TOM TOM CLUB on
    Island (Poly): ILPM 9686 (LP) ICM (Cass) CID (CD)
McVITIES GOLD BAR "Working In The Coal Mine" (Allen Tou
    ssaint) LEE DORSEY - *Old Gold: OG 9108 (7")*
M.& M's "The Candy Man"(Leslie Bricusse-Anthony Newley)
    from 'Willy Wonka & Chocolate Factory' (71) *Deleted*
MAGNET FURNITURE "Magic" (Bill Lyall-David Patton) by
    PILOT (74) *Old Gold: OG 9723 (7"s)*
MARY QUANT MAKEUP "She's So Fine" (Morley) THUNDER on
    'Thunder' *EMI: CDEMC 3570 (CD) EMTC 3570 (Cass)*
MAIL ON SUNDAY (1) "Sleeping Beauty" Ballet Op.66
    (Tchaikovsky) *(many recordings available)*
MAIL ON SUNDAY (2) "Blue Moon"(R.Rodgers-L.Hart) COWBOY
    JUNKIES on 'Blue Moon Revisited' - *Cooking Vinyl*

(Revolver) FRY 011CD (CDsingle) FRY 011(T) (7"/12")
note: TV version specially recorded (based on the
original Decca recording by Greta Keller) *DELETED*
MAIL ON SUNDAY (YOU Magaz.) "Mr.Sandman" (Pat Ballard)
CHORDETTES on 'Alan Freed R'N'R Collection' *Deja Vu
(Wynd-Up-T.Blood): DVLP 2130 (LP) DVMC 2130 (Cass)*
MALIBU (1) "Buy Off The Bar" (Lincoln Minott) 'Buy Off
The Bar' (LP) SUGAR MINOTT - *Black Roots (Jetstar)*
MALIBU (2) "One Love"/"People Get Ready" (B.Marley) BOB
MARLEY & THE WAILERS on 'Exodus' *Island: CID 9498
(CD) ILPM/ICM 9498 (LP/Cass)*
MALTESERS (1) "Dream Lover" (Bobby Darin) - BOBBY DARIN
Old Gold (Pinn): OG 9017 (7"s)
MALTESERS (2) "Flashdance" (Giorgio Moroder)-S/T-*Casabl
anca (Poly): PRICE(PRIMC) 111 (LP/CS) 811492-2 (CD)*
MANDATE AFTER SHAVE "Missing You" (J.Waite-M.Leonard-C.
Sandborn) JOHN WAITE on 'Missing You' (collect) *EMI
CDEMTV 53 (CD) TCEMTV 53 (Cass) EMTV 53 (LP)*
MANWEB - *SEE UNDER* 'ELECTRIC'
MARTINI (Orig Theme) "Dancin'Easy" (Chris Gunning) sung
by DANNY WILLIAMS *(Ensign-now deleted)*
MARTINI (New Theme) "The Quest" (Christopher Gunning)
(not available)
MASTERBLEND COFFEE "Violin Concerto in D.Major" Op.35
(Tchaikovsky) 1st m/m *(many recordings available)*
MATTESONS "La Premier Bon Heur Du Jour" by FRANCOISE
HARDY on 'Francoise Hardy's Greatest Hits' on *Vogue
(Discovery/Music Junction): 600 006 (CD)*
MAXELL TAPES (1) "Night On Bare Mountain" (Mussorgsky)
on Coll 'Commercial Breaks'/ 'Classic Experience'
MAXELL TAPES (2) "The Israelites" (D.Dekker-L.Kong) DES
MOND DEKKER & THE ACES - *Old Gold: OG 9268 (7"s)*
MAXELL TAPES (3) "Into The Valley" (R.Jobson-S.Adamson)
THE SKIDS on 'Fanfare' *Virgin: VM(C) 2 (LP/Cass)*
MAXWELL HOUSE (1) "The Mission" (Ennio Morricone) from
film -S/T- of the 1986 Robert De Niro-Jeremy Irons
movie *Virgin (Poly): CDV 2402 (CD) TCV 2402 (Cass)*
MAXWELL HOUSE (2) "Going Home" (Mark Knopfler) from
'Local Hero' -S/T- *Vertigo (Poly): 811 038-2 (CD)*
singles: *VER 81 (7") VERMC 81 (Cass) VERCD 81 (CDs)*
MAYNARDS JUST FRUITS based on "Gimme Dat Ding" (Mike Ha
zlewood-Albert Hammond) orig The PIPKINS (1970) on
Old Gold (Pickw): OG 9730 (7"s)
MAYNARDS WINE GUMS "Hoots Mon" (Harry Robinson) by LORD
ROCKINGHAM'S XI (1959) on *Decca (Poly): 882 098-2
(CDs) 882 098-4 (Cass) 882 098-7 (7")* also 'BRITISH
'BEAT BEFORE THE BEATLES VOL.3' *EMI CDGO 2048 (CD)*
MEMOREX TAPES "Nights In White Satin" THE MOODY BLUES
Moody Blues - *Old Gold (Pinn): OG 9349 (7"s)*
MERCANTILE CREDIT (1) "Coronation Scott" (Vivian Ellis)
'Famous Themes' *Grasmere: GRALP 10 (LP) GRTC 10 (C)*
MERCANTILE CREDIT (2) "Meditation" from 'Thais' (Massen
et) 'Encores You Love' (coll) *CFP (EMI): CDCFP 4543
(CD) CFP 4543 (LP) TC- (Cass) / others available*

MERCURY COMMUNICATIONS "In The Air Tonight" (Phil Colli
ns) PHIL COLLINS *Virgin: (CD)(TC)V 2185 (CD/Cas/LP)*
MERCURY COMMUNICATIONS (Harry Enfield/R.Branson) "Calli
ng All Workers" (Eric Coates) 'Historic Recordings'
ERIC COATES *HMV (EMI): CDHMV 1 (CD) TCHMV 1 (Cass)*
MERRYDOWN VINTAGE CIDER "Non-Stop" (John Malcolm) JOHN
MALCOLM ORCHESTRA on 'Sounds Visual' on *Radio Six
Productions (R6): RSY 603 (Cass) deleted*
METRO GTA NEW "Oh Yeah" (Dieter Meyer & Boris Blank) by
YELLO *-Mercury (Poly) 826 773-2 (CD) -4 (CS) -1(LP)*
MFI "Just My Imagination" (Norman Whitfield-Barrett Str
ong) orig TEMPTATIONS (1971) on 'Motowns G.Hits' on
Motown-Polydor (Poly):530105-2(CD) -4(Cass) -5(DCC)
MIDLAND BANK "Ode To Joy" from Symphony No.9 (Choral)in
D.min.Op.125 (Beethoven) *many recordings available*
MIDLAND BANK (Meridian A/C) "Turn Turn Turn" (Pete Seeg
er) *ORIG* (1965) THE BYRDS - *Old Gold: OG 9747 (7"s)*
MILK *Animated Bottles* "The Grasshopper's Dance" (Ernest
Bucalossi) PALM COURT THEATRE ORCH. 'Picnic Party'
Chandos: CHAN 8437 (CD) LBT 002 (Cass) LBR 002 (LP)
MILK (Wake Up To Milk) "Cool For Cats" (Glen Tilbrook-
Chris Difford) by SQUEEZE - 'Singles 45 and Under'
*A.& M. (Poly): CDA 64922 (CD) CAM 64922 (Cass) and
A.& M. AMCD 694 (CDs) AMMC 860 (Cass) AM 860 (7"s)*
MILK (Bob Geldof) "The Runner" (Jan Hammer)- JAN HAMMER
MCA (BMG): 'Snapshots' MCG(C)(DMGC 6039 (LP/CS/CD)
MILK (Cooler In A Can) "No Particular Place To Go" (Chu
ck Berry) CHUCK BERRY 'The Collection' *Castle Comm.
(BMG): CCSLP 194 (Dbl LP) CCSMC 194 (Cass)*
MILK - see also 'Scottish Dairies'
MILKY BAR "Home For Christmas Day" THE RED CAR AND THE
BLUE CAR *Virgin: VS 1394 (7"s) VSC 1394 (Cass)*
MILLER LITE (1) Quayside Ad "Bigger Isn't Better" from
'Barnum' (Cy Coleman-Michael Stewart) *TV Vers:* JOE
Campbell *(not available)* see 'Barnum' Films & Shows
MILLER LITE (2) "He Ain't Heavy He's My Brother" (B.Rus
sell-Bobby Scott) HOLLIES - *EMI: (TC)EMTV 11 (Cas/
LP) CDP 746238-2 (CD)* also on MFP: HR 8153 (Cass)
MILLER PILSNER All Of These Things Make Me Happy "Glad"
composed and sung by Tony Gibber *not available*
MINOLTA CAMERAS "You Are So Beautiful" (Billy Preston-
Bruce Fisher) by BONNIE TYLER *currently unavailable*
orig JOE COCKER (75) on 'The Essential Joe Cocker'
Polydor (Poly): 515 411-2 (CD) 515 411-4 (Cass)
MOBIL based on "24 Hours From Tulsa" (music by Burt Bac
harach) special lyrics *not available in this form*
MORRISSONS SUPERMARKETS "Mexican Hat Dance" (J.Tapatio)
JAMES LAST 'Trumpet A Go-Go' *Polydor 821 587-2 (CD)*
MOSS SECURITY ALARMS "Walk On By" (Burt Bacharach-Hal
David) orig DIONNE WARWICK *Old Gold: OG 9284 (7"s)*
MULLER MULLERICE "Captain Of Your Ship" (Kenny Young-B.
Yardley) REPARATA & DELRONS *currently unavailable*
MULTI-CHEERIOS (Nestle) "Chinese Dance" from 'Nutcrack
er Suite' (Tchaikovsky) *many versions all formats*

MURPHY'S IRISH STOUT (1) "Winter Wonderland" (Richard
    Smith-Felix Bernard) *many versions available*
MURPHY'S IRISH STOUT (2) "High Hopes" (Sammy Cahn-Jimmy
    Van Huesen) from film 'A Hole In The Head' (59) by
    FRANK SINATRA 'Screen Sinatra' *MFP: CDMFP 6052 (CD)*
MURPHY'S IRISH STOUT (3) "Someone's Rocking My Dream Bo
    at" (Leon Rene-Emerson Scott-Otis Rene)'Best Of INK
    SPOTS' *MFP (EMI):CDMFP 6064 (CD) TCMFP 50529 (Cass)*

N.S.P.C.C. (1) "Sorry Seems To Be The Hardest Word" (El
    lton John) ELTON JOHN 'G.Hits' *Poly: 846947-2 (2CD)*
    (2) "Tell Me There's A Heaven"(Chris Rea) CHRIS REA
    'Road To Hell' *WEA Magnet: 246 285-2 (CD) WX 317(C)*
NAPOLINA SAUCES "Max" (Paulo Conte) by PAOLO CONTE on
    East West (WEA): YZ 588 (7"s) YZ588CD (CDs)
NAT WEST "Crockett's Theme" (Jan Hammer) JAN HAMMER
    'Escape From Television' *MCA (BMG): MCLD(MCLC)19133*
NATIONAL EXPRESS "Together Again" (Buck Owens) versions
    RAY CHARLES 'Greatest C&W Hits' *Sequel-Knight (BMG)
    NEXTCD 100 (CD) NEXTLP 100 (LP) NEXTC 100 (Cass)*
    GLEN CAMPBELL 'Country' Capitol: *EG 260052-4 (Cass)*
    EMMYLOU HARRIS 'Elite Hotel' *WB (WEA): K(2)(4)54060*
NATIONAL POWER "The Right Stuff" (Bill Conti) -S/T- on
    Varese (Pinn): VCD 47250 (CD) with 'NORTH & SOUTH'
NATIONAL SAVINGS OPTION BONDS (1) "Let's Twist Again"
    (Kal Mann-Dave Appell) CHUBBY CHECKER on *Success
    (Taylors) 2083CD (CD) 2083MC (Cass)*
NATIONAL SAVINGS OPTION BONDS (2) "Morning Mood" from
    'Peer Gynt Suite No.1' Op.46 (Grieg) BERLIN PHILHAR
    MONIC ORCH (Von Karajan) *DG (Poly): 423 208-2 (CD)*
NATIONWIDE BUILDING SOC (1) (Letter / Special Dream)
    "Dreams" (John Trivers-Stanley Myers) *unavailable*
NATIONWIDE BUILDING SOC (2) "Life Is A Rock (But The
    Radio Rolled Me)" (Norman Dolph-Paul Di Franco) by
    REUNION (74) 'American Dreams 70's Vol.1' on *RCA
    (BMG): ND 90374 (CD) NK 90374 (Cass)*
NATIONWIDE ESTATE AGENCIES "All Together Now" (J.Lennon
    P.McCartney) from 'Yellow Submarine' *see under film*
NESCAFE (1) "Dawn" 'Peer Gynt Suite No.1" Op.46 (Grieg)
    'Classic Experience' *EMI: EMTVD 45 (2LPs) & Cass/CD*
NESCAFE (2) "I Can See Clearly Now" (Johnny Nash) on
    'JOHNNY NASH's Greatest Hits' *Epic: 465306-2 (CD)*
NESCAFE (3) Boat "Adagio" ('Spartacus') (Khachaturian)
NESCAFE ALTA-RICA (1) "La Colegiala" (Sopad) 'Cumbia
    Cumbia' - RODOLFO Y SU TIPICA RA 7 on *Ariola (BMG):
    122 992 (7"s) 612 992 (12"s) 662 992 (CDs) DELETED*
NESCAFE ALTA-RICA (2) "Pan Flute" (Gary Bell) p. Jeff
    Wayne Music *(not available)*
NESCAFE BLEND 37 "Black Coffee" (Ike & T.Turner) HUMBLE
    PIE from 'Eat It' *A&M: AMLS 6004 (LP-deleted) note:*
    TV version recorded by Steve Marriott not available
NESCAFE CAPPUCCINO "Dock Of The Bay" (Steve Cropper-O.R
    edding) OTIS REDDING *Old Gold: OG 9500 (7"s)*
NESTLE - *see under* brand name e.g. 'LION BAR'

NIKE (1) "Bo Diddley" (Bo Diddley)on 'In The Spotlight'
    BO DIDDLEY - *Chess (Poly): CHD 9264 (CD)*
NIKE (2) "Running Man" composed and performed by JOHN
    ZORN *(not available)*
NIKE (3) (AIR CROSS TRAINING) "Sergey Bubka" composed &
    conducted by MALCOLM McLAREN *(not available)*
NIKE (4) "Instant Karma" (John Lennon) JOHN LENNON from
    'Shaved Fish' *EMI: CDP 746642-2 (CD) (TC)PCS 7173*
NIKE (5) "Can I Kick It?" (Hoods-Reed) A TRIBE CALLED
    QUEST *Jive (BMG): JIVE(T)(CD) 265*
NIKE (6) "Little Wing" by JIMI HENDRIX on 'Axis Bold As
    Love" *Polydor (Poly): 847 243-2(CD) -4(Cass) -1(LP)*
NIKE (7/8) "Football" (David Ryder) and "Kids" (Dave St
    ricker) *original commissions and not available*
NISSAN CARS 'Flying' (John Harle) JOHN HARLE & OPERA
    HOUSE feat SARAH on *Internal Affairs-Zomba (BMG):
    KGBD 004 (CDs) KGBT 004 (12"s) KGB 004 (7"s)*
NISSAN CARS Swimming Pool Ad "Dance Of The Swans" from
    'Swan Lake' (Tchaikovsky) *many recordings available*
NISSAN MICRA "Combo-Beach-Teaser" (Steve Parsons) STEVE
    PARSONS *specially composed / not available*
NISSAN PRIMERA 16 Valve STEVE PARSONS *not available*
NIVEA LOTIONS "Blue Velvet" (Bernie Wayne-Lee Morris)
    BOBBY VINTON (63) on *Epic (Sony):* on 'Blue Velvet'
    Epic: 467570-2 (CD) -4(Cas) -1(LP)
NIVEA LOTIONS (2) "Avalon" (Bryan Ferry) 'Avalon' ROXY
    MUSIC - *EG (Virgin-Pol): EGCD 50 (CD) EGLP 50 (LP)*
NORWICH UNION "All The Way" (Sammy Cahn-J.Van Huesen)
    various vocal versions available
NORWEB - *SEE UNDER* 'ELECTRIC'
NUROFEN (1) "The Great Gig In The Sky" (Pink Floyd) on
    'The Dark Side Of The Moon' - PINK FLOYD on *Harvest
    CDP 746001-2 (CD SHVL 804 (LP) TC-SHVL 804 (Cass)*
NUROFEN (2) "Etude"(Francisco Tarrega) by MIKE OLDFIELD
    from ' The Killing Fields' -S/T- *Virgin: OVED 283
    (LP) OVEDC283(Cas) CDV2328 (CD)* also 'Gakkaen' (Aki
    ra Tamba) by ONO GAGAKU KAI SOCIETY ORCH on 'Japon'
    Ocora C.559018(CD) BOTH TRACKS: *Virgin VS 1328 (7")*
NUTCRACKER Terry's "Chinese Dance" from 'The Nutcracker
    Suite' (Tchaikovsky) *many recordings all formats*

OBSESSION PERFUME "Somewhere" (L.Bernstein-S.Sondheim)
    from WEST SIDE STORY -S/T- *Sony: 4677606-2 (CD)*
OIL OF ULAY (1) "First Time Ever I Saw Your Face" (Ewan
    MacColl) ROBERTA FLACK - *Old Gold: OG 9524 (7"s)*
OIL OF ULAY (2) "You Got What It Takes" (Berry Gordy-Ha
    rvey Fuqua-Raquel Davis) - MARV JOHNSON - *Stateside
    (EMI): SSL 6031 (LP)* / SHOWADDYWADDY - *Tiger (Poly)
    SHTV 1 (LP) SHMC 1 (Cass) SHCD 1 (Compact Disc)*
OIL OF ULAY (3) "Stay As Sweet As You Are" (Mack Gordon
    Harry Revel) *TV vers.not available* / NAT KING COLE
    'Love Is The Thing' *Capitol (EMI):CDP 746 648-2(CD)*
OLD ENGLAND SHERRY "There'll Always Be An England"(Ross
    Parker-Hugh Charles) VERA LYNN - *EMI: (TC) EMTV 28*

OLD SPICE (1) "Prima Vere" from 'Carmina Burana' (Carl
    Orff) *many recordings available*
OLD SPICE (2) "I Feel Good" (J.Brown) JAMES BROWN 'Very
    Best of James Brown' *Poly: 845 828-2(CD) -4(Cass)*
OLIVIO OLIVE OIL "Addio A Lugano" (Petro Gori) p.Joe &
    Co. *(unavailable)*
OPTREX (1) "Singin'In The Rain"(Nacio Herb Brown-Arthur
    Freed) - *see Films & Shows*
OPTREX (2) "I'm Wishing" (Larry Morey-Frank Churchill)
    'Snow White & Seven Dwarfs" *TV VERSION unavailable*
ORANGINA "Pida Me La" (Michel Berger) - The GIPSY KINGS
    not available
ORPHELIA AVON PERFUME "Chanson Triste" (Henry Du Parc)
    KIRI TE KANAWA - *EMI: EL 270135-2 (CD) -4 (CS)* also
    on *Philips: 416445-1 (LP) -4 (Cass) -2 (Comp Disc)*
OUTSPAN ORANGES "In The Summertime" (Ray Dorset) MUNGO
    JERRY - *see 'ANTI-DRINK DRIVING CAMPAIGN'*
OVALTINE "We Are The Ovaltineys Little Girls And Boys"
    THE OVALTINEYS *CJMO (Taylors): OVALP 1 (LP)* deleted
OVALTINE CHOCOLATE COLLECTION "My Baby Just Cares For
    Me" (Walter Donaldson-Gus Kahn) from 'Whoopee' (30)
    NINA SIMONE *Charly: CYZ 7112 (7")* also *EMI:EMTV 44*
OVALTINE LIGHT (1) "Fever" (John Davenport-Eddy Cooley)
    PEGGY LEE 'Million Selling Hits Of The 50s' *MFP
    MFP (EMI): CDMFP 6047 (CD) (TC)MFP 5847 (Cass/LP)*
OVALTINE LIGHT (2) "Hev Yew Gotta Loight, Boy?" (Alan
    Smetherst) SINGING POSTMAN (1966) orig on 'Best Of'
    EMI: GEP 8956 (EP) Starline: SRS 5063 (LP) deleted
OVALTINE OPTIONS "Mind Blowing Decisions" (John Wilder)
    HEATWAVE on 'Powercuts' *Epic (SM): 468921-2 (CD) -4*

P.& O.EUROPEAN FERRIES "Stompin'At The Savoy"(B.Goodman
    -Andy Razaf-Edgar Sampson-Chick Webb) BENNY GOODMAN
    'King Of Swing' *Pickwick:PWK 027(CD) HSC 3273(Cass)*
    also on *RCA Blue Bird (BMG): ND(NK) 90631 (CD/Cass)*
P.& O.FERRIES (1) "J'Attendrai" (B.Sievier-D.Olivieri-N
    Rastelli-L.Poterat) sung by TINO ROSSI 'Best Of'
    Capitol (EMI): CDEMS 1444 (CD) TCEMS 1444 (Cass)
P.& O.FERRIES (2) "La Mer" (Charles Trenet)
    SACHA DISTEL-*Ist Night (Pin): SCORE(C) 29 (7"/Cass)*
    CHARLES TRENET - *EMI: CDP 794464-2 (CD) EMS 1361 LP*
    BOBBY DARIN - *Old Gold: OG 9944 (7"s)*
PANASONIC (Cinema) "Imagination" (B.Some) BELOUIS SOME
    'Some People' *PARLOPHONE: EJ 240318-2(CD) -4(Cass)*
PANASONIC MS50 RECORDER "It's Over" (Roy Orbison-Joe Me
    lson) ROY ORBISON - *Old Gold: OG 9879 (7")* 'Legenda
    ry Roy Orbison' *Telstar: TCD 2330 (CD) STA(C)R 2330*
PANASONIC NICAM TV "Rondo" Finale from 'Eine Kleine Nac
    htmusik' Serenade No.13 in G.K525 (Mozart) *many rec
    odings available inc: 'Classic Experience 2' (EMI)*
PAXO STUFFING "I'm In The Mood For ('Ska') Love" (Jimmy
    McHugh-Dorothy Fields) sung by LORD TANAMO on *Moonc
    rest (Total-BMG): MOON 1009 (7"s) 12MOON 1009 (12")*
    also by TECHNIQUES on 'BaBaBoom' *Trojan: TRLS 265LP*

PEARL INSURANCE "Que Sera Sera" (J.Livingston-R.Evans)
   DORIS DAY on *Old Gold: OG 9091 (7"s)*
PEARL PENSIONS "As Time Goes By" (Herman Hupfeld) from
   'Casablanca' (1943) *see under FILMS & SHOWS*
PEARL SOAP - *see under* 'CUSSONS PEARL'
PEAUDOUCE BABY SLIPS "Dance Of The Hours" from 'La Gioc
   onda' (Ponchielli) *(many recordings available)*
PEAUDOUCE BABYKINI "Itsy Bitsy Teeny Weeny Yellow Polka
   Dot Bikini" (Paul Vance-Lee Pockriss) BRIAN HYLAND
   Old Gold (Pinn): OG 9598 (7") BOMBULARINA on *Carpet
   Polydor (Poly): CRPTX 1 (12"s) CRPT 1 (7"s)*
PEDIGREE CHUM 1st movement from 'New World Symphony' No
   9 in E.Min.Op.95 (Dvorak) *many recordings available*
PENTAX CAMERAS "Good Luck Charm" (Aaron Schroeder-Wally
   Gold) ELVIS PRESLEY *RCA (BMG): PD 90100-2 (2CD)*
PEPSI COLA (1) "It Takes Two" (William Stevenson-Sylvia
   Moy) ROD STEWART & TINA TURNER (1990) *W.Bros.(WEA):
   ROD 1(T)(C)(CD) (7"/12"/Cas/CD)* /orig (1966) MARVIN
   GAYE & KIM WESTON on *Motown (Poly): ZD 72397 (CD)*
PEPSI COLA (2) "Superfly Guy" Mark Moore-Pascal Gabriel
   S'EXPRESS *Rhythm King: CDLEFT 028(CDs) LEFT 028(T)*
PEPSI COLA (3) "The Best" (Knight-Chapman)- TINA TURNER
   'Foreign Affair' *Capitol:CDESTU 2103 (CD) ESTU 2103
   (LP) TCESTU 2103 (Cas) CL 543 (7") 12CL 543 (12"s)*
PEPSI COLA (4) "Seal Our Fate" (G.Estefan) GLORIA ESTEF
   AN - *Epic: 656773-7(7") -6(12") -4(Cass) -2(CDs)*
PEPSI COLA (5) "Rhythm Of My Heart" (Jordan-Capek) ROD
   STEWART - *W.Bros (WEA): W0017(7")(T=12")(C=Cas)(CD)*
PERRIER "I Put A Spell On You" (Jay Hawkins) SCREAMING
   JAY HAWKINS on 'Frenzy' *Edsel-Demon (Pinn): EDCD
   104 (CD) CED 104 (Cass)* also by ALAN PRICE on 'Best
   Of' *Castle (BMG): CDAR 1010 (CD) ARLC 1010 (Cass)*
   and NINA SIMONE 'Best Of' *Timeless/Phonogrm (Poly)
   822 846-2 (CD) TIMEC 10 (Cass) TIME 10 (LP)*
PERRIER (Keep One Below) "Groovin'" (Felix Cavaliere-E.
   Brigati) YOUNG RASCALS (67) *Old Gold: OG 9905 (7"s)*
PERRIER "Holding Out For A Hero" (Jim Steinman) from
   'Footloose' *see also* 'HERO AFTERSHAVE' (TV Ad)
PERSIL "Three Little Birds" (Don't Worry 'bout A Thing'
   BOB MARLEY *Island: BMW 1 (2LP) BMWC 1 (Cass)* + CD
PERSIL CONCENTRATED LIQUID (CHORAL AD) "Liquid Asset"
   (Ralph Allwood) prod.Joseph Glasman *(not available)*
PERSIL MICRO "I Remember You" (V.Schertzinger-J.Mercer)
   TV version *not available* / FRANK IFIELD on 'Best Of
   EMI Years' *EMI: CDEMS 1402 (CD) TCEMS 1402 (Cass)*
PERSIL MICRO (2) "Reet Petite" (Berry Gordy Jr-Tyran Ca
   rlo) orig JACKIE WILSON on *ACE: CDCH 913 (CD) or
   TBD: MCCD 017 (CD) or Ariola (BMG): 261 854 (CD)*
PERSIL WASHING UP LIQUID "There's No One Quite Like Gra
   dma" (Gordon Lorenz) by ST.WINIFRED'S SCHOOL CHOIR
   (1980) *MFP (EMI): TCMFP 5732 (Cass) FP 900 (7" del)*
PETITE TOYS "Va Pensiero" from Act 3 'Nabucco' (Verdi)
PEUGEOT 106 (1) "Respect" (O.Redding) ARETHA FRANKLIN
   Old Gold: OG 9102 (7"s)

PEUGEOT 106 (2) "Let The River Run"CARLY SIMON (Working
    Girls' *Arista (BMG): 662124 (CDs) 112124 (7")*
PEUGEOT 106 (3) "You're In My Heart" (Rod Stewart) ROD
    STEWART 'Best Of' *WB (WEA):926034-2 (CD) WX 314(C)*
PEUGEOT 106 KEY WEST / KEY LARGO SPECIAL EDITIONS "Open
    Your Heart" (Madonna Ciccone-Gardner Cole-Peter Raf
    elson) by MADONNA from 'True Blue' (86) *Sire (Wea):
    925 442-2 (CD) WX 54C (Cass) WX 54 (LP) & on single*
PEUGEOT 205 (1) "Just One Look" (D.Payne-G.Carroll) The
    HOLLIES - *EMI: EMTV 11 (LP) TC-EMTV 11 (Cass)*
PEUGEOT 205 (2) "The More I See You" (Mack Gordon-Harry
    Warren) - CHRIS MONTEZ - *Old Gold: OG 9146 (7"s)*
PEUGEOT 205 (3)"Working My Way Back To You"(Bob Gaudio)
    FOUR SEASONS - 'Greatest Hits' - *Platinum (Prism)*
PEUGEOT 205 (4) "See Me Feel Me" (Pete Townshend) from
    rock opera 'Tommy' (film 1975) Roger Daltrey vocal
    -S/T- *Polydor: 2657 014 (Dbl LP) 800 077-2 (CD)*
PEUGEOT 205 (5) "Look Of Love" (Martin Fry-Mark Lickley
    Stephen Singleton) ABC on 'Lexicon Of Love' *Neutron
    (Polyg): 810 003-2 (CD) NTRS 1 (LP) NTRSC 1 (Cass)*
PEUGEOT 205 (6) "Baby Please Don't Go" (Joe Williams) -
    THEM (1965) *London (Poly): LON(X)(CD)(CS) 292 (7"s/
    12"s/CDs/Cass)* also on Film -S/T- 'Days Of Thunder'
PEUGEOT 306 (1)(Drives The Imagination) (Karl Jenkins
    Mike Ratledge) *orig commission not available*
PEUGEOT 306 (2)"I Drove All Night" ROY ORBISON on 'King
    Of Hearts' *Virgin (EMI): CDVUS 58 (CD) VUSMC 58
    (Cass)* and *Virgin: VUS(C)(CD) 79 (7"/CDs/Cass)*
PEUGEOT 309 "Only You" (Buck Ram) - 1988 TV Ad version
    by JAR - *Chrysalis (CBS): CHS 3302 (7"s)   DELETED*
    PLATTERS version on *Old Gold (Pinn): OG 9485 (7"s)*
PEUGEOT 405 "Take My Breath Away"(G.Moroder-T.Whitlock)
    - BERLIN from -S/T- 'Top Gun' (Film 86) - *CBS 70296
    (LP) 40-70296 (Cas) CDCBS 70296 (CD) CBS 656361-7"*
    instrumental version see Coll 'SAXOPHONE ROMANCE'
PEUGEOT 405 (2) "Everyone's A Winner" (Errol Brown) HOT
    CHOCOLATE (78) on 'Very Best Of Hot Chocolate' -*EMI
    CDP 746375-2 (CD) EMTV 42 (LP) TC-EMTV 42 (Cass)*
PEUGEOT 605 "The Moldau" 2nd m/m from 'Ma Vlast' (My
    Country' (Smetana) Concertgebouw Orch.(A.Dorati) on
    Philips: 420 607-2 (2CD's) -4 (D.Cass) -1 (2LP's)
PHILIPS DCC "O Mio Babbino Caro" (Oh My Beloved Father)
    'Gianni Schicchi' (Puccini) *vers:* RENATA TEBALDI on
    'Famous Arias' *Decca (Poly): 433636-2(CD) -4 (Cass)*
PHILIPS ELECTRICAL "Hold On I'm Comin'" (Isaac Hayes &
    David Porter) SAM & DAVE on 'Soul Classics' - *Ocean
    (BMG-Wynd Up): OCN 2002-WL (LP) -WK (Cass) -WD (CD)*
PHILIPS LADYSHAVE "I Like Her Style" (Ronnie Bond) sung
    by Dave Lloyd *(not available)*
PHILIPS PHLISHAVE FOR MEN "Man Inside" (John Silverman)
    not available
PICNIC (Cadbury) "My Coo Ca Choo" (Peter Shelley) ALVIN
    STARDUST on 'Greatest Hits' on *Connoisseur (Pinn):
    CSALP 105 (LP) CSAPMC 105 (Cass) CSACD 105 (CD)*

PIMMS "Summertime" (George & Ira Gershwin) from 'Porgy & Bess' KIRI TE KANAWA 'Kiri Sings Gershwin' *EMI EL 270474-1/-4 / CDC747454-2 (CD) see Films & Shows*

PIONEER IN-CAR CD SYSTEM "Driver's Seat" SNIFF 'N' THE TEARS "Best Of Sniff'n'The Tears" *Chiswick (Pinn): CDWIK 102(CD) WIKC 102(Cass)* also on *Fun After All (Pinn):(CD)(12)(TF) FAA 115 (CDs/12"/7"/Cass)*

PIONEER MULTIPLAY CAR SYSTEM "Journey Is On The Inside" (Chris Christoffels) - Belgium *(not available)*

PIRELLI TYRES (1) "Nessun Dorma" (None Shall Sleep)from 'Turandot' (Puccini) GEOFF LOVE ORCH 'Opera Without Words' *EMI: CDP 746931-2 (CD)* PLACIDO DOMINGO 'The Essential Domingo' *DG: 429305-2 (CD) PDTVC 1 (Cass)* LUCIANO PAVAROTTI *Decca 417011-2 (2 CD's)*

PIRELLI TYRES (2) "Vesti La Giubba"'On With The Motley' from 'Pagliacci' (Leoncavallo) versions inc: FRANCO CORELLI *EMI: CDC 747851-2(CD)* JOSE CARRERAS *HMV: EX 290811-3 (2LP) EX 290811-5 (2Cas)* LUCIANO PAVAROTTI *Decca:414590-2(2CD)* JUSSI BJORLING *EMI:CDC 749503-2*

PIRELLI TYRES (3) "Riders On The Storm" (J.Densmore-Jim Morrison-Robbie Krieger-Ray Manzarek) THE DOORS on 'L.A.Woman' - *Elektra (WEA): K2-42090 (CD) K4-42090 (Cass) K-42090 (LP) / Old Gold (Pinn): OG 9520 (7")*

PIRELLI TYRES (4)(Sharon Stone Ad) "Choral" from 'Symph ony No.9' (Beethoven) plus "Worldly Woman" (Steve Parsons) *not available*

PIZZA HUT "Hot Hot Hot" by ARROW (84) on'Sound Of Soul' *Blatant (Castle Comm/BMG): BLATCD 11 (CD)*

PLAX DENTAL RINSE "Wheels" (Norman Petty) JOE LOSS ORCH 'In A Romantic Mood' - *EMI: CDP 746930-2 (CD)* / LEO KOTTKE 'Best Of Leo Kottke'- *EMI: CDP 746486-2 (CD)*

POLY COLOR "She's Got It" (orig by LITTLE RICHARD) on 'Here's Little Richard' *ACE (Pinn): CDCHM 128 (CD)*

POMAGNE "Pizzicato" from 'Sylvia' Ballet (Delibes) *(many recordings available)*

PONDS CREAM "Child" (Joe Campbell and Paul Hart) p.Joe & Co. *(not available)*

POT TV - *see under* 'GOLDEN WONDER POT TV'

POTTERTON BOILERS "This Ol' House" (Stuart Hamblen) SHAKIN' STEVENS - CBSCD 10047 (CD) 40-10047 (Cass)

POWERGEN - *see under* 'NATIONAL POWER'

PRESTIGE OVENWARE "What Becomes Of The Broken Hearted" (Riser-Dean-Weatherspoon) - JIMMY RUFFIN - *Motown (Poly): 530 057-2 (CD) 530 057-4 (Cass)*

PRETTY POLLY (1) "Move Over Darling" from film featur: DORIS DAY on 'A Portrait Of' on *Stylus (CD/Cass)*

PRETTY POLLY (2) "The Very Thought Of You" (Ray Noble) NEW MAYFAIR DANCE ORCHES with AL BOWLLY - *BBC (Pin) REB 649 (LP) ZCF 649 (Cass) BBC CD 649 (C.Disc)*

PRETTY POLLY (3) "Mario Mario" Love Duet Act 1 'Tosca' (Puccini) TV version: MARIO DEL MONACO with Renata Tebaldi on *Decca: 417 175-4DA (Cass)* OTHERS 'Great Love Duets' JOSE CARRERAS and Katia Ricciarelli on *Decca 421308-2(CD)* also GIACOMO ARAGALL & KIRI TE

KANAWA and Nat.Philh.Orch *Decca: 414 597-2 (2 CDs)*
PRETTY POLLY LEGACY "All Day And All Of The Night"(Ray
   Davies) The KINKS (64)'Kinks Collection' on *Castle
   Collectors (BMG): CCSCD 113 (CD) CCSMC 113 (2Cass)*
PRUDENTIAL (Whatever You Want In Life) "Prudential"
   (Nicholas Dodd) *not available*
PYRAMINTS Terry's 'Egyptian-Ella' (Walter Doyle) JACK
   HYLTON ORCH (1931) *available version:* TED WEEMS &
   HIS ORCH on 'Marvellous!' *Living Era-ASV (Koch Int)
   CDAJA 5029 (CD) ZCAJA 5029 (Cass)*

Q.C.SHERRY "Orchid Ella" (Pierre Arvay) published by
   De Wolfe Music *not available*
QUALITY STREET (1) "Dancin' In The Street" (M.Gaye-W.St
   evenson) MARTHA & VANDELLAS - *Motown (Poly)*
   DAVID BOWIE-MICK JAGGER - *EMI America: EA 204 (7"s)*
QUALITY STREET (2) "Magic Moments"(B.Bacharach-H.David)
   PERRY COMO *Old Gold: OG 9606 (7")* and 'When Housewi
   ves Had The Choice' *BBC: BBCCD 730 (2xCD) REQ(ZCQ)*
QE2 CRUISES "Elvira Madigan Theme" from 'Piano Concerto
   No.21 in C' (Mozart) *many recordings available*

RAC (New Knights Of The Road) "Gimme Shelter" (M.Jagger
   K.Richard) ROLLING STONES on 'Hot Rocks 1964-71'
   London (Poly): 820140-2 (2CD) -4 (Cas) also on "Let
   It Bleed" *London: 820052-2 (CD) SKL(KSKC) 5025*
RADION MICRO PLUS "In The Mood"(Andy Razaf-Joe Garland)
   GLENN MILLER ORCHESTRA *Old Gold: OG 9602 (7"s)*
RADOX BATH SALTS (1)" Lazy River" (Hoagy Carmichael-Sid
   Arodin) from 'Best Years Of Our Lives' (film 46) by
   HOAGY CARMICHAEL - *Connoisseur (Pinn): VSOPLP 103
   (LP) VSOPMC 103 (CS)* / also BOBBY DARIN 'Legend Of'
   Stylus (Pinn):SMR(C) 8504 (LP/CS) / LOUIS ARMSTRONG
   'S.Louis Blues' *Black Lion (C'point) INT 127.035 LP*
RADOX BATH SALTS (2) "Yaketty Yak" (J.Leiber-M.Stoller)
   COASTERS - *Old Gold (Pinn): OG 9089 (7"s)*
RADOX SHOWER FRESH "Singin'In The Rain" (A.Freed-N.Herb
   Brown) (52 G.Kelly movie) *see Films & Shows*
RAGU PASTA SAUCE (1) Aria "Largo Factotem" from 'Barber
   Of Seville' (Rossini) *(many recordings available)*
RAGU PASTA SAUCE (2) "Anvil Chorus" from 'Il Travatore'
   (Verdi) *(many recordings available)*
RAGU PASTA SAUCE (3) "La Donna E Mobile" - 'Rigoletto'
   (Verdi) *(many recordings available)*
RAGU PASTA SAUCE (4) "Vesto La Guibba" - 'I Pagliacci'
   (Leoncavallo) *(many recordings available)*
RAGU PASTA SAUCE (5) "Funiculi-Funicula" (Denza) vers:
   JOSE CARRERAS *Poly: 400015-2 (CD)* LUCIANO PAVAROTTI
   Decca: 410015-2 (CD) and 417011-2 (CD)
RAPPORT AFTER SHAVE "Let's Stay Together" by AL GREEN
   Hi-Demon (Pinn): HIUKCCD 130(CD) HIUKCASS 130(Cass)
REACTOLITE RAPIDE SUNGLASSES "Dance of the Sugar Plum
   Fairy" from 'Nutcracker Suite' (Tchaikovsky)
   many recordings available in all formats

REAL FIRES BRITISH COAL (1) "Will You Love Me Tomorrow"
(C.King-G.Goffin) SHIRELLES 'Hits Of The 60s' *Ocean
(Wynd Up) OCN 2008(WL)(WK)(WD)* / *Old Gold: OG 9286*
REAL FIRES BRITISH COAL (2) "A Room With A View" (Noel
Coward) NOEL COWARD *Happy Days (Con): CDHD 168 (CD)*
RED MOUNTAIN COFFEE "Shout" (Isley Bros) LULU on 'Somet
hing To Shout About' *Deram (Poly): 820 618-2 (CD)*
RED ROCK CIDER "Police Squad" Theme (Ira Newborn) from:
'NAKED GUN' *see under film* 'Naked Gun 2½'
Shadows theme (Hank Marvin) *not available*
REEBOK (1) (Sports) "Epic" (Chris Blackwell) *not avail.*
REEBOK (2) "Life Party" (2 Deep) 2 DEEP on *Atomic/A.& M
(Poly): WNR 821 (7") WNRT 821 (12") WNRCD 821 (CDs)*
REEBOK PLANET "Let's Do One" (Lisa Inayoue) "Do What I
Want" (Dominic Jennings) "What Could It Be" (Ingrid
Konupek) "Extreme" (Daniel Caccavo) *all unavailable*
REGIONAL RAILWAYS - *see under BRITISH RAIL*
RENAULT 19 "Temptation" (Paul Hardy-Joe Campbell) Joe &
Co sung by LESLEY GARRETT *not available*
RENAULT 19 ('Lunchtime' Ad) - *see RENAULT CLIO*
RENAULT 19 "House Of The Blue Danube" (MALCOLM McLAREN)
Epic (Son): WALTZ(C)(S)(T)4 (7"/Cass/CDs12")deleted
RENAULT 21 (1) "I Feel Free" (Clapton-Bruce) JACK BRUCE
Virgin: VS 875 (7"s) VS 875-12 (12"s) / also CREAM
on *Polydor: 817 172-1 (LP) 817 172-4 (Cass)*
RENAULT 21 (2) "The Prisoner Theme" (Ron Grainer) Music
ails and recordings see **TV Themes section**
RENAULT (21/25/E) "C'mon Let's Go" (R.Valens) RITCHIE
VALENS on 'Greatest Hits' *Antelope (Conifer): ANTC
52030 (CD)* TOMMY STEELE on 'The Rock'n'Roll Years'
See For Miles (Pinn): SEECD 203 (CD) SEE 203 (LP)
RENAULT CLIO ('Interesting' Ad) "Johnny & Mary" (Robert
Palmer) *TV vers.arr.by Carl Jenkins & Mike Ratledge
unavailable* / ORIG ROBERT PALMER track on 'Clues'
Island (Poly): CID(ICM)(ILPM) 9595 (CD/Cass/LP)
RENAULT ESPACE (as CLIO ad)
RENNIES "I'm Sitting On Top Of The World" (Lewis-Young-
Henderson) AL JOLSON 'Man & The Legend Vol.4' *Rhaps
ody (Presid): RHMD 4 (LP)* LES PAUL & MARY FORD 'Cap
itol Years' *EMI: (CD)(TC)EMS 1309 (CD-Cass-LP)*
RIDGEWAYS TEA "Soulful Africa" (Gary Bell) p.Jeff Wayne
Music *(not available)*
RIGHT GUARD "Three Little Birds" (Don't Worry 'bout A
Thing)(Bob Marley) BOB MARLEY & WAILERS on 'Legend'
Island: BMWCD 1 (CD) BMWCX 1 (Cass) BMWX 1 (LP)
RIMMEL COSMETICS "Silk" (Phil Sawyer) *not available*
RITZ BISCUITS "Love Theme" from 'Romeo & Juliet' (Proko
fiev) - London Symphony Orchestra (Andre Previn) on
EMI: CDS 749 012-8 (2 CD's) / many other versions
ROBINSONS MARMALADE "Calling All Workers" (Eric Coates)
see 'MERCURY COMMUNICATIONS' ad
ROCKY BAR (Fox's) based on "Rockin'Robin" *originally by*
BOBBY DAY (58) on 'Rockin'Robin' *ACE: CDCH 200 (CD)*
MICHAEL JACKSON (72) 'Best Of M.Jackson' *Motown BMG*

RONSEAL (1) "Bring It On Home To Me" (Sam Cooke) TV Ver
David Dundas *(unavailable)* | SAM COOKE - *RCA (BMG):*
PD 87127 (CD) 'The Man & His Music'| JOHN LENNON on
'Rock'n'Roll' *MFP: TC-MFP 50522 (Cass)* CDP 746707-2
RONSEAL (2) "Everything Is Beautiful" by RAY STEVENS -
Pickwick-Spot: SPR 8554 (LP) SPC 8554 (Cass)
ROSES (Cadbury) "Bring Me Sunshine" (S.Dee-Arthur Kent)
MORECAMBE & WISE *(Philips:del)* BRENDA LEE *(MCA:del)*
ROSS CHIP SHOP "Food Glorious Food" from 'Oliver' (Lio
nel Bart) - *see under* **FILMS & SHOWS**
ROSS STIR-FRY "Twist And Shout" (Isley) - THE BEATLES
from 'Please Please Me' - *Parlophone (EMI) PCS 3042*
(LP) TC-PCS 3042 (Cass) CDP 746435-2 (C.Disc)
ROVER 200 "Up Where We Belong" (from 'An Officer And A
Gentleman') Joe Cocker-Jennifer Warnes on *Island*
and (Poly): WIP 6830 (7"s) see also FILMS & SHOWS
ROVER 400 (1) "Nevertheless" (Bert Kalmar-H.Ruby) from
'Three Little Words' (Film 36 with Fred Astaire) TV
version by NILSSON on 'A Little Touch Of Schmilsson
In The Night' *see ROVER 800 for label & number*
ROVER 400 (2) "Unforgettable" (Irving Gordon) version
by NAT KING COLE on 'Unforgettable Nat King Cole' -
Capitol (EMI): CDEMTV 61 (CD) TCEMTV 61 (Cass)
ROVER 600 comp: Anthony and Gaynor Sadler *not available*
ROVER 800 "Lullaby In Ragtime" (Harry Nilsson)- NILSSON
on 'A Little Touch Of Schmilsson In The Night' *RCA:*
(BMG) NK 83761 (Cass) NL 83761 (LP) CD unconfirmed
ROVER 2000 "String Quartet No.2 In D.Minor" (Borodin)
Borodin String Quartet *(EMI): CDC 747795-2 (CD)*
ROVER GTI (Car Alarm Ad) "Old Folks" (Robinson-Hill) by
BEN WEBSTER (sax) on 'Live In Amsterdam' on *Charly*
(Charly): CDCHARLY 168 (CD only)
ROWENTA POWERMASTER "Aria-Ebben Ne Andro Lontana Act 1"
'La Wally' (Catalani) - RENATA TEBALDI - *Decca Jubi*
lee (Polyg): 414 205-1 (LP) 414 205-4 (Cass)
ROWNTREES JELLIES "Shakin' All Over" (Fred Heath-Guy Ro
binson) JOHNNY KIDD & PIRATES *EMI: CDKIDD 1 (2CD)*
ROYAL BANK OF SCOTLAND (1) "Sorcerer's Apprentice"(Paul
Dukas) - *(many recordings available)*
ROYAL BANK OF SCOTLAND (2) "Lieutenant Kije Suite"Op.60
London S.O.(Previn) *EMI: EG 290298-1 (LP) -4 (Cass)*
ROYAL BANK OF SCOTLAND (3) "Pictures At An Exhibition"
(Mussorgsky) *(many recordings available)*
ROYAL BANK OF SCOTLAND (4) "Playful Pizzicato" from 'A
Simple Symphony' Op.4 (B.Britten) *many recordings*
ROYAL BANK OF SCOTLAND (5) "Cursum Perficio" (Enya)from
'Watermark' ENYA - *WEA: 243875-2 (CD)-1 (LP)-4(Cas)*
ROYAL BANK OF SCOTLAND (6) "Savings Symphony" (Carl Dav
is) *(not available)*
ROYAL DOULTON CHINA "Enigma Variations Op.36" (Elgar)
(many recordings available)
ROYAL INSURANCE "I'm Gonna Sit Right Down and Write Mys
elf a Letter" (Joe Young-Fred Ahlert) *ORIG* by FATS
WALLER (35) *Official (Charly): OFFICIAL 3030-2 (CD)*

ROYAL MAIL (Love Letters) "Love Letters" (Victor Young-
   Edward Heyman) TV version: Maggie Ryder *unavailable*
ROYAL MAIL (St.Valentines Day) "Amore Bachiane" (Rossi
   Testoni) sung by Nuccia Bon Giavanni (EMI) *deleted*
ROYAL MAIL "Spread A Little Happiness" (Vivan Ellis-Ric
   hard Myers-Greatrex Newman) (Musical 'Mr.Cinders')
   Rev.London Cast 1983 TER (Koch): ZCTER 1069 (Cass)
RUMBELOWS "Don't Have Any More Mrs.Moore" (Harry Castli
   ng-James Walsh) TV version arr.by Richard Niles..*NA*
   originally LILY MORRIS (1926) currently unavailable
RYVITA (1) "You're The One That I Want" (John Farrar)
   'Grease' - *see* FILMS & SHOWS
RYVITA (2) "Bolero" (Ravel) 'Classics 2' - *Decca (Poly)*
   421 260-2 (CD) 421 260-4 (Cass) many other versions
RYVITA SESAME SEEDS "Fur Elise" Bagatelle No.25
   in A.minor (Beethoven) *(many recordings available)*

SAMSUNG TV'S "Sam's Song" (Lewis Quadling-Jack Elliott)
   BING CROSBY *MCA: MCL(C) 1607 (LP/Cass)* MIKE SAMMES
   SINGERS *Late Night Vinyl (Taylors) LNV 1 (2LP)* PHIL
   KELSALL *Grasmere (Tay): GRALP 25 (LP) GRTC 25 (Cas)*
SANATOGEN "Do You Feel Alright" (Chris Blackwell) *orig
   commission (not available)*
SAVE & PROSPER BUILDING SOCIETY "Minuet" (Boccherini)
SCHLOER MINERALS "I Get A Kick Out Of You" ('Anything
   Goes')(Cole Porter) GARY SHEARSTON *Old Gold:OG 9733*
SCHREIBER KITCHENS "Little Things Mean A Lot" (Carl Stu
   tz-Edith Lindeman) TV version sung by Linda Taylor
   (not available) / KITTY KALLEN on "Mid-Late 50s Bal
   lad Number Ones Vol.1" *Old Gold (Pinn):OG 3501 (CD)
   OG 2501 (Cass) OG 1501 (LP)* / TIMI YURO on "18 Unfo
   rgettable Ballads" *Mainline: 260403-2 (CD) -4 (Cas)*
SCHWEPPES MALVERN WATER "Symphony No.1-4th movement" by
   (Elgar) *many recordings available*
SCOTCH VIDEO TAPES "Not Fade Away" (B.Holly-N.Petty) by
   ROLLING STONES *(Decca)* and BUDDY HOLLY *(MCA)*
SCOTTISH & NEWCASTLE - *see* 'TARTAN SPECIAL'
SCOTTISH AMICABLE based on "I'm Just A Lucky So And So"
   (Duke Ellington) TV version sung by Lance Ellington
   (not available) / DUKE ELLINGTON with AL HIBBLER on
   Bluebird (BMG): PB 49197 (7"s)
SCOTTISH DAIRIES (MILK) "Don't You Forget About Me" (Ke
   ith Forsey-Steve Schiff) by SIMPLE MINDS on 'Glitte
   ring Prizes Simple Minds 1981-92' *Virgin: SMTVD 1
   (CD) SMTVC 1 (Cass) SMTVM 1 (MD) 463168 (DCC)*
SCOTTISH WIDOWS "Looking Good" (Tony & Gaynor Sadler)
   p.Logorythm Music *not available*
SEA FISH INDUSTRIES (1) "Shout" (Isley Bros) LULU & THE
   LOVERS - *Old Gold (Pinn): OG 9393 (7"s)*
SEA FISH INDUSTRIES (2) "Hold Tight Hold Tight" (I Want
   Some Seafood Mama)"(L.Kent-J.Brandow-L.Ware-W.Spots
   wood) ANDREWS SISTERS 'Sing Sing..'*MFP CDMFP 6044CD*
SEALINK (Lasting Impressions Ad) "Night Life" (R.Webb)
   De Wolfe Music *not available*

SEALINK "The Pleasure Cruise" (Harry Gifford-Frederick
   E.Cliffe) GEORGE FORMBY on 'George Formby' - *World*
   Records (EMI): SH 151 (LP deleted)
SEALY BEDS "In The Still Of The Night" (Cole Porter)
   FIVE SATINS from -S/T- 'Dirty Dancing' *RCA (BMG):*
   BD 86408 (CD) BK 86408 (Cass) BL 86408 (LP)
SEAT TOLEDO "I Want It All" (Queen) QUEEN *Parlophone*
   EMI: 'The Miracle' *CDPCSD 107(CD) TCPCSD 107(Cass)*
SECRET CHOC.BAR "Have You Seen Her" (Eugene Record-Bar
   bara Acklin) CHI-LITES on 'Very Best Of The Chi-Li
   tes' on *Music Club Int (TBD-MCI): MCCD 029 (CD)*
SEGA GAMES "Barber" (Richie Farmer) *not available*
SENSIQ COSMETICS "Strati Angelaki" (arr: Alex Yossifov)
   THE TRIO BULGARKA on 'Balkana: Music Of Bulgaria'
   Hannibal (Pinn): HNCD 1335 (CD) HNBC 1335 (Cass)
SENSODYNE TOOTHPASTE "Cry" (Kevin Godley-Lol Creme) by
   JOE GLASMAN *(not available)* orig (1985) GODLEY AND
   CREME on "Changing Faces" on *Polyd: 816 355-2 (CD)*
7 UP "Rain Rain Beautiful Rain" (Joseph Shambalala) The
   LADYSMITH BLACK MAMBAZO on 'Shaka Zulu' *W.Bros WEA:*
   WX 94C (Cass) 925582-2 (CD)
SHAPE YOGHURT - see under ST.IVEL
SHARP COMPACT DISC PLAYERS "Now Those Days Are Gone" by
   BUCKS FIZZ - *RCA: PD 70022 (CD) PK (Cass) PL (LP)*
SHARP'S EXTRA STRONG MINTS "Humoreske" Op.101 (Dvorak)
   (many recordings available)
SHARWOOD'S INDIA "Colours" (David Motion) *not available*
SHEBA CAT FOOD (1) "Lean On Me" (Bill Withers) CLUB NOU
   VEAU *W.Bros: W 8430(T) (7"/12")* /AL JARREAU *Topline*
   (K)TOP 173 (CS/LP) BILL WITHERS *Old Gold OG 9186 7"*
SHEBA CAT FOOD (2) "If" (David Gates) - BREAD 'Sound Of
   Bread' *Elektra (WEA): K 252062 (CD) K 452062 (Cass)*
SHEBA CAT FOOD (3) "When I Need You" (Albert Hammond-
   Carole B.Sager) LEO SAYER - *Old Gold: OG 9691 (7"s)*
SHEBA CAT FOOD (4) "There You Are" *not available*
SHELL (1) "Happy Valley" (theme)(Nick Portlock) *deleted*
SHELL (2) "I Want To Break Free" (Brian Deacon)
   QUEEN *EMI: QUEEN 2 (7") CDP 746016-2 (CD)*
SHELL (3) "No Particular Place To Go" (C.Berry) CHUCK
   BERRY '20 Great Tracks' *MFP (EMI): CD(TC)MFP 5936*
   (CD/Cass) also *Chess/MCA (BMG): CHLD 19116 (CD)*
SHIELD SOAP "The Continental" (Herb Madgison and Con
   Conrad) BOSTON POPS ORCH (J.Williams) on 'Salute To
   Hollywood' *Philips (Poly): 422 385-2 (CD)*
SHREDDED WHEAT "Coronation Scot" (Vivian Ellis) Queen's
   Hall Light Orchestra *see Collection 'Famous Themes'*
SHREDDIES (1) "Just Like Eddie" (Geoffrey Goddard) orig
   HEINZ - *Old Gold (Pinn): OG 9353 (7"s)*
SHREDDIES (2) "Ghostbusters" film theme (Ray Parker Jr)
   see under FILMS & SHOWS
SILKIENCE SELECTIVES "Respect" (Otis Redding) - ARETHA
   FRANKLIN - *Old Gold (Pinn): OG 9102 (7"s)*
SILKIENCE SHAMPOO "See Me Feel Me Touch Me" from 'Hair'
   (G.McDermott-J.Ragni-J.Rado) *see FILMS & SHOWS*

SILVIKRIN ACTIVE CARE "Bend Me Shape Me" (Scott English
Lawrence Weiss) AMEN CORNER *Old Gold: OG 9354 (7")*
SILVIKRIN HAIR SHAMPOO "Time After Time" sung by CYNDI
LAUPER - *Portrait: PRT 25792 (LP) 40-25792 (Cass)*
SIMPLE SOAP (Skin Care) "Simple Soap" (David Dundas)
not available
SINGAPORE AIRLINES "Singapore Serenade" 'You're A Great
Way To Fly' ANDREW THOMAS *Arena RIA 17 (7")deleted*
SINGAPORE AIRLINES (2) (orig music by Riley and Wilson:
not available) NOTE: similar to "Chung Kuo" (Vangel
is) from 'China' on *Polydor: 813 653-2 (CD)* ALSO:
"Chung Kuo Revisited" (Vangelis) ADDAMS & GEE on
Debut (Pinn): DEBT 3108 (7"s) DEBTX 3108 (12"s)
SKI YOGHURT "Apeman" (Ray Davies) *ORIG* THE KINKS (70)
on *Old Gold: OG 9579 (7"s)* ALSO 'The Hit Singles
Collection' *PRT (Castle-BMG): PYL(PYM)(PYC) 7002*
SKOL LAGER "Winners Song" ('I'm A Winner & You're A Win
ner') RALPH McTELL - *Mays (Spartan): ING 11 (7"s)*
SKY MULTI-CHANNELS PACKAGE "You're The First The Last
My Everything" (Barry White) BARRY WHITE on 'Let
The Music Play' *Pickwick: PWKS 4128P (CD) PWKMC
4128P (Cass,* also on *Old Gold: OG 9770 (7"s)*
SMIRNOFF VODKA (Reflections in Bottle Ad) "Midnight The
Stars And You" (H.Woods-J.Campbell-R.Connelly) *TV
version not available* orig: RAY NOBLE ORCHESTRA and
AL BOWLLY *Monmouth Evergreen Impt: MES 6816 (LP)*
SMITH'S CRISPS "Bobby's Girl" (H.Hoffmann-G.Klein) sung
by SUSAN MAUGHAM - *Old Gold (Pinn): OG 9247 (7"s)*
SNICKERS (Prev.Marathon) "Satisfaction" (M.Jagger-K.Ric
hards) - The ROLLING STONES on various compilations
SNICKERS (Superbowl)"Giants Of Sport"(J.Reids)*not avail*
SODA STREAM "Hippy Hippy Shake" (Chan Romero) by The
SWINGING BLUE JEANS on 'The Best Of The EMI Years'
EMI:CDEMS 1446 (CD) TCEMS 1446 (Cass)
SOFT & GENTLE DEODORANT "Move Closer" (Phyllis Nelson)
TV version: MASON JAMES *Soft G (Pinn): SOFTGCD 001
(CD) SOFTGMC 001 (Cass) SOFTGT001 (12"s) / orig by*
PHYLLIS NELSON (85) on *Collection* "All BY MYSELF"
on *Dover-Chrysalis (EMI): CCD 12 (CD)*
SOFT & GENTLE SHAMPOO (1) "Girls Just Want To Have Fun"
by CYNDI LAUPER - *Portrait: PRT 25792 (LP) 40- (CS)*
SOFT & GENTLE SHAMPOO (2) "The Heat Is On" (Glenn Frey)
GLENN FREY see 'Beverly Hills Cop 1' FILMS & SHOWS
SOFTLAN "The Stripper" (D.Rose) DAVID ROSE ORCHESTRA on
Old Gold (Pinn): OG 9451 (7"s)
SONY MUSIC SYSTEMS "Get Up I Feel Like Being A Sex Mach
ine" (Brown-Byrd-Lenhoff) JAMES BROWN & HIS FAMOUS
FLAMES *Polydor: COLE(X)(C)(CD) 15 (7"/12"/Cass/CD)*
SONY CAMCORDER "Teddy Bears Picnic" (Jimmy Kennedy-John
Bratton) Orig 1933 Recording HENRY HALL & HIS ORCH.
on 'All Aboard' *EMI: (TC)EMTX 101 (Cass/LP)*
SPILLERS ARTHUR'S "Sexy Eyes" (Robert Mather-Keith Steg
all-Chris Waters) DR.HOOK "Completely Hooked: Best
Of" *Capitol (EMI): 799209-2 (CD) TCESTV 2 (Cass)*

SPILLERS GOOD LIFE   "Cha Cha Cha" (Graham Preskett) p.
   Air Edel Music *(not available)*
SPILLERS PRIME *see under* 'WINALOT-PRIME'
ST.IVEL GOLD (1) (Tomato) "Ave Maria" (Bach-Gounod)
   (2) (Egg Soldier) "Meditation" ('Thais') (Massenet)
   (3) (Plum) "Men Of Steel" (Maj.Howe) *var.recordings*
ST.IVEL SHAPE TWINPOT "Think" (A.Franklin-Ted White)
   on 'Best Of Aretha Franklin' *Atlantic (WEA): 7567
   81280-2 (CD) 780 160-4 (Cass)*
ST.IVEL´SHAPE (1) sax intro from "Speedy Gonzales" (Bud
   dy Kaye-D.Hill-E.Lee) by PAT BOONE *Old Gold OG 9213*
ST.IVEL SHAPE (2) "1,2,3" (John Madara-David White-L.Bo
   risoff) *ORIG* LEN BARRY (65) *Old Gold: OG 9214 (7"s)*
STAINMASTER (Royal App) "Interferon" PARABOLA p.DeWolfe
   Music *not available*
STANDARD LIFE ASSURANCE "Wonderful Life" (Colin Vearnco
   mbe) by BLACK (1987) from 'Wonderful Life' *A.& M.
   (Poly): CDMID 166 (CD) CMID 166 (Cass)*
STELLA ARTOIS (Oil Painting Ad) "La Forza Del Destino"
   (Verdi) as used in 'Jean De Florette' see FILMS
STORK SPECIAL BLEND MARGARINE "Happy Birthday To You"
   (Mildred J.Hill-Patty S.Hill)
STREPSILS "Gymnopedie No.3" (Erik Satie) Anne Queffelec
   Virgin Class (Pol) VC 790754-2 (CD) -4 (Cass)
STROLLERS (Cadbury) "Wonderful Life" (Dave Dix-Robin Mi
   llar) by BLACK on 'Wonderful Life' on *A.& M. (Poly)
   CDA 5165 (CD) AMC 5165 (Cass) AMA 5165 (LP)*
SUN ALLIANCE (Norman At Fairground Ad) "Telstar" (Joe
   Meek) TORNADOS on '30 Years Of Number 1's Vol.3' on
   Connoisseur Coll (Pinn): TYNO(CD)(LP)(MC) 102
SUN PROGRESS (1) "Chinese Dance" 'The Nutcracker Suite'
   (Tchaikovsky) *many recordings available*
SUN PROGRESS (2) "Let The Sunshine In" from 'Hair' (Ger
   ome Ragni-James Rado-Galt McDermot) *see* TT 92 p.176
SUNDAY EXPRESS (1) "Rockit" (H.Hancock) HERBIE HANCOCK
   CBS 450625-1 (LP) -4 (C) / *Old Gold: OG 4001 (12"s)*
SUNDAY EXPRESS (2) "This Is It" (Van McCoy) MELBA MOORE
   on 'This Is It' *Sequel (BMG): NEXCD 195 (CD)*
SUNDAY MIRROR (1) "When Will I Be Famous" (Nich.Graham)
   BROS from 'Push' *CBS: CBS 460629-4 (Cass) -2 (CD)*
SUNDAY MIRROR (2) "The Best" (Knight-Chapman) orig (89)
   TINA TURNER 'Foreign Affair' *Capitol (EMI): CDESTU
   2103 (CD) TCESTU 2103 (Cass) ESTU 2103 (LP)*
SUNDAY PEOPLE "Every Kinda People" orig: ROBERT PALMER
   on 'Double Fun' *Island: IMCD 23(CD) ICM 9476(Cass)*
SURE SENSIVE "Jeepers Creepers" (Harry Warren-Johnny Me
   rcer) LOUIS ARMSTRONG from film 'Going Places' (38)
   on 'Jeepers Creepers' *Milan (RTM-Pinn): CDCH 602 CD
   C.602 (Cass) A.602 (LP)*
SURF MICRO PLUS (Clown) music (Paul Hart) *not available*
SWEETEX "Fill My Cup Lord" (Isiah Jones) TV version by
   Miriam Stockley-Lance Ellington-Richard Myhill (*not
   available*) version by COUNTRY SHACK on 'A Portrait'
   Sweet Folk All Recordings (Celtic Mus):SFA 056 (LP)

SWINTON INSURANCE "Flinstones Theme" (Hoyt Curtin)- see
   Collections 'Television's G.Hits Vol.1' (S.Screen)
SYBARIS PERFUME "Adagio In G.Minor" (Albinoni) -Academy
   Of St.Martin-In-The-Fields (Neville Marriner) HMV
   EMI: ASD 3017 (LP) TC- (CS) CDC 747391-2 (C.Disc)

T.A. "Ride On Josephine" (G.Thorogood) GEORGE THOROGOOD
   & THE DESTROYERS *Demon (Pinn): FIEND(CD) 55 (LP/CD)*
TAKE-A-BREAK MAGAZINE "Games People Play" (Joe South)
   JOE SOUTH - *Old Gold (Pinn): OG 9717 (7"s)*
TAMPAX "It's My Life" (Dr.Alban-Pop) DR.ALBAN *Logic Ar
   ista (BMG): 665330 (CDs) 115330 (7") 615330 (12"s)*
TANGO "When I'm Cleaning Windows' (G.Formby-F.Cliffe-H.
   Gifford) *ORIG* GEORGE FORMBY (film 36) 'Keep Your Se
   ats Please' on *Ditto (Pickwick): DTO 10204 (Cass)*
TANGO DIET "The Boss" (Tom Blades) *not available*
TARTAN SPECIAL (Scottish & Newcastle)(1 - Negative)
   'Negative' (Ronnie Paris) *not available*
TARTAN SPECIAL (Scottish & Newcastle)(2-Whoops-A-Daisy)
   "Something In The Air" (J.Keene) THUNDERCLAP NEWMAN
   (1969) *Old Gold: OG 9435 (7"s)*
TAUNTON BLACK CIDER "Make My Bay" (Pete Thomas) *record
   ing unavailable*
TAUNTON COOL CIDER "I'm A Wonderful Thing Baby" KID CRE
   OLE & COCONUTS - *Ze Island (Poly) IMA(C) 13 (LP/CS)*
TAUNTON DRY BLACKTHORN CIDER "Splish Splash" (B.Darin)
   BOBBY DARIN - *Old Gold: OG 9088 (7"s)*
TDK AR90 "Always Something There To Remind Me" (H.David
   Burt Bacharach) SANDIE SHAW *Old Gold: OG 9144 (7"s)*
TECHNICS CD PLAYERS "Walk On The Wild Side"
   (Lou Reed) LOU REED - *Old Gold (Pinn): OG 9635 (7")*
TENNENTS EXTRA (Designer Ad) "Nobody's Perfect" (Mike
   Rutherford) - MIKE & THE MECHANICS on 'Livin'Years'
   WEA: WX 203CD (CD) WX 203C (Cass) WX 203 (LP)
TENNENTS EXTRA (London Tube Ad) "Caledonia" (Dougie Mac
   Lean) by DOUGIE MACLEAN on 'Craigie Dhu' - *Dunkeld
   (Celtic Music): DUN 001 (CD)*
TENNENTS EXTRA "Money's Too Tight (To Mention)" (Mick
   Hucknall) SIMPLY RED on 'Picture Book' *Elektra WEA:
   960452-2 (CD) EKT 27C (Cass)*
TENNENTS EXTRA (Jaguar Car Ad) "Car Restorer" by Gary ·
   Bell - pub.Jeff Wayne Music *not available*
TENNENTS EXTRA (Father/Son Ad) "You Will Know When"
   composed & performed by ALAN PRICE *not available*
TENNENTS EXTRA "It's A Man's Man's World" - JAMES BROWN
   Polydor 825 714-2 (CD) 'Live' 823 003-2 (CD)
TENNENTS LA (Stage Door Ad) "Concert" composed and perf
   ormed by STEVE PARSONS *not available*
TENNENTS LA (Fairground Ad) composed and performed by
   Steve Parsons / p.Filmtrax *not available*
TENNENTS LA "Answer Me" (Silencers) - The SILENCERS
   RCA (BMG) PB 42283 (7") PT 42284 (12") PD 42284(CD)
TERRITORIAL ARMY "Ride On Josephine" GEORGE THOROGOOD
   & THE DESTROYERS *Demon (Pinn): FIEND(CD) 55 (LP/CD)*

TERRY'S - see under brand name e.g. 'ALL GOLD'
TESCO'S (1) (Dudley Moore) "In The Mood" (A.Razaf-J.Gar
    land) HENHOUSE FIVE PLUS TOO (RAY STEVENS) deleted
TESCO'S (2) "Carnival Of The Animals" (Saint-Saens)
    many recordings available in alml formats
TESCOS MULTI-SAVERS "One Two Three" (John Madara-David
    White-Leonard Borisoff) LEN BARRY Old Gold:OG 9214
TETLEY BITTER (Blues Riff) (Paul Hart) not available
TETLEY TEA (1) "Fun Fun Fun" (Brian Wilson) BEACH BOYS
    '.20 Golden Greats' Capitol (EMI): CDP 746738-2 (CD)
TETLEY TEA (2) "Windmills Of Your Mind" (Michel Legrand
    A.& M.Bergman) NOEL HARRISON Old Gold: OG 9090 (7")
TETLEY TEA (3) "I Get Around" (Wilson-Love) BEACH BOYS
    'Greatest Hits' EMI: CDEMTV 1 (CD) TCEMTV 1 (Cass)
TETLEY TEA (4) "Tea For Two" (Vincent Youmans-I.Caesar-
    Otto Harbach) from 'No No Nanette' / - TOMMY DORSEY
    ORCH (1959) Diamond Series RCA (BMG): CD 90127 (CD)
TETLEY TEA (5) "The Sorcerer's Apprentice" (Paul Dukas)
    The Ulster Orchestra (Vernon Handley) Chandos (Chan
    dos): CHAN 8852 (CD) ABTD 1469 (Cass)
TEXAS INSTRUMENTS "Romance" 2nd m/m 'Eine Kleine Nacht
    Musik' Serenade 13 in G for Strings K.525 (Mozart)
TEXSTYLE WORLD "It's Late"(Dorsey Burnette) RICK NELSON
    Liberty (EMI): CDEMC 3603 (CD) TCEMC 3603 (Cass)
THOMAS COOK TOURS (1) "Albatross" (P.Green) - FLEETWOOD
    MAC - see Collection 'MOODS 2'
THOMAS COOK TOURS (2)"Do You KnowWhere You're Going To"
    from 'Mahogany' Film S/T with Diana Ross see Films
THOMPSON HOLIDAYS (1) "Do it Again" (M.Love-B.Wilson)
    BEACH BOYS Capitol: CDEMTV 1 (CD) TC-EMTV 1 (Cass)
THOMPSON HOLIDAYS (2) "Song To The Siren" (Tim Buckley)
    TV version by Louise Rutkouski (not available) -LIZ
    COCTEAU (This Mortal Coil) 4AD: CAD(C) 411 (LP/Cas)
THOMPSON HOLIDAYS (3) "Groovin'" (Felix Cavaliere-Eddie
    Brigatti) The RASCALS on Film -S/T- 'Platoon' (87)
    WEA: 781742-2 (CD) WX 95 (LP) WX 95C (Cass)
THOMPSON HOLIDAYS (4) "We Do That We Don't Do That" by
    (Phil Sawyer) not available
THORNTONS TOFFEE "Blue Danube Waltz" (Johann Strauss)
THRESHER WINES "Canon In D" (Pachelbel) vers.on "The Cl
    assic Experience" EMI: EMTVD 45 (2CD) TC-EMTVC 45
    (Cass) or "Essential Classics" Poly: 431541-2(2CD)
TIMES NEWSPAPER "Preludium" (Grieg) Special Re-mix by
    music library TV version not available
TIMEX INDIGLO "Dance Of The Hours" from 'La Gioconda'
    (Ponchielli) many versions available (all formats)
TIMOTEI "Wonderful World" (Phil Sawyer) BEAUTIFUL WORLD
    East West (WEA*): YZ 717(C)(CD) (*not issued)
TIMOTEI MINERALS SHAMPOO (Waterfalls ad) orig composit
    ion by JENKINS-RATLEDGE productions not available
TINY TEARS DOLLS (Kenwood Parker) "Tiny Tears"
    p.Mingles Music not available
TIXYLIX MEDICINES "Dance Of The Sugar Plum Fairy" from
    'The Nutcracker Suite' (Tchaikovsky) many versions

TODAY NEWSPAPER "Day Of Wrath" from 'The Requiem Mass'
(Verdi) *many recordings available*
TOSHIBA TELEVISIONS "Thing-ummy-bob" (Gordon-Thomas-Hen
eker) from 'Happy As A Sandbag' (Mus.75) Orig Cast
Decca SKL5217 deleted TV ver.(Ken Barrie *not avail*)
TOYOTA "Book Of Days" (Enya) ENYA from "Shepherd Moons"
WEA: 9031 75572-2 (CD) WX 431C (Cass) WX 431 (LP)
TOYS'R'US "Walking In The Air" (Howard Blake) sung by
PETER AUTY from 'The Snowman' *CBSCD 71116 (CD) 40-C*
TREBOR SOFT MINTS "Mister Soft" (S.Harley) STEVE HARLEY
& COCKNEY REBEL *EMI:EDP 154677-3 (Dbl LP) CZ15 (CD)*
TRUSTHOUSE FORTE - *see under* 'FORTE'
TSB (1) "Morning Papers Waltz" Op.279 (Joha.Strauss II)
Chicago Symphony Orchestra (Carl Reiner) on *RCA*
Gold Seal (BMG): GD 60177 (CD) GK 60177 (Cass)
TSB (2) "Walking The Blues" (W.Dixon) WILLIE DIXON on
Deja Vu (Wynd-Up/T.Blood) DVLP(DVMC 2092 (LP/Cass)
TSB SPEEDBANK "Mony Mony" (B.Bloom-T.James-B.Gentry-R.
Cordell) TOMMY JAMES & THE SHONDELLS on 'Anthology'
Roulette (EMI): CZ 244 (CD) ROU 5004 (LP) TC-(Cass)
TUBORG LAGER (1) "Georgia On My Mind" (H.Carmichael-S.
Gorrell) RIGHTEOUS BROS 'Greatest Hits' *(Poly) (CD)*
MATT MONRO 'Matt Monro Sings' *MFP: DL411072-9 (Cas)*
T.W.A.AIRLINES "Massachusetts" (B.M.& R.Gibb) BEE GEES
Polydor: SPELP 83 (LP) SPEMC 83 (CS) 831 594-2 (CD)
TWEED PERFUME "Pastoral" from 'Symphony No.6 in F.Major
Op.68' (Beethoven) *many recordings available on all
formats*
TWIRL (Cadbury) "Take Five" (Paul Desmond) 'Kicks-Jazz
Dance 4" - *Affinity (Charly): AFFD 180 (LP)* also by
DAVE BRUBECK *Elite (Pickwick): ELITE 009CD (CD)*
TWIX "Executive Stress" (Phil Ramocon) pub.by SBK Music
not available
TWYNINGS TEA Excerpt from "Madam Butterfly" (Puccini)
many recordings available on all formats
TYCO TOYS "Thunderbirds" (Gray) BARRY GRAY ORCH 'A-Z OF
BRITISH TV THEMES' *Play It Again (Con): PLAY 004 CD*
TYPHOO FRESH BREW TEA "Pick Yourself Up" (Jerome Kern-
Dorothy Fields) 'Swing Time' *see FILMS & SHOWS*
TYPHOO TEA (1) "Rock Around The Clock" (Max Freedman-
Jimmy DeKnight) BILL HALEY/COMETS *Old Gold: OG 9220*
TYPHOO TEA (2) "Agadoo" (BLACK LACE) '16 Great Hits" on
Priority (BMG): LACECD 1 (CD) LACEC 1 (Cass)
TYPHOO TEA (3) "Peggy Sue" (B.Holly-J.Allison-N.Petty)
sung by BUDDY HOLLY on *Old Gold: OG 9222 (7"s)*
TYPHOO TEA (4) "I'm Into Something Good" (Carole King-G
erry Goffin) HERMAN'S HERMITS 'Best O.The EMI Years
Volume 1' *EMI: CDEMS 1415 (CD) TCEMS 1415 (Cass)*
TYPHOO TEA (5) "Jerusalem" (Hubert Parry) Orchestral ve
rsion *not available*
UNCLE BEN'S CLASSIC RECIPES "Fur Elise Bagatelle No.25"
(Beethoven) *(many recordings available)*
U.P.S. (UNITED PARCEL SERVICES) "Simple Task" (Geoffrey
Vilinski) *not available*

VANISH STAIN REMOVER "Take These Chains From My Heart"
  (F.Rose-H.Heath) RAY CHARLES on 'Greatest Country &
  Western Hits' *Next (Castle-BMG) NEXCD 100 (CD)*
VANITY FAIR MAGAZINE original music composed/performed
  by MICHAEL NYMAN *(not available)*
VANTAGE CHEMISTS "She'd Rather Be With Me" (Alan Gordon
  Garry Bonner) THE TURTLES - *Old Gold: OG 9155 (7"s)*
  'Best Of' *Music Club Int (TBD): MCCD 046 (CD)*
VAUXHALL "Layla" (Eric Clapton) DEREK AND THE DOMINOS
  DOMINOS *Old Gold: OG 9422 (7") RSO (Poly): 800014-2
  (CD)* also "Baker Street" (G.Rafferty) from 'City To
  City' GERRY RAFFERTY on *Fame-MFP: CDFA 3119 (CD)*
VAUXHALL ASTRA "Always On My Mind" (Wayne Thompson-Mark
  James-John Christopher) - WILLIE NELSON on 'Country
  Love' *Knight (BMG): KN(CD)(LP)(MC) 13001 (CD/LP/CS)*
  ELVIS PRESLEY 'All-Time Greatest Hits' *RCA (BMG: PD
  90100 (2xCD) PL 90100 (2xLP) PK 90100 (D.Play Cass)*
  PET SHOP BOYS 'Discography' *EMI(CD)TCPMTV3 (CD/Cas)*
VAUXHALL BELMONT "In The Depths of The Temple" 'Pearl
  Fishers Duet' (Bizet) *various recordings avaiable*
VAUXHALL CALIBRA "Tubular Bells Part 1" (Mike Oldfield)
  MIKE OLDFIELD *Virgin: CDV 2001 (CD) TCV 2001 (Cass)*
VAUXHALL CARLTON "Rondo from Horn Concerto No.4 in E.Fl
  at" KV 495 (Mozart) *many recordings available*
VAUXHALL CAVALIER (1) "Highway Patrol" (Ray Llewellyn)
  'Crimebusters' coll - *MFP 5768 (LP) TC-MFP 5768 (C)*
VAUXHALL CAVALIER (2) "Adagio" 'Spartacus' (The Onedin
  Line theme) (Khachaturian) *see TV THEMES Section*
VAUXHALL CAVALIER (3) "After You've Gone" (H.Creamer-T.
  Layton) from films 'For Me And My Girl' and 'Jolson
  Sings Again' *various available versions*
VAUXHALL CAVALIER (4) "Emperor Waltz" (Johann Strauss2)
  see Collect 'ESSENTIAL CLASSICS'
VAUXHALL CAVALIER (5) "Sledgehammer" (P.Gabriel) PETER
  GABRIEL on 'So' *Virgin: PGCD 5 (CD) PGMC 5 (Cass)*
VAUXHALL CLUB "Runaway" (D.Shannon-M.Crook) DEL SHANNON
  O.Gold: OG 9256 (7") Edsel: EDCD(CED) 121 (CD/Cass)
VAUXHALL GT ASTRA "True Love" (Cole Porter) from 'High
  Society' - see FILMS & SHOWS
VAUXHALL NOVA (1) "Hot In The City" (B.Idol) BILLY IDOL
  from 'Vital Idol' (Billy Idol) *on Chrysalis: (EMI):
  CCD 1502 (CD) ZCUX 1502 (Cass) CUX 1502 (LP)*
VAUXHALL NOVA (2) "La Bamba" (R.Valens) RITCHIE VALENS
  O.Gold: OG 9029 (7") /'Gr.Hits' *ACE: CDCHD 953 (CD)*
VAUXHALL NOVA (3) "Peter and The Wolf" (S.Prokofiev)
VAUXHALL NOVA (4) (Cartoon Car Ad) music Joe Campbell &
  Paul Hart (Joe & Co.) *not available*
VAUXHALL NOVA SPIN "How Much Is That Doggie In The Wind
  ow" (Bob Merrill) PATTI PAGE *Old Gold: OG 9482 (7")*
VAUXHALL SENATOR "The Long Ships" from 'Watermark'
  ENYA - *WEA: WX 199 (LP) WX 199C (Cas) WX 199CD (CD)*
VENEZIA PERFUME (Laura Biogitti) "Four Seasons Suite
  for Violin and Strings" Op.8 Numbers 1-4. (Vivaldi)
  Many recordings available all formats

VENO'S COUGH MIXTURE "Little Does She Know" (Burch-Doug
  las-Shuttleworth) adapt.from KURSAAL FLYERS 77 hit.
  the original on 'In For A Spin-Best Of The Kursaal
  Flyers' on *Line (Conifer): 900067 (CD)*
VEUVE DU VERNAY PERFUME "La Mer" (C.Trenet) CHARLES TRE
  NET 'Very Best Of' *EMI: CZ 314 (CD)*
VIDAL SASSOON WASH & GO "Big Girls Don't Cry" (Bob Gaud
  io-Bob Crewe) *orig* FRANKIE VALLI & FPIR SEASONS on
  Polygram: 513 119-2 (CD) -4 (Cass) -1 (LP)
VILEDA SUNSPLASH "Over On The Sunny Side" (Allan Flynn-
  Jack Egan) sung by AL BOWLLY with RAY NOBLE'S ORCH
  AL BOWLLY - *Old Bean (Conif): COLD(OLD) 6 (Cass/LP)*
VIMTO "Ain't That A Shame" (A.Domino-Dave Bartholomew)
  FATS DOMINO on 'The Fat Man Sings' *MFP (EMI): CDMFP
  5938 (CD) TCMFP 5938 (Cass)*
VIN DE PAYS "I Heard It Through The Grapevine" (Barrett
  Strong-Norman Whitfield) *various available versions*
VITTEL SPRING WATER "Aquarium" (Saint-Salens) *not avail*
VITALITE MARGARINE "The Israelites" (D.Dekker-Les Kong)
  DESMOND DEKKER & THE ACES - *Old Gold: OG 9268 (7"s)
  also Mooncrest (Total-BMG): (12)MOON 1009 (7"/12"s)*
VODAPHONE "Busy Line" - details under CELLNET ad
VOLKSWAGEN (93) "Call Me Irresponsible" (Sammy Cahn-Jim
  my Van Huesen) sung by DINAH WASHINGTON on 'Best Of
  Dinah Washington The Roulette Years' *EMI Roulette
  (EMI): CDROU 1054 (CD) TCROU 1054 (Cass)*
VOLKSWAGEN "Changes" (Alan Price) from 'O Lucky Man'(73
  Film) ALAN PRICE - *Ariola (BMG): 109911 (7") 609911
  (12"s)* 'Liberty' *4-10042(Cass) 260042 (CD) DELETED*
VOLKSWAGEN GOLF "I Wonder Who's Kissing Her Now" (J.How
  ard-F.Adams-W.Hough) RAY CHARLES - *Charly: CYZ 119
  (12") Topline TOP 126 (LP) KTOP 126 (C) CDTOP (CD)*
VOLKSWAGEN GTI "Young At Heart" (Robert Hodgens-Siobahn
  Fahey) - The BLUEBELLS (1984) *re-issued March 93 on
  London (Poly):LONCD 338 (CDsingle) LONCS 338 (Cass)*
VOLKSWAGEN PASSAT "God Bless The Child" (Arthur Herzog-
  Billie Holiday) BILLIE HOLIDAY - 'Lady & The Legend
  1952-56' - *Rhapsody (Presid): RHA(C) 6026 (LP/Cass)*
  BLOOD SWEAT & TEARS 'Greatest Hits' *CBS:CD 64803 CD*

WAGON WHEELS (1) "What A Mouth" (R.P.Weston) by TOMMY
  STEELE - *Pickwick-Spot: SPR 8531 (LP) SPC 8531 (CS)*
WAGON WHEELS (2) "Three Wheels On My Wagon"(Barry McGui
  re-Randy Sparks) NEW CHRISTY MINSTRELS '3 Wheels On
  My Wagon' *Ditto (Pickwick): DTO 10246 (Cass)*
WALDMANS STORES "Down Down" (F.Rossi-Robert Young) orig
  STATUS QUO (75) *Old Gold: OG 9566 (7"s)*
WALKERS CRISPS (Model Cars Offer) "633 Squadron" (Ron
  Goodwin) RON GOODWIN ORCH - *see FILMS & SHOWS*
WALKERS CRISPS "You'll Never Walk Alone" (R.Rodgers-O.
  Hammerstein) from 'Carousel' *var.recordings avail.*
WALKERS DOUBLE CRUNCH "Walk Like A Man" (Bob Crewe-Bob
  Gaudio) FRANKIE VALLI & FOUR SEASONS on 'Very Best
  Of' *Flying-Polydor (Polg): 513 119-2 (CD) -4 (Cass)*

WALKERS POPPADUMS "All Shook Up" (Otis Blackwell-Elvis
   Presley) - ELVIS PRESLEY - *Old Gold: OG 9704 (7"s)*
WALNUT WHIP Rowntrees "Demoiselles de Rochefort theme"
   (Michel Legrand) *(TV version unavailable)* ORIG on
   -S/T- 'Young Girls Of Rochefort' deleted
WALLS CORNETTO "O Sole Mio" (Di Capua) Neapolitan song
   'It's Now Or Never' ELVIS PRESLEY hit of 1960 based
   on this - *Old Gold (Pinn): OG 9742 (7"s)*
WALLS MAGNUM AFFAIR (1) "Affair" (Jasper Winge-Leisner)
   (2) "Pearls" (Michael Storey) *(not available)*
WALL'S ROMANZA "Come Back To Sorrento' (E. de Curtis-C.
   Aveling) FRANCO CORRELLI *EMI: CDC 747835-2 (CD)* and
   JOSEPH LOCKE 'Hear My Song' *MFP (EMI): (TC)DL 1033*
   ELVIS PRESLEY 'Surrender' *Old Gold: OG 9742 (7"s)*
WEETABIX (1) "Robin Hood" (Carl Sigman) DICK JAMES *see
   Coll* 'Hello Children Everywhere' *EMI:(CD)(TC)EM1307*
WEETABIX (2) "Run Rabbit Run" (Noel Gay-Ralph Butler)
   FLANAGAN & ALLEN *see Coll* 'HELLO CHILDREN VOL.3'
WEIGHT WATCHERS "You Can Get It If You Really Want" by
   JIMMY CLIFF - *Island: IRG 14 (LP) IRGC 14 (Cass)*
WHS (W.H.SMITH) "Stardust" (Hoagy Carmichael-Mitchell
   Parrish) *TV ver.unavailable / many other recordings*
WHAT'S ON Magazine "Just One Look" (Gregory Carroll-Dor
   is Payne) DORIS TROY on 'Soul Classics' *Ocean (BMG)
   WD(WK)(WL) 2002 (CD/Cass/LP)* / HOLLIES 'EP Collect'
   See For Miles (Pinn): SEECD 94 (CD) SEEK 94 (Cass)
WHIPSNADE ZOO "Out Of Africa Love Theme" (John Barry)
   JOHN BARRY -S/T- *MCA: DMCF 3310(CD) MCFC 3310(Cass)*
WHISKAS "Friends" by ARRIVAL - originally *Decca F.12986
   (1970-7"s)   F.13763 (1978-7"s) both now deleted*
WHITBREADS BEER "Abdul Abulbul Amir" (Percy French)
   PETER SKELLERN 'You're A Lady' *Pickwick: PWK 135 CD*
WILKINSON SWORD EDGE "Protector" (Olivier Bloch-Laine)
   specially recorded in Germany *not available*
WILLOW MARGARINE "On A Tree By A River ALittle Tom-Tit"
   'The Mikado' (G.& S.) D'Oyly Carte *Decca: 425 191-2*
WIMPY BARS "Come On Over To My Place" by THE DRIFTERS -
   Atlantic: K 10216 (7"s) K 60106 (Dbl LP) K4- (Cass)
WINALOT-PRIME "The Long March" (Chris Gunning) Barking
   Light - *Kennel (BMG): WOOF 1 (7"s) DELETED*
WINALOT WHOLEGRAIN (Singing Dogs) "I Like It" (Mitch Mu
   rray) originally 1963 by GERRY & THE PACEMAKERS on
   'The Singles plus' *EMI: CDP 746 602-2 (CD)*
WINNERS MAGAZINE "Built For Speed" (Motorhead) from 'No
   Sleep At All' MOTORHEAD *GWR (BMG) GW(CD)(TC)(LP)31*
WISPA (Cadbury) (1) "Serenade No.13 in G" from 'Eine Kl
   eine Nachtmusik' (Mozart) *many recordings available*
WISPA (Cadbury) (2) "We Do It" (Russell Stone) R.& J.
   STONE on '1976' *Connoisseur Collection (Pinn):
   YRNRCD 76 (CD) YRNRM 76 (Cass) YRNLP 76 (LP)*
WOOL "Canon In D" (Pachelbel) on 'Classic Experience'
   EMI: CDEMTVD 45 (2CD's) + LPs/Cass
WOOLMARK (LOVE FROM) "The Coldest Winter" (Roland Roman
   elli) p.Torpedo (France) *(not available)*

WOOLWICH BUILDING SOCIETY "Trois Gnossiennes" (Erik Sat
   ie) ANGELA BROWNRIDGE *EMI: CDEMX 9507 (CD) EMX 4120
   71-4 (Cass)* ANNE QUEFFELEC *Virgin: 790754-2(CD) -4*
WOOLWORTHS "Smile" (C.Chaplin) from Film 'Modern Times'
   on 'Tribute To Charlie Chaplin' *Decca 421263-4 (CS)*
WRANGLER JEANS (1) "Cross Town Traffic" (J.Hendrix)JIMI
   HENDRIX 'Singles Album' *Polydor: 827 369-2 (2xCD)*
   Polydor: PO 71 (7") PZ 71 (12"s) PZCD 71 (CDsingle)
WRANGLER JEANS (2) "You're Undecided"(J.& D.Burnette-P.
   Burlisson) by JOHNNY BURNETTE TRIO on 'Rock-A-Billy
   Boogie' *Bear Family (Rollercoaster): BCD 15474 (CD)*
WRANGLER JEANS (3) 'DJ Rap' (Ron-In) *not available*
WRIGLEYS SPEARMINT "All Right Now" (Andy Fraser & Paul
   Rodgers) by FREE on 'All Right Now' - *Island CITV 2*
   (CD) ICTTV 2 (Cass) ILPTV 2 (LP) 12IS 486 (12") CID
   486 (CDsingle) CIS 486 (Cass single)

YARDLEY BLACK VELVET "Love Theme" 'Romeo & Juliet' (68)
   (Nino Rota) *see FILMS & SHOWS*
YARDLEY COUNTRY GARDENS "English Country Garden" (Trad)
   (P.Grainger) Various recordings available
YARDLEY ENGLISH LAVENDER "Greensleeves" (Trad.attr.King
   Henry VIII) FRANCK THORNE ORCHEST on 'Pipe Dreams'
   Prestige-BBC (Pinn): CDPM 6002 (CD) (Z)PRIM 6002
YARDLEY FOREVER "When I Fall In Love"(V.Young-E.Heyman)
   orig by JERI SOUTHERN (52) NAT KING COLE (57)
YARDLEY LACE PERFUME "Elvira Madigan Theme" from 'Piano
   Concerto No.21 in C' (Mozart) *(many recordings)*
YARDLEY WHITE SATIN PERFUME "Nights In White Satin" The
   MOODY BLUES - *Old Gold (Pinn): OG 9349 (7"s)*
YORKSHIRE BANK Music composed by (Guildie Howes) P.Lass
   oo Music *unavailable*
YOU MAGAZINE (Orbis) "What A Difference A Day Made"
   Maria Grever-Stanley Adams) DINAH WASHINGTON on
   Mercury: 818 815-2 (CD) ESTHER PHILLIPS on 'Heart &
   Soul Girls' on *Knight (BMG): KN(CD)(MC)(LP) 12004*
YOUNGS SEAFOODS "Symphony No.8 in B.minor" 'Unfinished'
   (Schubert) *many recordings available*
YVES ST.LAURENT "Just Like Lovers" by INDIAN SUMMER on
   Strada (Total-BMG): STRAD 1 (7"s) 12STRAD 1 (12"s)

ZUBES (1) "Old Ned" (Steptoe & Son theme) (Ron Grainer)
   RON GRAINER ORCH *see Col* 'A-Z OF BRITISH TV THEMES'
ZUBES (2) "William Tell Overture" (Lone Ranger theme)
   (Rossini) *many recordings available*

---

for the very latest information why not subscribe to
TELE-TUNES *and have your book updated 3 times a year*
plus access to the telephone database information line

SEE PAGE 249 FOR DETAILS

BOOM BOOM & Other Songs From TV Commercials - V.A. p.93
   Movieplay (Tayl): MVP 5531 (CD) MPV 45331 (Cass)
      (see page 255)

CLASSIC COMMERCIALS - Var.Artists (Decca Recordings)
   Decca (Poly): 440 638-2 (CD) -4 (Cass)   p.1993
      (see page 258)

CLASSIC EXPERIENCE The - Various Artists & Orchs p.1988
   EMI: EMTVD 45 (Dbl LP) TC-(CS) CDEMTV 45 (Dbl CD)
CLASSIC EXPERIENCE 2 - Various Artists & Orchest p.1990
   EMI: CDEMTVD 50 (2CDs) / (TC)EMTVD 50 (2Cass/2LPs)
CLASSIC EXPERIENCE 3 - Various Artists & Orchest p.1991
   EMI: CDEMTVD 59 (2CDs) / (TC)EMTVD 50 (2Cass/2LPs)
CLASSIC EXPERIENCE 4 - Various Artists & Orchest p.1993
   EMI: CDEMTVD 72 (2CDs) (TC)EMTVD 72 (2Cass/2LPs)
      (All Listed in Tele-Tunes 1992/3)

COMMERCIAL BREAKS - Various Original Artists   p.1991
   Columbia (Sony Mus): 469048-2 (CD) 469048-4 (Cass)
      (see page 259)

ESSENTIAL CLASSICS - 33 Of The Greatest Classics p.1990
   DG (Poly): 431 541-2 (2CDs) -4(D.Cass) -1 (2LPs)
      (Listed in Tele-Tunes 1993)

ESSENTIAL OPERA - Various Artists   p.1991
   Decca (Poly): 433 822-2 (CD) -4(Cass) -1 (LP)
      (Listed in Tele-Tunes 1993)
ESSENTIAL OPERA 2 - Various Artists   p.1993
   Decca (Poly): 440 947-2 (CD) 440 947-4 (Cass)
      (Listed in Tele-Tunes 1993)

FAVOURITE TV CLASSICS (Volume 1) - Various Arts. p.1992
   Classics FP (EMI): CDCFP 4613 (CD) TCCFP 4613(Cass)
FAVOURITE TV CLASSICS (Volume 2) - Various Arts. p.1993
   Classics FP (EMI): CDCFP 4626 (CD) TCCFP 4626(Cass)
      (see page 265)

MIDNIGHT MOODS The Lighter Side Of Jazz: Various Arts.
   Verve (Polygram): 515 816-2 (CD) -4 (Cass)   p.1993
      (see page 280)

ORIGINALS - The Levi Jeans Ad Collection: Various Arts.
   Columbia (Sony Music): MOOD(C)(CD) 29   p.1993
      (see page 286)

ROUND MIDNIGHT 20 More Cool Cuts On The Lighter Side Of
   Jazz V.A. *Verve (Poly): 516 471-2(CD) -4(Cass) p.93*
      (see page 288)

STRESS BUSTERS: Music for a Stress-Less World - Various
   RCA Vic (BMG): 09026 60071-2 (CD) -4 (Cass) p.1993
      (see page 293)

A - *see under next word*

A.D.-ANNO DOMINI (BBC1 31/3/86) Mus sco (Lalo Schifrin) PARIS PHIL.ORCH *Import (Silva Screen): PCD 112 (CD)*

A.L.F.(USA)(ITV-25/4/87)*see Coll* 'AMERICAN TV THEMES 2'

A-TEAM The (USA)ITV from 29/7/83) Theme mus (Mike Post-Pete Carpenter) *Silva Screen (Con): FILM(C)(CD) 701 see Coll* 'TELEVISION MUSIC OF MIKE POST AND..'/'ITV AMERICA'/'ITV CHILDREN'S THEMES'/'GREAT TV THEMES4'

ABOUT FACE (Central from 6/11/89) theme (Denis King) *see Coll* 'LOVEJOY THE MUSIC OF DENIS KING'

ABSOLUTE BEGINNER'S GUIDE TO COOKERY (TSW 6/9/91) title theme based on Jack Strachey's "In Party Mood" (Hou sewives Choice) performed by MICHAEL ELPHICK & DON HENDERSON *Grasmere (Taylors): GRASS 4 (7"s)*

ABSOLUTELY (C4 22/8/90) title music (Pete Baikie) perfo rmed by PETE BAIKIE-MORWENNA BANKS & CAST........*NA*

ABSOLUTELY FABULOUS (BBC2 12/11/92) Music (Simon Brint) theme "This Wheel's On Fire" (Bob Dylan-Rick Danko) sung by JULIE DRISCOLL-ADRIAN EDMONDSON........*NA orig* JULIE DRISCOLL-BRIAN AUGER TRINITY '1968' on *Connoiss.Coll (Pinn): YRNRCD 68(CD) YRNRMC 68(Cass)*

ACCOUSTIC ROUTES (ORIG TV SOUNDTRACK) featuring Various Artists *Edsel/Demon (Pinn): NINETY 7 (CD)*

ACTIV-8 (BBC1 28/5/91) music (Richard Attree)........*NA*

ADDAMS FAMILY The (USA 64) Music from the original TV series by Vic Mizzy *RCA Imp (S.Screen): 61057-2(CD) -4 (Cass) see Coll* 'TELEVISION'S GREATEST HITS V.1'

ADULTERY (BBC2/Forum 15/6/93) theme (Roger Bolton)...*NA*

ADVENTURE GAME The (BBC2 2/2/84) "Duo In G.Major" Largo Rondo (Ferdinando Carulli) JOHN WILLIAMS and JULIAN BREAM 'Together' *RCA: 09026 61450-2 (CD) -4 (Cass)*

ADVENTURERS (BBC2 24/1/93) title mus (Michael Kamen).*NA*

ADVENTURES (C4 23/1/93) music composers: Ernie Wood-Dav id Skininer-Nigel Sawyer-Paal Griffiths-Pete Smith-Brendan Croker-Guy Fletcher-Kevin Stoney-Michael Wh alen-Tom Phillips *all original music.............NA*

ADVENTURES OF BLACK BEAUTY The (LWT 72 re-run C4 86) Theme "Galloping Home" (Denis King) - LONDON STRING CHORALE *see Collections* 'FAVOURITE TV THEMES'/'HIT THEMES 1'/'LOVEJOY'/'ITV THEMES'

ADVENTURES OF ROBIN HOOD The (ITV 17/2/56-1960) Theme mus (Carl Sigman) DICK JAMES *EMI:TCEM 1307 (Cass) CDS 791255-2 (CD)* GARRY MILLER on Coll 'TV CLASSICS Vol.1' *see also* 'Robin Hood'/'Robin Of Sherwood'

ADVENTURES OF ROBINSON CRUSOE The (BBC1 12/10/65) Music score (Gian Reverberi-Robert Mellin) Orig TV -S/T-score *Silva Screen (Con): FILM(C)(CD)705 (CD/Cass)*

ADVENTURES OF SHERLOCK HOLMES The (Granada 24/4/84) *see Coll* 'GRANADA STUDIOS TOUR'/'SHERLOCK HOLMES'

ADVENTURES OF TEDDY RUXPIN (ITV 3/7/92)Mus (Andrew Hugg ett) Songs composed and arr.by George Wilkins....*NA*

ADVENTURES OF WILLIAM TELL The (ITC 15/9/58-1959)theme sung by DAVID WHITFIELD 'Sings Stage & Screen Favou rites' *Pickwick: PWK 096 (CD) SDTO 2004 (Cass)*

ADVOCATES The (Scott TV 2/4/91) theme (Daryl Runswick)
    sung by JANICE KELLY (92) SHIRLEY HENDERSON (91).*NA*
AFRICAN SANCTUS (BBC1 78) A Mass For Love and Peace by
    DAVID FANSHAWE reiss: *Philips: 426 055-2/-4 (CD/CS)*
    also available Allmanna Sangen cond. by ROBERT SUND
    Proprius (Taylors): PR(C)(CD) 9984 (LP/Cass/CD)
AFTER HENRY (Thames 4/1/88) Theme "Three Quarter Blues"
    (George Gershwin) - Morton Gould Orchest- arranger:
    John Cacavas - *RCA Red Seal (BMG): GL 42747 (LP)*
AGAINST THE WIND (Austral.75) Theme (English-McCormick)
    see Coll 'GREAT TV THEMES VOLUME 2'
AGATHA CHRISTIE'S POIROT (LWT from 8/1/89) Music (Chris
    Gunning) -S/T-*Virgin: VTCD(MC) 8 (CD/Cass) deleted*
    theme music - see Collections 'FAVOURITE TV THEMES'
    /'HIT THEMES 1'/'20 TOP TV THEMES'
AIRWOLF (USA 84-ITV) Theme (Sylvester Levay) *see Coll:*
    'FANTASTIC TELEVISION THEMES'/'ITV AMERICA'
ALAS SMITH AND JONES (UKGold 6/11/92 orig BBC2 31/1/84)
    Music (Pete Brewis) Feat:MEL SMITH-GRIFF RHYS JONES
    previously available on BBC REB 527 ZCF 527 deleted
ALBION MARKET (Granada 30/8/85-9/86)Theme (Bill Connor)
    see Coll 'GRANADA STUDIOS SOUVENIR ALBUM'
ALEXEI SAYLE'S STUFF (UKGold 3/11/92 orig BBC 13/10/88)
    music (Simon Brint-Steve Jeffries) *not available*
ALFRED HITCHCOCK PRESENTS (USA 55) / ITV 60's) Theme
    "Funeral March Of A Marionette" (Gounod) on *Coll*
    'CHILLER' *Telarc (Con)* 'TELEVISION'S G.HITS VOL.1'
    Silva Screen / 'THEMES AND DREAMS' *Wisepack (TBD)*
ALIAS SMITH AND JONES (USA 71) BBC1 70's) Title Theme
    (Billy Goldenberg) *see Coll* 'GREAT TV THEMES VOL.3'
ALIEN YEARS The (Resolution Films Australia-88) ITV-
    9/6/91) music score (Bruce Smeaton)..............*NA*
ALL AT NUMBER 20 (Thames fr.10/2/86) theme (Denis King)
    see Coll 'LOVEJOY THE MUSIC OF DENIS KING'
ALL BLACK (BBC2 23/7/93) music (Mykael Riley)........*NA*
ALL CREATURES GREAT AND SMALL (UKGO 17/9/93 orig BBC1
    8/1/78) Title mus (Johnny Pearson) *see Colls* 'GREAT
    TV THEMES V.3'/'THEMES AND DREAMS'/'SOUNDS VISUAL'
ALL GOOD THINGS (BBC1 14/5/91) music (Bill Connor)...*NA*
ALL IN GOOD FAITH (Thames 11/4/88) Theme music "Klavier
    stuck in F" K.33b (Mozart) - DANIEL BARENBOIM - *HMV*
    (EMI): CDC 747384-2 (CD) EL 270382-4 (Cass)
ALL IN THE FAMILY (USA 71) "Those Were The Days" (Lee
    Adams-Charles Strouse) *Coll* 'TELEVISION'S G.HITS.3'
ALL IN THE GAME (Central/TVE 21/10/93) music comp/arr.
    (Chris Cawte) music superv: Graham Walker........*NA*
ALL OUR YESTERDAYS (Granada 10/9/87) "Yesterday" (John
    Lennon-Paul McCartney) - many recordings available
    including THE BEATLES - *Parlophone EMI: R 6013 (7")*
ALL OUR YESTERDAYS (Gr 60) "King Cotton" (John P.Sousa)
    PHILIP JONES BRASS - *Decca: 410.290-2 (CD)-4 (Cass)*
ALLO ALLO (BBC1 12/10/83-92) theme mus (Roy Moore-David
    Croft) *not available* other songs by cast members:
    (all deleted) see TELE-TUNES 1990

ALLOTMENT SHOW (BBC1 12/7/89) Theme "Lord Of The Dance"
(S.Carter) SYDNEY CARTER on "Lovely In The Dances"
Plant Life (Proj): PLR 032 (LP) / SPINNERS '18 Gold
en Fav' *EMI: (TC)NTS 165 (Cass/LP)* HOUGHTON WEAVERS
'Sit Thi Down' *Folk Heritage (Jazz Mus) (C)FHR 106*
ALMOST COMPLETE HISTORY OF THE 20TH CENTURY (Kudos/C4
6/10/93) original music (Julian Wastall).........*NA*
ALPHABET CASTLE (Carlton 10/9/93) music (Paul Reade).*NA*
ALY BAIN & FRIENDS (C4 Scotland 19/2/89)Shetland fiddle
player & guests - Music & Songs from the series on
'ALY BAIN & Friends' - *Greentrax (CM Celtic Music):*
TRAX 026 (LP) CTRAX 026 (Cass) CDTRAX 026 (CD)
see also under entry: 'SHETLAND SESSIONS'
AMERICAN FOOTBALL *see* TELE-TUNES 1992
AMERICAN LATE SHOW (BBC1 3/10/91) mus (Roger Bolton).*NA*
AN ACTOR'S LIFE FOR ME (BBC1 14/11/91) Title Theme from
'Pinocchio' (Disney 39) sung by Nick Curtis......*NA*
see under WALT DISNEY FILM INDEX and FILMS & SHOWS
AN ANGEL AT MY TABLE (C4/NZ-91) Music score (Don McGlas
han) -S/T- *Alhambra Imp (S.Screen): CDA 8925 (CD)*
AN ENGLISHWOMAN'S GARDEN (BBC2 24/9/93) m:John Keane.*NA*
AN EXCHANGE OF FIRE (Kestrel for C4 6/7/93) Music score
(Nick Bicat)....................................*NA*
ANASTASIA: THE MYSTERY OF ANNA (TV Film BBC1 10/7/88)
Music score (Laurence Rosenthal) Munich Philh Orch
Silva Screen (Con): FILMC 010 (Cass) SCCD 1015 (CD)
ANCIENT ART OF COOKERY (C4 3/1/89) m (Graham MacLean)*NA*
ANGEL & THE SOLDIER BOY The (Cartoon 89) BBC1-27/12/89
Music (CLANNAD) -S/T- *RCA (BMG): PD(PL)(PK) 74328*
ANGELS (Granada 2/6/92) theme music (Julian Wastall).*NA*
ANGLO-SAXON ATTITUDES (Thames/Euston Films 12/5/92)
theme and incidental music (Colin Towns).........*NA*
ANIMAL COUNTRY (Anglia 4/11/91)mus.(Guy Mitchelmore).*NA*
ANIMAL MAGIC (BBC1 70s-83) "Las Vegas" (Laurie Johnson)
see Collection 'SOUNDS VISUAL'
ANIMAL PASSIONS (BBC1 18/8/92) mus: (Gordon Gribben).*NA*
ANIMAL SQUAD (BBC1 4/1/85)"Time After Time" (Rod Argent
Robert Howes) BARBARA DICKSON *deleted*
ANIMAL SQUAD UNDERCOVER (C4 5/10/92) original music by
(Robert Howes and Rod Argent)...................*NA*
ANIMAL TRAFFIC (C4 15/5/88) Theme "Dominion" (Steve Jon
es-Steve Skaith) LATIN QUARTER on 'Swimming Against
The Stream' *RCA (BMG): PD(PK) 74037 (CD/Cass)*
ANIMALS OF FARTHING WOOD The (BBC1/EBU 6/1/93) music sc
(Detlev Kuhne) WDR Orchest (KRO Cologne) available
2CASS SPOKEN WORD: *BBC (Pinn): YBBC 1452 (2Cass)*
ANNA-BALLERINA (ITV (TVGO Munich 87) 30/12/91) music by
Sigi Schwab (Teldec Prod) *not available* / *other mus
ic taken from* 'Swan Lake' (Tchaikovsky)
ANNA OF THE FIVE TOWNS (BBC2 9/1/85) Title music (Nigel
Hess) LONDON FILM ORC - *see coll* 'SCREENS & STAGES'
ANNE OF GREEN GABLES (TV Canada-C4 2/1/87) also 'The Se
quel'(16/1/88)"Anne's Theme" (H.Hardy) HAGOOD HARDY
SLC (Movie Boulevard): CD Import

ANNIE ACROSS AMERICA (Angl.26/7/92) m: (Ray Russell).*NA*
ANNO DOMINI - *see under* 'A.D.'
ANOTHER WAR ANOTHER PEACE 1940-60 (BBC2 7/12/92) music
    score (Hans Guenter Wagener).....................*NA*
ANTIQUES ROAD SHOW (BBC1 18/2/79-1994) *orig theme* 'Bran
    dndenburg Concerto No.3 in G.Maj"(Bach) and 'Little
    Suite From Anna Magdalena Notebook' (J.S.Bach)
    85-89 series theme (Roger Limb - not available)
    89-94 series theme (Paul Reade - not available)
ANTON MOSIMANN NATURALLY (C4 6/9/91) mus (Adrian Burch-
    David Whitaker)................................*NA*
ANZACS (Australia-86 / BBC1 12/1/87) Theme music (Bruce
    Rowland) *see Coll* 'AUSTRALIA'S GREATEST HITS'
APPLEYARDS The (BBC 1950s first soap!) "Looking Around"
    (Colin Smith) *see Coll* 'MORE FAMOUS THEMES'
AQUA MARINA (ATV 60's) Music (Barry Gray) *see Coll* 'TV
    CLASSICS V.2'/'NO STRINGS ATTACHED'/'POWER THEMES'
    (vocal sung by GARRY MILLER) 'TV CLASSICS VOLUME 2'
ARE YOU BEING SERVED? (UKGO 10/9/93 orig BBC1 73) theme
    (Jimmy Perry-Penny Croft) by JOHN INMAN *DJM deleted*
ARENA (BBC2) Theme "Another Green World" (Brian Eno)
    BRIAN ENO *EG (Poly): EGMC 21 (Cass) EGCD 21 (CD)*
ARK The (BBC2/RTO Pict 19/1/93) music (John Keane)...*NA*
ARMY GAME The (ITV Granada 57-62) Theme feat Alfie Bass
    MICHAEL MEDWIN-BERNARD BRESSLAW on 'Hits Of 58' col
    MFP Hour Of Pleasure (EMI): HR 8175 (Cass only)
AROUND THE WORLD IN 80 DAYS (Michael Palin BBC1 14/7/91
    (11/10/89) Original music (Paddy Kingsland)......*NA*
AROUND THE WORLD IN 80 DAYS (TV mini series 90) Music
    score (Billy Goldenberg) with Irish Studio Symphony
    Orch - *Edel WG. (S.Screen): EDL 2518-1 (LP) -2 (CD)*
AROUND THE WORLD WITH WILLY FOG (BBC1) *see under entry*
    'WILLY FOG'
AROUND WHICKER'S WORLD (YTV September Films 24/7/92)
    theme music "Newsweek" (Graham De Wilde) new arrang
    ment. Orig BBC theme on *BBC-Pickwick: PWKS 645 (CD)*
AROUND WITH ALLIS (BBC2 15/3/85) "Music Box Dancer" (Fr
    ank Mills) JOHN MANN *Grosvenor (Taylors): GRS 1124
    (LP)* MANUEL & HIS MUSIC - *EMI: CDP 746932-2 (CD)*
ART ATTACK (TVS 15/6/90) theme music (Peter Miller-Ian
    Porter (Mr.Miller & Mr.Porter)...................*NA*
ART OF LANDSCAPE (C4 11/12/89-90) Various New Age and
    Classical Music Var.Arts. Coll: *New Note (Pinn):
    ALC(CD)11 (CD/Cass :V1) ALC(CD)12 (CD/Cass :V2)*
    'CLASSICAL LANDSCAPES' 12 Classic Music Tracks on
    Video: *Landscape (Sony Music): ALCV 2 (Video)*
ARTIFAX (BBC1-20/11/91) music (Kjartan Poskitt)......*NA*
ARTRAGEOUS (BBC2-DEF II 15/4/92) music (Snowboy).....*NA*
AS TIME GOES BY (BBC1 12/1/92) theme mus "As Time Goes
    By" (Herman Hupfeld) TV vers.sung by JOE FAGIN...*NA*
    see also under 'CASABLANCA'
ASHENDEN (BBC1 17/11/91) music (Stephen Oliver)......*NA*
ASK ODDIE (HTV 8/3/91) music (Paul Joyce)............*NA*
ASPEL & COMPANY (Thames 1/91) music (Ken Jones)......*NA*

ASTRO FARM (Filmfair/Central 18/9/92) mus: (Dave Cooke)
lyrics (Paul Field)...........................*NA*
ASTRONOMERS The (USA TV) Music score (J.A.C.Redford)
Intrada USA (Silva Screen): MAF 7018D (CD)
ATLANTIC REALM (BBC2 8/1/89) Music by CLANNAD on *BBC*
(Pinn): ZCF 727 (Cass) BBCCD 727 (CD) deleted
ATHLETICS (BBCTV 79-94)"World Series" (Keith Mansfield)
'BBC Sporting Themes' *BBC-Pickwick: PWKS 648 (CD)*
Also used "Fanfare For The Common Man" (A.Copland)
see also under 'WORLD ATHLETICS CHAMPIONSHIPS'
ATHLETICS (ITV Sport) "Hot Foot" (Rod Argent-Peter V.Ho
oke)see Coll 'FAVOURITE TV THEMES'/'20 TOP THEMES'
ATTACK OF THE KILLER TOMATOES (USA/BBC1 8/4/92) theme m
(John De Bello) mus (Shuki Levy) Marvel Prod USA.*NA*
AUF WIEDERSEHEN PET (Central 11/11/83 & 5/4/88) Themes:
"Breakin'Away"/"That's Livin'Alright"/"Back WithThe
The Boys Again" (David MacKay-Ken Ashby-Ian La Fren
ais) sung by JOE FAGIN / "Breakin'Away" and "That's
Livin'Alright" on 'The Best Of Joe Fagin' *Westmoor*
(Pinn/Taylors): CDWM 107 (CD) CWM 107 (Cass)
AUNTIE'S BLOOMERS (BBC1 29/12/91) m:(Keith Strachan).*NA*
AUSSIES (BBC1 Austr 87) 21/9/92) music (John Stuart).*NA*
AUSTRALIAN RULES FOOTBALL (C4/Broadcom Austral.18/7/92)
theme music (Frank Strangio)....................*NA*
AVENGERS The (ABCTV 65-69) Theme (Laurie Johnson) *see*
Coll 'A-Z OF BRITISH TV THEMES'/'ROSE AND THE GUN'/
'FAVOURITE TV THEMES'/POWER THEMES 90'/'TV CLASSICS
V.1'/'TV CLASSICS V.4' (as "The Shake")'ITV THEMES

B.& B. (Thames 19/6/92) music score (Jim Parker).,,,.*NA*
B.L.STRYKER (USA 89/ITV 4/5/91) Theme music (Mike Post)
see Coll 'ITV AMERICA'/'AMERICAN TV THEMES VOL.3'
BAD INFLUENCE (Yorkshire 29/10/92) mus (Ernie Wood)..*NA*
BAGDAD CAFE (USA 90/C4 12/9/91)Theme "Calling You" (Bob
Telson) from 88 film-S/T- sung by JEVETTA STEELE on
Island (Poly): CID 5718 (CD) ISTA(IC) 18 (LP/Cass)
BARNEY (BBC1 8/2/89) Title theme (Joanna Wyatt-Colin Fr
echter) THE MINI POPS / also "Love Your Dog" sung
by CARL WAYNE - *BBC (Pinn): RESL 233 (7"s) deleted*
BARNEY MILLER (USA 82 / C4 9/1/88) theme (Jack Elliot &
Allyn Ferguson) *see Collection* '4 AMERICA TWO'
BASKETBALL (C4 15/12/87) "Where Eagles Dare" (69 Film)
(RON GOODWIN) *EMI: CZ 21 (CD) TCEMS 1244 (Cass/LP)*
BATMAN (USA 66/C4 16/8/93) theme (Neal Hefti) *see Colls*
'CHILDREN'S WORLD OF TV THEMES' and FILMS & SHOWS
BATTLESTAR GALACTICA (USA 78-ITV) Theme (Glen A.Larson-
Stu Phillips) *see Col* 'FANTASTIC TELEVISION THEMES'
BAYWATCH (USA)(ITV 13/1/90) Theme (93)"Current Of Love"
(Kevin Savigar-Todd Cerney)sung by DAVID HASSELHOFF
Arista (BMG): 74321 17226-2 (CDs) -4 (Cass) -7(7"s)
also on 'Miracle Of Love' *Arista 74321 17618-2 (CD)*
-4 (Cass) prev.theme "Save Me" (Peter Cetera-David
Foster) PETER CETERA on 'One More Story' *Full Moon*
(WEA): WX 161(C)(CD) also on Coll 'ITV AMERICA'

BEAT THAT! (C4/Tiny Epic Vid-23/4/91) music (Mcasso).*NA*
BEAT The (Carlton/FCITV 4/1/93) theme (Paul K.Joyce).*NA*
BEAUTY AND THE BEAST (USA ITV 1/9/89) Music score (Don
   Davis) Suite on 'Hyperspace' *Prometheus (S.Screen):*
   PCD 120 (CD) Theme (Lee Holdridge) Song "The First
   I Loved Forever" sung by LISA ANGELLE -TV S/T music
   Capitol EMI: CDEST 2115(CD) TCEST 2115(Cas) deleted
BEER HUNTER The (C4 27/3/90) music (David Arch)......*NA*
BEETLE CALLED DEREK A (TVS 22/6/91) Theme music "The
   Carvery" performed by THE YES/NO PEOPLE..........*NA*
BEFORE COLUMBUS (Nat.Film Board Canada/Central 15/9/92)
   incidental music (Michael Rosas Cobian...........*NA*
BEHIND THE HEADLINES (BBC2 8/1/90) mus (John Miller).*NA*
BEIDERBECKE AFFAIR The (C4 4/93 orig 1985) music of BIX
   BEIDERBECKE performed by FRANK RICOTTI ALL-STARS &
   KENNY BAKER -S/T- on *Doormouse (Taylors): DM20CD*
   also 'Collection' on *Castle (BMG): CCSCD 350 (CD)*
BELLAMY RIDES AGAIN (BBC1 13/6/91)m:(Brian Gascoigne)*NA*
BEN CASEY (USA 60) *see* 'Televisions Greatest Hits 2'
BERGERAC (UKGold 7/11/92 orig BBC1 18/10/81) Theme mus
   (George Fenton) *Coll* 'BEST OF BBCTV THEMES' *deleted*
BERTHA (BBC1 1/4/85) Music (Guy Fletcher-Bryan Daly) on
   BBC-Pickwick: HSC 650 (CS) & REH 585 (LP) ZCR 585CS
BEST OF BRITISH (BBC1 22/4/87) Theme (Rob Waugh) arr.by
   Nicholas Raine: ROYAL P.O.- *RCA: PB 41389 (deleted)*
BETWEEN THE LINES (BBC1 4/9/92) theme mus (Hal Lindes)
   incid.score (Rick Wentworth (2) Colin Towns (1)..*NA*
BEVERLY HILLBILLIES The (USA 62) Theme "The Ballad Of
   Jed Clampett" sung by LESTER FLATT & EARL SCRUGGS -
   on 'Americana' *Columbia (SM): 468121-2(CD) -4(Cass)*
   also on *Collect.* 'TELEVISION'S GREATEST HITS VOL.1'
BEVERLY HILLS 90210 (ITV 12/1/91-USA Prod 90) theme mus
   (Jeffrey 'Skunk' Baxter & Stacy Widelitz) TV -S/T-
   W.Bros (WEA): 759924465-2 (CD) 759924465-4 (Cass)
   theme also on *Coll* 'ITV AMERICA' *(Silva Screen)*
BEWITCHED (USA 64-71 C4 86/87) Theme (Howard Greenfield
   Jack Keller)*see Coll* 'TELEVISION'S GREATEST HITS 2'
BEYOND THE SHADOWS (BBC1 4/4/93) mus (Frances Butt)..*NA*
BICYLE (BBC2 21/2/91) music (Ernie Wood).............*NA*
BIG BATTALIONS The (C4/Carnival 19/11/92) Music score
   composed/conducted by Christopher Gunning -S/T- *Hit*
   London (Poly): AHLCD 6(CD) AHLMC 6(Cass) AHL 6(LP)
BIG BREAK (BBC1 30/4/91) theme "The Snooker Song" (Mike
   Batt) from 'Hunting Of The Snark' *see* FILMS & SHOWS
   versions by CAPTAIN SENSIBLE and KENNY EVERETT
BIG BREAKFAST The (C4/Planet 24 from 24/9/92) album of
   v.arts *Arcade (Sony): ARC 3100082(CD) 3100094(Cass)*
BIG DEAL (UKGO 24/3/93 orig BBC1 14/10/84) Title theme
   (Bobby Gee) sung by BOBBY G 'Telly Hits 1' *deleted*
BIG EIGHT The (C4/Ideas 17/8/91) music (Big George)..*NA*
BIG GREEN BOAT SHOW The (Granada 30/3/93) music (Adrian
   Burch-David Whitaker).............................*NA*
BIG MATCH The (ITV) Theme "Aztec Gold" ROD ARGENT-PETER
   VAN HOOKE *see Coll* 'FAVOURITE TV THEMES'(The Match)

BIG ONE The (C4/HatTrick 5/2/92) theme "I Close My Eyes And Count to Ten"(Clive Westlake) DUSTY SPRINGFIELD 'Songbook' *Pickwick: PWKS 580 (CD) CN4 2107 (Cass)*
BIG PICTURE SHOW (C4 4/7/92) music (Justin Nicholls).*NA*
BIG STORY The (2020/Carlt.9/9/93) mus (Stephen Faux).*NA*
BIG WORLD (CAFE) (C4 19/2/89) Title theme composed and performed by COLDCUT on 'What's That Noise' on *Big Life (Cartel-R.Trade): CCUTLP 1 (LP) CCUTMC 1 (Cas)*
BILL COSBY SHOW (USA C4 86) theme music by Stu Gardner *see under* COSBY SHOW The
BILL The (Thames 16/10/84-93 also UKGold from 2/11/92) theme "Overkill" (Andy Pask-Charlie Morgan) *see Collection* 'ITV THEMES' *Pickwick: PWKM 4007 (CD)*
BILLY (USA-ITV 21/4/93) theme "I've Told Every Little Star" (Jerome Kern-Oscar Hammerstein II) by SONNY ROLLINS on 'Oleo' *Jazz Hour (Tayl): JHR 73552 (CD)*
BILLY WEBB'S AMAZING STORY (BBC1 3/1/91) theme (Steve Marshall) based on 'La Gazza Ladra' (Rossini)....*NA*
BIONIC WOMAN The (USA 76)Theme (Joe Harnell) Orchestral score on *5Jays (S.Screen Imp): 5JAYS 001/002 (2CDs)*
BIRDS OF A FEATHER (BBC1 16/10/89) Theme "What'll I Do" (Irving Berlin) *TV version unavailable* / MICHAEL CR AWFORD 'Songs from the Stage and Screen" on *Telstar (BMG): TCD 2308 (CD) STAR(STAC) 2308 (LP/Cas)* ELKIE BROOKS on 'Priceless' *Pickwick: PWKS 4086 (CD)*
BIRDSCAPE (C4 2/5/91) music score (Paul Lewis).......*NA*
BIRTH OF EUROPE (BBC2 6/10/91) mus (Terry Oldfield)..*NA*
BIRTHRIGHTS (BBC2 8/5/91)theme "Let The Slave" (William Blake-M.Westbrook) arr: Adrian Mitchell MIKE WESTBR OOK 'Bright As A Fire' *Original (Celtic): ORA 203LP*
BIT OF A DO, A (YTV 13/1/89) music (Ray Russell) theme sung by GEORGE MELLY-John Chilton's Feetwarmers..*NA*
BIT OF FRY & LAURIE A (BBC2 9/3/90) End Theme "Finale" from 'Carnival Of The Animals' (Saint-Saens)
BITEBACK (BBC1 17/11/91) music (Ron De Jong).........*NA*
BITSA (BBC1 8/1/91).Rick Juckes-Dave Benson Phillips.*NA*
BITTEN BY THE BUG (BBC2 20/1/92)m: Nick Lambuschagne.*NA*
BLACK AND WHITE (BBC1 11/4/88) Theme song (Something In side) "So Strong" (L.Siffre) - LABI SIFFRE on *China Chrysalis (EMI): (Z)WOL 9 (Càss/LP) 837369-2 (CD)*
BLACK AND WHITE MINSTREL SHOW The (BBC1 1950's-60's) The George Mitchell Minstrels with Dai Francis-Tony Mercer-John Boulter-Margaret Savage-Eve Blanchard 'Down Memory Lane' *MFP (EMI):CC 223 (CD)* 'The Black & White Minstrel Show' *EMI: CD(TC)IDL 105 (CD/Cass)*
BLACK BAG (C4 19/2/91) music (Amanda Alexander)......*NA*
BLACK BEAUTY *see* 'ADVENTURES OF BLACK BEAUTY'
BLACK BRITAIN (BBC2 7/1/91) orig music (Londonbeat)..*NA*
BLACK CANDLE The (TT 26/5/91) m:(Dominick Muldowney).*NA*
BLACK ON EUROPE (BBC2 25/6/91) theme (Errol Whitter).*NA*
BLACKADDER (BBC2 began 5/9/84) Theme music (Howard Good all) on 'BLACKADDER THE THIRD' *BBC (Pinn):ZBBC 1270 (2Cass) note:* Videos available: all **on** *BBC Videos: BBCV 4782 (series 1) 4785 (2) 4786 (3) 4787 (4)*

BLACKEYES (BBC2 29/11/89) Theme "Blackeyes" (Ferraris)
arr. by Max Harris *(not available)* versions by ROY
ROY FOX 'Strictly Instrumental' *Halcyon HAL 1 (LP)*
PALM COURT THEATRE ORCH 'Picnic Party' *Chandos:CHAN
8437(CD) LBR(T) 002(LP/Cass)* other mus "I'm Getting
Sentimental Over You" (G.Basman-N.Washington) - The
INK SPOTS 'Memories Of You' *MCA: MCLC 1743 (Cass)*
BLACKHEATH POISONINGS The (Central 7/12/92) mus score
(Colin Towns).................................*NA*
BLAKE'S 7 (BBC1 2/1/78) Theme music (Dudley Simpson)
GEOFF LOVE ORCH 'Superthemes' *MFP: 41 8103-4 (Cass)*
BLEAK HOUSE (BBC2 10/4/85) music (Geoffrey Burgon)...*NA*
BLIND DATE (LWT from 30/11/85) theme (Laurie Holloway)
additional music (Jonathan Sorrell).............*NA*
BLIND JUSTICE (BBC2 12/10/88) Music (Colin Towns) - *BBC
REB 714(LP) ZCF 714(Cass) BBCCD 714(CD)* all *deleted*
BLINKY BILL (BBC1 30/9/93) music (Guy Gross).......*NA*
BLOCKBUSTERS (Central from 29/8/83) Theme (Ed Welch) on
Grasmere (Taylors): GRASS 2 (7"s) with 'New Faces'
see also collect 'ITV THEMES'
BLOOD AND BELONGING (BBC2 11/11/93) title music (Gordon
Durity) *not available* / song "I've Got You Under My
Skin" (Cole Porter) sung by FRANK SINATRA on '20 Go
lden Greats' *EMI-Capitol: CDEMTV 10 (CD) TC- (Cass)*
BLOOD AND ORCHIDS (C4 USA Prod 88) music (Mark Snow).*NA*
BLOOD IS STRONG The (C4/Grampian 1/9/88) music composed
& performed by CAPERCAILLE with KAREN MATHESON -TV-
-S/T- *Survival (BMG): ZD 74993 (CD) ZK 74993 (Cass)*
BLOOD OF THE BRITISH (C4 18/6/86) Theme "Coronach" (Ian
Anderson-David Palmer) JETHRO TULL on '20th Anniver
sary' *Chrysalis (EMI): TBOXCD 1 (CDx4) TBOX 1 (Cas)*
BLOOD TIES (RAI Viac/ITV 6/9/93) music (Celso Valli).*NA*
BLOOMING BELLAMY (BBC1 16/7/93) mus (Brian Gascoigne)*NA*
BLOSSOM (USA/C4 24/4/92)theme (Mike Post-Stephen Geyer)
performed by DR.JOHN / other mus (Frank Denson) *see
Collection* '4 AMERICA TWO'
BLUE PETER (BBC1 27/10/58-1993) Theme "Barnacle Bill"
(Hornpipe) Orig SIDNEY ORCH ORCH *deleted* / MIKE OLD
OLDFIELD *Virgin (EMI): CDMOC 1 (2CD) CMOC 1 (2Cass)*
BOAT The (DAS BOOT) (BBC2 17/9/89 orig 21/10/84) Music
(Klaus Doldinger) -S/T- *W.Bros (WEA): K.58366 (LP)*
BOBBY DAVRO: PUBLIC ENEMY NO.1 (BBC1 5/9/92) theme mus
(Nigel Beaham-Powell)............................*NA*
BOBBY DAVRO: ROCK WITH LAUGHTER (BBC1 6/7/93) Music dir
(Paul Jury) theme "Rockin'The Night Away" sung by
Bobby Davro & Show Cast Singers..................*NA*
BOB'S YOUR UNCLE (Cent.27/4/91) music: (Andy Street).*NA*
BODGER AND BADGER (BBC1 13 /9/89) m: (Peter Gosling).*NA*
BODY AND SOUL (Red Rooster Prod for Carlton TV 8/4/93)
Music score (Jim Parker) TV -S/T- on *Hit-Chrysalis
(Polygram): AHLCD 11 (CD) AHLMC 11 (Cass)*
BONANZA (USA 59) Theme (David Rose) Lyrics (Jay Livings
ton-Ray Evans) *see Colls* 'GREAT TV THEMES VOL.1'/
'GREAT WESTERN THEMES'

BONJOUR LA CLASSE! (BBC1 15/2/93) mus (Philip Pope)..*NA*
BOOK GAME The (BBC2 27/8/85) Theme music "Rondo" from
   'Oboe Quartet E.Flat Major No.4' (Carl Stamitz)..*NA*
BOOKER 1993 (BBC2 2/11/93) mus (Dominique Legendre)..*NA*
BOOKMARK (BBC2 6/10/93) end song "Can You Forgive Her"
   (Tennant-Lowe) PET SHOP BOYS from 'Very' *Parlophone
   (EMI): CDPCSD 143 (CD) TCPCSD 143 (Cass) PCSD 143LP*
BOOKS BY MY BEDSIDE (TT 1/9/91) mus (Andy Sheppard)..*NA*
BOOM (C4 12/2/91) theme music (David Mindel).........*NA*
BOON (Central 14/1/86-1992) theme "Hi Ho Silver" (Jim
   Diamond-Chris Parren) sung by JIM DIAMOND on 'Jim
   Diamond' *Polydor (Polyg): 843 847-2 (CD) -4 (Cass)*
BOOT STREET BAND (BBC1 11/11/93) m: (Steve Marshall).*NA*
BORGIAS The (BBC1 14/10/81)Theme & music score (Georges
   Delerue) on *Prometheus (S.Screen): PCD 109 (CD)*
BORROWERS The (BBC1 8/11/92) Music (Howard Goodall)..*NA*
BOSWELL & JOHNSON'S TOUR OF THE WESTERN ISLES (Parav
   ision Prod/BBC2 27/10/93) orig music (Simon Fisher
   Turner) also feat MULL GAELIC CHOIR..............*NA*
BOTTOM (BBC2 17/9/91) theme music (The Bum Notes)....*NA*
BOUQUET OF BARBED WIRE (LWT 75/C4-83) Theme mus (Dennis
   Farnon) *see Coll* 'HIT THEMES 1-BEST OF BRITISH TV'
BOURNE IDENTITY The (TV USA 89) Theme & score (Lawrence
   Rosenthal) - FILM SYMPHONY ORCHESTRA Of PRAGUE on
   Intrada USA (Silva Screen): RVF 6005D (CD only)
BOWLS - *see under* 'WORLD BOWLS'
BOX OF DELIGHTS The (BBC1 21/11/84) Theme "Carol Sympho
   ny" (Hely-Hutchinson)The PRO-ARTE ORCH (Barry Rose)
   on *EMI: CDM 764131-2 (CD) -4 (Cass)*
BOXING (BBCTV) Main theme "Sir Percy" (Benson-Lewis) by
   Tony King Orchestra *(orig RCA 2238 7"s deleted)*
   other music used "Gonna Fly Now" (Bill Conti) from
   'Rocky' see FILMS & SHOWS / *related item* "Where's
   Harry?" Contenders (Frank Bruno-Harry Carpenter)
   Columbia: (12)DB 9136 (12"/7"s) deleted
BOY FROM ANDROMEDA The (NZ 90/BBC1 10/5/93) orig music
   (John Gibson)...................................*NA*
BOYS FROM THE BUSH (BBC1 25/1/91) music (Brian Lang).*NA*
BRADMAN (BBC2 Australian Prod) music (Garry Hardman).*NA*
BRAIN DRAIN (BBC2/Hat T.19/9/92) mus (Matthew Scott).*NA*
BRAIN GAME The (C4 25/5/92) music (Simon Etchell)....*NA*
BRASS (Granada 21/2/83) music (Kenyon Emrys-Roberts).*NA*
BRATPACK (Granada 4/1/93) theme music (Mr.Miller and
   Mr.Porter) *note:* 90 ser.music:Richard G.Mitchell.*NA*
BREAD (UKGO 3/11/92 and BBC 1/5/86-91) Theme mus "Home"
   (David MacKay) The CAST *BBC: RESL 186 (7"s) deleted*
BREADLINE BRITAIN (LWT-8/4/91) music (Kim Stevens)...*NA*
BRETTS The (Central 16/10/87) Theme (David Cullen-David
   MacKay) version by Richard Clayderman -*Decca (Poly)
   820 995-2 (CD) SKL 5345 (LP) KSKC 5345 (Cass)*
BRIAN CONLEY: OUTSIDE CHANCE (LWT 3/7/93) title theme
   (Andy Street-Paul Minett-Brian Leveson) sung by BR
   IAN CONLEY *unavailable.* note: "Brian Conley Sings"
   album available on *Dino (Pinn): DIN(CD)(MC) 54*

BRIDES OF CHRIST (C4 23/1/92) Music score (Mario Millo)
-S/T- *Alhambra (Pinn): A8936 (CD only)* / ALSO USED
"Hosanna In Excelsis" from Mass in B.Min.(J.S.Bach)
BERLIN RADIO SO (L.Maazel) *Polyg: 426657-2PSL2(2CD)*
BRIDESHEAD REVISITED (Gra 12/10/81) Mus Geoffrey Burgon
-S/T- *Chrysalis: (Z)CDL 1367 (CS/LP) CPCD 1367 (CD)*
see *Coll* 'BRIDESHEAD REVISITED'/'GRANADA STUDIOS'/
'REFLECTIONS'/'VISIONS'
BRIDGE The (C4/Europe 7/5/92) music (Jurre Haanstra).*NA*
BRIGHTON BELLES (H.Barclay/Carlton 7/9/93) Theme music
"Friendship" (Cole Porter) arr.by Denise Wharmby
and sung by QUEENS OF THE NIGHT..................*NA*
BRING'EM BACK ALIVE (USA 90)theme (Arthur B.Rubinstein)
see *Coll* 'AMERICAN TV THEMES-PRIMETIME COLL.VOL.2'
and 'FANTASTIC TELEVISION THEMES'/'ITV AMERICA'
BRINGING IT ALL BACK HOME (BBC1 NI/RTE-29/6/91) Opening
title music (Donal Lunny) closing mus (Eoin Duigan)
-S/T- with various artists on *BBC (Pinn): BBCCD 844
(2CD) ZCD 844 (Cass) REF 844 (2LP)*
BRITS 93 (Carlton 17/2/93) British Rec.Industry Awards
BRITS AWARDS ALBUM featuring *nominated artists* on
Polygram: 516 075-2 (2CD) -4 (2Cass) -1 (2LP)
BRITS 92 (BBC1 12/2/92) British Record Industry Awards
BRITS AWARDS ALBUM featuring *nominated artists* on
Polygram: 515 207-2 (2CD) 515 207-4 (2Cass) -1(2LP)
BRITTAS EMPIRE The (BBC1 3/1/91) mus (Frank Renton)..*NA*
BROND (C4 20/4/88 orig 87) "Secret Ceremony" (Bill Nels
on-Daryl Runswick) BILL NELSON on 'Duplex' *Cocteau
(Pinn): CDJCD 22 (CD) JCD 22 (2LP) TCJCD 22 (2Cass)*
BRONX ZOO The (USA)(C4 28/6/89)theme music (Gary Scott)
see *Coll* 'AMERICAN TV THEMES-VOL.1'/'4 AMERICA'
BROOKSIDE (C4 2/11/82-94) Theme music (Dave Roylance-
Steve Wright) on Collection 'SOAPS' *(MFP deleted)*
BROTHER FELIX...(C4 7/1/92) music (Esther Lamandier).*NA*
BROTHERS McGREGOR The (Granada 4/9/84) Theme (Derek Hil
ton) see *Collect* 'GRANADA STUDIOS SOUVENIR ALBUM'
BROTHERS The (UKGold 6/11/92 orig BBC1 71) Theme music
(Dudley Simpson) *Coll* 'Classic TV' *(MFP) deleted*
BRUCE FORSYTH'S GENERATION GAME (BBC1 6/9/90) "Life Is
The Name Of The Game" (B.Forsyth-Ian Wilson) BRUCE
FORSYTH *BBC deleted* / ROSEMARIE FORD 'I Wanna Dance
With Somebody' *Dover-Chrysalis (EMI):CCD(ZDD)ADD 26*
BRUSH STROKES (BBC1 12/10/87) theme "Because Of You" by
DEXYS MIDNIGHT RUNNERS on 'Very Best Of Dexys..' on
Mercury (Poly): 846 460-2 (CD) -4(Cass) -1(LP)
BUCK JAMES (USA 90) Theme music (Barry Goldberg)
see *Collection* 'AMERICAN TELEVISION THEMES VOL.3'
BUCK ROGERS IN THE 25TH CENTURY (USA 79 ITV) Theme (Stu
Phillips) see *Coll* 'FANTASTIC TELEVISION THEMES'
BUDDAH OF SUBURBIA The (BBC 3/11/93) Title Song and inc
idental music (David Bowie) sung by DAVID BOWIE and
ERDAL KIZILCAY feat LENNY KRAVITZ gtr -S/T- *Arista
(BMG): 74321 17004-2 (CD) 74321 17004-4 (Cass) also
74321 17705-2 (CDsingle) -4 (Cass single) -7 (7"s)*

BUDGIE (LWT 9/4/71-72) mus (Harry Rabinowitz) *see Coll*
    'HIT THEMES 1 - BEST OF BRITISH TV MUSIC'
BUGS BUNNY SHOW (Cartoon USA) *see Coll* 'BUGS BUNNY ON
    BROADWAY'/'CARL STALLING PROJECT'
BULLION BOYS The (BBC1 24/10/93) m:(Robert Lockhart).*NA*
BUNBURY TAILS The (C4 26/8/92) theme song "We're The Bu
    burys" (Barry, Maurice & Robin Gibb-David English)
    BEE GEES *others* "Bunbury Afternoon"/"Fight The Good
    Fight" (Gibb Bros) BEE GEES / "Up The Revolution"
    (Gibb Bros) ELTON JOHN / "Ride RajBun" (George Harr
    ison-David English) GEORGE HARRISON-RAVI SHANKAR *on*
    Polydor: (Poly): 515 784-2 (CD) 515 784-4 (Cass)
BURIED MIRROR (BBC2 22/4/92) music (Carl Davis)......*NA*
BURNING BOOKS (C4 20/10/91) music (Bill Padley)......*NA*
BUSH TUCKER MAN (Aus C4 17/5/92) m:(Rory O'Donoghue).*NA*
BUSINESS MATTERS (BBC2-6/6/91) mus: (Simon Davison)..*NA*
BUSMAN'S HOLIDAY (Granada 26/2/85) Theme (Peter Tatters
    hall-Mike Timoney) 'GRANADA STUDIOS SOUVENIR ALBUM'
BUTTERFLIES (BBC1 10/11/78-1983) theme "Love is Like A
    Butterfly" (Dolly Parton) *TV version sung by* CLARE
    TORRY *(EMI deleted)* / DOLLY PARTON version on Coll
    'Favourites' *Pickwick: PWKS 4116 (CD)*Park sequences
    Mus:'Adagio for Organ & Strings D.Minor' (Albinoni)
    'Classic Experience 2' on *EMI: CDEMTVD 50 (2CD's)*
BY THE SWORD DIVIDED (BBC1 6/1/85) Theme (Ken Howard-Al
    an Blaikley) Consort - *BBC: RESL 137 (7"s) deleted*
BYKER GROVE (BBC1 8/11/89-92) theme music (Martin Bramm
    er-David Brewis) sung by THE KANE GANG...........*NA*

CAGNEY AND LACEY (USA 81 BBC1 9/7/82 rerunBBC1 30/5/89)
    Pilot film (Loretta Swit/Tyne Daly) music by Nelson
    Riddle (unavailable) *Episodes 1-6* (Meg Foster/Tyne
    Daly) music: Mark Snow / theme "Ain't That The Way"
    (Michael Stull) sung by Marie Cain (unavailable)
    Episode 7 to end of series (Sharon Gless/Tyne Daly)
    Theme (BILL CONTI) *see coll:* 'CAGNEY & LACEY'
CALIFORNIA DREAMS (USA C4 25/4/93) Rock Band Drama Ser
    TV -S/T- *MCA (BMG): MCD 10718 (CD) MCC 10718 (Cass)*
CAMBERWICK GREEN (BBC1 66) Music by FREDDIE PHILLIPS
    see Collection 'THEMES FROM CHILDREN'S BBC'
CAMOMILE LAWN The (C4 5/3/92) music by STEPHEN EDWARDS
    based on 'String Quartet in F' (Ravel). Recordings:
    BRITTEN QUARTET *EMI: CDC 754346-2 (CD) EL 754346-4
    (Cass)* CHILINGIRIAN QUARTET *EMI: (CD)(TC)EMX 2156*
CAMPION (UKGO 9/1/93 orig BBC1 22/1/89) Theme music
    (Nigel Hess) *see Collect* '20 GREAT TV THEMES'
CAPITAL CITY (Thames 26/9/89) Theme music (Colin Towns)
    Music From Series on *First Night (Pinn): SCENECD 18
    (CD) SCENEC 18 (Cass)* / *see Coll* '20 TOP TV THEMES'
CAPITAL NEWS (USA 90/BBC1-1/8/91) Theme (Jan Hammer)
    see Collection 'AMERICAN TELEVISION THEMES VOL.3'
CAPTAIN PUGWASH (BBC 60s) "Trumpet Hornpipe" (Tradit)
    Captain Pugwash' Ships Crew QED with Firstmate H on
    Dingles (Spartan): SID 244 (7"s)

CAPTAIN SCARLET AND THE MYSTERONS (BBC2 1/10/93 orig
    ITV 29/9/67) music (Barry Gray) on colls 'A-Z OF BR
    ITISH TV THEMES' *Play It Again: PLAY 004 (CD)* and
    'TV CLASSICS VOLUME 1' *Castle Comm: MBSCD 412 (4CD)*
CAR 54-WHERE ARE YOU (USA 61/C4 87)*see Coll* 'TELEVISION
    'S GREATEST HITS VOLUME 2'
CARDIFF SINGER OF THE WORLD (BBC2 12/6/89) Signat.Tune
    "Voi Che Sapete" from 'Marriage Of Figaro' (Mozart)
    'Golden Opera Vol.2' *Decca: 414497-1(LP) -4(Cass)*
    TV vers.arr/performed: Peter Howell *(not available)*
CAROL AND COMPANY (Kalola USA/BBC1 6/9/93) theme music
    (Dan Foliart-Howard Pearl).......................***NA***
CARRERAS-DOMINGO-PAVAROTTI IN CONCERT (C4 7/9/90) The 3
    Tenors Concert recorded at the Baths Of Caracalla
    Rome on 7th July 1990. Feat JOSE CARRERAS, PLACIDO
    DOMINGO, LUCIANO PAVAROTTI. Orchestra consisting of
    200 musicians from Maggio Musicale of Florence and
    Teatro dell'Opera of Rome conducted by ZUBIN MEHTA.
    Decca (Poly): 430 433-2 (CD) -1 (LP) -4 (Cass)
CARSONS LAW (Australia ITV 88) Theme (Wayne Pearson)*see
    Collection* 'AUSTRALIAN TELEVISION'S GREATEST HITS'
CASTLE'S ABROAD (Anglia 30/6/91) theme mus 'Ode To Joy'
    (Beethoven) performed by ROY CASTLE..............***NA***
CASUALTY (BBC1 from 6/9/86-1994) Title theme music by
    (Ken Freeman).....................................***NA***
CATCHPHRASE (TVS from 12/1/86) music (Ed Welch)......***NA***
CATHEDRAL (LWT/Countrywide 19/4/92) md (David Hill)..***NA***
CATHOLICS AND SEX (C4 23/11/92) music (Nick Bicat)...***NA***
CATS (BBC2 15/11/91) Music score (Peter Howell)......***NA***
CATWEAZLE (LWT 1/3/70-71) theme music (Ted Dicks) *see
    Coll* 'A-Z OF BRITISH TV THEMES'
CAUGHT IN THE ACT (BBC1 10/1/92) music (Alan Parker).***NA***
CELEBRATION (Granada-Riverfront 17/3/91) theme music by
    Alex Balanescu-Tony Hinnigan (TEST DEPARTMENT)...***NA***
CELEBRATION: MAKING CONNECTIONS (Granada 24/2/92) music
    from "Thunder Before Dawn" (Various Artists) on
    Earthworks-Virgin: CDEWV 1 (CD) TCEWV 1 (Cass)
CELEBRITY SQUARES (Central 8/1/93) theme (Rick Turk..***NA***
CELTS The (BBC2 14/5/87) Music score comp/performed by
    ENYA -S/T/- *WEA: 4509 91167-2 (CD) WX 498C (Cass)*
    WX 498 (LP) theme on *WEA: YZ 705 (7"s)*
CENTURY FALLS (BBC1 17/2/93) music (David Ferguson)..***NA***
CERTAIN AGE A (BBC1 9/7/90) Theme "La Sicilienne" Op.78
    (Faure) Steven Isserlis (cell) Pascal Devoyon (pno)
    on *Hyperion (Taylors): CDA 66235 (CD) KA 66235 (LP)*
CHALKFACE (BBC2-6/5/91) theme song (ALAN PRICE)......***NA***
CHALLENGE ANNEKA (Mentorn/BBC1 from 8/9/89) theme music
    (David Mindell)...................................***NA***
CHAMPION THE WONDER HORSE (USA 56)(BBC1 7/11/92) theme
    song (Norman Luboff-Marilyn Keith) sung by FRANKIE
    LAINE *see Coll* 'HELLO CHILDREN VOLUME 2'
CHAMPIONS The (ITC 25/9/68 - 4/69) theme (Edwin Astley)
    see Col 'A-Z OF BRITISH TV THEMES'/'TV CLASSICS V2'
CHAMPIONS LEAGUE Football *see* 'EUROPEAN CHAMPIONS L..'

CHANCER (Central 6/3/90) theme (Jan Hammer) JAN HAMMER
on 'Escape From Television' also incl: 'Crockett's
Theme' *MCA (BMG): MCAD 10410 (CD) MCAC 10410 (Cass)*
CHANNEL 4 RACING (C4 88/94) Theme arrangement of the C4
sig music "Fourscore" (DAVID DUNDAS) *(Poly) deleted*
CHANNEL HOPPING (BBC1 11/10/92)theme MUSIC SCULPTORS.*NA*
CHANNELS OF RESISTANCE (C4 26/4/93) m.(Eric Lemoyne).*NA*
CHAPLIN PUZZLE The (Doc) Music score (Soren Hyldgaard)
cond Tony Bremner-S/T-*S.Screen (Con): FILMCD 128(CD)*
CHARLIE BROWN (Cartoon USA BBC) Theme: Amani A.W.Murray
'Happy Anniversary-A Jazzy Salute To Charlie Brown'
D.GRUSIN-L.RITENOUR-D.BRUBECK-J.WILLIAMS-G.MULLIGAN
and others *GRP USA (Pinn): GRP 9596-2 (CD) -4(Cass)*
CHARLIE CHALK (BBC1 20/10/88) Songs (Mike Redway) sung
KEN BARRIE *Redrock (AMT):ZCHARL 1(Cas) CDHARL 1(CD)*
CHARLIE'S ANGELS (USA 76) Theme (Jack Elliott-Allyn Fer
guson) *see Coll* 'TELEVISION'S GREATEST HITS VOL.3'/
CHARMER The (LWT 18/10/87) Theme "You're The Top" from
'Anything Goes' (Cole Porter) *see* FILMS & SHOWS
CHATEAUVALLON 'Fortune & Power' (C4 26/1/87) Mus (Vladi
mir Cosma) "When Fortune Reigns" RICHARD SANDERSON
with Hubert Leonard and VLADIMIR COSMA ORCH -S/T-
Carrere: CAL 225 (LP) CAC 225 (Cass) all deleted
CHECK OUT (C4/Div.from 15/5/90) mus (Debbie Wiseman).*NA*
CHEERS (USA C4 6/1/84-93) theme (Gary Portnoy-Judy H.
Angelo) *see Collects* 'GREAT TV THEMES VOL.1'(vocal)
'4 AMERICA' (instr) *orig* GARY PORTNOY *vers deleted*
CHEF! (BBC1 28/1/93) theme music "Serious Profession"
by OMAR / incidental music (Jakko M.Jakszyk).....*NA*
CHELSEA FLOWER SHOW 93 (BBC2 26/5/93) closing mus. "The
Mission" (Ennio Morricone) -S/T- *Virgin: CDV(TCV)
(MDV) 2402 (CD/Cass/MD)* also used "Pomp And Circums
tance No.2" (E.Elgar) *many recordings available*
CHELSEA FLOWER SHOW 92 (BBC2 1992/1991) music includes:
PENGUIN CAFE ORCHEST "From The Colonies" ('Broadcas
ting From Home" *EG (Virgin): EGCD 38 (CD)* / "Air A
Dancer"/"A Telephone And A Rubber Band" from 'When
In Rome' *EGCD 56 (CD)* / "Sketch"/"Perpetuum Mobile"
from 'Signs Of Life' *EGCD 50 (CD)* /other music used
"Prelude"('Holberg Suite Op.40) (E.Grieg) *many vers*
CHELTENHAM FESTIVAL (BBC1 14/3/89) Theme music"Odissea"
(Gian Reverberi-L.Giordiano) RONDO VENEZIANO - *Fanf
are (Mainline) RON 5(LP) ZCRON 4(Cass) CDRON 5 (CD)*
CHESS: *see under 'WORLD CHESS CHAMPIONSHIPS 1993'*
CHESTNUT SOLDIER The (HTV 20/11/91)mus (Danny Chang).*NA*
CHICO AND THE MAN (USA 74) Theme (Jose Feliciano) JOSE
FELICIANO on *RCA: ND 90123 (CD) NK 89561 (Cass)*
CHIEF The (Anglia from 20/9/91) theme (Nigel Beaham-Pow
ell-Bella Russell)..................................*NA*
CHILDHOOD (C4 1/3/92) music (Michael Whalen)........*NA*
CHILDREN IN NEED (BBC1 20/11/92) Theme 1989-93 "If You
Want To Help-Help Children In Need" (David Martin)
FINCHLEY CHILDREN'S MUSIC GROUP and CHOIRS (-)
see 'TELE-TUNES 1991' for all other recordings

CHILDREN OF THE NORTH (BBC2 30/10/91) music composed & conducted by Geoffrey Burgon....................*NA*
CHILDREN'S HOSPITAL (BBC1 19/10/93)m.(Debbie Wiseman)*NA*
CHILDREN'S ISLAND (ITV 22/2/92) mus (Hennie Bekker)..*NA*
CHIMERA (Anglia 7/9/91) Theme music "Rosheen Du" (Nigel Hess sung by Chameleon *see Coll* 'CHAMELEON'/'FAVOUR ITE TV THEMES'/'MAIGRET'/'20 TOP TV THEMES'
CHINA BEACH (USA/Sky 91) Theme music (John Rubinstein) *see Collection* 'AMERICAN TELEVISION THEMES VOL.3'
CHINESE DETECTIVE The (UKGO 1/3/93 orig BBC 30/4/81) Theme (Harry South) *BBC / MFP Collections deleted*
CHISH 'N' FIPS (Central 29/10/87) Songs (David Wood) 'The Chish'n'Fips Songbook' Mr.Wheeler & Mr.Fisher *First Night (Pinn): SCENE 11 (LP) SCENE C11 (Cass)*
CHOPPER SQUAD (Australia ITV 87) Theme (Mike Perjanik) *see Collec* 'AUSTRALIAN TELEVISION'S GREATEST HITS'
CHRONICLES OF NARNIA (UKGold 7/11/92 orig BBC 13/11/88) theme music (Geoffrey Burgon) *see Coll* 'BRIDESHEAD REVISITED' Story Cass 'Magicians Nephew' *BBC (Pinn) ZBBC 1109 (2Cass)* 'Lion The Witch And...*ZBBC 1110*
CHUCKLEVISION (BBC1 21/9/91) music (Dave Cooke)......*NA*
CHURCHILL (BBC1 15/1/92) orig music (Richard Holmes).*NA*
CIA (BBC1/NRK/Prime.24/6/92) music (Geoffrey Burgon).*NA*
CIRCLE OF DECEIT (YTV 16/10/93) music (Tim Souster)..*NA*
CIVIL WAR The (BBC2 30/3/91) theme "Ashokan Farewell" (JAY UNGAR) -S/T- incl: "Shenandoah"/"When Johnny Comes Marching Home" & others - KEN BURNS -S/T- on *Elektra-Nonesuch (WEA): 7559-79256-2(CD) -4(Cass)* ALSO AVAILABLE: "The Civil War-It's Music & Sounds" *Mercury Living Presence (Polyg): 432 591-2 MM2 (CD)*
CIVIL WAR (C4/Flashback 23/4/91) mus (Peter Brewis)..*NA*
CIVVIES (BBC1 22/9/92) opening title song "Go And Be Br ave" (Michael Storey) by LENNIE JAMES *not available* end title song "Brothers In Arms" DIRE STRAITS on *Vertigo (Poly): 824 499-2 (CD) VERH(C) 25 (LP/Cass)*
CLARENCE (UKGold 3/11/92 orig BBC2 4/1/88) theme "Sunny Side Up" (DeSylva-Brown-Henderson) *various versions*
CLARISSA (BBC2 27/11/91) music (Colin Towns).........*NA*
CLARKSON'S STAR CARS (BBC1 12/7/93) theme "Peter Gunn" (Henry Mancini)CINCINNATI POPS ORCH (Erich Kunzel) 'Mancini's G.Hits' *Telarc (Conifer): CD 80183 (CD)*
CLASS ACTION (C4 4/2/92) music (Justin Nicholls).....*NA*
CLASS OF THEIR OWN (Thames 29/6/92) m:(David Lawson).*NA*
CLASS RULE (BBC2 26/11/91) theme music "A Little Fugue" (J.S.Bach) performed by JACQUES LOUSSIER *(Start)*
CLASSIC ADVENTURE (BBC1 11/5/92) music (Nigel Hess) *see* 'FAVOURITE TV THEMES'/'MAIGRET AND OTHER TV THEMES'
CLIVE ANDERSON ON TV (C4 17/3/89) Theme "Yakekty Yak" (Jerry Leiber-Mike Stoller) original version by THE COASTERS *Old Gold: OG 9089 (7"s)*
CLOCHEMERLE (BBC2 4/10/91 orig 1972) music (Alan Roper) L'HARMONIE DU RHONE *BBC: RESL 8 (7"s 1972) deleted*
CLONING OF JOANNA MAY The (Granada 26/1/92) theme and incidental music (Rachel Portman)................*NA*

CLOSE TO HOME (LWT 1/10/89) Title theme (Brian & Warren Bennett) by PET SOUNDS *see Coll* '20 TOP TV THEMES'
CLOTHES SHOW The (BBC1 13/10/87-94)Theme "In The Night" (Tennant-Lowe) PET SHOP BOYS on 'Disco' *Parlophone: TC-PRG 1001 (Cass) CDP 746450-2 (CD)*
CLOWNING AROUND (BBC1 27/5/92) music (Peter Best) ..*NA*
CLUEDO (Granada 19/4/93) mus (Richard G.Mitchell-Kevin Malpass)......................................*NA*
COAST OF DREAMS (C4 17/2/92) music (Rick Fenn).......*NA*
COASTING (Granada 26/10/90) Theme (Peter Howitt & David MacKay) sung by PETER HOWITT *not available*
COLDITZ (UKGO 18/6/93 orig BBC1 19/10/72) "The Colditz March" (Robert Farnon) *see Collect* 'Big War Themes'
COLIN'S SANDWICH (UKGO 30/4/93 orig BBC2 18/10/88) mus "Rondo-Horn Concerto No.4 in E.Flat Maj" (Mozart) DAVID JOLLEY & Orpheus Ch.Or *DG (Poly):423377-2 /-4*
COLLECTING NOW (Best Of)(BBC1 10/7/91 orig 82-87) Theme "The Continental" (H.Magidson-C.Conrad) (TV version STEVE HARLEY unavailable) YEHUDI MENUHIN & STEPHANE GRAPPELLI on 'Top Hat' *MFP (EMI): CDCFP 4509 (CD)*
COLOUR EYE The (BBC1 3/6/91) "Java Jive" (M.Drake-B.Oak land) ANDY SHEPPARD Dave Defries & Jerry Underwood on *Antilles (Poly): AN(ANC)(ANCD) 8720 (LP/Cass/CD)*
COLOUR TV (BBC2 17/10/91) theme music (Roger Bolton).*NA*
COLUMBUS AND THE AGE OF DISCOVERY (BBC2 4/7/92) Music (Sheldon Mirowitz) *Narada Cinema (Pinn): CD 6002 CD*
COLTRANE IN A CADILLAC (Tiger Aspect/Meridian 4/5/93) theme mus "Benny Rides Again" BENNY GOODMAN ORCHES TRA *recording currently unavailable*
COME DANCING (BBC1 12/10/92) Theme song (Stewart James-Bradley James) sung by ROSEMARIE FORD............*NA* *previous theme* 25/6/90) Theme "Dancing Feet" (Andy Ross) on 'Dancing Feet' by ANDY ROSS on *President: PCOM 1107 (CD) PTLC 1107 (Cass) PTLS 1107 (LP)*
COME IN SPINNER (Aust.90-BBC1 30/6/91) Orig music (Mart in Armiger) Orig 40's songs arr.William Motzing and performed by VINCE JONES and GRACE KNIGHT. -S/T- on *Intuition Imp.(Pinn) INT 30732 (CD) INT 30734 (Cas)*
COMIC RELIEF 1993 (BBC1 12 Mar 93) Songs used included:
"Stick It Out" RIGHT SAID FRED *RCA:CD(CA)(12)COMIC1*
"We Can Build A Bridge" JUDDS *RCA: PD(PK)(PL) 90531*
"He Ain't Heavy He's My Brother" HOLLIES *EMI:CC 216*
"Father and Son" CAT STEVENS *Island: 840 148-2 / -4*
"Gnossiennes 1-6" (Erik Satie) *various recordings*
"Harvest For The World" The CHRISTIANS *Island Rec*
COMIC STRIP The (BBC2 1/2/90) *1/2:*(South Atlantic Raide rs) "Stand On It" (Beck-Bozzio) JEFF BECK-TERRY BOZ ZIO with TONY HYMAS on 'Jeff Beck's Guitar Shop' on *Epic: 463472-2(CD) -4(Cass) 3:*(GLC) "Ken" KATE BUSH *EMI:(CD)(12)EM 134 4:*(Oxford)music & title song by PRETENDERS+addit.mus (Simon Brint) *(not available)* 5 (Spaghetti Hoops) opening mus 'Funiculi Funicula' (Luigi Denza) ver: JOSE CARRERAS *Philips: 400015-2* LUCIANO PAVAROTTI *Decca: 410015-2 6* (Le Dogs)....*NA*

COMMONWEALTH GAMES 1990 (XIV) BBC1 24/1/90-3/2/90 Theme
"Nan Mai" (Welcome) Maori Anthem 'Be Strong Or Peri
sh' *not available* other items *LINK MUSIC* "Diamonds
On the Soles Of her Shoes" (P.Simon) *WEA: 925789-2
-4 (CD/Cass) CLOSING CEREMONY* "Now Is The Hour" by
(Maewa Kaihau-Dorothy Scott) sung by KIRI TE KANAWA
"This Is The Moment' by THE NEW ZEALAND ATHLETES.*NA*

COMMONWEALTH GAMES 1986 (XIII)(BBC 24/7/86) "Hundred Th
ousand Welcomes" ('Ceud Mile Failte') B.A.ROBERTSON
on Collection 'BBC Sporting Themes' *(BBC-Pickwick)*

COMPACT (BBC1 1962-65) Theme mus "City Movement" (Roger
Rôger) *see Coll* 'SOUNDS VISUAL'

COMPLETE SKIER The (C4 27/1/91) music (Simon James)..*NA*

COMPUTING FOR THE TERRIFIED (BBC1 education 21/2/93)
theme music (David Mitcham).....................*NA*

CONCERTO (C4/Cler.Medical 15/8/93) 6 programmes feat:
LONDON SYMPHONY ORCHESTRA (Michael Tilson Thomas)
and guest musicians Barry Douglas-James Galway-Stev
Isserlis-Alicia De Larrocha-Richard Stoltzman and
Kyoko Takezawa. *RCA (BMG): 09026 61782-6 to 09026
61787-6 (6 LASER DISCS) CD Numbers to be confirmed*

CONJUGAL RIGHTS (Gran 16/4/93) theme m.(Steve Brown).*NA*

CONNECTIONS (Granada 26/4/85) Theme (Bill Connor) *see
Coll* 'GRANADA STUDIOS SOUVENIR ALBUM'

CONNOISSEUR (BBC2 18/5/89) Theme: 1st m/mt Flute Sonata
No.4 in C (BWV 1030) (J.S.Bach) Roberto Fabbriciani
(flute) on *Frequenz (Conifer): 011-035 (CD)*

CONQUER THE ARCTIC (C4 12/1/91) mus pr.(Frits Hooft).*NA*

COOK REPORT (Central 22/7/87) mus (Darren S.Pullman).*NA*

COOL HEAD (Central 17/2/91) music (Philip Pope)......*NA*

COOL IT (BBC2 30/8/85) Feat PHIL COOL / Harmonica theme
(P.Cool) *Virgin (Poly): OVED(C) 228 (LP/Cass)*

COP ROCK (USA 90-BBC1 30/9/91) songs/title song "Under
The Gun" composed and performed by RANDY NEWMAN.*NA*

COPS (USA 90 SKY 91) theme "Bad Boys" (Inner Circle) on
'One Way' *RAS (Jetstar): RAS(CD)(MC)(LP) 3030*

CORONATION STREET (Granada 9/12/60-1994) Theme (Eric Sp
ear) *see Coll* 'GRANADA STUDIOS TOUR..'/'ITV THEMES'

COSBY SHOW The (USA C4 20/1/85) Theme (Stu Gardner-Bill
Cosby) *see Coll* '4 AMERICA: TV Themes From Ch.4'

COUNT DUCKULA (Thames 6/9/88)theme (Mike Harding) vocal
Sarah Harding *on Coll* 'KID'S THEMES' **deleted**

COUNTDOWN (C4 from 2/11/82-94) music (Alan Hawkshaw).*NA*

COUNTRY MATTERS (Granada 72) Theme (Derek Hilton) *see
Collection* 'GRANADA STUDIOS SOUVENIR ALBUM'

COUNTRY PRACTICE A (ITV Australia 88) Theme (Mike Perja
nik) *see* 'AUSTRALIAN TELEVISION'S GREATEST HITS'

COUNTRYMAN (BBC2 4/3/91) music (Keith Hopwood).......*NA*

COVER UP (USA BBC1 12/4/85) Theme "Holding Out For A
Hero" (Jim Steinman-Dean Pitchford) *see Collection*
'GREAT TV THEMES VOUME 3' and also 'FOOTLOOSE'-S/T-

COWLEY HIGH (Granada fr.11/11/92) various music includ:
"Get The Message" by ELECTRONIC album 'Electronic'
Factory (Pinn): FACD 290 (CD) FACTC 290 (Cass) & LP

COWRA BREAKOUT The (Austral-84/BBC1 7/6/91) Music score
(William Motzing)*see Coll*'AUSTRALIAN TV's GREATEST'
CRACKER (ITV 27/9/93) music com/per (Julian Wastall).*NA*
CRACKING THE CODE (BBC2 7/9/93) mus (Malcolm Clarke).*NA*
CRATER OF THE RAIN GOD (Zebra Films/C4 28/7/93) music
score (Brian Gascoigne)........................*NA*
CRAWL INTO MY PARLOUR (Ultra Flix Prod/BBC2 5/9/93)
orig music composed & peformed (Adriaan Strydom).*NA*
CRAWSHAW PAINTS ON HOLIDAY (JR Product for TSW 15/9/92)
theme music (Darren Elliot)....................*NA*
CRAZY COMPARISONS (Thames 18/6/91) mus(LBS Comm.mus).*NA*
CRAZY LIKE A FOX (USA ITV 19/1/86) Theme (Mark Snow)
previously on Coll 'SCREEN ACTION' *deleted*
CRIBB (Granada 79) Theme (Derek Hilton) *see Collection*
'GRANADA STUDIOS SOUVENIR ALBUM'
CRICKET (BBC 1/2) Theme "Soul Limbo" (Booker T.Jones)
BOOKER T.& MG's - *Stax (Pinn): Stax 808 (7"s)*
CRIME STORY (USA ITV 89) Theme "Runaway" (Del Shannon-
Max Crook) DEL SHANNON 'The Collection' *Line-Impact
(Conif): IMCD 9.00436 (CD) / Old Gold: OG 9256 (7")*
CRIME UNLIMITED (BBC1 28/4/92) theme m (Ian Butcher).*NA*
CRIMEWATCH (BBC1 7/6/84-93) Theme (John Cameron).....*NA*
CROSSROADS (Central 2/11/92 - 4/4/88 | 4510 episodes)
Orig theme 'Crossroads' (Tony Hatch) 64-87 *see Coll*
'A-Z OF BRITISH TV THEMES'/'TV CLASSICS VOL.4'
'Love Theme "The Summer Of My Life" (Simon May) *on
Coll* 'GREAT TV THEMES 1'/'Kings Oak' theme (Raf Rav
enscroft-Max Early) used 87-88 *Ariola 609912 (12"s)
deleted* / Tony Hatch theme also recorded by PAUL Mc
CARTNEY & WINGS *Parlophone: TC-PCTC 254 (Cass)*
CROSSWITS (Tyne-Tees from 6/1/87) music (Ed Welch)..*NA*
CRUFTS 91 (BBC1 12/1/91) theme music "Westway" (Herbie
Flowers) performed by SKY on 'Masterpieces' *Telstar
(BMG): TCD 2241 (CD) STAR 2241 (LP) STAC 2241 (Cas)*
CRYSTAL MAZE The (C4 15/2/90) music (Zack Laurence)..*NA*
CUBAN MISSILE CRISIS The (BBC2 7/10/92) original music
(Debbie Wiseman)...............................*NA*
CUCKOOLAND (BBC1 (NZTV) 8/84/91) mus (Jenny McLeod)..*NA*
CYBERZONE (BBC2/Broadsword 4/1/93) music (Ed Welch)..*NA*

DAD'S ARMY (BBC1 31/7/68-77 re-run 9/89) Theme "Who Do
Think You Are Kidding Mr.Hitler" (Jimmy Perry-Derek
Taverner) sung by BUD FLANAGAN / Original Cast Rec
ording *BBC (Pinn): ZBBC 1140(Cass)* theme *see Coll*
'A-Z OF BRITISH TV THEMES'/'TV CLASSICS VOLUME 3'
DAKTARI (USA 66) Theme music (Shelly Manne) *see Collect*
'TELEVISION'S GREATEST HITS 2'
DALLAS (UKGO 2/11/93 orig USA 80 and BBC1 1978-6/10/91)
(356 episodes) Theme (Jerrold Immel) *see Collection*
'GREAT TV THEMES VOLUME 2' *(Tring Int)*
DAME EDNA'S NEIGHBOURHOOD WATCH (ITV 19/9/92) title mus
comp/sung by Barry Humphries arr:Laurie Holloway.*NA*
DANCE ENERGY (BBC2 DEFII 15/10/90) theme music (Dave
Dorrell and Andrew Hale).......................*NA*

DANCEDAZE (C4 9/11/90) Theme "Breakaway" by BIG PIG on
   'Bonk' *A&M (Poly): CDA(AMC)(AMA) 5185 (CD/Cass/LP)*
DANCING (BBC2 24/1/93) title music (John Hill).......*NA*
DANGER MAN (ITC 11/9/60-68) re-shown C4 22/9/84) theme
   music "High Wire" (Edwin Astley) *see Coll* 'A-Z OF
   BRITISH TV THEMES'/'MAN FROM U.N.C.L.E.TV CLASSICS'
   'POWER THEMES 90'/'TV CLASSICS VOLUME 3'
DANGERMOUSE (Thames from 4/1/82-92)theme (Mike Harding)
   sung by SHEILA GOTT *on Coll* 'ITV CHILDREN'S THEMES'
DANIEL BOONE (USA 64) Theme (Paul Sawtell) *see Collect*
   'TELEVISION'S GREATEST HITS VOLUME 1'
DANNY BAKER AFTER ALL (BBC1 18/9/93) mus (Mark Kermode
   directing the RAILTOWN BOTTLERS)................*NA*
DARK HORSE (BBC1 12/5/93) orig music (Drew King).....*NA*
DARK SEASON (BBC1 14/11/91) Music (David Ferguson)...*NA*
DARLING BUDS OF MAY The (Yorkshire 7/4/91) theme music
   (Pip Burley) Music (Barrie Guard) ENGLISH LIGHT ORC
   ESTRA (Barrie Guard) *Soundtrack Music (EMI): CDEMC
   3612 (CD) TCEMC 3612 (Cass) all deleted 93* / spoken
   word Cass: *MCI (TBD): TALKMC 015 (2Cass) 016 (2Cass*
DARTS (BBC) Theme music "Cranes" (Douglas Wood) DOUGLAS
   WOOD GROUP *see Coll* 'BBC SPORTING THEMES' *deleted*
DAS BOOT (W.Germany) - *see under* 'The BOAT'
DAVE ALLEN (Carlton/Noel Gay 7/1/93) theme "Blarney's
   Stoned" (Alan Hawkshaw) arr:David Mindel *orig avail
   able Columbia Studio 2 (EMI): TWO 391 (LP) deleted*
DAVID COPPERFIELD (UKGO 13/6/93 orig BBC1 19/10/86)orig
   music (Stephen Deutsch)........................*NA*
DAVRO (TVS 17/3/90) music director (Andy Street).....*NA*
DAY THE WORLD CHANGED (BBC2 15/1/92) mus (Roy Mason).*NA*
DAYS AND NIGHTS OF MOLLY DODD (USA-86/BBC1-15/7/90)
   Theme music (Patrick Williams) *see Collection*
   'AMERICAN TELEVISION THEMES VOLUME 3'
DAYS OF MAJESTY (Granite Prod for YTV 2/6/93) orig mus
   (Barrington Pheloung) TV -S/T- on *London (Polygram)
   828 427-2 (CD) 828 427-4 (Cass)*
DAZZLING IMAGE (C4 8/6/92) theme (David Cunningham)..*NA*
DE GAULLE AND FRANCE (BBC2) mus (Marc-Olivier Dupin).*NA*
DEA (USA-BBC1 30/10/91) title music (Micahel Kamen)..*NA*
DEAD GOOD SHOW The (Gran 9/11/92) theme "Beat Girl"
   (John Barry) *Play It Again (S.Screen) PLAY 001 (CD)*
DEAR JOHN *(UK)* (BBC1 22/7/91 orig 17/2/86) theme 'Dear
   John' (John Sullivan) sung by JOAN BAXTER........*NA*
DECISIONS DECISIONS (C4 8/1/93) mus (Francis Shaw)..*NA*
DEFENDERS OF THE WILD (YTV 12/1/92) mus (Ernie Wood).*NA*
DELIA SMITH'S SUMMER COLLECTION (BBC2 4/5/93) theme mus
   "Summertime" (George Gershwin) *BBC arrangement...NA
   other recordings - see 'PORGY & BESS' p.206 TT 1993*
DEMOB (Talkback/YTV 15/10/93) Music comp/orchestrated
   by Peter Martin / Music co-ordinator: Helen Sava.*NA*
DEMPSEY & MAKEPEACE (LWT 11/1/85) Theme (Alan Parker)
   see Coll 'HIT THEMES 1 - BEST OF BRITISH TV MUSIC'
DEPARTMENT S (ITC 9/3/69) Theme (Edwin Astley) *see Coll*
   'A-Z OF BRITISH TV THEMES'/TV CLASSICS VOLUME 2'

DESERT SONG (SURVIVAL SPECIAL) (Anglia-20/11/91) Music
    score (Ray Russell) *not available* / SONGS from 'The
    Joshua Tree' by U2 *Island: CID U26(CD) UC26 (Cass)*
DESMOND'S (H.Barclay Prod/C4 5/1/89-1994) Theme "Don't
    Scratch My Soca" (Trix Worrell-John Collins)....*NA*
DESPERADO (USA) Granada 29/9/90 Title theme music (Don
    Henley-Glenn Frey) THE EAGLES (73) 'Greatest Hits'
    Asylum (WEA): 960 342-2 (CD) K4 53017 (Cass)
DETECTIVES The (BBC1/Celador 27/1/93) theme mus (Keith
    and Matthew Strachan)...........................*NA*
DEVELOPING STORIES (BBC2 3/5/92) 'Lucia' (Max Jocson)*NA*
DEVICES AND DESIRES (Anglia 4/1/91) theme music "Elegy"
    (Richard Harvey) *prev.on* 'Impressions' *(KTel) delet*
DICK BARTON (ITV 78) Theme "Devil's Galop" (Charles Wil
    liams) *see Coll* 'FAMOUS THEMES'(1)
DICK POWELL SHOW (THEATRE) (USA 61/C4 7/1/93) "Dick Pow
    ell"/"Nervous Teaser" (themes) (Herschel Burke Gilb
    ert) orig on *London Dot HLD 9655 (7"s 1962) deleted*
DICK TURPIN (LWT 6/1/79) Theme (Denis King) *see under*
    'LOVEJOY' *Collection*
DICK VAN DYKE SHOW The (USA 61) Theme (Earl Hagen) *see*
    Coll 'TELEVISION'S GREATEST HITS VOL.1'
DID YOU SEE (BBC2 80-93) orig ser.(1980-88 with Ludovic
    Kennedy) theme music 'Think Big' (Francis Monkman)
    (20/10/91-93 w.Jeremy Paxman) title theme (Anthony
    & Gaynor Sadler) *both themes unavailable*
DIFFERENT WORLD, A (USA series C4 from 22/9/88) theme
    music (Stu Gardner-Bill Cosby-Dawnn Lewis) sung by
    ARETHA FRANKLIN *version on Collect:* '4 AMERICA TWO'
DIG (C4 Tartan TV 19/4/91) title mus (Mike Walker)...*NA*
DINOSAUR (Granada 1/9/91) music (Gerhard Heinz)......*NA*
DINOSAURS The (USA TV Series 93) Music score (Peter Mel
    nick) TV -S/T- *Narada Cinema (Pinn): ND 66004 (CD)*
DIRK BOGARDE: BY MYSELF (C4 11/1/92)theme music "Here's
    What I'm Here For" (Harold Arlen) arr. Roger White
    saxophone solo by Dave Woolfson..................*NA*
DIRTY BEASTS & REVOLTING RHYMES (Central 2/4/91) theme
    mus "Three Blind Mice" arr./perf: Graham Goodwin..*NA*
DIRTY DANCING (USA 90 ITV 18/10/91) theme "(I've Had)
    The Time Of My Life" (F.Previte-J.De Nichola-D.Mark
    owitz)BILL MEDLEY-JENNIFER WARNES *see* FILMS & SHOWS
DISGUISES (Granada 25/2/93) theme mus (Mike Timoney).*NA*
DISPOSSESSED The (C4/YTV 4/9/91) music (Ernie Wood)..*NA*
DISTRICT NURSE (UKGold 8/11/92 orig BBC1 10/1/84) music
    (David Mindell) *BBC deleted*
DIVINE INSPIRATION (LWT 6/6/93) mus (Debbie Wiseman).*NA*
DIVORCE (BBC2 16/5/91) title music (Malcolm Clarke)..*NA*
DIVORCING DADDY (Scot TV 28/6/91) m:(Phil Cunningham)*NA*
DIXON OF DOCK GREEN (BBC1 55-76) Theme "An Ordinary Cop
    per" (JEFF DARNELL) Jack Warner *(BBC deleted)*
DIZZY HEIGHTS (BBC1 18/2/93) theme music (Ken Bolam).*NA*
DJ's HEAVEN (BBC2 25/9/93) title mus (James Taylor)..*NA*
    also used "Whole Lotta Love" (Led Zeppelin) by CCS
    'WHOLE LOTTA LOVE' *EMI:CDEMS 1426 or CDP 797553-2CD*

DOCTOR AT THE TOP (BBC1 21/2/91) theme "Bond Street Par
ade" (Alan Tew) *see next item* incid mus (Ed Welch)
DOCTOR FINLAY (Scottish TV 5/3/93) mus (Richard Harvey)
played by The Scottish Chamber Orch (R.Harvey) Orig
TV -S/T- on *Total (BMG):TOTCD 2 (CD) TOTMC 2 (Cass)*
DOCTOR FINLAY'S CASEBOOK (BBC1 60s) Theme "A Little Sui
te" (Trevor Duncan) Orch Of The Light Music Society
(V.Dunn) *HMV: ESD 7063 (LP) deleted*
DOCTOR IN THE HOUSE (LWT 70) theme music (Alan Tew) *see*
Coll 'A-Z OF BRITISH TV THEMES'
DOCTOR KILDARE (USA 61) Theme music (Jerry Goldsmith)
vocal "Three Stars Will Shine Tonight" by RICHARD
CHAMBERLAIN - *Old Gold OG 1012 (LP) OG 2012 (Cass)*
DOCTOR QUINN: MEDICINE WOMAN (USA/ITV 28/5/93) orig mus
ic (William Olvis).....................................*NA*
DOCTOR WHO (BBC1 23/11/63-93) orig theme (Ron Grainer)
'THIRTY YEARS AT THE RADIOPHONIC WORKSHOP' **(BBC)**
Music by Various Artists *BBC (Pinn) BBCCD 871 (CD)*
COLLS: 'A-Z OF BRITISH TV THEMES'/'FAVOU.TV THEMES'
(1) 'DR.WHO - VARIATIONS ON A THEME' by various
composers - *Silva Screen (Con): FILMCD 706 (CD)*
(2) 'EARTHSHOCK' (Classics Vol.1) BBC Radiophonic
Workshop music composed & performed by Ron Grainer
Peter Howell-Malcolm Clarke-Dudley Simpson-Delia De
rbyshire-Roger Limb *S.Screen (Con): FILMC(CD) 709*
(3) 'THE FIVE DOCTORS' (Classics Vol.2) various com
posers - *Silva Screen (Con): FILMCD 710 (CD)*
(4) 'THE CURSE OF FENRIC' (mus: Mark Ayers) *Sil.Scr*
(Con): FILMCD 087 (CD)
(5) 'MYTHS & OTHER LEGENDS (mus: Mark Ayres) *Silva*
Screen: FILMCD 088 (CD)
(6) 'DR.WHO AND THE PESCATONS' (mus: Kenny Clayton)
Silva Screen (Con): FILMCD 707 (CD)
(7) 'GREATEST SHOW IN THE GALAXY' (mus: Mark Ayres)
Silva Screen (Con): FILMCD 114 (CD)
(8) '.GENESIS OF THE DALEKS' (BBC1 series feat Tom
Baker) Music score from 5 series (Dudley Simpson)
Silva Screen (Conifer): FILMCD 134 (CD)
(9) 'GHOSTLIGHT' (BBC1 ser. feat Sylvester McCoy)
Music sc (Mark Ayres) *S.Screen (Con):FILMCD 133(CD)*
(10) 'THE MISSING STORIES': Power Of The Daleks
(BBC-Pinn) *ZBBC 1433 (2Cass)* **and Fury From The Deep**
(BBC-Pinn) *ZBBC 1434 (2Cass)*
(11) 'TOMB OF THE CYBERMEN' (BBC) *BBC (Pinn):*
ZBBC 1343 (2Cass)
DOCTORS TO BE (BBC2 26/10/92) theme music (Elizabeth Pa
rker) BBC Radiophonic Workshop.....................*NA*
DOG CITY (J.Henson/C4 17/10/93) theme (Phil Balsam)..*NA*
DOG'S LIFE The (BBC2 23 /9/93) orig mus (Simon Park).*NA*
DOGTANIAN AND THE THREE MUSKEHOUNDS (BBC1 3/1/85) Music
(Guido & Maurizio De Angelis) Christopher Laird *see*
Coll 'THEMES FROM CHILDREN'S BBCTV'/'ITV CHILDREN'S
DOING IT WITH YOU...IS TABOO (C4 5/10/93) music (Robert
Doyle and Ingmar King).............................*NA*

DOMESDAY (BBC1 23/11/86) Music (CLAIRE HAMMILL) 'Domesd
    ay' - *Coda (WEA): CODS 21 (7"ep) CODS 21T (12"s)*
DONOVAN THE DIVINER (BBC2 18/5/89) Theme from 'The Roma
    nce Of Harp & Flute'- THELMA OWEN & PHILLIPA DAVIES
    on *IMP (Pickwick): PCD 835 (CD) CIMP(C) 835 (LP/CS)*
DON'T LEAVE ME THIS WAY (BBC1 30/5/93) mus.score (Colin
    Towns)*(not available)* end song "Don't Leave Me This
    Way" sung by OTIS REDDING *Atlantic Recording (WEA)*
DON'T TELL FATHER (BBC1 26/4/92) theme (Nick Ingham).*NA*
DON'T WAIT UP (UKGold 28/1/93 orig BBC1 25/10/83) signa
    nature music (Nick Ingham)......................*NA*
DOOGIE HOWSER MD (USA)(BBC1-5/9/90)theme (Mike Post).*NA*
    see Coll 'AMERICAN TV THEMES-PRIMETIME COL.VOL.2' &
    'TELEVISION MUSIC OF MIKE POST AND PETE CARPENTER'
DOWN AMONG THE BIG BOYS (BBC Sc.One 19/9/93) orig music
    (Ray Russell-Simon Chamberlain)..................*NA*
DOWN HOME (C4 1/3/86) V.Art -S/T- *Lismor (Celtic Music)*
    LIFL 7011 LP-Vol 1) LIFL 7012 (LP-Vol 2) LIFC (Cas)
DOWN TO EARTH (C4 6/11/90) music (Anne Dudley).......NA
DRAGNET (USA 50s) Theme (Walter Schumann) *see Collect*
    'TELEVISION'S GREATEST HITS 1'
DRAGON HAS TWO TONGUES The (C4 17/6/87) Music (Robin Wi
    lliamson) -S/T- *TER (Conif): (ZC)TER 1133 (Cass/LP)*
DREADED LURGI The (BBC2 17/9/91) title mus (Vangelis)*NA*
DREAM MACHINE (C4 17/11/91) music (Peter Howell).....*NA*
DREAM ON (USA 90/C4 9/8/91) theme m (Michael Skloff) on
    Collection '4 AMERICA TWO'
DREAMSTONE The (Central 25/9/90)*Theme song* "Better Than
    A Dream" (M.Batt) MIKE BATT Album / Billy Connolly-
    Ozzy Osbourne-Frank Bruno-Gary Glitter-Bonnie Tyler
    Mike Batt-London P.O.- *Adventure (CBS): ADVT(CD)(C)*
    (LP) 1001 (CD/Cass/LP) deleted
DRUG WARS:Camarena (USA 89/BBC1 16/7/91) music: Charles
    Bernstein-Charles Calello-Al Kooper-Warren Zevon &
    Jorge Strunze with Ardeshir Farah...............*NA*
DUCHESS OF DUKE STREET The (UKGold 2/11/92 orig BBC 76)
    theme (Alexander Faris) *see Coll* 'ITV THEMES'
DUET (C4 29/1/91 USA Prod 87) theme mus (Buddy Budsen)
            and sung by URSULA WALKER & TONY FRANKLIN..*NA*
DUKES OF HAZZARD (USA 79) Theme 'Good Ol'Boys' (WAYLON
    JENNINGS) *see* Coll 'TELEVISION'S GREATEST HITS 3'/
    'GREAT TV THEMES VOL.1'
DUNGEONS AND DRAGONS (BBC2 83) Theme (Johnny Douglas)
    'On Screen' with JOHNNY DOUGLAS STRINGS on *Dulcima*
    (Taylors-T.Blood): DLCD 110 (CD) DLCT 110 (Cass)
DUTY FREE (Yorkshire 13/2/84) music (Peter Knight)...*NA*
DUTY MEN The (BBC2 29/10/87) Theme "Watching You" (Mich
    ael Kamen) M.KAMEN-SASHAZOE *BBC:12RESL 215 deleted*
DYNASTY (UKGO 8/3/93 orig BBC1 82 (USA 80) theme music
    (Bill Conti) *see Collection 'GREAT TV THEMES VOL.3'*

EARLY TRAVELLERS IN NORTH AMERICA (BBC2 23/7/92) music
    (Tot Taylor)....................................*NA*
EAST (BBC2 4/6/90) title music (Harjinda Bopari).....*NA*

EASTENDERS (BBC1 19/2/85-1994) *Theme* (Simon May-Leslie
   Osborne) Orig version SIMON MAY ORCHESTRA *see Coll:*
   'GREAT TV THEMES V.3' **EASTENDERS** (BBC1) theme (new
   arrangement) from 11/7/93 SIMON MAY *Polyd: PZCD 268
   (CDs) POCS 268 (Cass) PO 268 (7"s)* NOTE: incl.vocal
   vers. by SHARON BENSON "I'll Always Believe In You"
EAT UP (Stephens/Kerr C4 6/10/93) mus (Pete Baikie)..*NA*
EAT YOUR GREENS (C4 7/4/93)*see under 'GROW YOUR GREENS'*
ECHO FOUR-TWO (Assoc.Rediff.24/8/61-25/10/61) theme mus
   ic (Laurie Johnson) *see Coll* 'TV CLASSICS VOL.4'
ED CASE SHOWCASE (BBC2 8/5/92) theme mus (Jim Wafer).*NA*
EDD THE DUCK (BBC2 7/10/90) Theme "Awesome Dude" ON *BBC
   (Pinn): EDD 001 (7"s)* BBC Childrens TV Link Puppet
EDGE OF DARKNESS (BBC2 10/5/92 orig 4/11/85)Theme music
   ERIC CLAPTON-MICHAEL KAMEN *BBC:12/ZCRESL178 deleted*
EDINBURGH NIGHTS (BBC216/8/93)t.music (Andrew Poppy).*NA*
EDWARD AND MRS.SIMPSON (Thames 8/11/78 & 19/5/86) Music
   (Ron Grainer) singer Jenny Wren -S/T- *RK: deleted*
EERIE INDIANA (USA/C4 23/3/93) music theme (Gary Chang)
   on '4 AMERICA TWO' *Primetime (S.Screen):TVPMCD 803
   (CD/Cass)* song "ForeverWare" by Dean Friedman....*NA*
8.15 FROM MANCHESTER (BBC1 21/4/90) theme music based
   on 'Find Out Why' by The INSPIRAL CARPETS (orig) on
   Cow (Nine Mile/Cartel): DUNG 5(T)(CD) (7"/12"/CDs)
EL C.I.D. (Gran 7/2/90) Theme "Go For It" (Mike Moran)
   Performed by GEORGIE FAME - *Food For Thought/Music
   For Nations (Pinn): YUM 119 (7"s)*
ELDORADO (BBC1 6/7/92- 9/7/93) Theme music (Simon May)
   song "When You Go Away" (Simon May) sung by JOHNNY
   GRIGGS on *Hit-Chrysalis (Poly): HLC 3 (CDs) HLK 3
   (Cass) HLS 3 (7"s)* also includes instrumental theme
ELIZABETH R (UKGO 20/6/93 orig BBC1 17/2/71) music by
   David Munrow and The Early Music Consort. theme mus
   "The Leaves Are Green" (William Byrd) *BBC deleted*
ELIZABETH R (Documentary BBC1 6/2/92) original music by
   (Rachel Portman).................................*NA*
ELVIS: GOOD ROCKIN' TONIGHT (USA 89 orig C4-3/4/90) mus
   (Bob Mann-Steve Tyrell-Jimmy Z) performed by Ronnie
   McDowell *not available* orig ELVIS material on *RCA*
EMINENT VICTORIANS (BBC2 18/9/89) "Serenade For Strings
   In C.Op.48" (Tchaikovsky) Berlin P.O.on Teldec (*ASV
   Pinn): ZK8.43312 (CD) CY4(AZ6) 43312 (Cass/LP)*
EMMERDALE (FARM) (Yorkshire TV 16/10/72-1994) Theme mus
   ic (Tony Hatch) *see Coll* 'A-Z OF BRITISH TV THEMES'
   'TV CLASSICS VOL.4'
EMPTY NEST (USA/C4 18/8/89)Theme "Life Goes On" (George
   A.Tipton-John Bettis) by BILLY VERA & BEATERS....*NA*
ENCHANTED APRIL (BBC2 orig 5/4/92 rpt 14/3/93) music sc
   (Richard Rodney Bennett) conductor: Neil Richardson
   -S/T- *Bay Cities (Silva Screen): BCD 3035 (CD)*
ENCIRCLED SEA The (C4 6/7/90) Music (ROBERT BOYLE)-S/T-
   Silva Screen (Con) FILMCD 076 (CD) FILMC 076 (Cass)
ENDLESS GAME The (C4 20/8/89) Music by ENNIO MORRICONE
   -S/T- *Virgin: (TCV)(CDV) 2602 (Cass/CD) all deleted*

E.N.G. (C4 29/4/91)/(Alliance-Canada 89) theme music by (Mickey Erbe-Maribeth Soloman)...................*NA*
ENTERTAINMENT EXPRESS (BBC1 8/1/93) mus (Tot Taylor).*NA*
ENTERTAINMENT USA (BBC2 15/4/83) Theme "I'll Slap Your Face" (Jonathan King) 'Many Faces Of Jonathan King' *Music Club Int (TBD): MCCD 108 (CD) MCTC 108 (Cass)*
EQUALIZER The (USA 29/10/86) Theme (STEWART COPELAND) -TV S/T- *IRS: MIRFC 1029 (Cass) DMIRF 1029 (CD)*
ESTHER INTERVIEWS.. (BBC1 14/7/88) Theme "Gymnopedie No 3"(Erik Satie orchestration Debussy) ANGELA BROWNRIGE *EMI: CDEMX 9507 (CD) EMX 412071-1(LP)-4(Cass)* CECILE OUSSET - *EMI: CDC 747225-2 (CD)*
EUROCOPS (C4 5/3/90) Theme (Jan Hammer) JAN HAMMER on 'Snapshots' *MCA (Poly): (D)MCG(C) 6039 (CD/LP/Cass)*
EUROPE BY DESIGN (BBC1 16/8/92) Mus (Dominic C.Collins)
EUROPE EXPRESS (C4 6/1/89) theme mus (David Stevens).*NA*
EUROPE ON THE BRINK (BBC2 12/1/93) title theme music (Martin Kiszko)......................................*NA*
EUROPEAN ATHLETIC CHAMPIONSHIPS (BBC1 26/8/86)Theme mus "Going Home" (Mark Knopfler) *see* 'LOCAL HERO' film
EUROPEAN CHAMPIONS LEAGUE Football (ITV Sport 25/11/92) "Champion League Anthem" (Tony Britten)..........*NA*
EUROPEAN FIGURE SKATING CHAMPIONSHIPS (BBC 1/2) theme music "Mornings At Seven" (James Last) JAMES LAST & HIS ORCHESTRA on 'Happy Heart' *Polydor (Polygram) 839 643-2 (CD) -4 (Cass) see also* 'ICE SKATING'
EUROPEAN FOOTBALL CHAMPIONSHIP 1992 (Sweden) 10/6/92 ITV Coverage: *THEME:* "You Are The Number One" by UNION featuring PAUL YOUNG (Mike & Mechanics) on *Jive (BMG): JIVCD 309 (CDs) JIVE 309 (7"s) deleted* BBC Coverage *THEME:* "Ode To Joy" 4th m/ment 'Choral Symphony No.9' (Beethoven) BERLIN PHILHARMONIC ORCH *DG-Polygram: 415832-2 (CD) many versions available*
EUROPEAN SWIMMING CHAMPIONSHIPS - see under 'SWIMMING'
EUROVISION SIGNATURE MUSIC "Te Deum In D.Major" (Marc-Antoine Charpentier) Academy Of St.Martin-In-The Fields (Neville Marriner) *EMI: CDC 754 284-2 (CD)* also English Chamber Orch *EMI: CZS 767 425-2 (2CD)*
EUROVISION SONG CONTEST (1993) (Ireland) (BBC1 15/5/93) *93 WINNING SONG:* "In Your Eyes" (Jimmy Walsh) sung by NIAMH KAVANAGH for IRELAND scored 187 pts (25 Countries) *Arista: 74321 15415-2(CDs) -4(Cass) -7(7")* *93 UK ENTRY:*"Better The Devil" (Dean Collinson-Red) SONIA (164 pts- 2nd) *Arista (BMG): 74321 14687-2CDs*
EUROVISION SONG CONTEST (1992) (Sweden) (BBC1 9/5/92) *92 WINNING SONG:* "Why Me"(Johnny Logan)LINDA MARTIN scored 155 points (23 Countries) *Columbia (Sony M) 658131-7 (7"s) 658131-4 (Cass) deleted* *92 UK ENTRY:* "One Step Out Of Time" (Tony Ryan-Paul Davies-Victor Stratton) MICHAEL BALL (139 pts- 2nd) *Polydor: PZCD 206 (CDs) PO 206 (7") POCS 206 (Cass)*
EUROVISION SONG CONTEST (1991) (Rome) (BBC1-4/5/91) *91 WINNING SONG:* "Fangad Av En Stormvind' (Captured By A Love Storm) CAROLA (Sweden) scored 146 points

continued...
   (22 Countries) *RCA (BMG):PB 44649(7")* *PD 44650(CDs)*
   also "Le Dernier Qui A Parle" (Last One Who Speaks)
   AMINA (France) 146 Ppts *Philips: PH 45 (7")* *PHMC 45
   91 UK ENTRY* "A Message To Your Heart" (Paul Curtis)
   SAMANTHA JANUS (47 Points - 11th) *Hollywood (Pinn):
   HWD(T)(CD)104 (7"/12"CDs)* / SEE ALSO *AWARDS SECTION*
EUROVISION SONG CONTEST (1990) (Yugoslav)(BBC1 5/5/90)
   90 WINNING SONG "Insieme 1992" (All Together Now)by
   TOTO COTUGNO (Italy) scored 149 pts (22 countries)
   on *Odeon (EMI): (12)ODO 113 (12"s/7"s) deleted*
   90 UK ENTRY "Give A Little Love Back To The World"
   (Paul Curtis) sung by EMMA (87 points placed 6th)
   recorded on *Big Wave (BMG): BWR 33 (7"s) deleted*
EUROVISION SONG CONTEST (1989) (Switzerl) (BBC1-6/5/89)
   89 WINNING SONG "Rock Me" sung by RIVA (Yugoslavia)
   scored 137 points (1st) (22 countries) *unavailable*
   89 UK ENTRY "Why Do I Always Get It Wrong" (Second)
   130pts (Brian Hodgson-John Beeby) perf: LIVE REPORT
   Brouhaha (Priority):CUE 7(7"s) 12CUE 7(12") deleted
EUROVISION SONG CONTEST (1988) (Ireland) (BBC1-30/4/88)
   1988 WINNING SONG: "Ne Partez Pas Sans Moi" sung by
   CELENE DION (Switzerland) - *unavailable in the U.K.*
   scored 137 points (1st place) (21 countries in all)
   1988 UK ENTRY: "Go" sung by SCOTT FITZGERALD - 136
   points (2nd) - on *PRT (PRT): PYS 10 (7"s) deleted*
EUROVISION SONG CONTEST (1987) (Belgium) (BBC1-9/5/87)
   1987 WINNING SONG: "Hold Me Now" composed & sung by
   JOHNNY LOGAN (Ireland) - *Epic: Log 1 (7"s) 451073-1
   (LP) 451073-4 (Cass)* / 172 points / (1st placed)
   1987 UK ENTRY: "Only The Light" (Richard Peebles)
   RIKKI - *OK: OK 010 (7"s) OKL (12"s)* / 47 pts (13th)
EUROVISION SONG CONTEST (1986) (Norway) (BBC1-3/5/86)
   1986 WINNING SONG: "Jaime La Vie" I Love Life - by
   SANDRA KIM (Belgium)-*Carrere: CAR(T) 398 (7"s/12s)*
   scored 176 points (1st) (20 countries in all)
   1986 UK ENTRY: "Runner In the Night" by RYDER on *10
   Virgin: TEN 1 (7") deleted* 72 points and placed 7th
EUROVISION SONG CONTEST (1985) (Sweden) (BBC1-4/5/85)
   1985 WINNING SONG: "La Det Swinge"(Let It Swing) by
   BOBBY SOCKS *RCA: PB 40127 (7")*(123pts) 19countries
   1985 UK ENTRY: "Love Is" performed by VIKKI on *PRT
   7P/12P 326 deleted* scored 100 points / placed 4th
EUROVISION SONG CONTEST (1984) (Luxembourg) BBC1-5/5/84
   1984 WINNING SONG: "Diggi-Loo Diggi-Ley" - HERREY'S
   MCA: PAN 5 (7") scored 145 pts (1st) / 19 countries
   1984 UK ENTRY: "Love Games" by BELLE &THE DEVOTIONS
   CBS: A4332 (7") deleted scored 63 points placed 7th
EUROVISION SONG CONTEST (1983) (Munich Ger)BBC1 23/4/83
   1983 WINNING SONG: "Si La Vie Est Cadeau" (If Life
   Is A Gift) by CORRINE HERMES on *Poly: POSP 597 (7")
   deleted* scored 142 pts (1st) 20 Countries in all
   1983 UK ENTRY: "I'm Never Giving Up"by SWEET DREAMS
   Ariola: ARO 333 (7") deleted (79 points placed 6th)

EUROVISION SONG CONTEST (1982) (England) BBC1 24/4/82
   1982 WINNING SONG: "Ein Bisschen Friden" (A Little
   Peace) by NICOLE on *CBS A2467 (7"s)*(scored 167pts)
   1982 UK ENTRY: "One Step Further" by BARDO on *Epic*
   A.2265 (7"s) scored 76points (7th) (18 countries)
EUROVISION SONG CONTEST (1981) (Dublin Eire)BBC1 4/5/81
   1981 WINNING SONG: "Making Your Mind Up" by BUCKS
   FIZZ on *RCA: RCA 56 (7"s)* scored 136 pts placed 1st
   20 countries in all taking part */GERMANY placed 2nd*
EVENING SHADE (USA/C4 26/7/93) theme mus (Snuff Garrett
   Clarke Rigsby-Kevin Stoller) Version on '4 AMERICA
   TWO' *Primetime (Conif): TVPMCD(TVPMC) 803 (CD/Cass)*
   ORIG SERIES THEME "Blueberry Hill" by FATS DOMINO
   (Al Lewis-Larry Stock-Vincent Rose) by FATS DOMINO
   'Best Of' *EMI-Liberty: CZ111 (CD) / MFP:CDMFP 6026*
   see also Coll '4 AMERICA TWO' themes collection
EVER DECREASING CIRCLES (BBC1 29/1/84-1989) Theme music
   "Prelude No.15 Op.34 Allegretto" (D.Shostakovich)
EVERY SILVER LINING (BBC1 27/5/93) mus (Steven Edis).*NA*
EXECUTIVE STRESS (Thames 10/86)Theme "Why We Fell In Lo
   ve" (A.L.Webber-T.Rice) JULIE COVINGTON *unavailable*
EXTRA (BBC2 DEF Series 19/9/90) Theme music by WILLIAM
   ORBIT based on "Atom Dream" from 'Strange Cargo 2'
   IRS (EMI): EIRSACD 1041 (CD) EIRS(C) 1041 (LP/Cass)
EXTREME EAST (BBC2 26/7/92) music (Kampec Dolores)...*NA*
EYE OF THE STORM (Meridian 8/1/93) mus (Henry Marsh).*NA*
EYEWITNESS (LWT 15/1/89)Theme mus (Rod Argent-Peter Van
   Hooke) *see* '20 Great TV Themes' collection

FACE OF TUTANKHAMUN The (BBC2 (Chronicle) 20/11/92)
   Music score (Howard Davidon).....................*NA*
FACE TO FACE (BBC 60-rerun 88) Theme music 'Overture'
   'Les Francs-Juges' (Op.3) (Berlioz) *various records*
FACING UP TO AIDS (BBC1 6/1/91) "Body Talk" IMAGINATION
   on 'Body Talk' *RCA (BMG): ND(NK) 74322 (CD/Cass)*
FAITH IN THE FUTURE (LWT 4/8/91)theme(Terry Seabrook)*NA*
FALCON CREST (USA-81)(ITV 18/1/82) theme (Bill Conti)
   see Coll 'AMERICAN TV THEMES VOLUME 2'
FALKLANDS WAR The (C4/Fine Arts Prod 13/1/92) theme mus
   Paddy Kingsland *not available* ALSO USED: music from
   'Symphony No.1 In B.Flat Minor'(Sir William Walton)
   LONDON PHILH.OR.(B.Thomson) *CHANDOS: CHAN 8862 (CD)*
FALL & RISE OF REGINALD PERRIN (UKGO 6/11/93 or BBC 76)
   theme (Ronnie Hazlehurst) *Polyd 2384.107 LP deleted*
FALL GUY The (USA 81) Theme "The Unknown Stuntman"
   (G.Larson-Stu Philips) *Coll* 'ITV CHILDREN'S THEMES'
FALLEN HERO (Granada 78) Theme music (Derek Hilton) *see*
   Collection 'GRANADA TOURS SOUVENIR ALBUM'
FAME (USA BBC1 12/2/85)· Title song sung by Erica Gimpel
   RCA: PK 89257 (Cass) see Coll 'GREAT TV THEMES V.1'
FAME IN THE 20TH CENTURY (BBC1 6/1/93) Music sco (Carl
   Davis) *CLIVE JAMES BBC (Pinn): ZBBC 1458 (2 Cass)*
FAMILIES (Granada from 23/4/90-1993) Title theme music
   composed & performed by MATTHEW SCOTT *not available*

FAMILY AFFAIRS (BBC1 19/10/92) music (Xian Vassie)...*NA*
FAMILY AT WAR A (C4 Granada) 26/8/89 (first shown 1970)
    Theme: 1st m/m Symph No.6 in E.M (Vaughan Williams)
    London Symp Orch (A.Previn) *RCA (BMG) RD 89883 (CD)*
    New Phil Orch (A.Boult) *HMV (EMI): CDC 747215-2(CD)*
    see Collections: 'GRANADA STUDIOS SOUVENIR ALBUM'
FAMILY MATTERS (BBC1 3/1/90) music (Matthew Scott)...*NA*
FAMILY NESS The (BBC1 5/10/84) Title music (Roger/Gavin
    Greenaway) -S/T- *BBC (Pinn): REC(ZCR) 530 (LP/Cass)*
FAMILY OF SPIES (USA/ITV 1/9/91) music (Paul Chihara)*NA*
FAMILY PRIDE (Central 30/6/91) music: Jasmine Cafe...*NA*
FAMILY TIES (USA C4 6/7/85) Theme "Without Us" (Jeff Ba
    rry-Tom Scott) DENEICE WILLIAMS-JOHNNY MATHIS *not
    available / by var.arts on PMF (Kingdom):90685-2 CD
    see also collection* '4 AMERICA TWO'
FAMOUS FOR FOUR MINUTES (C4 Watson Prod 5/91) Theme mus
    "The Very Thought Of You" (Ray Noble) performed by
    AL BOWLLY with New Mayfair Dance Orch (Ray Noble)
    on 'The Very Thought Of You' *EMI Cedar: CZ 306 (CD)*
FAMOUSLY FLUENT (BBC1 3/1/93) theme (Simon Davison)..*NA*
FANTASTIC FACTS (Carlton 16/6/93) mus (Anne Dudley)..*NA*
FANTASTIC MAX (BBC1 13/9/89) theme (Clark Gassman and
    Michael Tavera) *on Coll:* 'KIDS THEMES' **deleted**
FAR FLUNG FLOYD (BBC2 13/7/93) theme " Waltz In Black"
    The STRANGLERS on 'Meninblack" *Fame (MFP-EMI): CDFA
    3208 (CD) TCFA 3208 (Cass)*
FAR PAVILIONS The (C4 7/2/88 orig 3/1/84) Music (Carl
    Davis) ethnic co-ordinator for Indian Music (Tripti
    Pandey) -S/T- *Chrysalis (Z)CDL 1464 (CS/LP)* **deleted**
FAST FRIENDS (BBC1 30/3/91) music (Tony Gibber)......*NA*
FATAL INVERSION A (BBC1 10/5/92) m: (David Ferguson).*NA*
FATHER CHRISTMAS (C4-25/12/91) Music (Mike Hewer) perf
    Phoenix Chamber Orch (Julian Bigg) narrated by Mel
    Smith -S/T- *Columbia 469475-2 (CD) -4(Cass) -1(LP)*
FATHER DEAR FATHER (UKGold 4/11/92 orig Thames 68)theme
    (Gordon Franks) **deleted**
FATHER DOWLING INVESTIGATES (USA 89)(ITV 23/3/91) theme
    music (Dick De Benedictis)........................*NA*
FAWLTY TOWERS (BBC2 75 rerun 88) Theme (Dennis Wilson)
    Collection 'BEST OF BBC TV THEMES' **deleted**
FEAST OF CHRISTMAS (C4 24/11/92) music (John Altman).*NA*
FEDERATION CUP - *see under TENNIS*
FELIX THE CAT (USA/BBC1 25/9/93) title music (Mark Moth
    ersbaugh) score music (Winston Sharples).........*NA*
FIDDLY FOODLE BIRD (BBC1 8/1/92) title song (Bob Saker-
    Jonathan Hodge) +Stuart Leathwood-Julian Littman on
    MFP (EMI): CDMFP 5958 (CD) TCMFP 5958 (Cass)
FIFTEEN STREETS The (TTees 20/8/89) m: (Colin Towns).*NA*
FIFTEEN-TO-ONE (C4 11/1/88-94)mus dir (Paul McGuire).*NA*
FIGHT AGAIN (BBC 15/5/93) orig music (Peter Bennett).*NA*
FIGHTING FOR GEMMA (Granada 10/11/93) mus score (Ilona
    Secazc) *not available* theme song "My Girl" (William
    Robinson-Ronald White) by OTIS REDDING on 'The Coll
    ection' *Castle Com (BMG): CCSCD(CCSMC)339 (CD/Cass)*

FILIPINA DREAMGIRLS (BBC1 15/9/91) Theme "Dreaming" (Si
    mon Brint-Lise Mayer) sung by HOPE AUGUSTUS......*NA*
FILM 93 (BBC1 72-94) *Theme* "I Wish I Knew How It Would
    Feel To Be Free" (Billy Taylor-Dick Dallas) BILLY
    TAYLOR *on Coll* 'MOODS 2' also by JOHNNY PEARSON on
    'THEMES AND DREAMS' *President (Pres):PRCD 132 (CD)*
    Movie News link music "Groove Merchant" TOMMY CHASE
    QUARTET *Stiff: CDSEEZ 66 (CD)(Z)SEEZ 66 (Cass/LP)*
    Top Ten link Music "Commuter" (Murray Monroe)....*NA*
    additional music "Watersports" (Patrick Wilson)..*NA*
FIND A FAMILY (Central 12/2/89)Theme "Find Me A Family"
    (A.Clarke-T.Hicks) HOLLIES *EMI: EM 86 (7") deleted*
FINDERS KEEPERS (TVS 12/4/91) music (Simon Etchell)..*NA*
FINE ROMANCE A (LWT 6/1/84) Title song(J.Kern-D.Fields)
    sung by Judi Dench *(unavailable)* / Yehudi Menuhin &
    Stephane Grappelli - *EMI: (TC)EMD 5504 (Cass/LP)*
FIRE AND ICE (LWT 26/12/86) Torvill & Dean Special with
    Music (Carl Davis) London Philharmonic Orchestra on
    1st Night: CASTC 7 (Cass) CASTCD 7 (CD) deleted
FIRE IN THE BLOOD (BBC2 30/1/92)mus (David Ferguson).*NA*
FIREBALL XL5 (ATV/ITV 25/3/63) Music (Barry Gray) *see*
    Coll 'A-Z OF BRITISH TV THEMES'/'TV CLASSICS VOL.1'
FIREMAN SAM (BBC/SC4-88) Theme: Ben Heneghan-Ian Lawson
    sung by MALDWYN POPE *see* Themes From Children's BBC
    'All In A Good Cause' Spoken Word *BBC(Pin):YBBC1483*
FIRM FRIENDS (TT/Zenith 16/6/92) music (Alan Parker).*NA*
FIRST AMONG EQUALS (Granada 30/9/86) Theme (Richard Har
    vey) *see Collect:* 'GRANADA STUDIOS SOUVENIR ALBUM'
FIRST BORN (BBC1 30/10/88) Theme music (Hans Zimmer)
    previously on 'WORLD OF BBCTV THEMES' *now deleted*
FIRST CLASS COUNTY (Gran/YTV 25/4/93)m.(Cath Baxter).*NA*
FIRST LETTER FIRST (BBC1 5/1/93)m:(Mark Newby Robson)*NA*
FIRST OF THE SUMMER WINE (BBC1 5/9/88) *Opening theme*
    "Sweet And Lovely" (G.Arnheim-H.Tobias-J.Lemare) -
    AL BOWLLY with RAY NOBLE'S ORCH - *EMI: SH 107822-1*
    (LP) -4 (Cas) Closing theme "Ain't That The Way It
    Goes" JACK PAYNE ORCH *Golden Age (MFP) now deleted*
FIRST TUESDAY (YTV-ITV 83-2/11/93) mus (Adrian Burch).*NA*
FIVE CHILDREN & IT (BBC1 9/1/91) music: Michael Omer.*NA*
FLAME TREES OF THIKA (Thames 10/7/83) Music (K.Howard-A
    Blaikley) VIDEO SYMPHONIC / *see Coll* 'REFLECTIONS'
FLEA & THE GIANTS (C4 26/6/91)m: (Marc Olivier-Dupin)*NA*
FLIGHT OF THE CONDOR (BBC2 14/10/87) Theme 'Floreo De L
    lamas' (Marquez) -S/T- INTI ILLIMANI & GUAMARY *see*
    Coll 'IMAGINATIONS'
FLIGHT OVER SPAIN (C4 30/8/89) Spanish music composed
    and played by Jaime Perez.....................*NA*
FLINTSTONES The (USA 61/85) "Meet The Flinstones" (Hoyt
    Curtin) *see Coll* 'TELEVISION'S GREATEST HITS VOL.1'
FLOWERING PASSIONS (C4 13/6/91) music (Francis Shaw)
    -S/T- *Silva Screen (Con): FILM(C)(CD) 116 (Cass/CD)*
FLOYD ON..(BBC2 23/9/86) Theme "Peaches"/"Waltzinblack"
    (Stranglers) THE STRANGLERS on 'The Collection' on
    Fame (MFP-EMI): (CD)(TC)FA 3230 (CD/Cass/LP)

FLOYD ON OZ (BBC2 11/4/91) details as previous entry
FLOYD ON SPAIN (BBC2 18/8/92) orig music (Ian Butcher &
    Andrew Wilson *not available)* ALSO USED "Waltz In Bl
    ack"(The Stranglers) THE STRANGLERS on 'Collection'
    Fame (EMI): (CD)(TC)FA 3230 (CD/Cass) and also used
    "Canarios" performed by JOHN WILLIAMS
FLYING DOCTORS (BBC1 (Australian Prod) 1/10/85) theme
    music (Garry McDonald and Laurie Stone) -S/T- on
    OneMone Auatralia (Silva Screen): IMICD 1015 (CD)
FOLLOW THE MONEY (BBC2 23/2/92) music (James Simpson &
    Philip Pope)..*NA*
FOLLOW YOUR NOSE (Tyne-Tees 13/5/92) mus (John Cook).*NA*
FOLLYFOOT (Yorkshire 70's) Theme "The Lightning Tree"
    (Steve Francis) *see Collect.*'ITV CHILDREN'S THEMES'
FONTAMERA (RIA/C4 18/8/91) music (Robert De Simone)..*NA*
FOOD & DRINK (BBC2 27/10/87) 93/94 series theme (Simon
    May) *not available* previous theme arrangements of
    "Food Glorious Food" from 'Oliver' (Lionel Bart) by
    Henry Dagg / Joe & Co *unavailable /* see also OLIVER
FOOD FILE (C4 5/2/92) theme music (Nigel Beaham-Powell
    and Bella Russell)...............................*NA*
FOOTBALL:*see* BIG MATCH-FOOTBALL ITALIA-GRANDSTAND-MATCH
    OF THE DAY-SAINT AND GREAVSIE-THE MATCH-WORLD CUP
    FOOTBALL-EUROPEAN CHAMPIONS LEAGUE
FOOTBALL ITALIA (Chrysalis for C4 12/9/92) theme music
    "I'm Stronger Now" (Steve DuBerry-Ben Chapman) by
    DEFINITIVE 2 on *Deconstruction (BMG): 743211 2473-2
    (CDsingle) 743211 2473-1 (12"s)*
FOR ALL MANKIND (BBC1 20/7/89) Music (Brian Eno-Dan Lan
    ois) BRIAN ENO 'Apollo' *EG (Poly): EG(CD)(MC) 53*
FOR BETTER OR WORSE (C4 28/9/89) Theme "Dance Of The Su
    gar Plum Fairy"'The Nutcracker Suite' (Tchaikovsky)
FOR LOVE OR MONEY (C4/Wall2Wall 5/1/93) Commercial M.*NA*
FOR THE GREATER GOOD (BBC2 20/3/91) theme music (Andy
    McCluskey) ORCHESTRAL MANOEUVRES IN THE DARK.....*NA*
FOR THE LOVE OF ADA (UKGO 9/9/93 orig Thames 70) theme
    music (Ron Grainer).................................*NA*
FOR THE TERM OF HIS NATURAL LIFE (BBC1 (Aust) 16/6/85 &
    1989) Music score (Simon Walker) -S/T- *OneMone Aust
    (Silva Screen): IMICD 1001 (CD)*
FOR THOSE I HAVE LOVED (Mutual Prod 1984/BBC1 21/7/91)
    Music score (Maurice Jarre) -S/T- on *General Music
    (Italy Imp-S.Screen): 803055 (LP) 804055 (Cass) and
    803073 (LP-Vol.2) 804073 (Cass-Vol.2)*
FOREIGN FIELD, A (BBC Scr.One 12/9/93) original music
    (Geoffrey Burgon) harmonica (Tommy Reilly).......*NA*
FOREVER GREEN (LWT 26/2/89) Theme (Patrick Gowers) *see
    Colls* 'FAV.TV THEMES'/'HIT THEMES 1'/'20 TOP TV...'
FOREVER KNIGHT (TV USA 92) Music score (Fred Mollin)
    see Collection 'VAMPIRE CIRCUS'
FORGET-ME-NOT FARM (BBC1 13/11/90) mus (Mike Amatt)..*NA*
FORSYTE SAGA The (BBC1 67) Theme mus "Elizabeth Tudor"
    from 'Three Elizabeths Suite' (Eric Coates) *see Col*
    'TV CLASSICS 2'/'A-Z OF BRITISH TV..'/'GREAT TV...'

FORTUNES OF WAR (BBC1 11/10/87) Theme (Richard Holmes)
PAVELS RUMANIAN ENSEMBLE *see*'BEST OF BBC TV'*deleted*
F.O.T. (False or True) (BBC2 Scotland 25/7/93) music by
(Hilary Brooks).................................**NA**
FRAGGLE ROCK (TVS 7/1/84) Theme (Philip Balsam-Dennis
Lee) THE FRAGGLES *RCA -(BMG): PL(PK) 70221 (LP/Cas)*
see collection 'ITV CHILDREN'S THEMES'
FRAGILE EARTH (C4 13/1/91) music (Phil Sawyer) other
music by various composers (specially composed)..**NA**
FRANCE MEANS BUSINESS (BBC2 9/2/93) mus: (Max Early).**NA**
FRANK SINATRA (CBS USA TV mini-series) -TV- Soundtrack
9362 45091-2 (CD) 9362 45091-4 (Cass)
FRANK STUBBS PROMOTES Noel Gay Prd for Carlton 12/7/93)
theme "Hard Business" (Brian May) sung by BRIAN MAY
incidental music (Neil McArthur)................**NA**
FRANKIE'S HOUSE (Anglia 9/5/92) theme and incidental
music (Jeff Beck and Jed Lieber) TV -S/T- on *Epic
(Sony M): 472 494-2 (CD) 472 494-4 (Cass) -1 (LP)*
WINNER OF 1993 BAFTA FOR BEST ORIGINAL TV MUSIC
FRANKIE'S ON..(Central 21/6/92) mus (Jonathan Cohen).**NA**
FRANK'S PLACE (USA)(C4 24/8/90)*opening mus* "Do You Know
What It Means" (Louis Alter-Eddie De Lange) LOUIS
ARMSTRONG '20 Golden Pieces' *Bulldog (Presid): BDL
(BDC) 2007 (LP/Cass) closing theme* "How Long Blues"
(Leroy Carr-Ann Engberg) COUNT BASIE-JIMMY RUSHING
FRED (BBC2 1/10/84) Theme "Carnival Of Venice" (Briccia
ldi) by JAMES GALWAY on *RCA (BMG): PL(PK)(PD) 70260*
FREDDIE AND MAX (Thames 12/11/90) Theme "Let's Call The
Whole Thing Off" (G.& I.Gershwin) arr. David MacKay
sung by the cast *unavailable* /from 'Shall We Dance'
FREE FOR ALL   (C4 Filmit 16/2/93) mus (Andy Roberts).**NA**
FRENCH FIELDS (UKGold 5/11/92 orig Thames 5/9/89) music
(Alan Parker)..................................**NA**
FRESH FIELDS (Thames 9/85) Theme mus "Pick Yourself Up"
(Jerome Kern-Dorothy Fields) from 'Swing Time' (36)
Y.MENUHIN & S.GRAPPELLI *EMI: (TC)EMD 5504 (Cass/LP)*
FRESH PRINCE OF BEL-AIRE (BBC2 14/1/91)..Will Smith..**NA**
FRIDAY AT THE DOME (C4 Holmes Assoc-3/5/91) title music
(Paul Oakenfield-Steve Osborne)................**NA**
FRIDAY ON MY MIND (BBC1 15/5/92) theme and incidental
music (Daemion Barry and Julian Wastall)........**NA**
FRIDAY THE 13TH (TV Series) (USA 89)(ITV-13/7/90) Music
score (Fred Mollin) TV -S/T- on *GNP Crescendo USA
(S.Screen): GNPD 8018 (CD) GNPS(5) 8018 (LP/Cass)*
FROCKS ON THE BOX (TVS 9/87) Theme "Largo" WORKING WEEK
Virgin: TCVEGD 19 (Cass) CDVE 19 (CD)
FROM THE EDGE (BBC2 22/7/92) title mus (Mik Scarlet).**NA**
FROM WIMPS TO WARRIORS (BBC2 11/6/91)m: Clif Brigden.**NA**
FRUITY PASSIONS (BBC2 21/5/90) music (Henry Dagg)....**NA**
FUGITIVE The (USA ABC/QM 1963-66) theme music (Pete Rug
olo) *see Coll* 'TV CLASSICS VOLUME 2' *(Castle Comm)*
FULL MONTY The (Gran.29/10/93) music (Mike Woolmans).**NA**
FULL STRETCH (Meridian 5/1/93) music (Andy Roberts)..**NA**
FULL TREATMENT (Tham 25/4/91) mus (Maciej Hrybowicz).**NA**

FULL WAX (BBC1 19/1/91) (N.Beaham-Powell/B.Russell)..*NA*
FUNNY BONES (SC4/BBC Ent 29/9/92) music (Ernie Wood).*NA*
FUNNY BUSINESS (BBC2 22/11/92) music (Kenny Craddock-
   Colin Gibson)...............................*NA*
FUTURE COOKS (BBC2 29/8/93) theme mus.arr. (Dave Cooke)
   of 'Arrival Of The Queen Of Sheba' (Handel)......*NA*
   many versions inc: SCOTTISH CHAMBER ORCH (Alexander
   Gibson) 'Baroque Classics' *Chandos: CHAN 6527 (CD)*

GAELIC GAMES (Chrysalis TV Irel. for C4 19/6/93) Theme
   "Book Of Days" (Enya-Roma Ryan) fr "Shepherd Moons"
   WEA (WEA): 9031 75572-2 (CD) -4 (Cass) -1 (LP)
GALAHAD OF EVEREST (BBC2 9/12/91)m: (Steve Marshall).*NA*
GALLOWGLASS (BBC1 10/1/03) music sc (David Ferguson).*NA*
GAMBIT (BBC2 (WG) 15/2/91) mus (Paul Vincent Gunia)..*NA*
GAME SET AND MATCH (Gran 3/10/88)Music (Richard Harvey)
   Chrysalis: CCD 1692 (CD) (Z)CHR 1692 all deleted
GAMES IN QUESTION The (C4 28/8/88) Theme "Ode To Joy"
   'Symph No.9 In D.Min' Op.125' (Choral) (Beethoven)
GAMESMASTER (C4 7/1/92) music (Julian Walstall)......*NA*
GARDEN CLUB (C4 1/3/91) music (Stuart Gordon).......*NA*
GARDENER'S DIRECT LINE (BBC Leeds from 19/8/87) Theme
   "And Do They Do" (MICHAEL NYMAN) on 'Zoo Caprices'/
   'And Do They Do' on *TER (Conif): (CD)(ZC)TER 1123*
GARDENER'S WORLD (BBC2 19/2/93) theme music to 1993
   series (Nick Webb-Greg Carmichael)..............*NA*
GARDENERS GUIDE A (C4 24/8/90) Theme mus "Petite Fleur"
   (Sidney Bechet) CHRIS BARBER with MONTY SUNSHINE on
   'Sleepy Shores' *Old Gold: OG 3703(CD) OG 2703(Cass)*
GARDENS BY DESIGN (BBC2 4/1/91) music (Roger Limb)...*NA*
GARDENS WITH BORDERS (YTV for C4 22/1/93) title music
   (Paul and Suzy Brown)..........................*NA*
G.B.H. (C4 6/6/91) Music (Richard Harvey and Elvis Cost
   ello)-S/T- music by ELVIS COSTELLO & RICHARD HARVEY
   on *DEMON (Pinn): DSCD 4(CD) DSCASS 4(Cass) DSLP4 LP*
GENERAL ELECTION 1992 (9/4/92) *Political Party Themes:-*
   CONSERVATIVE: "Abdelazer" incidental mus Z570 (Purc
   ell) Empire Brass arr.A.L.Webber *EMI:CDC 749277-2CD*
   LABOUR: "My Land Your Land" (Michael Kamen) by The
   ALARM on 'b' side of "Rescue Me" *IRS: IRM 150 (7"s)*
   LIBERAL DEMOCRAT: "Paddy's Tune" arr.by Bobby Gee
GENERAL ELECTION 1987 (BBC 11/6/87) Theme "Arthur" RICK
   WAKEMAN - *A.& M: (Poly) CDA(CAM) 64515 (CD/Cass)*
   used for previous (1983/1979) Gen.Elections (BBC)
GENERAL HOSPITAL (ITV 70's series) *theme (1)* "Girl In
   The White Coat" (Derek Scott) *theme (2)* "Red Alert"
   (Johnny Pearson) both *see Colls* 'TV CLASSICS VOL.3'
GENERATION GAME *see* 'BRUCE FORSYTH'S GENERATION GAME'
GENERATIONS (C4 23/3/87) Theme "Windmills Of Your Mind"
   (Michel Legrand-Alan & Marilyn Bergman)from 'Thomas
   Crown Affair' NOEL HARRISON *Old Gold: OG 9090 (7")*
GENTLE TOUCH The (LWT 1/9/84) Theme (Roger Webb) ROGER
   WEBB ORCH - *Chandos: LBT 007 (Cass) see also Collec*
   'HIT THEMES 1 BEST OF BRITISH TV MUSIC'

GEOFFREY SMITH'S WORLD OF FLOWERS (BBC2 11/1/84) Theme
    "Mayfair Concert" (H.Conzelmann-Delle Haensch) MAYF
    AIR BAROQUE ORCH - *BBC: (ZCR)REH 524 (LP) deleted*
GEORGE AND MILDRED (UKGold 2/11/92 orig Thames 76)theme
    (Johnny Hawkesworth) *deleted*
GERMANS The (C4/Tham 30/1/92) music (Richard Wright).*NA*
GET BACK (BBC1/Alomo 26/10 92) music (Ray Russell)...*NA*
GET SMART (USA 9/65-C4 8/92) theme (Irving Szathmary)
    see coll 'TELEVISION'S GREATEST HITS VOL.1'
GET WET! (WSNTV91/ITV 10/9/93) music (Michael Lynch).*NA*
GHOST TRAIN (Tyne-Tees 21/4/90) music (John Cook)....*NA*
GHOSTS OF OXFORD STREET (C4 25/12/91) Mus: Var.Artists
    -S/T- *RCA (BMG) PD 75233(CD) PK 75233(Cass) deleted*
GHOSTS OF THE PAST (BBC1 8/10/91) "Liverpool Oratorio"
    (Paul McCartney-Carl Davis) featur: KIRI TE KANAWA-
    SALLY BURGESS-JERRY HADLEY-WILLARD WHITE Royal Liv
    erpool Philh.Choir (Liverpool Cathedral) and Royal
    Liverpool Orch.(Carl Davis) on *EMI: CDPAUL 1 (CD)
    also CDS 754371-2 and TCPAUL 1 (Cass) PAUL 1 (LP)
    HIGHLIGHTS - CDC 754642-2 (CD) EL 754642-4 (Cass)*
GIBBERISH (BBC1 Celador16/3/92) mus (Keith Strachan).*NA*
GIMME 5 (Tyne-Tees 25/4/92) title music (John Cook)..*NA*
GINGERBREAD GIRL (YTV 9/4/93) theme "Sweet Gingerbread
    Girl" (Michel Legrand-Alan & Marilyn Bergman) arran
    ged by John Mealing and sung by JANET DIBLEY.....*NA*
GIRL FROM TOMORROW (BBC1 3/5/91) mus (Ian Davidson)..*NA*
GLADIATORS (LWT 10/10/92) theme music (Muff Murfin) on
    Polydor (Poly): ATOR 1(T)(CD)(MC) (7"/12"/CDs/Cass)
    'GLADIATORS ALBUM' (Var.Arts) *Polyg: 515 877-2 (CD)
    -4(Cass)* Volume 2 'Return' *516 517-2(CD) -4(Cass)*
GLASGOW BY THE WAY (C4 9/8/88) Theme mus "Sneakyville"
    SECESSION - *Siren (Virgin-Poly): CDSRN 11 (CD)*
GLASS (BBC2 2/8/90 and 8/9/85) *Theme* "Karelia" 'K.Suite
    Op.11' (Sibelius) / "Flower Duet" 'Lakme' (Delibes)
GLOBAL IMAGE (C4 13/1/92) music perf: ADEYI ABREHET..*NA*
GLORIA (BBC1 27/4/92) title music (Tot Taylor)......*NA*
GO FISHING (C4 9/6/91) theme music (David Lindsay)...*NA*
GO GETTERS (YTV 12/7/91) orig music (Chris Norton)...*NA*
GOGGLE EYES (BBC2 24/3/93) music (Jim Parker)........*NA*
GOING FOR A SONG (BBC1 71) Theme "Prelude" -'The Birds'
    (Respghi) *several classical recordings available*
GOING FOR GOLD (BBC1 12/10/87-1994) theme music (Hans
    Zimmer-Sandy McClelland)......................*NA*
GOING LIVE (BBC1 26/9/87) theme (Peter Gosling) *previou
    sly on Coll* 'CHILDREN'S WORLD OF TV THEMES' *deleted*
GOING STRAIGHT (UKGO 20/4/93 orig 24/2/78) theme (Dick
    Clement-Tony Macauley) by RONNIE BARKER *EMI deleted*
GOLDEN GIRLS The (USA)(C4 1/8/86) Theme "Thank You For
    Being a Friend" (A.Gold) *TV version unavailable*
    ANDREW GOLD on 'Never Let Her Slip Away' *Pickwick
    954831615-2 (CD) -4 (Cass) also var.artists collect
    on PMF (Kingdom): 90681-2 (CD)*
GOLDEN PALACE (USA 92 C4 14/4/93) theme "Thank You For
    Being A Friend" (Andrew Gold) *see entry above*

GOLDEN YEARS The (Stephen King's) (C4 2/1/93) Music sco
(Joe Taylor) title song composed/performed by DAVID
BOWIE on 'Station To Station' *EMI: CDEMD 1020 (CD)*
GOLDEN YEARS The (C4 12/11/92) mus (Debbie Wiseman)..*NA*
GOLDRING AUDIT (C4 Juniper 9/1/92) mus (David Arch)..*NA*
GOLF (BBC1/2) theme music "Chase Side Shoot Out" (Brian
Bennett) BRIAN BENNETT orig on 'Sporting Themes' on
BBC: REH 348 (LP) ZCR 348 (Cass) both deleted note:
version on 'GOLD' collection *Telstar: TCD 2563 (CD)*
GOLF AND ALL IT'S GLORY (BBC2 14/7/93) m:(Dick Fioca)*NA*
GONE TO SEED (Central 13/11/92) Mus THE GUTTER BROTHERS
F.Beat/Demon (Pinn): XX(CD)(MC)(LP) 21 (CD/Cass/LP)
GONE TO THE DOGS (Central 29/11/91) mus.sup (Graham Wal
ker) theme comp & sung by THE GUTTER BROTHERS -S/T-
F.Beat/Demon (Pinn): XX(CD)(MC)(LP) 21 (CD/Cass/LP)
GOOD BOOK GUIDE The (BBC1 3/1/93) theme music (Peter Ho
well (BBC Radiophonic Workshop)..................*NA*
GOOD GUYS The (Thames 3/1/92) mus (Debbie Wiseman) *see
Collections* 'FAVOURITE TV THEMES'/'HIT THEMES 1'
GOOD LIFE SHOW The (Gran. 28/5/91) mus:(Peter Salem).*NA*
GOOD MORNING MISS BLISS (USA 88/ITV 15/7/91)song "These
Are The Best Of Times"(Charles Fox-Mark Meuller).*NA*
GOOD MORNING WITH ANNE & NICK (BBC1 12/10/92) title mus
ic (Alan Coates-Kim Goody)......................*NA*
GOOD SEX GUIDE The (Prospect Pict for Carlton 14/1/93)
featuring various oldies / theme music...........*NA*
GOOD WOMAN OF BANGKOK The (TRUE STORIES) (C4 7/5/92)
"Aria Di Madama Lucilla" ('Vado, Ma Dove? Oh Dei!')
KV.583 (Mozart) sung by DAME JANET BAKER (mezz-sop)
with SCOTTISH CHAMBER ORCH on *Erato: ECD 88090 (CD)*
GOODBYE CRUEL WORLD (BBC2 6/1/92) music (Barrington
Pheloung)..*NA*
GOODIES The (UKGold 2/11/92 orig BBC1 71) music (Bill
Oddie-Michael Gibbs) *deleted*
GOODNIGHT SWEETHEART (BBC1 18/11/93) theme (Ray Noble)
mus (Anthony & Gaynor Sadler) sung by NICK CURTIS
not avail / orig: AL BOWLLY *EMI: CDP 794341-2 (CD)*
GORDON THE GOPHER (BBC1 1/91) theme (Craig Lindsey)
previously 'CHILDREN'S WORLD OF TV THEMES' *deleted*
GRACE & FAVOUR (BBC1 10/1/92) theme (R.Moore-D.Croft)*NA*
GRAND NATIONAL 90/91/92 (BBC Grandstand) opening music
theme "Champions" (CARL DAVIS) *see* FILMS & SHOWS
GRAND PRIX (BBC 78-93) Theme "The Chain" FLEETWOOD MAC
WB (WEA): K456344 (C) K256344 (CD) also Coll 'GOLD'
GRANDSTAND (BBC1 began 8/10/58 - 1994)
Title theme 1976-1994 (Keith Mansfield) SOUND STAGE
ORCH *see Coll* 'FAVOURITE SPORTING THEMES' / *Orig 58
theme* "News Scoop"(Stevens) *Col* 'On The Air'*deleted*
Opening menu "Bad Love" (Eric Clapton) 'Journeyman'
ERIC CLAPTON *WB (WEA): 926074-2(CD) WX 322C (Cass)*
'Final Results' sequence "The Way It Is" (Hornsby)
BRUCE HORNSBY & THE RANGE *RCA(BMG): PD(PK)(PL)89901*
Additional Link Music "The Race" (D.Meyer-B.Blank)
YELLO 'Flag' *Mercury: 836 426-2(CD) -4(Cass) -1(LP)*

GRANGE HILL (BBC1 1978-93) *Theme music (78-89)* "Chicken
    Man" (ALAN HAWKSHAW) - *BBC Pickwick: HSC 650 (Cass)
    1990-91 Theme* (PETER MOSS) *not available*
GRANPA (Film Car C4/31/12/89) Music (Howard Blake) with
    Sarah Brightman and Peter Ustinov -S/T- on *Columbia
    (Sony Music) CDHB 1 (CD) HBC 1 (Cass) HB 1 (LP)*
GRAVY TRAIN The (Goes East) (C4 27/6/90+28/10/91) Theme
    music (John Keane)................................*NA*
GREAT AUSTRALIAN BOAT RACE (C4 4/10/86) "Down Under" by
    MEN AT WORK - *Epic: (CD)(40)EPC 85669 (CD/Cass/LP)*
GREAT COMMANDERS The (7th Art Prod/C4 21/11/93) Orig
    music (Simon Farmer-Michael Portman)..............*NA*
GREAT EXPECTATIONS (Dickens) (UKGO 14/11/93 orig BBC1
    10/7/83) music composed & conducted (Paul Reade).*NA*
GREAT EXPECTATIONS (Dickens) (HTV-Primetime-Disney Chan
    nel 21/7/91) music score (Ken Thorne)............*NA*
GREAT EXPECTATIONS (BBC1 8/4/91) mus:(Peter Howell)..*NA*
    end theme "Shoulder To Shoulder" from series 'Roads
    To Freedom' sung by GEORGIA BROWN *(Cube - deleted)*
GREAT MOGHULS The (C4 2/2/90) Theme music (Tim Souster-
    Shanti Sharma) -S/T- *Silva Screen: FILM(C)(CD) 064*
GREAT RUSSIAN WRITERS (C4 2/9/92) music (E.Manukian).*NA*
GREATEST AMERICAN HERO The (USA 81)Theme mus (Mike Post
    -Pete Carpenter) JOEY SCARBURY *see Collection*
    'TELEVISION'S GREATEST HITS VOLUME 3'
GREED AND GLORY (C4 18/10/92) music (Julian Wastall).*NA*
GREEDYSAURUS GANG (BBC1 27/9/93) music (Kick Prod)...*NA*
GREEN MAN The (BBC2 28/10 90) music (Tim Souster)....*NA*
GRIM TALES (C4 14/4/89) music (Ged Haney-Clive Bell).*NA*
GRIZZLY ADAMS - *see* 'LIFE AND TIMES OF GRIZZLY ADAMS'
GROTBAGS (Central 4/9/91) tile theme (Colin Campbell)
    performed by CAROL LEE SCOTT....................*NA*
GROW YOUR GREENS (Wall To Wall Prod for C4 2/4/93) also
    'EAT YOUR GREENS' series / music Real Music Comp.*NA*
GROWING PAINS (BBC1 16/5/92) Music director: Nigel Hess
    theme song "I Could Care For You" (Nigel Hess) sung
    by NICK CURTIS *see Coll*' MAIGRET & OTHER TV THEMES'
GROWING PAINS OF ADRIAN MOLE The (Thames 5/1/87) *see
    under* 'Secret Diary Of Adrian Mole'
GROWING RICH (Anglia 28/2/92) m:(Dominic Muldowney)..*NA*
GROWING UP WILD (BBC2 26/9/93) music (Steve Everitt).*NA*
GUILTY The (Central 8/6/92) music sco (Hal Lindes)...*NA*
GUITARRA! (C4 12/8/88 orig 17/3/85)-TV S/T- with JULIAN
    BREAM - *RCA (BMG): RD 86206 (CD) /RL(RK) 85417 (2)*
GULDENBERG INHERITANCE The (Germany ZDF 87)(ITV 6/5/91)
    original music score (Eberhard Schoener).........*NA*
GUN LAW (USA 55-75) Theme (Koury-Spencer) *see Collect*
    'GREAT WESTERN THEMES' Ser.orig known as GUN SMOKE

HADLEIGH (Yorkshire 29/10/69-1976) Theme m (Tony Hatch)
    see Coll 'A-Z OF BRITISH TV THEMES'/'TV CLASSICS 3'
HANGAR 17 (BBC1 10/1/92) title music (Martin Cook)...*NA*
HANNAH HAUXWELL (YTV 16/2/92) "Hanna's Theme" (Martin
    Bullard)..*NA*

HANCOCK (BBC1 60's) Theme music (Derek Scott) *see Coll* 'A-Z OF BRITISH TV THEMES'/'TV CLASSICS VOL.2'

HANGIN'WITH MR.COOPER (USA/C4 16/7/93) theme song (Denz il Foster-Thomas McElroy) performed by Dawnn Lewis-Holly Robinson with En Vogue.....................*NA*

HANNAY (Thames 6/1/88) theme (Denis King) *see Collect:* 'LOVEJOY'/'ITV THEMES'

HAPPENING The (C4 6/9/91) theme mus (Jools Holland)..*NA*

HAPPY DAYS (USA 74 / re-run C4 27/2/89) *orig opening theme* "Rock Around The Clock" (Jimmy De Knight-Max Freedman) BILL HALEY & THE COMETS *Old Gold: OG 9220 Title theme* "Happy Days"(Norman Gimbel-Charles Fox) PRATT & McLAIN 'TELEVISION'S GREATEST HITS VOL.3' 'GREAT TV THEMES VOLUME 1'/'ITV THEMES'

HAPPY EVER AFTER (UKGO 31/5/93 orig BBC1 74) theme mus (Dennis Wilson) recorded on *Polydor (deleted)*

HAPPY FAMILIES (BBC2 6/5/92) music (Roger Bolton)....*NA*

HAPPY FAMILIES (BBC1 6/11/89) music (Richard Attree).*NA*

HAPPY FAMILIES (BBC1 18/9/93) music (David Mindel)..*NA*

HAPPY MEMORIES (BBC1 16/10/91) theme "What A Wonderful World" (G.Weiss-G.Douglas) sung by LOUIS ARMSTRONG *Old Gold: OG 9419 (7"s)*

HARD TIMES ON PLANET EARTH (USA Touchst 89)(ITV 4/5/91) orig music score (Joseph Conlan)................*NA*

HARDBALL (USA 90 ITV 28/8/91) Theme (Sylvester Levay)*NA*

HARRY (Union Pic/BBC1 18/9/93) music (Tony McAnaney).*NA*

HARRY AND THE HENDERSONS (USA 90 BBC1 27/9/91) theme "Your Feet's Too Big" (Ada Benson-Fred Fisher & Ink Spots) TV version sung by LEON REDBONE *unavailable* orig versions by THE INK SPOTS and FATS WALLER (36) *see FILMS & SHOWS* 'BIG FOOT & THE HENDERSONS' *(MCA)*

HARRY ENFIELD'S GUIDE TO OPERA (C4 4/3/93) selection of Opera Classics by OPERA NORTH conductor PAUL DANIEL *EMI: CDC 754785-2 (CD) CDC 754785-4 (Cass)*

HARRY ENFIELD'S TELEVISION PROGRAMME (BBC2 2/4/92)theme mus (Kate St.John) additional mus (Simon Brint)..*NA*

HARRY'S GAME (Yorkshire 25/10/82) Music (Paul Brennan) CLANNAD 'Past Present' *RCA (BMG): PD(PK)(PL) 74074 RCA (BMG): 74321.118127 (7"s) 74321.118124 (Cass) 74321.118122 (CDs) see Coll* 'VISIONS'/'IMAGINATIONS' 'GREAT TV THEMES VOLUME 2'

HARRY'S MAD (Central 4/1/93) music (Nigel Beaham-Powell and Bella Russell) Available SPOKEN WORD Cassette *BBC (Pinn): YBBC 1395 (Cass)*

HAVE GUN-WILL TRAVEL (USA 57) Theme "Ballad Of Paladin" (Richard Boone-J.Western-Sam Rolfe)- JOHNNY WESTERN on 'Americana' *Columbia (SM): 468121-2(CD) -4(Cass)*

HAVE I GOT NEWS FOR YOU (BBC2 from 28/9/90) signature tune (Big George)................................*NA*

HAWAII 5-0 (USA 68-80) BBC1-30/10/91 Theme (Morton Stev ens) *see Coll* 'TELEVISION'S GREATEST HITS VOLUME 1' 'GREAT TV THEMES VOLUME 2'

HAWAIIAN EYE (USA 59) Theme (M.David-J.Livingston) *see Coll* 'TELEVISION'S GREATEST HITS VOLUME 2'

HEAD OF THE CLASS (USA86)(BBC1 9/3/87) theme (Ed Alton)
   see Coll 'AMERICAN TV THEMES-Primetime Coll.Vol.2'
HEAD OVER HEELS (Carnival/Carlton 11/1/93) title song
   (Don Black-Richard Kerr) sung by Nicholas Haverson
   TV -S/T- feat theme and orig ROCK'n'ROLL songs on
   Telstar (BMG):TCD(STAC)(STAR) 2649 (CD/Cass/LP)
HEADS AND TAILS (BBC 80) *coll* 'THEMES FROM CHILDREN'S'
HEALTH EXPERIMENT (Angl.17/5/91) mus (Dirk Higgins)..*NA*
HEARSAY (BBC2 13/8/91) Title mus (Shirley Thompson)..*NA*
HEART OF SOWETO (BBC2 16/3/91) music (Peter Spencer).*NA*
HEART OF THE MATTER (BBC1 1978-94) *Theme (89-94)* Title
   music (Jonathan Gibbs) BBC R.Workshop *unavailable*
   Theme (85-88) "Loisada" (JOE JACKSON) *A.& M.(Poly):*
   (AMLX)(CXM) 65000 (CD/Cass) Theme (78-84) "From The
   Top" (Bach arranged by John Williams)
HEARTBEAT (YTV 10/4/92) theme "Heartbeat" (Norman Petty
   Bob Montgomery) NICK BERRY on 'HEARTBEAT' *Columbia*
   (Sony M): 471900-2 (CD) 471900-4 (Cass) -1 (LP) and
   Volume 2 *Columbia (Sony M): 475529-2 (CD) -4 (Cass)*
   BUDDY HOLLY on *Pickwick: PCD 888(CD) HSC 3199(Cass)*
HEARTS OF GOLD (BBC1 29/10/88) Title theme (Lynsey De
   Paul orig by GOLD *CBS: CBS 654501-7 (7"s) deleted*
   song "Ave Maria" (Bach-Gounod) performed by LESLIE
   GARRETT and AMANDA THOMPSON from 26/10/93 programme
   on *Int.Affairs-Jive (BMG): KGBD(KGBM) 012 (CD/Cass)*
HEIDI (ITV/Intertel 3/5/92) music (Siegfried Franz)..*NA*
HEIGHTS The (SKY 21/10/92) Music from Group 'HEIGHTS'
   Capitol (EMI): CDEST 2189 (CD) / Cassette deleted
HEIMAT (Homeland) (Germany 84/BBC2 19/4/86 and 22/1/93)
   music score (Nikos Mamangakis)..................*NA*
HELD IN TRUST (C4 5/4/86) "Music In Trust" -S/T- with
   ALISON KINNAIRD & BATTLEFIELD BAND - *Temple (Gordon
   Duncan-Celtic Mus) (C)TP 022 (CS/LP) COMD 2010 (CD)*
HELLO DO YOU HEAR US C4 3/2/90 mus (Alexei Rybnikov).*NA*
HELP SQUAD The (TVS 19/5/91) music (Simon Webb)......*NA*
HELP YOURSELF (BBC1 10/3/92) theme (Rod Thompson)....*NA*
HENRY'S CAT (BBC1 13/9/84) Music (Peter Shade) Narrator
   Bob Godfrey *Theme on* 'CHILDREN'S THEMES' *(Pickwick)*
HERE'S ONE I MADE EARLIER (BBC2 17/10/93) music incl:
   'Barnacle Bill' (Hornopipe) (BLUE PETER theme) and
   incidental mus.composed/played by Peter Gosling..*NA*
HEROES The (TVS 2/4/89) HEROS 2 **(The Return)**(15/12/91)
   Music score (Peter Best) both -S/T- on *Silva Screen
   (Conif): FILMC 112 (Cass) FILMCD 112 (CD)*
HIGH CHAPARRAL The (USA BBC1 67) Music (David Rose) *see
   Coll* 'GREAT TV THEMES VOLUME 2'
HIGHWAY (TTees 9/84) 'Highway Companion' Harry Secombe-
   Bernard Cribbins-Wendy Craig-Guards Chapel Choir &
   ROD THOMPSON (theme) *Word: WRDR(WRDC) 3033 (LP/CS)*
   'Highway Of Song' *(Starblend) HWAY 1 (LP) ZC (Cass)*
   theme also on collection 'ITV THEMES'
HIGHWAY TO HEAVEN (USA)(ITV 7/6/87) theme (David Rose)
   see Coll 'AMERICAN TV THEMES-PRIMETIME COLL.VOL.2'
   and 'FANTASTIC TELEVISION THEMES'

HILL STREET BLUES (USA 80-ITV/C4 80s) Theme (Mike Post)
    Music from orig scores on 'Hill Street Blues' Coll:
    Silva Screen (BMG):FILM(C)(CD) 702 (Cas/CD) also on
    Coll 'MAGNUM P.I.'/'CAGNEY & LACEY & OTHERS'/'GREAT
    TV THEMES V.4'/'TV MUSIC OF MIKE POST'/'ITV THEMES'
HISTORY MAN The (BBC2 8/10/82) Theme: GEORGE FENTON on
    Food For Thought: YUM 110 (7"s) c/w 'Bergerac'
HIT AND RUN (BBC2 2/1/90) Theme music "Oh Yeah" (Dieter
    Meyer-Boris Blank) YELLO on 'New Mix In One Go' on
    Mercury (Poly): 826773-2 (CD) MERD(C) 95 (2LP/2Cas)
HITMAN AND HER The (Granada from 3/9/88) theme "Cocoon"
    (Elvine Tess) TIMERIDER on 'Are You Ready For This'
    PWL (WEA): HFCD 22 (CD) HFC 22 (Cass) HF 22 (LP)
HITCHHIKERS GUIDE TO THE GALAXY (UKGO 23/3/93 orig BBC2
    BBC2 81) *Theme* (Tim Souster) *Other Mus* (Paddy King
    sland) *BBC:ZBBC 1035 (Cass set) BBCCD 6001(CD set)*
HOGAN FAMILY The (USA 88 BBC1 12/8/91) Theme "Together
    Thru The Years" (Charles Fox-Stephen Geyer) sung by
    ROBERTA FLACK / add.music by Bruce Miller........*NA*
HOGAN'S HEROES (USA 65 C4-86) *see Coll* TELEVISION'S GRE
    ATEST HITS VOLUME 2'/'4 AMERICA TWO'
HOLD THE DREAM (C4 5/5/87) Theme (Barrie Guard) - ELKIE
    BROOKS - *Legend (Poly:) LMA(T)(CD) 1 (LP/Cass/CD)*
    ee also under 'WOMAN OF SUBSTANCE A'
HOLIDAY 92/93 (BBC1 7/1/92) theme (Paul Hardcastle)..*NA*
HOLIDAY 89-91 (BBC1) *Theme* "Holiday Romance" composed &
    performed by GORDON GILTRAP *(not available)*
    Link music "The Long Ships" from 'Watermark' sung &
    composed by ENYA *WEA: WX 199(C)(CD) (LP/Cass/CD)*
HOLIDAY 86 (BBC1 7/1/86)Theme "Holiday Suite" SIMON MAY
    ORCH *BBC (Pinn): REB 594 (LP) ZCF 594 (Cas) deleted*
HOLIDAY 80-85 (BBC1) Theme "Heartsong" (Gordon Giltrap)
    GORDON GILTRAP - *Old Gold: OG 9235 (7"s)*
HOLLYWOOD GREATS (USA-C4 2/8/92) music (Jep Epstein).*NA*
HOLLYWOOD REPORT (C4/Central) music (David Mindel)...*NA*
HOLLYWOOD UK (BBC2 5/9/93) music (Steve Beresford)...*NA*
HOLLYWOOD WIVES (USA 4/9/89) Title song (Jan Buckingham
    Jeff Silbar) LAURA BRANIGAN / Music (Lalo Schifrin)
    see Coll 'MAGNUM P.I. THE AMERICAN TV HITS ALBUM'
HOME AND AWAY (Australia)(ITV from 13/2/89) *Title theme*
    (Mike Perjanik)sung by KAREN BODDINGTON & MARK WILL
    IAMS *1st Night: SCORE 19 (7")* "Living Without Your
    Love" by IMAGES *1st Night: SCORE(L) 25(7"/12")*
HOME ON SUNDAY (BBC1 30/6/85) Theme music "Impromptu No
    3 in G.Flat Maj Op.90" (Schubert)
HOME SERVICE The (C4 Cen 29/7/89) Theme "Build A Little
    Home" (Al Dubin-Harry Warren) - ROY FOX & HIS BAND
    with DENNY DENNIS - *Joy (President): JOYD 285 (LP)*
HOME SHOW The (Thames 14/7/92) music (Alan Brown)....*NA*
HOME TO ROOST (Yorks 24/10/87)Theme "Consider Yourself"
    (Lionel Bart) from 'Oliver' *see* FILMS & SHOWS
HOMICIDE: LIFE ON THE STREET (USA/C4 15/11/93) Main the
    me (Lynn F.Kowal) incidental score (Jeff Rona)...*NA*
HOOKED (Granada 26/1/92) theme music (Cath Baxter)...*NA*

HOOPERMAN (USA)(ITV 17/4/88) theme music (Mike Post)
see *Coll* 'AMERICAN TV THEMES VOL.1'/'TELEVISION MUS
IC OF MIKE POST'/'ITV THEMES'
HOPE IT RAINS (Thames 3/6/91) mus: (Graham de Wilde).*NA*
HORIZON (BBC2) Title music (Wilfred Josephs).........*NA*
HORSE OF THE YEAR SHOW (BBC1)Theme mus "A Musical Joke"
from 4th m/m Symph No.40 in G.min (Mozart) *various
recordings incl:* 'Horse Of The Year Show' *Coll* BAND
OF ROYAL CORPS OF TRANSPORT *Bandleader ZCBND 1001Cas*
HORSEMAN RIDING BY. A (UKGO 18/4/93 orig BBC 24/9/78)
Theme "A Country Canter" (Michael Hankinson) *see
Coll* 'Famous Themes Remember These'*Grasmere (Tayl)*
HOSPITAL WATCH (BBC1 2/9/91) Theme "La Serenissima" (Gi
an Reverberi-L.Giordano) RONDO VENEZIANO on 'Venice
In Peril' *Fanfare (Mainline): CD(ZC)RON 1 (CD/Cass)*
HOT METAL (LWT 16/2/86) Theme "Papers" (Alan Price) per
formed by ALAN PRICE *Trojan: TRO 9083 (7"s) deleted*
HOUSE OF CARADUS The (Granada 78) Theme: JOHNNY PEARSON
'Themes & Dreams' coll - *President: PRCD 132 (CD)*
HOUSE OF CARDS (BBC1 18/11/90) music (Jim Parker)....*NA*
HOUSE OF ELIOTT The (BBC1 31/8/91) music (Jim Parker)*NA*
HOUSE PARTY - see 'NOEL'S HOUSE PARTY'
HOUSE STYLE (ITV 8/1/91) music (Keith Hopwood).......*NA*
HOUSTON KNIGHTS (USA) Theme (Dennis McCarthy-George Doe
ring) *see Collec* 'AMERICAN TELEVISION THEMES VOL.3'
HOW DO YOU MANAGE (BBC1 12/4/92) mus (Simon Davison).*NA*
HOW DOES YOUR GARDEN GROW (C4 (Ulster TV) 3/1/92) music
(John Anderson)..................................*NA*
HOW TO SAVE THE EARTH (C4 5/5/92) m:(Steve Marshall).*NA*
HOW WARS END (C4 8/1/91) orig music (Carl Davis).....*NA*
HOWARDS' WAY (BBC1 1/9/85-25/11/90) Theme (Simon May-Le
slie Osborne) *see Coll* 'GREAT TV THEMES VOLUME 3'
HUCKLEBERRY HOUND (USA Cartoon) *see Coll* 'TELEVISION'S
GREATEST HITS VOLUME 2'
HUMAN ELEMENT (BBC2 16/5/92) music (Malcolm Clarke)..*NA*
HUMAN JUNGLE The (ITC 63/C4 87) Theme (John Barry) JOHN
BARRY ORCH 'Hit and Miss' *C5-See For Miles (Pinn):
C5CD 516 (CD) C5-516 (Cass)*
HUMDINGERS (BBC1 3/6/91) music (Simon Etchell).......*NA*
HUNDRED ACRES A (Antelope West/C4 23/2/90) Theme (Nigel
Hess) - *see Coll* 'MAIGRET'/'FAVOURITE TV THEMES'
HUNT THE PIE (Granada 8/3/93) music (Mike Woolmans)..*NA*
HUNTER (USA77)(ITV 5/85) mus (Mike Post-Pete Carpenter)
see Coll 'AMERICAN TV THEMES VOLUME 1'/'TELEVISION
MUSIC OF MIKE POST'/'GREAT TV THEMES VOLUME 1'
HUNTERS IN THE WORLD (BBC1 Bristol 2/8/93) music score
(Brian Gascoigne)..............................*NA*
HURRAY FOR TODAY USA (YTV 12/11/90)mus (Adrian Burch)*NA*
HURRICANES The (Scottish TV Ent/DIC 2/11/93) music by
(Michael Tavera-Reed Robbins-Mark Simon).........*NA*
HYPNOTIC WORLD OF PAUL McKENNA The (Celador for Carlton
19/10/93)music (Keith Strachan-Matthew Strachan).*NA*
HYPOTHETICALS (Brian Lapping Asso/Granada/BBC2 17/5/93)
music (Howard Davison)..........................*NA*

I **CAN DO THAT** (YTV 10/7/91) theme song (Adrian Burch & David Whitaker).................................*NA*

I **DREAM OF JEANNIE** (USA 65/C4 30/9/87) Theme (Hugo Mont enegro-Buddy Kaye) *see* 'TELEVISION'S GR.HITS VOL.1'

I **LOVE LUCY** (USA 50s and C4-89) Musical Highlights from series on *USA Imp (Sil.Screen): SM(C) 1951 (LP/Cas)* *see also Coll* 'TELEVISION'S G.HITS VOLUME 1'

I **LOVETT** (BBC2 Scotland) music (David McNiven).......*NA*

I **MARRIED JOAN** (USA 50s) Theme on *Coll* 'TELEVISION'S GR GREATEST HITS VOLUME 2'

I **SPY** (USA 65) Music (Earle Hagen) *see Coll* 'TELEVISION 'S GREATEST HITS VOLUME 2'

ICE SKATING (BBC 78-93) Theme "Mornings At Seven" JAMES LAST ORCH 'Happy Heart' *Poly: 839643-2(CD) -4(Cass)*

ICE SKATING (ITV 88-93) Themes "Industrial Report" (Gra ham de Wilde p.KPM Mus) and "Ergotron" (Podlasinsky p.Kanda Music) - *both recordings unavailable*

IF **THE WORST HAPPENS** (BBC1 8/8/93) mus David Stevens.*NA*

IF **WISHES WERE HORSES** (C4 29/10/91)mus: Dave Corbett.*NA*

IF **YOU SEE GOD TELL HIM** (BBC1 11/11/93) music director (Simon Brint) theme song "Orange Coloured Sky" (Mil ton DeLugg-Willie Stein) sung by CLAIRE MARTIN *not available* / orig: (1950) NAT KING COLE on 'Big Band Cole' *EMI Capitol: CDP 796259-2 (CD) or CZ 436 (CD)*

I'**LL FLY AWAY** (USA Lorimar/C4 14/6/93) Theme and Music score (W.G.Snuffy Walden) **theme on Coll** '4 AMERICA TWO' *see Collect* / episode one opening song "All I Could Do Was Cry" sung by ETTA JAMES available on 'Chess Masters' *Chess-MCA (BMG): CHLD 19168 (CD)*

IN **SEARCH OF THE DEAD** (BBC2 Wales 3/10/92) theme music "Lauda Jerusalem In E.Minor" RV 609 (Vivaldi) The Montiverdi Choir EBS (Gardner) on *DG 429 565-2 (CD)*

IN **SICKNESS AND IN HEALTH** (UKGO 17/7/93 or BBC1 1/9/85) theme music comp/sung by CHAS AND DAVE *BBC deleted*

IN **SOLIDARITY** (BBC2-2/2/91) music (Dave Brooks)......*NA*

IN **SUSPICIOUS CIRCUMSTANCES** (Granada 30/3/92) theme mus ic (Matthew Scott)................................*NA*

IN **THE LINE OF DUTY** (TV) Music sco (Mark Snow) TV -S/T- *Intrada (Koch Int): MAFCD 7034 (CD)*

IN **THE WILD** (Tigress/Meridian 5/7/93) Music sco (Nigel Beaham-Powell and Bella Russell)...............*NA*

IN **TIME OF WAR** (TVS 6/2/92) theme music "Sospiri" Op.70 for Strings Harp and Organ (Elgar) *many recordings*

IN **WITH MAVIS** (C4/YoYo 17/792) music (Roger White)...*NA*

INCREDIBLE HULK The (USA 78) Theme music (Joe Harnell) Orchestral score on 'Film & TV music of Joe Harnell *5Jays Imp (Silva Screen): 5JAYS 001/002 (2CDs)*

INDUSTRIAL SYMPHONY NO.1 (USA/C4 9/5/92) Music (Angelo Badalamenti) Lyrics (David Lynch) voc: JULEE CRUISE *Warner Bros (WEA): 925859-2 (CD) -4 (Cass) -1 (LP)*

INSIDE VICTOR LEWIS SMITH (BBC2 1/11/93) title music by (Dave Stewart) addit.music (Elizabeth Parker)....*NA*

INSPECTOR ALLEYN MYSTERIES (BBC1 18/4/93) Closing theme (Anne Dudley) Orig music (Ray Russell)..........*NA*

INSPECTOR GADGET (Cartoon ITV 13/6/85) *see Coll* 'TELEVI
    SION'S GREATEST HITS VOLUME 3'
INSPECTOR MORSE (Central 25/12/87-93) Theme (Barrington
    eloung) -S/T- with Classics *Virgin (EMI):* (Vol.1)
    VTCD 2 (CD) VTMC 2 (Cas) VTLP 2 (LP) / (Vol.2) *VTCD
    14 (CD) VTMC 14(Cass)* / (Vol.3) *VTCD 16 (CD) VTMC
    16 (Cass) see Coll* 'FAVOURITE TV THEMES'/'20 TOP..'
    TV -S/T- COLLECT.(Vol.1/2/3) Virgin: TPAK 27 (3CDs)
    spoken word cass: *MCI (TBD): TALKMC 013/014 (4Cass)*
INSPECTOR WEXFORD - *see* 'RUTH RENDELL MYSTERIES The'
INTERFACE (C4/Same Pr 24/3/92) music (Paul Riordan)..*NA*
INTERNATIONAL ATHLETICS - *see under* 'ATHLETICS'
INTERNATIONAL SHOWJUMPING *see under* 'HORSE OF THE YEAR'
INTERNATIONAL TENNIS (BBC Maj.Competitions) "Brave New
    World" from 'War Of The Worlds' (JEFF WAYNE) on *CBS
    96000 (2LPs) 40-(Cass) see also under* 'WIMBLEDON'
INTERNATIONAL VOLLEYBALL (C4 10/1/88) Theme "Always On
    My Mind" (Willie Nelson) PET SHOP BOYS *EMI (CD/Cas)*
INVADERS The (USA 66) Theme music (Dominic Frontiere)
    see Coll 'GREATEST SCI-FI HITS VOLUME 2'
INVISIBLE ENEMIES (C4 12/7/92)mus (Michael Atherton).*NA*
IPSO FACTO (BBC1 3/12/91)(New Pardesi Music Machine).*NA*
IRISH R.M.The (C4 12/7/84) Music score (Nick Bicat) TV
    -S/T- *Ritz: RITZLP(MC) 011 (LP/Cass)*
IRONSIDE (USA 67) Theme music (Quincy Jones) *see Collec*
    'TELEVISION'S GREATEST HITS VOLUME 1'
ISLAND OF GHOSTS: *see under* 'MADAGASCAR'
ISRAEL: A NATION IS BORN (C4 19/3/92) original music by
    Mischa Segal and orchestrated by William Ashford.*NA*
IT AIN'T HALF HOT, MUM! (UKGO 26/5/93 orig BBC1 72) mus
    "Meet The Gang" (Jimmy Perry-David Croft) performed
    by The Cast orig record on *EMI:EMC 3074 LP) deleted*
IT'LL BE ALLRIGHT ON THE NIGHT (Thames 1981-89) theme
    music (Rod Argent-Peter Van Hooke)...............*NA*
IT'LL NEVER WORK (BBC1 9/11/93) music (Depeche Mode).*NA*
ITALIANS The (BBC2 4/9/92) title music (Jim Parker)..*NA*
ITN NEWS (Orig 60's-70's theme) 'Non Stop' John Malcolm
    Orch *see Coll* 'SOUNDS VISUAL' *see also* 'NEWS AT 10'
ITV ATHLETICS - *see Collections* 'FAVOURITE TV THEMES'
ITV NATIONAL WEATHER Identity Music "ITV Logo" (David
    Dundas) *see Coll* '20 Top TV Themes'
ITV TELETHON (ITV 7/92) theme "Give A little Bit" by
    SUPERTRAMP *A.& M.: AMCD(AMMC/AM) 007 (CDs/Cass/7")*
IT'S MY CITY (BBC1 18/6/89) Theme "Forgotten Town" (Hen
    ry Priestman) CHRISTIANS *Island (Poly) CID(ICT)9876*
IT'S MY PLEASURE (BBC2 17/11/87) Theme "Souvenir" (Hump
    hreys-Carter) OMD 'Architecture & Morality'(Dindisc
    Virgin): (CD)DID(C)1 (CD/LP/Cas) also (CD)(TC)OMD1
IVOR THE ENGINE (BBC1 77) Theme (Vern Elliott) Stories
    and music from the series on *BBC: ZCM 517 (Cass)*

JACK DEE SHOW (C4 26/2/92) m.assoc (Graham K.Smith)..*NA*
JAMES RANDI PSYCHIC INVESTIGATOR (Gran 17/7/91) music
    (Robert Lockhart).................................*NA*

JAMES WHALE RADIO SHOW The (Yorkshire 7/4/89) Theme Mus "Bimbo" (Mark Platts-Phil & Mark Scott) MUSIC FORCE on *Flair (Priority-BMG): FLA 110 (7"s)*

JAPANESE LANGUAGE & PEOPLE (BBC2 14/9/91)(Clive Bell)*NA*

JASON KING (ITC 15/7/71-72) Theme mus (Laurie Johnson) *see Collections* 'ROSE AND THE GUN The'

JAZZ DETECTIVE The (HTV 27/4/92) music (Mark Thomas).*NA*

JEEVES AND WOOSTER (Granada from 22/4/90) Music (Anne Dudley) -S/T- *EMI:CDEMC 3623 (CD) TCEMC 3623 (Cass)*

JEOPARDY! (Meridian-R.Grundy 22/2/93) mus (Rick Turk)*NA*

JERUSALEM: OF HEAVEN AND EARTH (Nomad Films 1983 / BBC2 5/9/93) orig music (Frank Strangio)..............*NA*

JETSONS The (USA 62) (BBC1 10/7/90) Theme (Hoyt Curtin) *see Coll* 'TELEVISION'S GREATEST HITS VOLUME 1'

JEWEL IN THE CROWN The (Granada 9/1/84 & C4 9/85) Music (George Fenton)-S/T- *Chrysalis (ZC)CDL 1465 deleted see Coll* 'GRANADA STUDIOS SOUVENIR'/'ITV THEMES'

JIM'LL FIX IT (BBC1 1975-93) title song (David Mindel) *previously* 'CHILDREN'S WORLD OF TV THEMES' *deleted*

JOE 90 (ATV/ITC 29/9/68-69) Music (Barry Gray) *see Coll* 'F.A.B.-THUNDERBIRDS'/'NO STRINGS ATTACHED'/'POWER THEMES 90'/'MAN FROM UNCLE'/'ITV CHILDREN'S THEMES' 'TV CLASSICS VOLUME 1' ("Joe 90-Main Theme")

JOHN SESSIONS TALL TALES (BBC2 19/1/91) theme 'Concerto for Violin and Orchestra in D.Major Op.77' (Brahms)

JOHN TOVEY'S EATING ON A PLATE (BBC2 25/9/91) theme mus ic (Martin Kiszko)..............................*NA*

JOHNSON & FRIENDS (BBC2 30/7/91) music (Chris Neal)..*NA*

JOHNNY BALL REVEALS ALL (Cen.18/3/92)m:(Martin Cook).*NA*

JOHNNY STACCATO (USA 59) theme music (Elmer Bernstein) *see Collection* '4 AMERICA TWO'

JOINT ACCOUNT (BBC1 26/1/89) music (Colin Cowles)....*NA*

JOKER IN THE PACK (BBC1 22/5/92) mus (Simon Etchell).*NA*

JOKING APART (BBC2 7/1/93) theme mus "Fool If You Think It's Over" (Chris Rea) *arr.& sung by* Kenny Craddock *not available* / CHRIS REA version on 'New Light Thr ough Old Windows' *WEA: 243841-2 (CD) WX 200C (Cass)*

JOSIE (C4 1/5/91) music (Richard Vranch-Simon Brint).*NA*

JOSHUA JONES (BBC1 7/1/92) Title song (Ben Heneghan-Ian Lawson) sung by MALDWYN POPE..................*NA*

JOY TO DRIVE A (C4/HTV 10/8/92) theme mus "King Of The Road" (Roger Miller) by ROGER MILLER on *Old Gold: OG 9480 (7"s) + BMG: CDCST 51 (CD) CSTK 51 (Cass)*

JUDY FINNIGAN DEBATE (Gran.5/9/93) m:(Amos Zamorski).*NA*

JUKE BOX JURY (BBC2 24/9/89) Theme "Hit And Miss" (John Barry) Courtney Pine on *Antilles-Island (Poly): ANN 11 (7"s) 12ANN 11 (12"s)* / orig 1959 theme by JOHN BARRY 7 + 4 *see Coll* 'JOHN BARRY BEST OF THE EMI Y'

JULIET BRAVO (UKGold 5/11/92 orig 30/8/80) theme (Derek Goom arrangement of melody by Bach) *BBC deleted*

JUNIPER JUNGLE (BBC1/Storm Group Prd 8/1/93) title song comp/sung by BOBBY BALL / incid.score Paul Joyce.*NA*

JUST A GIGOLO (Central 8/4/93)title theme song (Richard Vranch) sung by TONY SLATTERY.................*NA*

JUST GOOD FRIENDS (UKGold 4/11/92 orig BBC1 22/9/83)
Theme (John Sullivan) sung by PAUL NICHOLAS *K.Tel:
ONCD 3334 (CD) ONE 1334 (LP)*
JUST SO STORIES (BBC1/Bevanfield 7/4/92) Kick Prod...*NA*
JUST US (Yorkshire 18/2/92) mus (Christopher Norton).*NA*
JUST WILLIAMS (C4-7/85) "Green Onions" (B.T.Jones) BOOK
ER T & MGs: *Old Gold OG 9499 (7") WEA: K40072 (LP)*
JUSTICE GAME The (BBC1 7/4/89) "Waterfront" (Jim Kerr)
SIMPLE MINDS on 'Sparkle In The Rain' *Virgin (Poly)
CDV 2300 (CD) V 2300 (LP) TCV 2300 (Cass)*
JUTE CITY (BBC1-27/10/91) Theme (David A.Stewart) DAVID
A.STEWART *Anxious RCA (BMG): ZB 45043 (7") ZT 45044
(12"s) ZD 45044 (CDs)* Complete -S/T- on *Anxious RCA
(BMG): ZD 75187 (CD) ZK 75187 (Cass) ZL 75187 (LP)*

KABADDI (C4 Endboard Prod-5/5/91) theme "Raqs" (Sheila
Chandra-Steve Coe-Martin Smith) sung by SHEILA CHAN
DRA on 'Silk' on *Indipop Records (R.Trade/Indidpop)
SILK 001CD (CD) SILK 001(LP) / SILK 001MC (Cass)*
KAPPATOO II (Tyne-Tees 9/4/92) mus (Debbie Wiseman)..*NA*
KAZUKO'S KARAOKE KLUB (C4 25/5/89) Th: "Do The Karaoke"
(K.Hohki-K.Taguchi) FRANK CHICKENS 'Klub Money' *Fly
ing Leckords (Cartel) STIR 002X (LP) SYZZLE 2 (7"s)*
KEEPING UP APPEARANCES (BBC1 from 29/10/90-93) Title th
eme music (Nick Ingman).........................*NA*
KENNEDY'S The (Brook Prod for Thames 13/10/92) original
music (Michael Bacon).........................*NA*
KERSPLAT (C4 13/1/91) (Julian Wastall-Daemon Barry)..*NA*
KEVIN & CO (BBC1 12/11/92) theme music (Roger Limb)..*NA*
KEVIN'S COUSINS (BBC1 9/1/92) theme mus (Roger Limb)..*NA*
KEY TO REBECCA The (TV Mini series) Music score (J.A.C.
Redford) -S/T- *Prometheus (Silva Scr): PCD 123 (CD)*
KICKSTART (BBC1 27/8/85) Theme mus "Be My Boogie-Woogie
Baby" (R.Vaplus) MR.WALKIE-TALKIE *prev on Collect
'FAVOURITE SPORTING THEMES' (MFP) deleted*
KIDNAPPED (LWT 78) Mus (Vladimir Cosma) "David's Theme"
see Coll 'GREAT TV THEMES VOLUME 1' (David Balfour)
KILROY (BBC1 from 12/10/87) theme (Robert Howes).....*NA*
KIND OF LOVING A (Granada 4/4/82) Theme (Derek Hilton)
see Collection 'GRANADA STUDIOS SOUVENIR ALBUM'
KINNOCK: THE INSIDE STORY (LWT 18/7/93) music scored by
(Robert Childs)...............................*NA*
KINSEY (BBC1 2/4/91) theme music (Dave Greenslade)...*NA*
KIRI TE KANAWA & ANDRE PREVIN - *see 'Together'*
KNIGHT & DAYE (USA 89 BBC1 7/6/92) theme "Night & Day"
(Cole Porter) FRANK SINATRA '20 Golden Greats' *Deja
Vu (TBD): DVCD 2015 (CD) DVMC 2015 (Cass)* Inciden
tal music score (David Michael Frank)...........*NA*
KNIGHT RIDER (USA 82 ITV) Theme (G.A.Larson-S.Phillips)
Colls 'FANTASTIC TELEVISION.'/'GREAT TV THEMES V.3'
KNIGHTMARE (Anglia 7/9/87-93) Theme music composed and
performed by ED WELCH..........................*NA*
KNOTS LANDING (USA BBC1 79) Theme (Jerrold Immel) *see
Coll* 'BEST OF BBC TV THEMES' *deleted*

KOJAK (USA 73) Theme (Billy Goldenberg) *see Coll* 'GREAT
TV THEMES'/'TELEVISION'S G.HITS 3'/'MY KIND OF MUS'
KON-TIKI MAN The (BBC-18/4/90) Music (Ragnar Bjerkreim)
with Film Symphony Orch Of Prague conductor: Stefan
Koniek-S/T-*BBC: BBCCD 780(CD) ZCF 780(Cass) deleted*
KUNG FU (USA 71) Music (Jimmy Helms) theme *see Collect*
'GREAT TV THEMES VOLUME 3'
KYTV (BBC2 from 3/5/90) music (Phil Pope)...........*NA*

L.A.LAW (USA)(ITV 7/9/88) theme (Mike Post) *see Collect*
'AMERICAN TV THEMES VOL.1'/'GREAT TV THEMES VOL.3'/
'TELEVISION MUSIC OF MIKE POST'/'ITV THEMES'
L.A.:Stories (WOW prod BBC2 25/4/93) m.(Jimmy Harry).*NA*
LABOUR OF LOVE, A (BBC2 27/2/93) title music (Nigel Bea
ham Powell and Bella Russell)..................*NA*
LACE (USA) (YTV orig 8/9/84 re-run 1990) Music composed
and performed by NIC BICAT....................*NA*
LADY CHATTERLEY (BBC1 6/6/93) Music from "Appalachia"
(Delius) / "Hammersmith Prelude" (Holst) / "Venus"
from 'The Planets Suite' (Holst) played by London
Philharmonic Orch (conductor Barry Wordsworth)....*NA*
versions: "Appalachia" by ROYAL PHILHARMONIC ORCHES
(Richard Hickox) *Decca (Poly):425156-2(CD) -4(Cass)*
"Hammersmith Prelude" *Mercury (Poly):432 009-2 (CD)*
"Venus" (The Planets) *var.recordings on all formats*
LAND OF HOPE (C4 Austr) mus (M.Perjanik-J.Flanagan)..*NA*
LAND OF HOPE AND GLORIA (Thames 24/6/92) theme song by
(Sheila Ferguson-Erwin Keiles) SHEILA FERGUSON...*NA*
LAND OF THE GIANTS (USA 68 / C4 10/1/93) theme music by
(John Williams) *see Collection* '4 AMERICA TWO'
LARAMIE (USA 59 re-run BBC2 86) Theme music (Cyril Mock
ridge) *see Collection* 'GREAT WESTERN THEMES'
LAST NIGHT OF THE PROMS (BBC1 15/9/90) - 'Music For The
Last Night Of The Proms' featuring: Royal Philharmo
nic Orch (Sir Charles Groves) and Chorus with Sarah
Walker (soprano) - *Cirrus Dig.Classics (Castle-BMG)
CTVCD 501 (CD) CTVMC 501 (Cass) CTVLP 501 (LP)*
LAST OF THE SUMMER WINE The (BBC1 12/11/73-1994) Theme
(Ronnie Hazlehurst) RONNIE HAZLEHURST *CBS deleted*
LATA IN HER OWN VOICE (C4 13/1/91) the music of Indian
film playback singer LATA MANGESHKAR featuring orig
film music by S.D.Burman and other composers. Some
material is available via *EMI (India) Records/Tapes*
LATE NIGHT WITH LETTERMAN (USA C4 28/7/87) "Viewer Mail
Theme" (Henry Mancini) on 'James Galway Greatest Hi
ts Vol.2' *RCA (BMG): 09026 61178-4 (Cass) -2 (CD)*
LAUREL & HARDY *see under Collections* 'LAUREL & HARDY'
LAVERNE & SHIRLEY (USA 76)Theme "Making Our Dreams Come
True" (Norman Gimbel-Charles Fox) CYNDI GRECCO *see
Coll* 'TELEVISION'S GREATEST HITS VOLUME 3'
LAW AND HARRY McGRAW The (USA 88 ITV 12/2/92) theme
music (Richard Markowitz)......................*NA*
LAW AND ORDER (BBC1 8/4/91 USA 89) Theme (Mike Post)
see Collection 'AMERICAN TELEVISION THEMES VOL.3'

LAZARUS AND DINGWALL (BBC2 1/2/91) mus (Simon Brint).*NA*
LE MANOIR (C4 YTV 24/7/92) theme music "Images For Orch
   estra" (Debussy) played by The CBSO (Simon Rattle)
   EMI: CDC 749947-2 (CD) -4 (Cass) other incidental
   music: "Prelude A L'Apres-Midi D'Faun" (Debussy)
   LSO (Andre Previn) *EMI: CDC 747001-2 (CD) -4 (Cass)*
LEARNING TO FAIL (BBC2 7/1/92) music (Peter Moser)..*NA*
LEAVING (BBC2 2/5/85) Theme (R.Hazlehurst) Ronnie Hazle
   hurst Orch-*BBC (Pickwick): HSC 649 (LP) PWKS 649 CD*
LEAVING OF LIVERPOOL The (Austr/BBC Co Pr BBC1 15/7/93)
   Music score (Peter Best) -S/T- *OneMone Australia
   (Silva Screen): IMICD 1019 (CD)*
LEGEND OF PRINCE VALIANT The (USA King 92/ BBC1 6/4/93)
   mus (Steve Sexton-Gerald O'Brien-Marc Jordan) feat:
   EXCHANGE -S/T- *Mesa (Movie Boulevard):R2.79040 (CD)*
LENIN: THE TRAIN (TV mini-series) Mus (Nicola Piovani)
   Milan (Silva Screen): CDCH 381 (CD)
LET THE BLOOD RUN FREE (Australia Med.Arts-C4 29/8/92)
   theme and incidental music (Al Mullins)..........*NA*
LIFE AND LOVES OF A SHE-DEVIL The (BBC2 8/10/86) Theme
   "Warm Love Gone Cold" (Peter Filleul) by CHRISTINE
   COLLISTER *Coll* 'BEST OF BBC TV THEMES' *deleted*
LIFE AND SOUL (LWT 25/7/93) theme music (Phil Binding-
   Simon Moore)..*NA*
LIFE AND TIMES OF DAVID LLOYD GEORGE (BBC2 4/3/81)Theme
   'Chi Mai' (Ennio Morricone) *see Coll* 'REFLECTIONS'
   'MUSIC OF ENNIO MORRICONE'
LIFE AND TIMES OF GRIZZLY ADAMS (USA 78) theme "Maybe"
   (Thom Pace) instrumental version ('The Man From The
   Mountains') *see Coll* 'GREAT TV THEMES VOLUME 3'
LIFE AND TIMES OF HENRY PRATT The (ITV/Red Rooster Prod
   9/11/92) Music composed by Peter Skellern........*NA*
LIFE IN THE FREEZER (BBC1 18/11/93) m:(George Fenton).*NA*
LIFE IN PIECES, A (BBC2 26/12/90) theme mus 'Piano Conc
   erto No.2 in C.Minor' (S.Rachmaninov) *many versions*
LIFE WITHOUT GEORGE (UKGO 4/5/93 or BBC1 12/3/87) theme
   music composed and sung by PENNY CROFT...........*NA*
LIFEBOAT (Central 27/4/93) music (Anthony Phillips)..*NA*
LIFESENSE (BBC1 11/11/91) Music (Paul Hardcastle)....*NA*
LIFT OFF! (ABC Australia/C4 4/1/93) title music (Chris
   Neal-Frank Strangio-Paul Grabowsky)..............*NA*
LIGHT OF EXPERIENCE The (BBC2 76-87) Theme "Doina De Ja
   le" - GHEORGE ZAMFIR *see Coll* 'REFLECTIONS' *(CBS)*
LILLIE (LWT 24/9/78) Theme music (Joseph Horovitz) *see
   Collection* 'HIT THEMES 1 BEST OF BRITISH TV MUSIC'
LILLIPUT IN ANTARCTICA (Cousteau Society/BBC1 2/8/93)
   theme music "Antarctica" (Vangelis) VANGELIS on
   'Themes' *Polydor (Polyg): 839 518-2 (CD) -4 (Cass)*
   other mus.from 'Out Of The Cool' album by GIL EVANS
   ORCH *Impulse-New Note MCA (Pinn): MCAD 5653(CD)* and
   "Concertos Pour Mandoline" (Vivaldi) on *Erato (WEA)
   2292-45668-2 (CD) 2292-45670-4 (Cass)*
LINCOLN (USA TV Docum.series) Music score (Alan Menken)
   -S/T- *USA Import (S.Screen): 54752-2 (CD) -4 (Cass)*

LIONS TOUR 93 (ITV Sport/Scottish Prov 26/6/93) theme (Charlie Skarbek) arr.of Holst's "Jupiter" (Planets Suite) **note** vocal version by KIRI TE KAANAWA "World In Union" *see p.118 TT1993 under World Cup Rugby 91*

LIPSTICK ON YOUR COLLAR (C4 21/2/93) opening title song (Edna Lewis-George Goehring) sung by CONNIE FRANCIS closing music "The Man With The Golden Arm" played by BILLY MAY ORCH. *SOUNDTRACK feat sel.of 28 oldies Polygram: 516 086-2 (CD) 516 086-4 (Cass) -1 (LP)*

LIQUID TELEVISION (BBC2 13/5/91) (Mark Mothersbaugh).*NA*

LITTLE HOUSE ON THE PRAIRIE The(USA 74 rpt C4-13/10/91) theme (David Rose) *Coll* '4 AMERICA TWO'/'GREAT TV.'

LITTLE PICTURE SHOW The (ITV/Diverse Prod 5/1/93) music (Howie Bernstein).................................*NA*

LITTLE WIZARDS (USA Marvel/Akom Prod/C4 4/10/92) music (Haim Saban-Shuki Levy)......................*NA*

LIVE AID CONCERT 85 (13/7/85) Rockin'All Over The World (John Fogerty) STATUS QUO on *Old Gold:OG 9567 (7"s)*

LIVE AND KICKING (BBC1 2/10/93) theme music (David Arnold and Paul Hart).........................*NA*

LIVER BIRDS The (BBC1 14/4/69-5/1/79) theme music 'On A Mountain Stands A Lady' (trad) sung by THE SCAFFOLD 'Best Of' *EMI: CDEMS 1436 (CD) TCEMS 1436 (Cass)*

LIVERPOOL ORATORIO *see 'GHOSTS OF THE PAST'*

LIVING DANGEROUSLY (BBC1 12/11/92) theme and incidental mus (Elizabeth Parker BBC Radiophonic Workshop)..*NA*

LIVING ISLAM (BBC2 14/4/93) music by ROHAN...........*NA*

LIVING SOAP The (BBC2 15/10/93) theme mus "Renaissance" by M PEOPLE from 'Elegant Slumming' *De Construction (BMG): 74321 16678-2 (CD) -4 (Cass) -1 (LP)*

LIZA WITH A 'Z' (USA TV Concert 1972) -S/T- featur LIZA MINNELLI reissue *Sony Coll: 982994-2 (CD) -4 (Cass)*

LOCOMOTION (BBC2 31/10/93) title music (Roger Bolton) original music (Howard Davidson)..................*NA*

LODGE The (Central 7/4/93) music (Peter Davis).......*NA*

LONDON BOAT SHOW The (BBC2 12/1/87) Theme "Vivaldi' SKY *Telstar (BMG): TCD 2241 (CD) STAC 2241 (Cass)*

LONDON MARATHON The (BBC1 13/5/84-93) Theme "The Trap" (Ron Goodwin) *see Coll* 'MY KIND OF MUSIC'

LONDON UNDERGROUND (English Channel Prod/BBC2 5/10/92) theme "Things That Make You Go H'mmm" C.& C.MUSIC FACTORY *Sony Music: 467814-2 (CD) -4 (Cass) -1 (LP)*

LONDON'S BURNING (LWT 20/2/88-94) Theme mu (Simon Brint Rowland Rivron) *see Collect* 'FAVOURITE TV THEMES'/ 'HIT THEMES 1 BEST OF BRITISH TV'/'20TOP TV THEMES'

LONE RANGER The (USA 1949 re-run C4 88) Theme "William Tell Overture" (Rossini) *many recordings available*

LONESOME DOVE (USA TV/BBC1 30/8/93) Music score (Basil Poledouris) -S/T- *USA Impt (Movie Boulevard):- (CD)*

LONESOME PINE SPECIALS The (USA 88/C4 6/11/90) Theme by JERRY DOUGLAS "Dhaka Rok" from 'Under The Wire' (J. Douglas) *MCA (BMG): MCAD(IMCA(C) 5675 (CD/LP/Cass)*

LOOK AT IT THIS WAY (BBC1/Arts & Ent. 22/11/92) theme and incidental music (Stanley Myers)............*NA*

LOOK The (BBC2 20/9/92) theme "What Is Life" (Che Faro
      Senza) from 'Orpheus and Eurydice' (Gluck) / other
      mus "Into The Night" (Tennant-Lowe) PET SHOP BOYS
LOOSE CANNON - *see under* MAX MONROE
LORD MOUNTBATTEN THE LAST VICEROY (ITV 4/86)Music (John
      Scott) R.P.O.-S/T- *TER (Con): (ZC)TER 1113 (Cas/LP)*
LOSE A MILLION (Carlton 22/9/93) mus (Simon Etchell).*NA*
LOST EMPIRES (Granada 24/10/86) Music (Derek Hilton) on
      TER (Conif): (CD)(ZC)TER 1119 (CD/Cass/LP)
LOST IN SPACE (USA 65) *see Coll* 'TELEVISION'S GREATEST
      HITS VOLUME 1'/'GREATEST SCI-FI HITS VOUME 3'
LOTUS EATERS The (UKGO 12/9/93 orig BBC 71) theme "Ta
      "Ta Trena Pou Fyghan" STAVROS XARAHAKOS *BBC deleted*
LOU GRANT (USA 77/C4 84) Theme (Patrick Williams) *see
      Coll* 'CAGNEY & LACEY & OTHER AMERICAN TV THEMES'
LOVE AND HATE (BBC1 13/8/91) mus: (Eric N.Robertson).*NA*
LOVE AND REASON (BBC2 1/9/93) music (John Keane).....*NA*
LOVE BOAT (USA 77) Title theme (Charles Fox-Paul Willia
      ms) *see Coll* 'TELEVISION'S GREATEST HITS VOLUME 3'
LOVE DIVIDED A (C4/C.Contact 3/6/91) mus: (Sabreen)..*NA*
LOVE FOR LYDIA (LWT 77) Theme (Harry Rabinowitz) *see Co
      llection* 'HIT THEMES 1 BEST OF BRITISH TV MUSIC'
LOVE HURTS (BBC/Alomo 3/1/92-1994) mus (Alan Hawkshaw)
      "Love Hurts" sung by PETER POLYCARPOU -S/T- album:
      EMI:CDSTM 4 (CD) TCSTM 4 (Cass) title theme also on
      EMI: CDEM 259 (CDs) TCEM 259 (Cass) EM 259 (7"s)
LOVE LUST & LONELINESS (BBC1 20/4/93) m.(David Lowe).*NA*
LOVEJOY (BBC1 10/1/86-1994) theme (Denis King) *see Coll*
      'LOVEJOY AND OTHER ORIGINAL TV THEMES'
LOVERS The (Granada 71) Theme (Derek Hilton) *see Collec*
      'GRANADA STUDIOS SOUVENIR ALBUM'
LUCKY CHANCES (USA/ITV 29/7/92) m:(Billy Goldenberg).*NA*
LUCKY LADDERS (Anglia 21/3/88) music (Mike Moran)....*NA*
LUV (BBC1 9/3/93) theme mus 'Intermezzo from Cavalleria
      Rusticana' (Mascagni) *on* 'ESSENTIAL CLASSICS' *DG
      Poly: 431 541-2 (2CD) -4 (2Cass)* also on 'CLASSICS
      OF THE SILVER SCREEN' *Telarc (Conif): CD 80221 (CD)*

MACGREGOR ACROSS SCOTLAND (BBC1/Wildview Prod 18/7/92)
      theme music (Jimmie MacGregor) incidental music by
      Dougie MacLean. examples on 'Craigie Dhu' album on
      Dunkeld (Celtic Music/Topic): DUN 001 (CD/Cass)
MACGYVER (USA-88)(BBC1 8/4/89)theme mus (Randy Edelman)
      see Coll 'AMERICAN TV THEMES VOLUME 2'
MADAGASCAR: ISLAND OF GHOSTS (SURVIVAL) Anglia 13/11/91
      Orig music: ROSSY on 'Island Of Ghosts' *Real World
      (Virgin): CDRW 19 (CD) RWMC 19 (Cass)*
MADE IN HEAVEN (Granada 24/7/90) Theme "Love Is The Swe
      etest Thing" (Ray Noble) sung by PETER SKELLERN on
      'Skellern' *Ariola (BMG): 260 490 (CD) 410 490 (Cas)*
      AL BOWLLY with RAY NOBLE *EMI: CZ 306 (CD)*
MADE IN THE USA (C4/Panoptic 24/4/92) theme music (Pop
      Tarts and Jimmy Harry).........................*NA*
MAGIC CROWN The (Border 24/5/91)(Eduardo Armentaros).*NA*

MAGIC OR MEDICINE (Primedia/C4 14/6/93) Music composed
  and performed by Aaron Davis and John Lang.......*NA*
MAGIC ROUNDABOUT The (BBC1 64) Theme (Alain Legrand)
  see Coll 'THEMES FROM CHILDREN'S BBC'
MAGNUM; P.I. (USA from 80) Theme music (Mike Post-Peter
  Carpenter) *see Coll* 'MAGNUM P.I.'/'CAGNEY & LACEY'
  'TELEVISION MUSIC OF MIKE POST & PETE CARPENTER'
MAHABARAHTA (C4 9/12/90 Music composed and performed by
  TOSHI TCHUCHITORI -S/T- on *Real World (Virgin-Poly)*
  CDRW 9 (CD) RWLP 9 (LP) RWMC 9 (Cass)
MAHABARAT (BBC2 14/4/90) 91 pt Hindi serial / Playback
  singer: MAHENDRA KAPOOR on "Dillan Dee Gal" on *Star*
  (Backs): SSRLP 5106 (LP) SC 5106 (Cass)
MAIDEN VOYAGES (20:20 prod for C4 26/4/93) title music
  (Mary and Andrew Phillips)......................*NA*
MAIGRET (BBC1 1961)Theme (Ron Grainer) *see Coll* 'A-Z OF
  BRITISH TV THEMES'/'TV CLASSICS VOLUME 2'
MAIGRET (Granada 9/2/91) Theme music (Nigel Hess) *Eagle*
  (BMG): EAGLE 14 (7"s) vocal by OLIVE SIMPSON *see*
  Coll 'MAIGRET & OTHER TV THEMES'
MAIN EVENT The (BBC1/Grundy 1/5/93) mus: (Rick Turk).*NA*
MAKING ADVANCES (BBC1 26/7/93) music (Alan Lawrence).*NA*
MAKING HAY (C4/Fulmar 31/5/93) theme music "Galop" by
  Leslie Howard (in style of Shostakovich).........*NA*
MAKING OUT (BBC1 6/1/89) Theme music "Vanishing Point"
  NEW ORDER - *Factory (Pin): FACD 263 (CDsingle)* also
  vocal version on 'Technique' - *Factory FACT 275(LP)*
  FACT 275C (CS) FACD 275 (CD) -with incidental music
MAKING TIME (BBC1 7/3/93) music (Mark Pringle).......*NA*
MALGUDI DAYS (C4 P.Raag-21/4/91) music (Sharang Dev).*NA*
MAN ALIVE (BBC2 82) Theme music (Tony Hatch) *see Collec*
  'A-Z OF BRITISH TV THEMES'/'TV CLASSICS VOLUME 3'
MAN FROM U.N.C.L.E. The (USA/NBC/MGM 1964-1967) reshown
  (BBC2 fr 11/9/92) Theme music (Jerry Goldsmith) *see*
  Collect:'MAN FROM UNCLE-MUSIC FROM CULT TV CLASSICS'
  'TELEVISION'S G.HITS VOL.1'/'GREAT TV THEMES VOL.4'
MAN IN A SUITCASE (ITC 27/9/67-68) Theme (Ron Grainer)
  see Coll 'A-Z OF BRITISH TV THEMES'/'TV CLASSICS V2'
MAN ON THE RIM (Australia/ABC 88/BBC1 6/8/93) original
  music (Peter Best)...............................*NA*
MAN WHO LIVED AT THE RITZ The (USA-88-ITV-11/8/91) mus:
  (Richard Rodney Bennett) add.mus.(Alan Snelling).*NA*
MANCUSO FBI (USA)(BBC1 3/9/90) theme music (Susan Hamil
  ton-Doug Katsaros) *see Coll* AMERICAN TV THEMES V.1
MANHATTAN CABLE (C4 (USA)1/5/91) theme mus (POP TARTS &
  C.P.ROTH) on *World Of Wonder (Pacific): WOW 24 (LP)*
MANNIX (USA/1967-74) Theme music (Lalo Schifrin) *see*
  Collect:'MAN FROM UNCLE-MUSIC FROM CULT TV CLASSICS'
MANOR OF ULLOA The (TVE Spain 85/C4-8/8/91) music by
  (Juan J.Garcia Caffi)............................*NA*
MAP OF DREAMS (C4 1/87) Music composer/performer (Bill
  Nelson) -S/T- *Cocteau: JCCD (CD) deleted*
MAPP AND LUCIA (C4 LWT 14/4/85) Theme (Jim Parker) on
  'Off The Record' *Sierra: FEDD 1010 (2LP) deleted*

MARCH OF TIME The (C4 13/9/89) Theme song "Now" (Robert Wright-George Forrest) from Musical 'The Song Of Norway' by PERRY COMO also by AL MARTINO *deleted*

MARCO (Thames 15/3/90) Link music "Workin'On It"(C.Rea) CHRIS REA on 'New Light Through Old Windows' - *WEA: WX 200(C)(CD)* / Theme (Michael A.Moran) *unavailable*

MARCUS WELBY MD (USA 68) *see Collec* 'TELEVISION'S GREATEST HITS VOL.3'

MARKSMAN The (BBC1 4/12/87)Music (Peter Filleul-Richard Thompson) "My Time" sung by CHRISTINE COLLISTER on -S/T- *BBC: REB 660 (LP) ZCF 660 (Cass) all deleted*

MARLENE MARLOWE INVESTIGATES (BBC1 25/9/93) music (Ken Bolam)..*NA*

MARRIED WITH CHILDREN (USA ITV 8/1/89) Theme "Love And Marriage" (S.Cahn-J.Van Huesen) orig: FRANK SINATRA 'Capitol Coll.Series' *Capitol (EMI): C4-92160 (Cas) also by var.artists on PMF (Kingdom): 90681-2 (CD)*

MARSHAL The (HTV 24/4/93) music arranged by Mark Thomas "Concerto Grosso" for Oboe & Strings (Allesandro Marcello) *various recordings on CD and Cass*

MARSHALL CHRONICLES The (USA 90/C4 11/7/91) Music and end title theme (Barry Goldberg) Song "Falling In Love" composed & sung by RANDY NEWMAN on 'Land Of Dreams' *W.BROS (WEA): K925782-2 (CD)-4(Cass)-1(LP)*

MARY TYLER MOORE SHOW (USA 70) Theme (Sonny Curtis) *see Coll* 'TELEVISION'S GREATEST HITS VOL.2'

MARY WHITEHOUSE EXPERIENCE BBC2 3/1/91 (Simon Brint).*NA*

M*A*S*H (USA 71-84 BBC2) Theme "Suicide Is Painless" (J.Mandel-M.Altman) THE MASH *Old Gold: OG 9759 (7")* *see Collection* 'GREAT TV THEMES Volume 1'

MASTERCHEF (BBC1 2/7/90) music (Richard G.Mitchell)..*NA*

MASTERMIND (BBC 72-93)Theme "Approaching Menace" (Neil Richardson) *see under* collection 'SOUNDS VISUAL'

MATCH OF THE DAY (BBC1 from 1970) Theme (Barry Stoller) *see Coll* 'GREAT TV THEMES VOLUME 4'

MATCH The (Coca-Cola Cup)theme "You Are The Number One" (Mike Rutherford) UNION feat Paul Young (Mike & The Mechanics) *Jive (BMG):JIVECD 309 (CDs) JIVE 309 7"s*

MATCH The (ITV Sport 30/10/88) Theme "Goal Crazy" (Rod Argent-Peter Van Hooke) *see Coll* '20 TOP TV THEMES'

MATTERS OF TASTE (C4 2/1/91) (N.B-Powell-Tim Walter).*NA*

MAVERICK (USA 57) Title theme (Paul Francis Webster-David Buttolph) *see Coll* 'GREAT WESTERN THEMES'

MAVIS CATCHES UP WITH...(Pineapple Prod/Thames 15/9/92) theme music (Dominick Miller......................*NA*

MAX MONROE: LOOSE CANNON (USA 90) Theme music "Tied Up" (Dieter Meyer-Boris Blank) by YELLO on their 'Flag' album *Mercury (Poly): 836426-2 (CD) -4(Cass) -1(LP)*

MAY TO DECEMBER (BBC1 3/4/89)Theme mus "September Song" (Kurt Weill-Maxwell Anderson) from 'Knickerbocker Holiday'(44)'September Affair'(50) *TV version....NA* MATT MONRO *MFP: CDMFP 6003(CD)* FRANK SINATRA *Capit: ED260177-4 (Cass)* KEN MACKINTOSH ORCH 'Mac's Back' *President: PLCD 532 (CD) other versions available..*

ME AND MY GIRL (LWT 31/8/84) Theme (Peter Skellern) *see*
    Coll '20 GREAT TV THEMES'
ME YOU AND HIM (Thames) m:(Lawrence Frewer-Nick King)*NA*
MEASURE FOR MEASURE (BBC2/Windfall 6/5/93) theme music
    (Brendan Croker).......................................*NA*
MEDAL OF HONOR (USA TV Ser) Symphonic Score (Richard
    Stone) *Import (Silva Screen): PCD 106 (CD)*
MEDIC (USA 55) Theme "Blue Star" (Victor Young-Edward
    Heyman) GLEN GRAY CASA LOMA ORCH *Capitol: EMS 1147
    (LP) TC (Cas)* CYRIL STAPLETON- *Decca RFLD 49 (2LPs)*
MEDICS (Granada 31/3/92) music (Jonathan Whitehead)..*NA*
MEDICS (Granada 14/11/90) orig music (Robert Lockhart)
    performed by BLACK..................................*NA*
MEGAMANIA (Thames 8/4/92) music (Michael Burdett)....*NA*
MELVIN & MAUREEN (BBC1 9/1/92) mus (Jonathan Cohen)..*NA*
MEMENTO (C4 15/4/93) music score (Michael Kamen).....*NA*
MEN (USA)(ITV 8/2/92) theme (James Newton Howard) *see*
    Coll 'AMERICAN TV THEMES PRIMTIMEE COLL.VOL.2'
MEN BEHAVING BADLY (Thames 18/2/92) mus (Alan Lisk)..*NA*
MEN TALK (C4 23/7/92) theme music (Nigel Beaham-Powell-
    Bella Russell).....................................*NA*
MEN'S ROOM The (BBC2 25/9/91) music (Andy Roberts) end
    song"I Am A Woman" (Andy Roberts-Sarah Jane Morris)
    sung by SARAH JANE MORRIS..........................*NA*
MERLIN OF THE CRYSTAL CAVE (BBC1 11/91) Music score by
    (Francis Shaw) MUNICH SYMPHONY ORCH (Francis Shaw)
    Silva Screen (Conifer): FILMCD 089 (CD)
MIAMI VICE (USA orig BBC1 4/2/85) Theme (JAN HAMMER)
    'Best Of Miami Vice' *MCA: 241 746-2/-4/-1(CD/Cs/LP)*
    'MIAMI VICE 1' including theme and items by Glenn
    Frey-Chaka Khan-Tina Turner-Phil Collins-Mel Melle
    MCA (BMG): MCLD 19024 (CD) MCLC 19024 (Cass)
    MIAMI VICE 2' theme + items by Phil Collins-Gladys
    Knight-Steve Jones-Andy Taylor-Roxy Music-Patti Lab
    elle - *MCA (BMG): MCLD 19090 (CD) MCLC 19090 (Cass)*
    "ESCAPE FROM TELEVISION" (Jan Hammer Collection) -
    MCA: MCAD 10410 (CD) MCAC 10410 (Cass)
MICHAEL BALL (Carlton 8/7/93) Music dir (Michael Reed)
    album "Always" *Polydor: 519 666-2 (CD) -4 (Cass)*
MICHAEL WINNER'S TRUE CRIMES - *see* 'TRUE CRIMES'
MIDNIGHT CALLER (USA)(BBC 28/1/89) theme (Brad Fiedel)
    see Coll 'AMERICAN TV THEMES VOL.1'
MIKE & ANGELO (Thames 17/10/91) mus (David Stafford).*NA*
MIKE HAMMER (USA 83 revival) Theme "Harlem Nocturne"
    (Earle Hagen) KEN MACKINTOSH ORCH on 'Mac's Back'
    President: PLCD 532 (CD) see coll 'MAGNUM PI'
MILLENIUM (BBC2 UK/Canada Co-Prod 3/1/93) Music score
    (Hans Zimmer) music arranged and performed by Mark
    Mancina -S/T- *Narada Cinema (Pinn): ND 66001 (CD)*
MINDER (Thames 11/9/80) "I Could Be So Good For You"
    (Gerard Kenny-Pat Waterman) orig DENNIS WATERMAN on
    EMI 5009 7"s deleted see Coll GREAT TV THEMES V.1'
MINE EYES HAVE SEEN THE GLORY (C4 7/3/93) orig music by
    (Jim Parker)..*NA*

MINI-DRAGONS (BBC2 27/8/92)ser.mus (Richard Einhorn).*NA*
MIRACULOUS MELLOPS (C4/(Austr)20/9/92) theme "We Need A
   Miracle" (Chris Harriott-Dennis Watkins).........*NA*
MIRIAM STOPPARD HEALTH & BEAUTY (Yorkshire TV 23/7/92)
   music composed and performed (Adrian Burch)......*NA*
MISS MARPLE (BBC1 from 26/12/84) theme music (Alan Blai
   kely-Ken Howard) theme & incidental music on -S/T-
   EMI: CDEMC 3648 (CD) TCEMC 3648 (Cass)
MISS WORLD (shared between BBC/ITV until 1988) - Theme
   "Miss World" (W.Pritchard) *Col* 'MORE FAMOUS THEMES'
MISSION EUREKA (C4 24/7/91) mus (Paul Vincet Gunia)..*NA*
MISSION IMPOSSIBLE (USA 60s re-run BBC2 87) Music (Lalo
   Schifrin) plus NEW 91 series music (John E.Davis)
   -S/T- *GNP (S.Screen): GNPD(GNP-5) 8029 (CD-Cass)*
MISTER MEN (BBC1 73) - *see under* 'Mr.Men'
MISTRAL'S DAUGHTER (ITV 16/5/93 orig 1/1/86) music by
   (Vladimir Cosma) -S/T- *Carrere deleted* / theme song
   "Only Love" (V.Cosma-N.Gimbel) sung by NANA MOUSKOU
   RI on Hits Collect *Polydor:836 497-2 (CD) -4 (Cass)*
MISTRESS OF SUSPENSE (HTV 25/8/92)m:(Georges Delerue)*NA*
MISTRESS The (UKGO 2/7/93 orig BBC2 17/1/85) *Theme* Over
   ture Italian Girl In Algiers" (Rossini) *(many vers)*
   Link mus 'A Girl In Winter (Alan Tarney) SKY *Ariola*
MODEL WORLD (BBC1 9/88) Theme 'Trains & Boats & Planes'
   (B.Bacharach-H.David) SHADOWS on *MFP: CDMFP 6002 CD*
   BILLY J.KRAMER *EMI: EG260189-1(LP) MFP: HR8150(Cas)*
MOJO WORKING (C4 24/6/692) theme mus (Graeme Pleeth).*NA*
MOMENT OF TRUTH (Clark/C4 10/6/93) m:(Marina Mowatt).*NA*
MONARCHY The (LWT 16/8/92) theme music (Steve Nieve).*NA*
MONEY PROGRAMME The (BBC2 4/66-88) 'Theme From The Carp
   etbaggers' (Elmer Bernstein) 'The Cat' JIMMY SMITH
   Verve: 810 046-2 (CD) / 1989-94 theme *not available*
MONKEES The (USA 66) Theme (Tommy Boyce-Bobby Hart) THE
   MONKEES *Old Gold: OG 9123 (7"s)* also on'Then & Now-
   Best Of The Monkees' *Arista: 257874(CD) 407874(Cas)*
MONTY PYTHON'S FLYING CIRCUS (BBC2 5/10/69-1974) Theme
   music "Liberty Bell March" (John Phillip Sousa)
   following items are on *Charisma/Virgin* except*
   'Another M.Python Record'*CASCD 1049 (CD) CHCMC 79*
   'Contractual Obligation' *CASCD 1152 (CD) CHCMC 34*
   'Instant Record Collection'*CASCD(MC) 1134 (CD/Cass)*
   'Live At Drury Lane'*(EMI•) CDVIP 104 (CD) TCVIP 104*
   'Matching Tie and Handkerchief' *CASCD 1080 (CD)*
   'Monty Python Sings' *MONT(C)(D) 1 (LP/Cass/CD)*
   'Monty P.Previous Record' *CASCD 1063 (CD) CHCMC 80*
   'The Holy Grail'-S/T-*CASCD 1103 (CD) CHCMC 17 (Cas)*
   'The Final Rip-Off' *Virgin CDMP1 (CDx2) MPDC1(Cass)*
MOOMIN (TVI Finl/Marina Fra/BBC1 7/9/93) open/closing
   music (Pierre Kartner) score (Sumio Shiratori)...*NA*
MOON AND SON (UKGO 16/6/93 orig BBC1 4/1/92) mus (Denis
   King) *see Coll* 'LOVEJOY & OTHER ORIGINAL TV THEMES'
MOONLIGHTING (USA BBC2 29/5/86) Title theme (Al Jarreau
   Lee Holdridge) AL JARREAU 'Moonlighting' *MCA (BMG):
   MCLD(MCLC)19091 (CD/Cass) Col1* 'GREAT TV THEMES V2'

MOP AND SMIFF (BBC1 4/4/85) Theme "Two Of A Kind" -MIKE
   AMATT *see Coll* 'THEMES FROM CHILDREN'S BBC'
MORE THAN A GAME (BBC1 19/5/92) music (David Chilton-
   Nick Russell-Pavier)............................*NA*
MORE WINNERS (C4 Austr.27/5/91) music (Michael Atkinson
   and Yuri Worontschak)...........................*NA*
MORECAMBE & WISE SHOW The (BBC1 66-84) Various themes:
   "Bring Me Sunshine"/"Positive Thinkin'"/"We Get Alo
   ng So Easily Don't You Agree" sung by MORECAMBE and
   WISE on 'Get Out Of That' *EMI: ECC 29 (Cass only)*
MORK AND MINDY (USA 78 / C4 16/3/93) theme music (Perry
   Botkin Jnr) *see Collection* '4 AMERICA TWO'
MOSAIC (BBC1 22/11/92) music (Xian Vassie)...........*NA*
MOTOR SHOW The (Gran 29/3/92) music (Kevin Malpass)..*NA*
MOTORCITY MUSIC YEARS (C4 8/9/93) theme music co-produc
   ed by Delroy Maclean-Brian Travers...............*NA*
MOTORMOUTH (TVS from 3/9/88) Theme music (Peter Miller-
   Ian Porter) MR.MILLER-MR.PORTER '20 TOP TV THEMES'
MOUNTBATTEN *see under* 'Lord Mountbatten'
MOVE OVER DARLING (BBC1 5/3/90) "Move Over Darling" (T.
   Melcher-Hal Kantner-Joe Lubin) DORIS DAY on 'A Port
   rait Of Doris Day' *Stylus: SMD(C)(R)984 (CD/Cas/LP)*
   note: TV version by PAMELA STEPHENSON *not available*
MOVIE GAME The (BBC1 3/4/91) music (Stan Shaw).......*NA*
MOVIE MAHAL (C4 10/9/89) Selec.of Indian Film -S/T- mus
   ic on 'Movie Mahal Vol.1' - *Globestyle-Ace (Sterns-
   Pin): CDORBAD 054 (CD) ORBAD 054 (LP) Vol.2 CDORBAD
   056 (CD) ORBAD 056 (LP) Vol.3 CDORBAD 059 (CD) & LP*
MOVIEWATCH (C4 17/1/93) music (Jonathan Whitehead)...*NA*
MR.& MRS. (Border 18/1/84) theme music "Be Nice To Each
   Other" (T.Hatch-Jackie Trent) TONY HATCH and JACKIE
   TRENT *see Collect* 'TV CLASSICS VOLUME 4' *(Castle)*
MR.BENN (BBC1 from 1970) Theme (Don Warren)on 'Military
   Bands Play Favourite Themes' *Conifer: CFRC 503 (LP)*
MR.BLOBBY - see under NOEL'S HOUSE PARTY
MR.DON AND MR.GEORGE (C4 25/8/93) Mus (Pete Baikie)..*NA*
MR.ED (USA 60 re-run C4 3/87) *see Coll* 'TELEVISION'S GR
   EATEST HITS VOLUME 1'
MR.LUCKY (USA CBS 59/Brav 8/9/93) theme music (Henry Ma
   ncini) on 'Mancini's Greatest Hits' CINCINNATI POPS
   ORCHESTRA (Erich Kunzel) *Telarc (Con) CD 80183 (CD)*
MR.MAGOO (USA Cartoon 50's) *see Coll* 'TELEVISION'S GREA
   TEST HITS VOLUME 3'
MR.MEN & LITTLE MISSES (BBC1 76) Arthur Lowe-Pauline Co
   llins-John Alderton - *MSD: KIDM 9002/3 (Cassettes)*
MR.PALFREY OF WESTMINSTER (Thames 5/85) Theme music:
   'Oboe Concerto No.2 in D.Min Op.9'(Tomaso Albinoni)
MR.ROSE (Granada 17/2/67-5/12/68) theme music "Mr.Rose
   Investigates" (Snow) *see Coll* 'TV CLASSICS VOL.3'
MR.SMITH'S GARDENING PROGRAMMES (BBC2 78-85) Theme "Pip
   er In The Meadow" (Trad.) YORKSHIRE IMPERIAL METALS
   BAND - *Polyphonic: (C)PRL 006 (Cass/LP)* also by THE
   GRENADIER GUARDS on *MFP: CC 247 (CD) HR 8176 (Cass)*
   see also 'Geoffrey Smith's World Of Flowers' (BBC)

MR.WAKEFIELD'S CRUSADE (BBC2 Wales 22/4/92) music score
   (Rachel Portman) conducted by David Snell........**NA**
MR.WROE'S VIRGINS (BBC2 24/2/93) music composed and per
   formed by Roger Eno-Brian Eno....................**NA**
MUNSTERS The (USA 63) Title theme (Jack Marshall) **see**
   Coll 'TELEVISION'S G.HITS V.1' **and** '4 AMERICA TWO'
MULBERRY (BBC1 24/2/92) theme song "These Are Mulberry
   Days" (Chris Adonis-Chris Nicolaides) arranged by
   Steve Parr and sung by KARL HOWMAN...............**NA**
MUPPET SHOW The (ITV 76/BBC1 86) Theme (Sam Pottle) **see**
   Coll'GREAT TV THEMES VOL.1'/'TELEVISION'S G.HITS 3'
MURDER IN EDEN (BBC1 NI 19/7/91) music (Bill Connor).**NA**
MURDER MOST HORRID (BBC2 14/11/91) Title theme (Simon
   Brint) sung by Ruby Turner......................**NA**
MURDER OF QUALITY,A (Thames 10/4/91) music score (Stanl
   ey Myers).......................................**NA**
MURDER ORDAINED (USA 87/BBC1 20/7/92) mus(Mark Snow).**NA**
MURDER SHE WROTE USA (ITV 26/5/85) theme (John Addison)
   see Coll 'AMERICAN TV THEMES VOL.1'
MURDER SQUAD (Thames 4/2/92) music (Martin Kiszko)...**NA**
MURDERERS AMONG US (TV Mini-series) Music score (Bill
   Conti) -S/T- **Bay Cities (S.Screen): BCD 3004 (CD)**
MUSHROOM PICKER The (BBC2 3/2/93)mus (Roger Jackson).**NA**
MUSIC GAME The (C4/HTV 8/5/92)music different each week
MUSICAL ROUTES (Music Box prod for YTV 21/5/93) Theme
   music (Adrian Burch-David Whitaker)..............**NA**
MY BROTHER TOM (Australia 86/C4-6/7/91) music score by
   (Garry McDonald and Laurie Stone)...............**NA**
MY DEAD DAD (C4/Scottish TV Prod 28/7/92) **Opening theme**
   "Nothing But Blue Skies" arr: Dave Mindel-Don Gould
   sung by JOCELYN BROWN / **Closing theme** "What Goes Up
   Must Come Down" arr: Dave Mindel-Don Gould sung by
   TOMMY BLAZE / **also used** "Can't Quit Your Love"...**NA**
MY FAMILY AND OTHER ANIMALS (BBC1 17/10/87) Theme compo
   sed by Daryl Runswick with Ken Barry (whistling)
   Collec 'BEST OF BBC TV THEMES' **deleted**
MY SECRET IDENTITY (ITV Canada/Telefilm/Sunrise-2/9/91)
   title song composed and performed by FRED MOLLIN.**NA**
MY TWO DADS (USA C4 from 10/5/90) theme "You Can Count
   On Me" (Greg Evigan-Lenny Macallso-Michael Jacobs)
   see Coll '4 AMERICA'
MY WILDERNESS REPRIEVED (BBC2 8/4/93) Theme music "Minu
   et" from 'A Downland Suite' (John Ireland) ENGLISH
   CHAMBER ORCHESTRA (Conduct: David Garforth) **Chandos
   (Chandos): CHAN 8390 (CD) ABTD 1112 (Cass)**
MYSTERIES OF EDGAR WALLACE The (ITV 60's) Theme "Man Of
   Mystery" (Michael Carr) by THE SHADOWS 'In The 60s'
   MFP (EMI): CDMFP 6076 (CD) (TC)MFP 5873 (Cass/LP)

NAKED CITY (Rapido Prod/C4 23/7/93) title theme music
   (Comanchee Creek) music editor (John Godfree)....**NA**
NAKED CITY The (USA 58-62) Theme music (Billy May) KEN
   MACKINTOSH OR 'Mac's Back' **President: PLCD 532 (CD)**
NAKED HOLLYWOOD (BBC2 24/2/91) music (Roger Bolton)..**NA**

NAKED VIDEO (BBC2 Scot 12/5/86) mus (David McNiven)..*NA*
NAME OF THE ROOM (BBC2 4/1/93) music (Elizabeth Parker:
  BBC Radiophonic Workshop).........................*NA*
NANNY KNOWS BEST (BBC1 12/9/93) music (Ken Bolam)....*NA*
NAT KING COLE SHOW (USA 1957) (C4 8/4/90) Songs From TV
  Series sung by NAT KING COLE on 'Shooting High' on
  Capitol (EMI): (CD)(TC)EMS 1370 (CD/Cass/LP)
NATION (BBC2 28/7/92) Music (David Arch).............*NA*
NATURAL LIES (BBC1 31/5/92) music (Richard Harvey)...*NA*
  song "Endless Sleep" (Jody Reynolds-Dolores Nance)
  JODY REYNOLDS (1959) *Old Gold: OG 9015 (7")* also on
  Magnum Force (MMG): MFLP 066 (LP) also recorded by
  MARTY WILDE *Philips: 848 168-2 (CD) 848 168-4(Cass)*
NATURE (BBC2 3/4/92) music (Elizabeth Parker) BBC RW.*NA*
NATURE PERFECTED (C4 15/11/91) music (Max Early).....*NA*
NATURE WATCH (Centr 26/5/92) theme (Paul Buckmaster).*NA*
NEAREST AND DEAREST (Granada 72) Theme (Derek Hilton)
  see Collection 'GRANADA STUDIOS SOUVENIR ALBUM'
NEAT AND TIDY (USA C4 12/2/88) "Guitar Man"(Jerry Reed)
  by ELVIS PRESLEY *RCA: PD 89473 (CD) NL(NK) 89168*
NEIGHBOURS (Australia 85 BBC1 27/10/86-94)*Theme* (Jackie
  Trent-Tony Hatch) orig BARRY CROCKER version on
  Pickwick: HSC 645 (Cass) PWKS 645 (CD)
NELLIE THE ELEPHANT (Central 8/1/90) Theme (Peter Hart-
  Ralph Butler) LULU *Phonogram: NEL(MC) 1 deleted*
  MANDY MILLER *on* Coll 'HELLO CHILDREN EVERYW..Vol.1'
NEVER MIND THE QUALITY, FEEL THE WIDTH! (UKGO 6/9/93 or
  ig ABC/Thames 25/11/67) theme music (Bob Miller).*NA*
NEVER THE TWAIN (UKGold 6/11/92 orig Thames 7/9/81) mus
  (Jack Trombey)...................................*NA*
NEW ADVENTURES OF BLACK BEAUTY (LWT 1/9/90) Theme "Gall
  oping Home" (Denis King)*see* Coll '20 TOP TV THEMES'
NEW AGE (C4 27/1/91)mus (Mike Ray-Lorraine Anderson).*NA*
NEW ATTITUDE (BBC2 USA-29/10/90) music (Kurt Farquhar)
  theme sung by SHERYL LEE RALPH...................*NA*
NEW AVENGERS The (IDTV 22/10/76-78) Theme Music (Laurie
  Johnson) *see* Coll 'ROSE AND THE GUN'/'ITV THEMES'
NEW FACES OF.. (Central 10/9/88) Title theme (Ed Welch)
  1ch) *Grasmere (Tayl): GRASS 2 (7")* & 'Blockbusters'
NEW LASSIE The (USA 89 BBC1 3/6/91) theme music (Al Bur
  ton-Timothy Thompson and whistle by Les Baxter)..*NA*
NEW STATESMAN The (C4 9/87) Theme "Promenade" 'Pictures
  At An Exhibition" (Mussorgsky) arr.by Alan Hawkshaw
NEWMAN & BADDIEL IN PIECES (BBC2 20/9/93) theme music
  (The SUNDAYS)....................................*NA*
NEWHART (USA)(C4 12/7/86) theme music (Henry Mancini)
  see Coll 'AMERICAN TV THEMES VOLUME 1'
NEWS AT TEN (ITN 3/7/67-93) Theme "The Awakening" '20th
  Century Portrait'(JOHNNY PEARSON) orig full version
  see Coll 'SOUNDS VISUAL' *see also under* 'ITN NEWS'
NEWSNIGHT (BBC2 from 28/1/80) theme (George Fenton)..*NA*
NEXT BIG THING The (Wild+Fresh Pr.for C4 25/4/93) theme
  music (Julian Stewart Lindsay)...................*NA*
NICE TOWN (BBC2 18/11/92 music score (Colin Towns)...*NA*

NICE WORK (BBC2 4/10/89) music (Rachel Portman)......*NA*
NIGEL MANSELL'S INDIE CAR 93 (Carlton 17/7/93) theme by
  Steve Duberry *not available* / incidental music "The
  Beatmaster's Tribal Buzz Mix" by The SHAMEN on *One*
  Little Indian (Pinn): 88TP12 (12") 88TP7CD (CDsing)
NIGHT COURT (USA/ITV 91) Theme music (Jack Elliott)
  see Coll 'AMERICAN TELEVISION THEMES VOL.3'
NIGHT OF THE RED HUNTER (New Zealand/BBC1 23/7/92) md
  (Peter Blake) recording and mix (Graham Ridding).*NA*
NIGHTINGALES (C4 27/2/90) Theme "A Nightingale Sang In
  Berkeley Square" (Eric Maschwitz-Jack Strachey-Mann
  ing Sherwin) *TV ver.(Clever Music)..NA* / PALM COURT
  THEATRE ORCH + LINDA MURRAY *Chandos: CHAN 8856 (CD)*
NIGHTMARE YEARS The (C4 9/5/92) mus (Vladimir Cosma).*NA*
NIGHTSHIFT (BBC2 23/5/93) music (David Poore)........*NA*
999: (BBC1 Bristol 25/6/92) theme mus (Roger Bolton).*NA*
NINETIES The (BBC2 28/3/93) music (Martin Kiszko)....*NA*
NO EASY WALK (C4 29/8/87) Theme "No Easy Walk To Freed
  om" JANET KAY *Local/CSA:7(12)LR 012 (7"/12")deleted*
NO FRILLS (BBC1 5/9/88) Theme "Swipesy Cakewalk" (Scott
  Joplin) on 'Joplin's Greatest Hits' with DICK HYMAN
  RCA Victor (BMG): GD 60842 (CD) GK 60842 (Cass)
NO HIDING PLACE (ITV 16/9/59-67) Theme (Laurie Johnson)
  see Coll'A-Z OF BRITISH TV THEMES'/'TV CLASSICS V4'
NO KIDDING (BBC1-14/10/91) music (Debbie Wiseman)....*NA*
NO LIMITS (BBC2 10/87) Theme (J.King) by Jonathan King
  BBC: RESL 218 (7") and 'Entertainment USA' *deleted*
NO MORE NIGHTINGALES (BBC1 6/10/91) m.(Roger Bolton).*NA*
NODDY (Cosgrove Hall/BBC1 17/9/92) m: (Paul K.Joyce).*NA*
NOEL EDMONDS CONCORDE SPECIAL (BBC1 13/4/90) "Sirius"
  (Alan Parsons) from 'Eye In The Sky' ALAN PARSONS
  PROJECT - *Arista (BMG): 610004 (CD) 204666 (LP)*
NOEL'S ADDICTS (BBC1 P.Mill 14/4/92) music (David Lowe-
  Julian Ronnie)..*NA*
NOEL'S HOUSE PARTY (BBC1 fr.23/11/91) md Ernie Dunstall
  "Mr.Blobby" *Destiny/Total (BMG): CDDMUS 104 (CDs)*
  CADMUS 104 (Cass) DMUS 104 (7"s)
NOMADS (C4 3/9/92) m: Howard J.Davidson (Final Touch)*NA*
NORTH AND SOUTH (USA ITV 8/12/86) music sc (Bill Conti)
  S/T - *Varese (S.Screen): 704 310 (LP) C704 310 (CS)*
  see Coll 'AMERICAN TV THEMES VOLUME 1'
NORTH STAR: THE TV MOVIE (USA 90) theme (Brad Fiedel)
  see Coll 'FANTASTIC TELEVISION THEMES'
NORTHERN EXPOSURE (USA/C4 16/3/92)theme: David Schwartz
  -S/T- *with V/A - MCA (BMG):MCD(MCC) 10685 (CD/Cass)*
  theme also on Coll '4 AMERICA TWO' *see Collections*
NOT ONLY...BUT ALSO... (BBC2 4/11/90 orig 1965) theme
  "Goodbyee" (P.Cook-Dudley Moore) PETE & DUD on 'The
  Clean Tapes' on *RIO (AMT): RDC 1206 (Cass)*
NOT POTS (C4 13/3/90) theme music (Ken Howard).......*NA*
NOT WITH A BANG (LWT 25/3/90) Theme (Rod Argent-Peter
  Van Hooke) ROD ARGENT and PETER VAN HOOKE - *Total*
  (BMG): WEEK 100 (7") c/w 'The Piglet Files' Theme
NOTES AND QUERIES (BBC2 7/1/93)mus (Peter Griffiths).*NA*

NURSES (USA Touchst./C4 28/8/92) theme song "Here I Am"
   (George Aliceson Tipton-John Bettis).............*NA*
NUTT HOUSE The (USA)(BBC2 14/10/89) music (Lance Rubin)
   see Coll 'AMERICAN TV THEMES VOLUME 2'

OASIS (Zenith for Carlton 12/1/93) mus YES/NO PEOPLE.*NA*
OBSESSIONS (BBC2 16/3/92) theme mus (David Stevens)..*NA*
OCEAN CHALLENGE (BBC2 2/5/93) Music by ENYA from albums
   'Watermark' *WEA: 243875-2 (CD) -4 (Cass)* and 'Sheph
   erd Moons' *WEA: 9031 75572-2 (CD) -4 (Cass)*
ODD COUPLE The (USA 70 BBC rerun 89) theme (Neal Hefti)
   see Coll 'GREAT TV THEMES VOLUME 4'
OFF THE BACK OF A LORRY (B.Lapping/BBC1 18/10/92) title
   music (Debbie Wiseman)........................*NA*
OFF THE COURSE (BBC2 Scot 12/1/88)Theme "The Way It Is"
   BRUCE HORNSBY & RANGE *RCA (BMG): PL(PK)(PD) 89901*
OK2 TALK FEELINGS (BBC1 6/1/91) mus (Richard Attree).*NA*
OLD BOY NETWORK (Central 16/2/92) mus (Dave Mackay)..*NA*
OLD COUNTRY (C4 3/6/85) Theme "Recuerdos DeLa Alhambra"
   (Francisco Tarrega) by JOHN WILLIAMS on *CBS 61843
   (LP) 40-61843 (Cass)* / Orig TV Title 'Out Of Town'
OLD DEVILS The (BBC2 16/3/92) music (John Altman)....*NA*
OLD GREY WHISTLE TEST (BBC2 Rock Series 70s-80s) Theme
   "Stone Fox Chase" (Buttrey-Haley-McCoy)orig by AREA
   CODE 615 *(Polydor deleted) see also* 'Whistle Test'
OLD MAN AND THE SEA The (Yorkshire / 90) Music by Bruce
   Broughton -S/T- *Intrada (S.Screen): RVF 6008D (CD)*
OLIVER TWIST (UKGO 22/8/93 orig BBC1 13/10/85) theme &
   incidental music (Dudley Simpson)..............*NA*
OLLY'S PRISON (BBC2 28/5/93) Radiophonics: Peter Howell
OLYMPIC GAMES 1992 (BBC 8/92) BBC theme mus "Barcelona"
   (Freddie Mercury-Mike Moran) FREDDIE MERCURY-MONSER
   RAT CABALLE on *Polydor* / Also available: 'BARCELONA
   GAMES MEDLEY LP' famous arias performed by PLACIDO
   DOMINGO-JOSE CARRERAS-MONSERRAT CABALLE-GIACOMO ARA
   GALL-TERESA BERGANZA-JUAN PONS-City Of Barcelona SO
   (G.Navarro) *RCA (BMG): 09026 61204-2 (CD) -4(Cass)*
   'Amigos Para Siempre' (Andrew Lloyd Webber) by JOSE
   CARRERAS-SARAH BRIGHTMAN *(Polydor) /*
OLYMPIC GAMES 1988 (BBC1-2 / ITV-C4 17 Sep-2 Oct 1988)
   FULL DETAILS LISTED IN TELE-TUNES 1993
OLYMPIC WINTER GAMES *see* 'WINTER OLYMPIC GAMES'
ON THE AIR (USA/BBC2 24/7/93) m:(Angelo Badalamenti).*NA*
ON THE BIG HILL (Granada 15/11/88) Music (Guy Fletcher-
   Brendon Croker) on *Silvertone (BMG): ORE(C)(CD) 501*
ON THE LINE (BBC2 17/5/90) Title theme (Hugh Matier-Ste
   ve Martin) JINGLE JANGLES *Coll* '20 TOP TV THEMES'
ON THE UP (BBC1 from 4/9/90) Opening music "Concerto Gr
   ossi in A.op.6 no.11" 1st m/m (Handel) by GUILDHALL
   STRING ENSEMBLE - *RCA (BMG): RD(RK) 87921 (CD/Cass)*
   Closing theme composed and sung by DENNIS WATERMAN
   and arranged by Ray Russell...................*NA*
ONE BY ONE (UKGold 4/11/92 orig BBC1 29/1/84) theme mus
   (Michael Omer)................................*NA*

ONE FAMILY (C4/Fragile 29/12/92) mus (Rajap Dholakia)*NA*
ONE FOOT IN THE GRAVE (BBC1 4/1/90-1994) title song com
posed and sung by ERIC IDLE..................*NA*
ONE FOOT IN THE PAST (BBC2 4/6/93)mus.(Roger Bolton).*NA*
ONE GAME The (Central 4/6/88) Theme "Saylon Dola"(Nigel
Hess) sung by CHAMELEON *see Coll* 'FAVÓURITE TV THEM
ES'/'20 GREAT TV THEMES' also *Eagle: FLY(CD)(MC)100*
ONE IN FOUR (BBC2 2/2/87) Theme (Mark Williams-Pino Fru
miento) HEART & SOUL *see* Collect.'20 Top TV Themes'
ONE MAN AND HIS DOG (BBC2 1976-1994) Title theme (Alan
Benson) BBC recording..........................*NA*
ONE TO WIN (BBC1 21/9/91) music (Patrick C.Lyons)....*NA*
100 GREAT PAINTINGS (BBC2 5/9/82) Theme "String Quartet
No.11 in F.Minor Op.95" (Beethoven)
100 PER CENT (BBC1 10/1/92) theme music composed & perf
ormed by (That Petrol Emotion)..................*NA*
ONEDIN LINE The (UKGold 5/11/92 orig BBC1 15/10/71) mus
theme 'Adagio' from Spartacus Ballet (Khachaturian)
ONLY FOOLS AND HORSES (BBC1 8/9/81-92) Theme composed
and performed by JOHN SULLIVAN..................*NA*
ONLY JOKING (LWT/Hewland 25/4/92) theme (Simon Webb).*NA*
OPEN ALL HOURS (BBC1 76 rpt 1/91) music (Max Harris).*NA*
OPENING SHOT (LWT 10/7/93) theme arrangement of 'South
Bank Show' theme ("Caprice in A.Minor No.24 from
'Themes and Variations'" (Paganini)..............*NA*
ONE FAMILY (C4/Fragile 29/12/92) mus (Rajap Dholakia)*NA*
OPERATION HOSPITAL (C4 5/1/93) mus (Ronald De Jong)..*NA*
OPINIONS: BRITAIN 93 (Open Media Prod/C4 21/2/93) music
(Robert Lockhart-Steve Parr).....................*NA*
OPPORTUNITY KNOCKS (BBC1 from 31/3/87) theme "Star" (Do
reen Chanter) KIKI DEE 'Spotlight On Kiki Dee' on
Rocket (Poly): 848 359-2(CD) -4(Cass deleted)
OPPOSITES ATTRACT (BBC1 21/9/91) music and songs compos
ed and performed by DEREK GRIFFITHS...............*NA*
ORANGES ARE NOT THE ONLY FRUIT (BBC2 10/1/90) Music by
Rachel Portman - 2 Story Cass *BBC (Pinn): ZBBC 1151*
ORCHESTRA! (C4 6/1/91) Sir Georg Solti and Dudley Moore
Television Guide to Orchestral Music -S/T- from the
series on *Decca: 430 838-2(CD) -4(Cass) -1(LP)*
ORCHID HOUSE The (C4 21/2/91) music (Michael Storey).*NA*
ORDINARY PEOPLE (C4 30/1/90) Theme music "Piano Trio In
G.Minor Opus 11" (Fanny Mendelssohn-Hensel) Cologne
Clementi Trio - *Largo (Impetus): LARGO 5103 (CD)*
ORNAMENTAL KITCHEN GARDEN The (BBC2 28/9/90) Theme "Sal
ut d'Amour" Op.12 (Elgar) - Bournemouth Sinfonietta
Chandos: CHAN 8371 (CD) CBT(CBR) 1016 (Cass/LP)
other mus 'Reverence' (Chris Payne) *(not available)*
OTHER AMERICAS The (Central/C4 12/10/92) theme music by
(Juan Luis Guerra)................................*NA*
OTHER SIDE OF PARADISE (Central 22/2/92) original music
(Martin Armiger)..................................*NA*
OUR BACKYARD (C4 11/6/91) music (Tony Flynn)........*NA*
OUR HOUSE (ITV 60's series) theme music (Maxim-Hudis)
see Coll 'TV CLASSICS VOLUME 3' *(Castle Comm)*

OUT (C4 Alfalfa 26/6/91) music (Julian Wastall)......*NA*
OUT OF AFRICA (Afro Wisdom Prod for C4 11/7/93) music
    (Charlie Hart-Amadouo Saho)....................*NA*
OUT OF DARKNESS (BBC2 7/9/92) title mus (Salif Keita)*NA*
OUT OF SIGHT (C4 Domino 22/3/92) theme m: (Nigel Beaham
    -Powell & Bella Russell)......................*NA*
OUT OF THE RUINS (BBC 7/12/89 -'Aid For Armenia') Music
    score (Michael Nyman) MICHAEL NYMAN on *Silva Screen
    (Conifer): FILMCD 063 (CD) FILMC 063 (Cas)*
OUT OF THIS WORLD (USA 9/4/90)Theme "Swingin'On A Star"
    (Johnny Burke-Jimmy Van Heusen) BIG DEE IRWIN and
    LITTLE EVA on '60s Mix Vol.2' *Stylus: SMD 855 (CD)*
OUT OF TOWN (TVS) - *see under* 'Old Country'
OUTER LIMITS The (USA 63/64) Theme music (Dominic Fron
    tiere) TV -S/T- on *GNP USA (Silva Screen-Conifer):
    GNPD 8032 (CD) GNP5 8032 (Cass)*
OUTSIDE CHANCE: - see BRIAN CONLEY
OUTSIDE TIME (Ffilmiau Br C4 13/8/91) mus (Messiaen).*NA*
OVER MY DEAD BODY (USA 90)(BBC1 11/1/91) theme (Lee Hol
    dridge) *see Coll* 'AMERICAN TELEVISION THEMES VOL.3'
OVER THE RAINBOW (Meridian 11/7/93) mus (Ray Russell)
    lyrics and singer (Angeline Ball)...............*NA*
OWEN MD (BBC1 70s) Theme "Sleepy Shores" Johnny Pearson
    JOHNNY PEARSON ORCH - *Old Gold: OG 9792 (7"s) also
    see Coll* 'SOUNDS VISUAL'/'GREAT TV THEMES VOLUME 1'
OWL TV (C4/Owl TV/Thames 1/8/93) m:(Andrew Phillips).*NA*
    previous theme "Got To Move" (Jonathan Goldsmith-
    Tim Ryan) sung by CREE SUMMER FRANCKS............*NA*
OX TALES (USA 89) music (Haim Saban-Shuki Levy)......*NA*

P's & Q's (BBC2 13/8/92) theme "Goodbye And Thank You"
    FRANK LUTHER from 'Manners Can Be Fun'*not available*
PACIFIC STATION (USA)(C4 27/7/93) theme mus "Rescue Me"
    (Carl Smith-Raynard Miner) performed by Margo Thund
    er-Phaedra Butler-Rise Engermann) *not available*
    orig (1965) version: FONTELLA BASS on "Sisters Of
    Soul" *Roots-Provogue (Pinn-Tayl): RTS 33024 (CD)*
PACKAGE PILGRIMS (Anglia 10/1/93) theme music "Voice Of
    Peace" (Nick Glennie Smith)....................*NA*
PADDINGTON (BBC1 74) Theme "Size Ten Shuffle" (Herbert
    Chappell) *see Coll* 'THEMES FROM CHILDREN'S BBC'
    (BBC) Spoken word cassette with Michael Hordern on
    BBC (Pinn): YBBC 1481 (Cass)
PALLISERS The (UKGO 7/6/93 orig BBC1 74) theme (Herbert
    Chappell) NEW PHILHARMONIA ORCHESTRA *BBC deleted*
PANDORA'S BOX (BBC2 10/6/92) orig music (Jon King-Andy
    Gill)...*NA*
PANORAMA (BBC1 11/11/53-1994) Various Themes including:
    80-94 Theme "Today It's You"Aujourd Hui C'est Toi"
    from 'A MAN AND A WOMAN' (66-Francis Lai) available
    -S/T- Musidisc (Pinn): 10129-2 (CD) -4 (Cass)
    Orig 50s Theme "Openings & Endings" (Robert Farnon)
    on 'London Calling' *Grasmere (Tayl): GRALP(GRTC) 30*
PAPER MAN The (BBC2 8/5/91) music score (Chris Neal).*NA*

PARADISE (USA 88 BBC1 from 5/7/89) mus:Jerrold Immel.*NA*
PARADISE CLUB The (BBC1 19/9/89) Music (David Lawson)
   with Pride-Stan Tracey Big Band-Denis Lotis-Carmel
   -S/T- *BBC: BBCCD(REB)(ZCF) 764 (CD/LP/Cass) deleted*
PARADISE POSTPONED (Thames 15/9/86) Theme '1st movement
   Cello Concerto' (Elgar) *many recordings available*
   Orig Music (Roger Webb) *Columbia: SCX 6706 deleted*
PARALLEL 9 (BBC1/Roach) theme music (Ed Welch).......*NA*
PARAMOUNT CITY (BBC1 25/5/91) theme "Things That Make
   You Go Hmmm" (C.& C.MUSIC FACTORY) *Columbia (Sony)*
   467814-2 (CD) -4 (Cass) -1 (LP)
PARENTHOOD (USA 90 Imagine Prod-MCA /BBC2 4/6/93) theme
   RANDY NEWMAN (title song on Film -S/T- on *Reprise*
   USA (Silva Screen Imp): 926001-2 (CD)
PARKER LEWIS CAN'T LOSE (USA) Theme (Dennis McCarthy)
   see Coll 'AMERICAN TELEVISION THEMES VOL.3'
PARNELL AND THE ENGLISHWOMAN (BBC2 9/1/91) music (Jim
                Parker) theme performed by JAMES GALWAY...*NA*
PARTISANS OF VILNA (TV Doc) Music from orig -S/T- on
   Flying Fish (CMD/Proj): FF70450 (CD) FF90450 (Cass)
PARTNERS IN CRIME (LWT 16/10/83) Mus (Joseph Horovitz)
   performed by RICHARD RODNEY BENNETT-MARIAN MONTGOME
   RY *see Coll* 'HIT THEMES 1-BEST OF BRITISH TV MUSIC'
PARTRIDGE FAMILY The (USA 70) Theme: Hugo Montenegro
   see Coll 'TELEVISION'S GREATEST HITS 2'
PASSION FOR ANGLING (BBC2 5/9/93) m:(Jennie Muskett).*NA*
PASSPORT (BBC1/Mentorn 6/6/93) music (David Mindel)..*NA*
PAST AFLOAT The (BBC1 5/5/85) Theme "Serenade For Strin
   gs In E.Maj Op.22" (Dvorak) *various recordings*
PATRIK PACARD (BBC1 6/4/92) Foreign product.Title song
   post-prod by ECO Studiós.(unidentified vocalist).*NA*
PAUL HOGAN SHOW The (Best Of) (Australia 82 / C4 7/91)
   theme (Tchaikovsky)*Coll* 'AUSTRALIA'S GREATEST HITS'
PAUL MERTON-THE SERIES (C4 25/9/91) Kokomedia music..*NA*
PAVAROTTI IN THE PARK (C4 25/12/91) LUCIANO PAVAROTTI
   The Hyde Park Summer Concert 1991 - *Decca (Polyg):*
   436 320-2 (CD) 436 320-4 (Cass) 436 320-1 (LP)
PEACOCK SCREEN (C4 30/12/91) title mus (Roger White).*NA*
PENMARRIC (UKGold 3/11/92 orig BBC1 12/10/79) theme mus
   (Richard Hartley) *BBC deleted*
PENNIES FROM HEAVEN (BBC2 7/2/90 prev.shown 1/12/1978) ʼ
   1930's music re-recorded from orig 78's / Complete
   recordings of over 65 songs used in the BBC series:
   (orig on BBC) now re-issued on *Connoisseur Collect*
   (Pinn): POTTCD 300 (2CD) POTTMC 300 (2Cass)
PEOPLE FIRST (C4/Same Pr 24/3/92) mus (Paul Riordan).*NA*
PEOPLE'S GAME The (C4 31/3/91) music (Rod Anderson and
   Jason Mayo)....................................*NA*
PERFECT HERO, A (LWT 17/5/91) Theme "The Bells Of Hell
   Go Ting-a-ling-a-ling" (Richard Holmes)..........*NA*
PERFECT SCOUNDRELS (TVS from 22/4/90) mus (2nd series)
   (Nigel Hess) *see Coll* 'MAIGRET & OTHER TV THEMES'
   music (1st ser) Richard Blackford-John Cameron...*NA*
PERPETUAL MOTION (BBC2 2/1/92) music (David Stevens).*NA*

PERRY MASON (USA 58) Theme (Max Steiner) *see Collection*
    TELEVISION'S GREATEST HITS VOLUME 1'
PERRY MASON: CASE OF... (BBC1 13/4/91 USA) theme (Fred
    Steiner) music (Dick de Benedctis)
PERRY MASON: RETURN OF PERRY MASON (BBC-(USA)-31/3/90)
    Theme (Fred Steiner)- JERRY GOODMAN on 'It's Alive'
    Private (BMG): 259642 (CD) 409642 (Cas) 209642 (LP)
PERSUADERS The (ITV 17/9/71-72) Theme mus (John Barry)
    see Collection 'GREAT TV THEMES VOLUME 4'
PETER GUNN (USA 58) Theme (Henry Mancini) DUANE EDDY
    with ART OF NOISE *China: WOLD 2 (LP) ZWOLD 2 (Cass)*
    TV -S/T- *Impt (Silva Screen): 1956-2 (CD) -4 (Cass)*
    see Coll 'MANCINI'S G.HITS'/'GREAT TV THEMES VOL.4'
PETER THE GREAT (USA TV mini series 87) Music (Laurence
    Rosenthal) *S.Screen: SCCD 1011 (CD) FILMC 006 (Cas)*
PHANTOM OF THE OPERA (BBC1 19/8/90) (Charles Dance) Mus
    (John Addison) -S/T- *Coloss.(S.Screen): XCD 1004CD*
PHIL COOL (Central 1/8/92) music dir (Pete Baikie)...*NA*
PICK OF THE WEEK (YTV 6/10/91) theme "Unsquare Dance"
    DAVE BRUBECK on *Elite (Pickwick): ELITE 009CD (CD)*
PICTURE OF HEALTH, A (BBC2 17/7/93) mus (Roger Limb).*NA*
PIG ATTRACTION The (HTV 6/5/93) PINKY & PERKY with TIM
    Tim Whitnall *Telstar (BMG): TCD 2668 (CD) STAC 2668
    (Cass) STAR 2668 (LP)* also available: PINKY & PERKY
    New Song Compilation *EMI: CD(TC)EMS 1470 (CD/Cass)*
PIGLET FILES The (LWT-7/9/90) Theme (R.Argent-P.Van Hoo
    ke) ROD ARGENT-P.VAN HOOKE *Coll* '20 TOP TV THEMES'
PILGRIMAGES (C4 14/11/90) theme mus "Sakura" (Yuqijiro
    Yocoh) played by JOHN WILLIAMS (gtr) on Masterworks
    (Sony): DCT 40140 (Dbl Cass) DC 40140 (Dbl LP) also
PINK PANTHER The (BBC1-2 USA Cart 64) Theme (Henry Manc
    ini) JAMES GALWAY & HENRY MANCINI ORCH on *RCA (BMG)
    RD(RK) 85315 (CD/Cass) Coll* 'MANCINI'S GREAT.HITS'
PINKY AND PERKY (BBC 60's) New Compilation of Songs on
    EMI: CDEMS 1470 (CD) TCEMS 1470 (Cass)
PIRATES OF DARK WATER (USA/BBC1 7/4/92) mus (Tom Chase-
    Steve Rucker) md (Bodie Chandler) Hanna-Barbera..*NA*
PLAIN TALES FROM NORTHERN IRELAND (BBC2 2/9/93) music
    (Michael Klein)..................................*NA*
PLANNED MIRACLE The (BBC2 23/9/91)mus David Ferguson.*NA*
PLAY AWAY / PLAY SCHOOL (BBC1-2 / 1964-88) Songs from
    both series featuring Jonathan Cohen-Brian Cant-Don
    Spencer-Johnny Ball-Rick Jones-Lucie Skeaping-Carol
    Chell-Floella Benjamin-Lionel Morton-Toni Arthur-Jo
    hnny Silvo-Chloe Ashcroft / *MFP: TC-DL 1114 (2Cass)*
PLAY IT SAFE (BBC1 5/1/92) music (Martin Cook)..*NA* also
    used "The Clapping Song" (Lincoln Chase) orig (65)
    SHIRLEY ELLIS *Old Gold: OG 9161 (7"s)*
PLAYBOX (Central 31/10/88)Feat Keith Chegwin-Pat Coombs
    Music from series - *Rio Digital: RD(CASS)LP 1204*
PLAYDAYS: Lizzie Singalong (BBC) *BBC (Pinn): YBBC 1490*
PLAZA PATROL (YTV 15/7/91) theme mus (Alan Hawkshaw).*NA*
PLEASE SIR (LWT 68) theme music (Sam Fonteyn) *see Coll*
    'A-Z OF BRITISH TV THEMES'

POINTS OF VIEW (BBC 2/10/61-94) 80s Theme "When I'm 64" (Lennon-McCartney) BEATLES *Parlophone: CDP 746442-2 (CD)* 91-94 theme (BBC Radio.Workshop) *not available*
POIROT *see under* 'AGATHA CHRISTIE'S POIROT'
POLE TO POLE (BBC1 21/10/92) music (Paddy Kingsland).*NA*
POLICE RESCUE (BBC1 3/4/91 Australia-90) music theme by (Martin Armiger) on Collect "More Great Australian Film & TV Themes" *ABC Australia Imp: 512 306-2 (CD)*
POLICE SQUAD! (USA 4/3/82) Theme mus (Ira Newborn) IRA NEWBORN on 'Naked Gun 2½' Film -S/T- *see p.197 TT93*
PONDLES The (Central 16/9/87) Songs (Dave Cooke)TV Cast *PRT: KIDM 9001 (Vol.1 Cass) KIDM 9002 (Vol.2 Cass)*
POPEYE (USA Cart 40's) *Coll* 'TELEVISION'S G.HITS VOL.1'
POSTCARDS FROM DOWN UNDER (BBC2 8/4/91) theme "Outback" (Garry Dial) by JAMES MORRISON on 'Postcards From Down Under' - *WEA Int: 255697-2(CD) -4(Cass) -1(LP)*
POSTMAN PAT (BBC1 from 5/7/82-1994) music (Bryan Daly) narrated and sung by KEN BARRIE *Post Music (Pinn): PPCD 101 (CD) PMC 101 (Cass)* also available with KEN BARRIE-CAROL BOYD *BBC (Pinn): YBBC 1491 (Cass)* VOL.2 *Post Mus (Pinn):PPCD 102 (CD) PPMC 102 (Cass)* 'Postman Pat Sings Children's Favourites' with KEN BARRIE *Red Rock (TBD): RKC 018 (Cass) RKC 013 (Cas)*
POT OF GOLD (Centr/Grundy 28/78/93) mus.dir Colin Keyes
POT BLACK / JUNIOR POT BACK (BBC2 72-86) "Black & White Rag" (George Botsford) WINIFRED ATWELL on 'Winnie's Piano Party' *President: PLCD 531 (CD) (TC)PLE 531*
POTSWORTH & CO (USA) BBC1 2/1/91 m:(Michael Taverea).*NA*
POWER & THE GLORY (BBC2 4/10/91) mus Paddy Kingsland.*NA*
POWER GAME The (ITV 65) theme mus (Cyril Stapleton) *see Coll* 'A-Z OF BRITISH TV THEMES'/'TV CLASSICS VOL.2'
PRAISE BE! (BBC1 18/5/93) music (Gary Scargill-Peter Ol royd) *not available* /orig theme 'Lord Of The Dance' (Sydney Carter) - *see* 'ALLOTMENT SHOW' for details
PRESS GANG The (Central 16/1/89) theme mus (Peter Davis John Mealing-John G.Perry).....................*NA*
PRIDE AND PREJUDICE (UKGO1/8/93 orig BBC2 13/1/80) ori ginal music (Wilfred Josephs)....................*NA*
PRIME SUSPECT (Grana 7/4/91) music (Stephen Warbeck).*NA*
PRIME SUSPECT 2 (Gran 15/12/92) m: (Stephen Warbeck).*NA*
PRIME SUSPECT 3 (Gran 1994) music: (Stephen Warbeck).*NA*
PRISONER The (C4 23/9/92 prev:19/9/83 orig:ITV 29/9/67) 17 part series starring Patrick McGoohan with Music by (RON GRAINER & others) -S/T- *Silva Screen (Con):* (theme music on Vol.1) (Vol.2 feat music of Philip Green-Robert Farnon-J.S.Petit+"The Age Of Elegance" *FILM(C)(CD) 042 (Vol.1) / FILM(C)(CD) 084 (Vol.2) FILM(C)(CD) 126 (Vol.3)* / add.item 'PRISONER THEME" + 'DANGER MAN' (Edwin Astley Orch) and "DRY BONES" (Four Lads) on *Bam Caruso (Rev-APT): NRIC 112 (CDs)*
PRISONER CELL BLOCK H (Australia 79-87)(UK 84-93) Theme "On The Inside" (Alan Caswell) sung by LYNNE HAMILT ON with instrumental theme *A1 (BMG): A1 311 (7"s) see COLLECT* 'AUSTRALIAN TELEVISION'S GREATEST HITS'

PRISONERS OF CONSCIENCE (BBC2 27/11/89) Theme "Fragile"
     (G.Sumner) STING from 'Nothing Like The Sun' *A.& M.*
     CDA 6402 (CD) AMA 6402 (LP) AMC 6402 (Cass)
PRISONERS OF THE SUN (NATURAL WORLD)BBC2 19/1/92) music
     (John Alder and Steve Levine).................*NA*
PRIVATE EYE (USA 87/BBC1 24/3/92) theme (Joe Jackson)*NA*
PRIZE The (BBC2 4/7/93) music (Paul Foss)...........*NA*
PROFESSIONALS The (LWT 30/12/77-83) Theme (Laurie Johns
     on) *see Coll* 'ROSE & THE GUN'/'FAVOURITE TV THEMES'
     'HIT THEMES1 BEST OF BRITISH TV MUSIC'/'ITV THEMES'
PROFILES OF NATURE (C4 16/6/91) music (Ron & Dave Harri
     son)...*NA*
PROSTITUTE (Fr/C4 27/9/93)orig music (Serge Kochyne).*NA*
PUBLIC FACE: (C4 18/3/91) music/sounds (Ron Geesin)..*NA*
PULASKI (BBC1 2/10/87) Theme (Brian Bennett) - SHADOWS
     see Collect 'WORLD OF BBC TV THEMES'
PULSE The (C4/Diverse 16/2/93) mus (Jim Sutherland)..*NA*
PUNCH DRUNK (BBC1 4/1/93) music (David McNiven)......*NA*
PUPPY DOG TALES (BBC1 24/9/92) mus (Derek Wadsworth).*NA*
PUSH THE BOAT OUT (BBC2 26/6/91) m: (Phil Cunningham)*NA*

Q MILLIGAN (BBC2 5/9/93) "Q Theme" (Spike Milligan) on
     'BRITISH COMEDY CLASSICS' *EMI: ECC 7 (2Cass)*
QD - THE MASTER GAME (C4 29/7/91) theme music (Graham
     De Wilde)..*NA*
QUANTUM LEAP (USA 89)(BBC2 13/2/90) theme (Mike Post)
     -S/T- with orig music & songs on *GNP (Silva Screen)*
     GNPD 8036 (CD) GNP-5 8036 (Cass) see *also* Colls:-
     'AMERICAN TELEVIS.THEMES V.2'/'FANTASTIC TV THEMES'
QUATERMASS EXPERIMENT The (BBC & Film 55) Main theme
     "Mars" from 'Planets Suite' (Gustav Holst)
QUESTION OF COLOUR, A (BBC2 12/7/93) theme music (Jean
     Louis Valero) song "Mood Indigo" (Duke Ellington-I.
     Mills) sung by DEE DEE BRIDGEWATER...............*NA*
QUESTION OF SPORT A (BBC1 1969-92) Theme (Richie Close)
     Coll 'BBC SPORTING THEMES' *deleted*
     Competition Music "There Are More Questions Than An
     swers" JOHNNY NASH 'Greatest Hits' *Epic 465306-2 CD*
QUESTION TIME (BBC1 from 25/9/79-1993) Theme music by
     Stanley Myers *not available*
QUINCY (USA 76) Theme (Glen A.Larson-Stu Phillips) *see*
     Coll 'TELEVISION'S GREATEST HITS VOL.3'/'GREAT TV
     THEMES VOLUME 1'
QUO VADIS (TV Film Italy C4 11/2/86) Music (Piero Picci
     one) -S/T- *Gen.Music Italy (S.Screen) GM 30716 (LP)*

RAB C.NESBITT (BBC2 fr. 27/9/90) mus (David McNiven).*NA*
RACING FROM AINTREE (BBC1 5/4/90) Theme "The Mission"
     (Ennio Morricone) *see* FILMS & SHOWS 'THE MISSION'
RACING GAME The (BBC2 5/5/92) music (Peter Filleul)..*NA*
RADIO ROO (BBC1 25/2/91) mus (J.Cohen-Wayne Jackman).*NA*
RAILWATCH (BBC1 13/2/89) Theme "High Energy Express"
     (PAUL GREEDUS) on 'Power Cuts' *Focus (John Fiddy*
     Music): FCD 101 (CD only)

RAILWAY CARRIAGE GAME (BBC1 9/1/85) Theme "Coronation
    Scot" (Vivian Ellis) *see Coll* 'FAMOUS THEMES'
RAINBOW SERPENT (C4 2/4/91) music (Peter Miller).....*NA*
RALLY CHALLENGE (BBC2 12/2/90) "Karla With A K" (Rick
    Chertoff) HOOTERS 'One Way Home' *CBS: 450851-2 (CD)*
RALLY REPORT (BBC2 19/11/89) Theme "Duel" (PROPAGANDA)
    ZTT (Isl-Poly) ZTIQ 3 (LP) ZCIQ 3 (CS) CID 126 (CD)
RAPIDO (BBC2 20/10/88) m: (Anne Dudley) ART OF NOISE.*NA*
RAWHIDE (USA 57) Title song (Dimitri Tiomkin-Ned Washin
    gton) sung by FRANKIE LAINE *Old Gold: OG 9665 (7"s)*
    vers 'Round-Up' *Telarc (Conifer): CD 80141 (CD)*
READY STEADY GO! (ITV 9/8/63-23/12/66) Re-run (C4) 1985
    Orig theme "Wipeout" (SURFARIS) *Old Gold:OG 9171 7"*
    Most remembered theme "5-4-3-2-1" (MANFRED MANN)
REAL CHARLOTTE The (Gran 16/6/91) m: (Paul Corbett)..*NA*
REAL HIGHLAND FLING A (ITV 92) Var.arts -S/T- 'Amazing
    Grace' *Scotdisc (Con): CDITV 556(CD) KITV 556(Cass)*
REAL McCOY The (Thames 19/9/90) Theme "Stompin' At The
    Savoy"(B.Goodman-E.Sampson-C.Webb) THE INK SPOTS on
    'Whispering Grass' *Flapper (HMundi):PASTCD9757 (CD)*
REAL McCOY The (BBC2 10/5/91) title music composed and
    performed by (JAZZIE-B and WILLIE MOWAT).........*NA*
REALMS OF THE RUSSIAN BEAR The (BBC2 15/11/92) Music
    (Martin Kiszko) conducted by Harry Rabinowitz....*NA*
REAR WINDOW (C4 11/4/90) music (Julian Bahula).......*NA*
RECORD BREAKERS (BBC1) Music during record attempts:-
    "Pipeline" from 'Amonia Avenue' - ALAN PARSONS PRO
    JECT on *Arista (BMG): 206·100 (LP) 406100 (Cass)*
RED ARCTIC (BBC2 2/7/91) music (Ryiuchi Sugimoto)....*NA*
RED DWARF (BBC2 15/2/88-1993) Music and theme song by
    (Howard Goodall) with "Tongue Tied" featuring THE
    CAT (Danny John-Jules) on *EMI: (TC)EM 286 (Cass/7")*
    also on *CDEM 286 (CDs) 12EM 286 (12")* **without theme**
RED FOX   (LWT 8/12/91) music (Alan Parker)...........*NA*
REDUNDANT (BBC2 30/1/92) theme music (Roger Bolton)..*NA*
REDEMPTION SONG (BBC2 30/6/91) Title song (Bob Marley)
    BOB MARLEY & WAILERS on 'Uprising' *Island (Polyg):*
    CID 9596 (CD) ICM 9596 (Cass) ILPM 9596 (LP)
REILLY-ACE OF SPIES (Thames 9/83) Theme from 'Romance'
    (Shostakovich) arr Harry Rabinowitz *see Collections*
    'IMAGINATIONS'/'GREAT TV THEMES VOLUME 4'
RELATIVE VALUES (BBC2 19/5/91) theme (Andrew Poppy)..*NA*
REMINGTON STEELE (USA)(BBC1 3/9/83) mus (Henry Mancini)
    Coll 'AMERICAN TV THEMES VOLUME 2'/'COPS & ROBBERS'
REMOTE CONTROL (C4 8/1/91) music (Andy Gangaden).....*NA*
REPORTAGE (DEF II Series) (BBC2 2/11/88) Title theme by
    COLDCUT on 'What's That Noise' on *Big Life (Cartel-*
    Rough Trade): CCUTLP 1 (LP) CCUTMC 1 (Cass)
RESCUE (Scottish 8/1/90) Music: Rod Argent-Robert Howes
    -S/T- feat ROD ARGENT & ROBERT HOWES *Stylus(Stylus)*
    HONEYCD 14 (CD) HONEYL 14 (LP) HONEYC 14 (Cass) del
RESNICK:Lonely Hearts (BBC1 31/3/92) m:(Bill Connor).*NA*
RETURN OF DOGTANIAN (ITV 8/1/91) theme (Guido/Maurizzio
    De Angelis) *see under* 'Dogtanian & 3 Muskehounds'

RETURN OF SHERLOCK HOLMES The (Granada 9/7/86)*see under entry* 'SHERLOCK HOLMES'
RETURN OF THE ANTELOPE (Granada 17/1/88) Theme (Wilfred Josephs) *see* coll 'Granada Studios Souvenir Album'
RETURN OF THE MAN FROM U.N.C.L.E. (USA) theme (Jerry Goldsmith) *see Coll* 'FANTASTIC TELEVISION THEMES'
RETURN OF THE PSAMMEAD (BBC1 6/1/93) m:(Michael Omer)*NA*
RETURN OF THE SAINT The (ITV 78) Theme (Irving Martin-Brian Dee) *see Coll* 'A-Z OF BRITISH TV THEMES'/'TV CLASSICS VOLUME 1' *(Castle Comm)*
RHYTHMS OF THE WORLD (BBC2 25/4/92) theme music (Dennis Bovell) *not available / VIDEOS AVAILABLE ON ISLAND*
RICH MAN POOR MAN (USA-ITV 75) Music score (Alex North) -S/T- re-issue *Varese (Pinn): VSD 5423 (CD) also on* 'GREAT TV THEMES VOLUME 2'
RICH TEA & SYMPATHY (YTV 5/7/91) theme (Ray Russell-Sally Howard)sung by PATRICIA HODGE-DENNIS QUILLEY.*NA*
RICHARD AND JUDY SHOW The (Granada 5/7/92) theme music (Mike Moran)..................................*NA*
RICHARD DIGANCE (LWT 20/7/91) music (Mcasso Prod)....*NA*
RICHEST WOMAN IN THE WORLD The (ITC/87-15/9/91) Theme: "I Found A Million Dollar Baby" (Dixon-Warren-Rose) BING CROSBY 'Early Years' *Neovox (VJM): NEOVOX911LP*
RIDERS (Anglia Films 2/5/93) orig music (Roger Webb).*NA*
RIDES (BBC1 19/2/92) music (Bill Connor) "Rides" (Bill Connor-Carole Hayman) sung by SHEILA GOTT........*NA*
RIFF-RAFF ELEMENT The (BBC1 2/4/93) original mus (Tony McAnaney) orchestrated by (Marcus Brown).........*NA*
RIFLEMAN The (USA 58) Theme music (Herschel Burke Gilbert) see Collect 'TELEVISION'S GREATEST HITS VOL1'
RIGHT TO REPLY (C4) Theme "Broadcast News" BILL NELSON on 'Duplex' *Cocteau (Pin):(TC)JCD(CD) 22 (CS/LP/CD)*
RIK MAYALL PRESENTS (Granada 20/5/93) original music by Barrington Pheloung..............................*NA*
RIN TIN TIN (USA 56) 'TELEVISION'S GREATEST HITS VOL.1'
RING MY BELL (C4 25/10/91) music (Pop Tarts).........*NA*
RING OF SCORPIO (BBC1 19/6/92) mus (Martin Armiger)..*NA*
RIPTIDE (USA) theme (Mike Post-Pete Carpenter) *on Coll* 'TELEVISION MUSIC OF MIKE POST AND PETE CARPENTER'
RIVER The (BBC1 20/10/89) Theme composed/sung by DAVID ESSEX on 'Touching The Ghost' *Lamplight (Total-BMG) LAMPCD 1 (CD) LAMPLP(MC) 1 (LP/Cass)*
ROAD RUNNER (USA Cartoon) *see Coll* 'TELEVISION'S GREATEST HITS VOLUME 2'
ROBIN HOOD 'The Adventures Of' (TV) *see* 'Adventures Of Robin Hood' (ITC series with Richard Greene)
ROBIN OF SHERWOOD (HTV 28/4/84)Theme "Robin (The Hooded Man)" CLANNAD on 'Past Present' *RCA (BMG): PD 74074 (CD) PK (Cass) / 74321.118127 (7"s) 74321.118124 (Cass) 74321.118122 (CDs)*
ROBINSON CRUSOE (BBC1 60s) *see* 'ADVENTURES OF ROBINSON'
ROBINSON CRUSOE & MAN FRIDAY (Filmed TV Mini series 88) Music score (Maurice Jarre) -S/T- *Prometheus Import (Silva Screen): PST 501 (LP)*

ROCKFORD FILES (USA 75)Theme (Mike Post-Pete Carpenter)
   see Coll 'TELEVISION MUSIC OF MIKE POST & PETE CARP
   ENTER'/'GREAT TV THEMES VOLUME 3'
ROCKLIFFE'S BABIES (UKGO 20/9/93 orig BBC1 9/1/87) mus:
   (Paul Hart-Joe Campbell) JOE & CO with Corona Stage
   School Choir *BBC Collection (BBCCD 705 - deleted)*
ROD AND EMU (ITV FilmFair) theme (Keith Hopwood).....*NA*
ROGER MELLIE (C4 31/12/92) theme music (Danny Chang).*NA*
RONSON MISSION (BBC DEFII 9/9/93) music The PIXIES...*NA*
ROOBARB (BBC1 70's) music (Johnny Hawksworth) new SHAFT
   'Roobarb & Custard' (Pritchard-Hughes-Hawksworth)
   (Ffrreedom (Poly): TAB(X)(MC)(CD) 100 (singles)
ROOT INTO EUROPE (Cent/Aspect 17/5/92)(Clever Music).*NA*
ROOTS SCHMOOTS (Hawkshead/C4 8/3/93) orig mus (Robert
   Neufeld) title music sung by MOSHE HASCHELL......*NA*
RORY BREMNER (BBC2 from 20/4/90) music (Anne Dudley).*NA*
RORY BREMNER WHO ELSE (C4 9/10/93) mus (Mingles Mus).*NA*
ROSEANNE (USA C4 from 27/1/89) theme music (Dan Foliart
   Howard Pearl) *see Coll* '4 AMERICA'
ROSIE AND JIM (Cent 3/9/90) Mus (Andrew McCrorie-Shand)
   'Rosie & Jim's Song Party with *Rebecca Nagan-Robin
   Stevens MFP (EMI):CDMFP 5964 (CD) TCMFP 5964 (Cass)*
   'Rosie & Jim's Christmas' *MFP: TCMFP 6100 (Cass)*
ROUGH GUIDE TO THE AMERICAS (BBC2 DEF2 20/10/93) commis
   sioned orig music (Carl McIntosh)................*NA*
ROUGH GUIDE TO THE WORLD (BBC2 DEF2-21/6/89) End Theme
   "Money God" composed and performed by BIG PIG on
   'Bonk' *A.& M.: CDA(AMA)(AMC) 5185 (CD/LP/Cass)*
ROUND THE BEND (Yorkshire (Hat Trick) 20/5/91) music by
   (Philip Pope-Big George-Simon Franglen)..........*NA*
ROYAL ASCOT (BBC1 22/6/90) **Theme** "Odissea" (G.Reverberi
   -L.Giordano) RONDO VENEZIANO on *Fanfare (Mainline):
   CDRON 5 (CD) ZCRON 5 (Cas) RON 5 (LP)* Fashion Link
   Music "Regata Dei Dogi" on 'Venice In Peril' RONDO
   VENEZIANO *Fanfare (Mainl): CDRON 1(CD) ZCRON 1(Cas)*
ROYAL CELEBRATION,A (BBC1 26/9/93) mus (Anne Dudley).*NA*
   Songs "I've Been Loving You Too Long" OTIS REDDING
   "Let's Dance" CHRIS REA on 'Dancing With Strangers'
ROYAL COLLECTION (Antelope/Icon Films/C4 18/10/92) orig
   music (Carl Davis) conduct MUNICH SYMPHONY ORCH..*NA*
ROYAL GARDENS (BBC2 9/10/92) music (Raf Ravenscroft and
   Charles Olins) RAVENSCROFT PARTNERSHIP...........*NA*
ROYAL HERITAGE (BBC1 77 rep 86)Theme "Zadok The Priest"
   'The Coronation Anthem' (Handel) *many recordings*
ROY'S RAIDERS (BBC1 20/7/91) title theme "On My Bike"
   (David Essex) sung by WILLIAM VANDERPUYE.........*NA*
RUBBISH KING OF THE JUNGLE(A For Animation/HTV 29/6/93)
   theme mus (Andre Jacquemin-David Howman)........*NA*
RUBY WAX - *see under* 'HIT AND RUN' and 'FULL WAX, The'
RUGBY SPECIAL (BBC2 78-90) "Holy Mackerel" (Brian Benne
   tt) *see Coll* 'BBC SPORTING THEMES' *deleted*
RUGBY WORLD CUP 1991 *see under* 'WORLD CUP RUGBY 1991'
RUMPOLE OF THE BAILEY (Thames 1978-93) Theme by Joseph
   Horovitz - *Columbia (EMI): DB 9143 (7"s) deleted*

RUNAWAY BAY (YTV 9/1/92) orig mus & title song (Romano Mushmarra) sung by DANA DAWSON.................*NA*
RUNNING WILD (LWT 6/3/87) incidental music (Denis King) *see* 'LOVEJOY' *Coll* / **RUNNING WILD** (LWT 3/87) Theme (Catherine Stock-John Worth) SHADES *Sierra deleted*
RUPERT (Scottish/Nelvana Prod 23/9/92) music (Milan Kym licka) Cantus Productions.....................*NA*
RUPERT (ITV 70's) Theme "Rupert The Bear" (Ron Roker & Len Beadle) by JACKIE LEE *PRT: 7P 337 (7") deleted*
RUSS ABBOT SHOW The (BBC1 6/9/86-91) theme m: "Songs Of Joy" (Gary Roberts-Ian Paul) sung by RUSS ABBOT..*NA*
RUSSIAN NEW MUSIC (C4 30/1/92)(10pt series) 'Document' CDbox set featuring NEW Music from Russia: The 80's 80's on *Leo (Pinn): CDLR 801/808 (CDx8)*
RUTH RENDELL MYSTERIES The (TVS 19/6/88) Music by BRIAN BENNETT -'The Ruth Rendell Mysteries' **(Var.Artists)** *EMI Soundtrack: CDSTM 2 (CD) TCSTM 2 (Cass)* / ALSO: Brian Bennett (1) *Pickwick: PWKS 546 (CD) HSSC 3286* Brian Bennett (2) *Polydor: 847524-2 (CD) -4 (Cass)*

S.& M. (C4 Hat-Trick 6/11/91) Theme (Pete Thomas)....*NA*
SAILOR (BBC 11/1/84) Theme "Sailing" (Gavin Sutherland) ROD STEWART *WEA: K16600 (7"s) 926034-2 (CD) WX314C*
SAINT The (ITC 4/10/62-69) Theme mus (Edwin Astley) *see Coll* 'A-Z OF BRITISH TV THEMES'/'TV CLASSICS VOL.1'
SAINT & GREAVSIE (LWT 5/10/85-93) Theme: 1988-93 "Aztec Gold" ROD ARGENT-PETER VAN HOOKE *see Collection* '20 TOP TV THEMES'/'ITV THEMES'
SAINT ELSEWHERE (USA 82-89) Theme (Dave Grusin) Orig on *GRP USA: GRPA 1006 (LP) GRPC 1006 (Cass)*
SAM SATURDAY (LWT 27/6/92) music (Rick Wentworth)....*NA*
SANTA BARBARA (USA ITV 7/9/87) "If Ever You're In My Arms Again" PEABO BRYSON *Elektra: 960362-1(LP)-4(Cas)*
SATURDAY NIGHT LIVE (USA)(BBC2 7/11/92) featuring CHEVY CHASE-JOHN BELUSHI-DAN ACKROYD-GILDA RADNOR-RICHARD PRYOR-JANE CURTIN-LILY TOMLIN-LARAINE NEWMAN-DON PARDO BAND - *Laughing Stock (Pinn): LAFFC 9 (Cass)*
SATURDAY ZOO (Channel X/C4 16/1/93) music dir (Janette Mason) with Cris Bonacci-Yolanda Charles-Michelle Drees (female band) / theme music.................*NA*
SCARECROW & MRS.KING (USA 83) Mus: Arthur B.Rubinstein Williams-Fairey Engin.Band *Grasmere: GRTC 17 (Cass)*
SCARLET AND BLACK (BBC1 31/10/93) orig music composed and conducted by (Jean Claude-Petit)............*NA*
SCHOFIELD'S EUROPE (BBC1 14/11/91) mus (Simon Brint).*NA*
SCIENCE FICTION (Yorks.22/9/92) mus (Robert Hartley).*NA*
SCOOBY-DOO (USA Cartoon 70) 'TELEVISION'S GREAT.HITS 3'
SCREAMING (BBC1 15/3/92) theme "Dome Epais"("The Flower Duet") from 'Lakme' (Delibes) TV vers.arr.by Ronnie Hazlehurst and sung by Maryetta Midgley & Alexandra Gordon *available by:* LESLEY GARRETT on 'DIVA' *Silva Screen (Con): SONG(C)(CD) 903 (Cass/CD) SILVACD 105 (CDs) SILVATC 105 (Cass)* also: MADY MESPLE-DANIELLE MILLET *EMI: CDS 74930-2 (2CD)*.H/Lights *CDM 763447-2*

SEA HUNT (USA 58) Theme (Ray Llewellyn) Coll *see Collec*
    'TELEVISION'S GREATEST HITS VOLUME 2'
SEA TREK (BBC1 7/10/91) music (Roger Limb)...........*NA*
SEAQUEST DSV (USA/ITV 16/10/93) theme (John Debney)..*NA*
SEAN'S SHOW (C4/Chan.X 15/4/92) music (Tony De Meur).*NA*
SECOND CHANCE (BBC1 9/3/92) Title theme composed and
    performed by MIKE HARDING.......................*NA*
SECOND RUSSIAN REVOLUTION The BBC2 31/5/91 music score
    (Debbie Wiseman)...............................*NA*
SECOND THOUGHTS (LWT 3/5/91) theme "Our Love Is Here To
    Stay" (George/Ira Gershwin) 'The Goldwyn Follies'
    (38) 'An American In Paris' (52) *see* FILMS & SHOWS
SECRET AGENT (BBC2 28/10/92) m:(Barrington Pheloung).*NA*
SECRET CABARET WITH SIMON DRAKE (C4 Open Media Product.
    15/1/92) music (Robert Lockhart)................*NA*
SECRET DIARY OF ADRIAN MOLE The (Thames 85) Theme "Prof
    oundly In Love With Pandora" (C.Jankel-I.Dury) -IAN
    DURY *EMI 5534 (7") deleted* see also 'GROWING PAINS'
SECRET GARDEN The (BBC1 75 & 85) Theme "The Watermill"
    (Ronald Binge) on 'Music For A Country Cottage' on
    EMI: CDGO 2039 (CD) TCGO 2039 (Cass)
SECRET HISTORY (C4 14/11/91) music (Andrew Claxton)..*NA*
SECRET LIFE OF MACHINES The (Artifax/C4 from 15/11/88)
    theme mus "The Russians Are Coming" based on 'Take
    5' (Paul Desmond) by VAL BENNETT on Coll 'Rebel Mus
    ic' *Trojan (Pinn): CDTRD 403 (2CD) TRLD 403 (2LP)*
SECRET OF THE SAHARA (RAI/ZDF/TFI Co.Prod ITV 12/9/93)
    Music score (Ennio Morricone) -S/T- *RCA France Imp
    (available through 'MOVIE BOULEVARD' mail order)*
SECRET WORLD OF SEX, A (BBC2/Domino Prod91/rpt 1/2/93)
    title music (Jim Parker).......................*NA*
SECRETS OF THE MOORS (C4 HTV/Forum 23/7/92) theme and
    incidental music taken from 'The Wasps' (Vaughan Wi
    lliams) LONDON PHILHARMONIC ORCH (Sir Adrian Boult)
    EMI: CDM 764020-2 (CD) EG 764020-4 (Cass)
SEEKERS (Central 25/4/93) music sco (Daryl Runswick).*NA*
SEINFELD (USA 90)(BBC2 6/10/93) mus (Jonathan Wolff).*NA*
SELLING HITLER (Thames 11/6/91) music (John Keane & Tim
    Souster) new lyrics (Howard Schuman)............*NA*
SENSE OF BELONGING (C4 30/6/91) music (Piers Partridge-
    Adrian Harman).................................*NA*
SEPARATE BUT EQUAL (BBC2 16/6/93) music (Carl Davis).*NA*
SEPTEMBER SONG (Granada 1/3/93) mus (Richard Harvey).*NA*
SESAME STREET (USA 70's) Theme (Joe Raposo-Stone-Hart)
    Coll 'GREAT TV THEMES V.2'/'TELEVISION'S G.HITS V3'
SEVEN FACES OF WOMAN -*see Collect* 'FAVOURITE TV THEMES'
77 SUNSET STRIP (USA 57) Theme (Mac David-Jerry Livings
    ton) *see Coll* 'TELEVISION'S GREATEST HITS VOLUME 1'
SEX NOW (LWT 21/7/91) theme music (Graeme Pleeth.....*NA*
    Songs "People Are Still Having Sex" (LaTOUR) *Polyd:
    PO 147 (7") PZ 147 (12") PZCZ 147 (CD) POCS 147(MC)*
    "Let's Stick Together" (BRYAN FERRY) *EG (Virgin)*
SEXUAL IMPERATIVE The (C4/Genesis/13WNET 7/1/93) music
    score (Terry Oldfield)..........................*NA*

SHADOW The (BBC2 27/7/91) music (Simon Davison)......*NA*
SHADOWS OF THE HEART (Australia 90/BBC1 12/7/92) Origin
   al music (David Hirschfelder)...................*NA*
SHAKA ZULU (ITV 22/6/91) music composed & performed by
   DAVE POLLECUTT -S/T- *Impt (S.Screen): CDC 1002 (CD)
   also:* 'Shaka Zulu' by LADYSMITH BLACK MAMBAZO GROUP
   Warner Bros (WEA): 7599 25582-2 (CD) WX 94C (Cass)
SHAKESPEARE: ANIMATED TALES (BBC Wales/SC4/C4/Soyuzmult
   film/Christmas Films 9/11/92) Music (Michail Meerovi
   ch) SYMPHONY ORCHESTRA OF MOSFILM CORPORATION ....*NA*
SHAKING THE HEAVENS (BBC2 4/8/92) theme (Ben Park)...*NA*
SHAPE OF THE WORLD The (Granada 28/4/91) music score by
   (Richard Harvey) assist: Harry Gregson-Williams..*NA*
SHARP END The (BBC1 12/4/91) orig music (Bill Connor)
   end title theme vocal by SLIM GAILLARD...........*NA*
SHARPE (Celtic/Central 5/5/93) original music (Dominic
   Muldowney-John Tams).............................*NA*
SHELLEY (UKGO 12/7/93 prev Thames 28/7/92 orig 1979)
   theme music (Ron Grainer).......................*NA*
SHERLOCK HOLMES (Granada) 'Adventures'/'Return'/'Sign'
   Music (PATRICK GOWERS) St.Paul's Cathedral Choir &
   Gabrieli String Qu.& Wren Or. *TER: (CD)(ZC)TER 1136*
SHETLAND SESSIONS The (BBC2 2/9/92) VARIOUS ARTISTS on
   'Shetland Sessions Vol.1-2' *Lismor (Taylors-Gordon
   Duncan): LCOM 7021/7022 (CD) LICS 7021/7022 (Cass)*
   INCLUDES Intro Theme "The Constitution" (Aly Bain)
   and Outro Theme "Scalloway Lasses" (Aly Bain)
   see also under entry 'ALY BAIN AND FRIENDS'
SHIRALEE The (BBC1 Australian Pr) music (Chris Neal).*NA*
SHIRLEY'S WORLD (ATV 1971) "Shirley's Theme"/"Rickshaw
   Ride" m: (Laurie Johnson) *see Coll* 'ROSE & THE GUN'
SHOESTRING (UKGold 2/11/92 orig BBC1 30/9/79) theme mus
   (George Fenton) *Coll* 'BEST OF BBC TV THEMES'*deleted*
SHOGUN (BBC1 20/11/82 and 3/8/85) Music (Maurice Jarre)
   -S/T- *RSO USA (S.Screen): RSO 3088 (LP) CTI 2088Cas*
SHOOT THE VIDEO (C4 4/9/93) mus (Darren Elliot-King).*NA*
SHOULDER TO SHOULDER (BBC1 3/10/93 orig 1974) incid.mus
   (Stanley Myers)theme song from "March Of The Women"
   (Dame Ethel Smyth) sung by GEORGIA BROWN & Cast..*NA*
   "Land Of Hope And Glory" (Edward Elgar and Arthur
   Benson) Benson sung by DAME CLARA BUTT on the album
   'Heart Of Empire' *Flapper (Pinn): PASCD 7012 (CD)*
SHOW JUMPING - *see under* 'HORSE OF THE YEAR SHOW'
SHOWBIZ PEOPLE (BBC1 29/6/92) theme m: "Arrival" (Benny
   Andersson-Bjorn Ulvaeus) ABBA from 'The Hits 2' on
   Pickwick (Pickwick): PWWKS 500 (CD)
SHRINKS (Thames 13/2/91) theme mus (Debbie Wiseman)..*NA*
SIDE BY SIDE (BBC1 27/4/92) theme mus (David MacKay).*NA*
SIGN ON (C4/Tyne-Tees 28/3/92) theme mus (John Cook).*NA*
SILENTS The (C4 series 88) Music (Carl Davis) - *Virgin
   Classics (Poly): VC 790785-2 (CD) -4 (Cass)*
SILK ROAD The (ITV 23/6/87) 'Silk Road Suite' (KITARO)
   with L.S.O. 'Silk Road 1' *(Polydor) 823 736-2 (CD)*
   'Silk Road 2' *(Polydor) 817 532-1 (LP) -4 (Cass)*

SIMON AND SIMON (USA 82) Theme (Michael Towers-Barry De Vorzon) *see Coll* 'GREAT TV THEMES VOLUME 2'

SIMPLE TRUTH The (BBC 12/5/91) theme "The Simple Truth" composed/sung by CHRIS DE BURGH on *A & M: RELF 785 (7"s) RELMC 785 (Cass) RELCD 785 (CDs) / A CHARITY SINGLE IN AID OF THE CAMPAIGN FOR KURDISH REFUGEES*

SIMPLY THE BEST (C4/HTV 4/8/92) theme (Simon Park)...*NA*

SIMPSONS The (Sky One Satellite 90) music by (Loren) on 'The Simpsons Sing The Blues' incl "Do The Bartman" *Geffen (BMG): GEFD 24308 (CD) GEF(C) 24308 (LP/Cas)*

SIN WITH BRUCE MORTON (C4 2/6/93) mus (Blair Cowan)..*NA*

SINGING DETECTIVE The (BBC1 16/11/86 and repeated 6/88) *Story* (Dennis Potter) *Theme music* "Peg O' My Heart" (Fred Fisher-Alfred Bryan) arr by Max Harris & His Novelty Trio / orig on BBC re-issued on *Connoisseur Collect (Pinn): POTTCD 200 (2CD) POTTMC 200 (2Cass)*

SINGLES (Yorkshire 27/1/88) music (Johnny Pearson)...*NA*

SIR FRANCIS DRAKE (ABC/ATV 12/11/61-29/4/62) theme mus: (Ventura) *see Coll* 'TV CLASSICS VOLUME 3'

SISTER WENDY'S ODYSSEY (BBC2 21/11/92) theme and incidental music (Roger Bolton).......................*NA*

SITTING PRETTY (BBC1 19/11/92) Theme (John Sullivan) MD: Ed Welch "Sitting Pretty" sung by DIANE BULL.NA

SIX MILLION DOLLAR MAN (USA 72 reshown BBC1-8/90) Theme (Oliver Nelson) 'Dynamic Sound Of Johnny Gregory' *Philips: 846 833-2 (CD) 846 833-4 (Cass)*

SIX WIVES OF HENRY VIII (UKGO 1/8/93 orig BBC1 1/1/70) music (David Munrow) performed by The Early Music Consort arr.& conducted by David Munrow *BBC deleted*

SIXTHIRTYSOMETHING (C4 14/8/91) m:Jonathan Whitehead.*NA*

SKI SUNDAY (BBC2 72-93) Theme mus "Pop Looks Bach" (Sam Fonteyn) *see Coll* 'BBC SPORTING THEMES' *deleted*

SKY AT NIGHT The (BBC1 24/4/57-94) Theme "At The Castle Gate" from 'Pelleas et Melisande' Op.46 (Sibelius) *also:* 'The Music Of Patrick Moore' EVER READY BRASS BAND (Geoffrey Brand) featur 'Halley's Comet March' *Conifer: CFRC 511 (LP) MCFRC 511 (Cass)*

SLAP MAXWELL STORY The (USA BBC2 21/1/89) mus (Patrick Williams) *see Coll* 'AMERICAN TV THEMES VOLUME 2'

SLEDGEHAMMER (USA 88 ITV 12/1/89) Theme (Danny Elfman) *see Coll* 'AMERICAN TELEVISION THEMES VOLUME 3'

SLEEPERS (BBC2 10/4/91) music score (David Dundas-Rick Wentworth)...*NA*

SMALL OBJECTS OF DESIRE (BBC2 22/2/90) theme mus (David Stevens)...*NA*

SMELL OF REEVES & MORTIMER The (Channel X/ BBC 21/9/93) music (Peter Brewis-Jim Moir-Bob Mortimer).......*NA*

SMURFS The (Cart 70s) *see Coll* 'GREAT TV THEMES VOL.4'/ 'TELEVISION'S GREATEST HITS VOLUME 3'

SNAKES AND LADDERS (C4 17/10/89) Theme "I've Seen The Future" (Jim Parker-Lawrence Marks-Maurice Gran).*NA*

SNAPPER The (BBC2 4/4/93) theme "Can't Help Falling In Love With You" (George Weiss-Hugo & Luigi)performed by LICK THE TINS *Mooncrest (BMG): CRESTCD 012 (CD)*

SNAPSHOTS (C4 6/1/93) music (Julian Stewart Lindsey). *NA*
SNOOKER (BBC Sport) Theme mus."Drag Racer" DOUGLAS WOOD
   GROUP - *for details see under* 'WORLD SNOOKER'
SNOW SHOW The (BBC2 18/2/93) title m: (Andrew Poppy). *NA*
SNOWMAN The (C4 Cartoon 24/12/85) Music (Howard Blake)
   Narr: Bernard Cribbins with The Sinfonia Of London
   Song "Walking In The Air" sung by PETER AUTY -S/T-
   Columbia (Sony Music) CD 71116 (CD) 40-71116 (Cass)
SNUB TV (BBC2 DEFII 8/1/90) theme "Human Nature" (Gary
   Clail) prod by Adrian Sherwood / on *Perfecto (BMG)*
   PB(PK) 44401 (7"/Cass) PT 44402 (12") PD 44404 (CD)
SO HAUNT ME (BBC1 23/2/92) theme music (Rolfe Kent)..*NA*
SO YOU THINK YOU'VE GOT TROUBLES (BBC1 Alomo) 17/10/91)
   theme music (Fiachra Trench)......................*NA*
SO YOU WANT TO PLAY GOLF (BBC2/BBC Ent 10/10/92) theme
   music (Steve Martin-Hugh Matier).................*NA*
SOFTLY SOFTLY (BBC1 60's-70's) Theme music (David Fansh
   awe) on 'Dynamic Sound Of Johnny Gregory' - *Philips*
   846 833-2 (CD) 846 833-4 (Cass)
SOLDIER SOLDIER (Central 10/6/91) music (Jim Parker). *NA*
SOLO (UKGO 2/4/93 orig BBC2 11/1/81) theme "Air Russe"
   'Op.107 Variation for Flute & Piano' (Beethoven)
SOLVE MY PROBLEM (Gran 31/3/92) music (Mike Timoney). *NA*
SOME MOTHERS DO 'AVE 'EM (BBC1 74-79 rpt at various int
   ervals) theme mus (Ronnie Hazlehurst) orig recorded
   by RONNIE HAZLEHURST ORCH on *Polydor (now deleted)*
SOMEBODY'S CHILDREN (Scottish 26/4/90)Theme "The Circle
   Game" (Joni Mitchell) TV Version by MAIRIE McINNES
   (not available) JONI MITCHELL on 'Ladies Of The Can
   yon' *Reprise (WEA): K2-44085 (CD)K1 (LP)/ K4 (Cass)*
SON OF THE MORNING STAR (BBC1 mini-ser.17/12/92) Music
   score (Craig Safan) -S/T-*Intrada (Koch): MAF 7037CD*
SONG FOR EUROPE 1993 (BBC1 9/4/93) *Winning song* "Better
   The Devil You Know" (Dean Collinson-Redd) sung by
   SONIA *Arista (BMG): 74321 14687-7(7")-4(Cass)-2(CD)*
   note: "So Much Of Your Love" (placed 2nd) and "Our
   World" (3rd) are on SONIA's album 'Better The Devil
   You Know' *Arista (BMG): 74321 14980-2(CD) -4 (Cass)*
SONG FOR EUROPE 1992 (BBC1 3/4/92) *Winning song:* "One
   Step Out Of Time" (Tony Ryan-Paul Davies-Victor Str
   atton) by MICHAEL BALL *Polydor: PZCD(PO)(POCS) 206*
   SONG FOR EUROPE *see also* 'EUROVISION SONG CONTEST'
SONGS AND MEMORIES (C4 19/9/92) t.mus (Roger White)..*NA*
SONGS OF PRAISE (BBC1 from Oct 1961) current signature
   music (Robert Prizeman)..........................*NA*
SONNY SPOON (USA) theme music (Mike Post) - *see Collect*
   'AMERICAN TV THEMES VOLUME 1'/TELEVISION MUSIC OF
   MILE POST AND PETE CARPENTER'
SONS AND DAUGHTERS (Australia ITV 19/10/83) Title song
   (Peter Pinne-Don Battye) sung by KERRI & MICK *see*
   Coll 'AUSTRALIAN TELEVISION'S GREATEST HITS'
SOOTY SHOW The (ITV 5/1/83-93) Theme (Matthew Corbett)
   'SOOTY & CO.' *MFP (EMI): TCMFP 6103 (Cass) see also*
   Collection 'ITV CHILDREN'S THEMES'

SORRY! (UKGold 8/11/92 orig BBC1 12/3/81) theme music
(Gaynor Colborne-Hugh Wisdom).....................**NA**
SOUL (BBC2 12/4/92) music (Peter Howell) BBC R.Works.**NA**
SOUND STUFF *(C4) - see 'Together' (Kiri Te Kanawa)*
SOUNDS OF THE 60s (BBC2 5/10/91)theme (Roger Bolton).**NA**
SOUNDS OF THE 70s (BBC2 16/1/93)theme (Roger Bolton).**NA**
SOUTH BANK SHOW The (LWT 1978-94) Theme "Caprice In A.
Minor No.24" from 'Themes and Variations 1-4' (Paga
nini) Featuring ANDREW & JULIAN LLOYD WEBBER - *MCA:
MCLC 1816 (Cass) DMCL 1816 (CD)*
SPACE 1999 (ITC 4/9/75-77) Music (Barry Gray) *see Coll:*
'F.A.B.- THUNDERBIRDS'/'NO STRINGS ATTTACHED'
SPACESHIP EARTH (C4 21/2/91) theme (Gavin Greenaway).**NA**
SPACEVETS (BBC1 29/9/92) music (Dominic Glynn).......**NA**
SPAIN IN THE SHADOW OF THE SUN (C4)(Edward Shearmur).**NA**
SPAIN MEANS BUSINESS (BBC2 8/9/93) music (Rick Fenn).**NA**
SPAIN ON A PLATE (BBC2 15/5/92) mus (Richard Attree).**NA**
SPARKY'S MAGIC PIANO (USA TV animation BBC1 17/4/88)
Orig 1960 version composed by Ray Livingston featur
ing Henry Blair and Ray Turner with the 'Sonovox'
talking voice on *EMI: CDEMS(TCEMS) 1466 (CD/Cass)*
SPECIALS (BBC1 25/9/91) theme music (Proetan Orc)....**NA**
SPENDER (BBC1 8/1/91) theme music (Tony McAnaney)....**NA**
SPENSER FOR HIRE (USA 85)(BBC1 12/9/89) theme (Steve Do
rff-Larry Herbstritt) *Coll* 'AMERICAN TV THEMES V.1'
SPIDER (BBC1 26/9/91) theme music (Jeff Stevenson)...**NA**
SPIDERMAN (USA 78) "Spiderman" (Ellis) / *see Collection*
'TELEVISION'S GREATEST HITS VOLUME 3'
SPIDERMAN & HIS AMAZING FRIENDS (BBC1 6/10/83)Title mus
plus "Iceman"/"Firestar" (Johnny Douglas) by Living
Sound on *Dulcima (Taylors): DLCS 102 (7"s)*
SPIRIT OF FREEDOM (C4/Illuminations/Antenne2 19/11/92)
Orig music (Denis Barbier).......................**NA**
SPIRIT OF TREES (RTE/C4 23/10/92) mus (John Collins).**NA**
SPITTING IMAGE (Central 6/86) 'Spit In Your Ear' V.Arts
Virgin (EMI) CDVIP 110 (CD) TCVIP 110 (Cass)
SPLENDID HEARTS (BBC2 Bristol 16/10/92) title music by
(Nigel Beaham-Powell and Bella Russell)..........**NA**
SPOOKS OF BOTTLE BAY The (Fugitive Prod/Carlton 9/9/93)
music (Charlie Skarbek-Richard Blanshard)........**NA**
SPORTRAITS (Transw.Int/ITV 26/6/93) mus (Paul Frost).**NA**
SPORTSMASTERS (ITV 25/8/90) Theme "Calypso" (J.M.Jarre)
JEAN MICHEL JARRE on 'Waiting For Cousteau' *Polydor
843614-2(CD) -4(Cass)see also* 'GRAND SPORTSMASTERS'
SPORTSNIGHT (BBC1 70-93) title theme (Tony Hatch) *see*
Coll 'A-Z OF BRITISH TV THEMES'/'TV CLASSICS VOL.4'
SPYSHIP (BBC1 9/11/83) Theme "A Cold Wind" (Richard Har
vey) Royal Philhar Orch with vocal by JUNE TABOR on
collection 'Hooked on Themes' *K-Tel: ONCD 3435 (CD)*
SQUADRON (BBC1 80) Theme (Anthony Isaac) 'Military Band
Coll' - *Conifer: CFRC 503 (LP) MCFRC 503 (Cass)*
SQUARE DEAL (LWT 3/9/88) Title theme (Brian Bennett)
see Coll '20 GREAT TV THEMES'
ST. - *see under* 'SAINT...'

STAB IN THE DARK A (C4 5/6/92) music (David Arch)....*NA*
STALAG LUFT (Yorkshire 27/10/93) mus (Stanley Myers).*NA*
STANDING ROOM ONLY (BBC2 23/9/91)mus (Mykaell Riley).*NA*
STANLEY AND THE WOMEN (Central 28/11/91) music (Barring
   ton Pheloung).....................................*NA*
STAR CHAMBER (C4 16/2/92) theme music (Chris Andrews-
   Jonathan Sorrel)..................................*NA*
STAR COPS (BBC2 6/7/87)Theme "It Won't Be Easy" (J.Hayw
   ard) JUSTIN HAYWARD *Coll* 'BEST OF BBCTV TH.'*deleted*
STAR PETS (BBC1 24/9/92) title music (Nigel Hopkins).*NA*
STAR TEST (C4 4/4/89) theme mus (Jonathan Sorrell and
   Chris Andrews)....................................*NA*
STAR TREK (USA 66) Theme music (Alexander Courage) *note*
   all STAR TREK items are distributed by SILVA SCREEN
   25TH ANNIVERSARY (The Astral Symphony) Featur music
   inc theme *Milan (Pinn) 262 832 (CD) 412 832 (Cass)*
   CLASSIC SERIES V.1 *GNPD 8006 (CD) GNP-5 8006 (Cass)*
   CLASSIC SERIES V.2 *GNPD 8025 (CD) GNP-5 8025 (Cass)*
   CLASSIC SERIES V.3 *GNPD 8030 (CD) GNP-5 8030 (Cass)*
   SOUND EFFECTS (60) *GNPD 8010 (CD) GNP-5 8010 (Cass)*
   TV SCORES V.1 with R.P.Orch - *CBS USA: LXE 703 (CD)*
   TV SCORES V.2 with R.P.Orch - *CBS USA: LXE 704 (CD)*
STAR TREK: THE NEXT GENERATION (USA 88) (BBC2-26/9/90)
   New Theme (Jerry Goldsmith-Alexander Courage) plus
   music by Dennis McCarthy - *all dist.by Silva Screen*
   Volume 1 - *GNPD 8012 (CD) GNP-5 8012 (Cass)*
   Volume 2 - *GNPD 8026 (CD) GNP-5 8026 (Cass)*
   Volume 3 - *GNPD 8031 (CD) GNP-5 8031 (Cass)*
STAR TREK: DEEP SPACE NINE (USA/SKY1 15/8/93) Music by:
   (Dennis McCarthy-Jay Chattaway) -S/T- *GNP USA (Sil.*
   Screen): GNPD 8034 (CD) GNP-5 8034 (Cass)
STAR TREK (Films) - *see FILMS & SHOWS section*
STARSKY & HUTCH (USA 75) Theme "Gotcha" (Tom Scott) *see*
   Coll 'GREAT TV THEMES VOLUME 3' *note:* Other themes
   were by Lalo Schifrin and Mark Snow *(now deleted)*
START YOUR OWN RELIGION (BBC1 6/9/92) m:(Andrew Neve)*NA*
STATEMENT OF AFFAIRS,A (Carl.8/3/93) m: (Hal Lindes).*NA*
STATES OF AMERICA (C4 12/4/93) m.(Elizabeth Bennett).*NA*
STATES OF MIND (BBC2 8/7/92) music (Thomas A.Naunas).*NA*
STATES OF TERROR (BBC1 17/11/93) mus (Mark T.White)..*NA*
STAY LUCKY (Yorkshire 8/12/89) music (Danny Chang-Mike
            Price) theme sung by DENNIS WATERMAN.....*NA*
STAY TOONED (BBC1 from 17/3/90) theme (Mark Pringle).*NA*
STEPTOE & SON (BBC 64) Theme "Old Ned" (Ron Grainer)
   see Coll 'A-Z OF BRITISH TV THEMES'/'TV CLASSICS 3'
   Original Cast Recording on *BBC: ZBBC 1145 (Cass)*
STEVEN SPIELBERG'S AMAZING STORIES (USA Amblin/MCA-BBC1
   19/4/92) music (John Williams)....................*NA*
STINGRAY (ATV/ITC 6/10/64 reshown BBC2 11/9/92) Music
   (Barry Gray) *see Coll:* 'F.A.B.-THUNDERBIRDS' and
   'ITV CHILDREN'S THEMES'/'A-Z OF BRITISH TV THEMES'
   'TV CLASSICS VOLUME 1' *(vocal sung by* GARRY MILLER)
STINGRAY (USA-90) Theme (Mike Post and Pete Carpenter)
   see Collection 'AMERICAN TELEVISION THEMES VOL.3'

STOLEN CHILDHOOD (C4 14/10/89) Theme 'Cradle Song' Wieg
    enlied Op.49 No.4 'Lullaby' (Brahms) MARY O'HARA on
    'World Of Music' *MFP: CDMFP 6073 (CD) (TC)MFP 5870*
STORM FROM THE EAST (BBC/NHK Co-Prod BBC2 10/8/93) orig
    music (Richard Attree) ....*NA*
STRANGERS (Austr/C4 14/3/93) music (Matthew Brown)...*NA*
STRATHBLAIR (BBC1 Scot 3/5/92) music (Michael Gibbs).*NA*
STREET LEGAL (C4 25/4/93) theme mu.(Howard Davidson).*NA*
STREET The (USA 88/C4 7/7/91) theme (Jack Holder)....*NA*
STREETHAWK (USA 84 ITV)Theme by TANGERINE DREAM on *Jive*
    Electro: JIVE(T) 101 (7"/12") Coll 'FANTASTIC TV..'
STREETS OF SAN FRANCISCO (USA 72) Theme (Pat Williams)
    'Dynamic Sound Of JOHNNY GREGORY'*Phil:846 833-2(CD)*
STREETWISE (TVS 25/9/89) music (Rod Thompson)........*NA*
STRICTLY CLASSIFIED (Gran 25/4/93)m.(Patrick Dineen).*NA*
STUDIO 5B (USA 89 BBC2 20/6/89) theme music (Mike Post)
    see Coll 'TELEVISION MUSIC OF MIKE POST'
SUE LAWLEY (Granada 1/4/91) music (Craig Pruess).....*NA*
SULLIVANS The (Australia 79) Theme (Geoff Harvey) *see*
    Coll 'AUSTRALIAN TELEVISION'S GREATEST HITS'
SUMMER WITH SELIK (BBC1 20/8/93) music (Dave Hewson).*NA*
SUMMER'S LEASE (BBC2 1/11/89) Theme m: "Carmina Valles"
    (Nigel Hess) sung by CHAMELEON on 'Chameleon'- *Fly*
    (Total-BMG): FLYCD 100 (CD) FLYLP(MC) 100 (LP/Cas)
    see Collection 'FAVOURITE TV THEMES'
SUMO (Cheerleader/C4 from 26/1/88) orig music composed
    & performed by PETE QUINTON 'Sumo Music CD' *only*
    available from CHEERLEADER PRODUCT. (081 995 7778)
SUNDAY SUPPLEMENT (Centr.16/5/93) mus (Chris Taylor).*NA*
SUPERBODS (BBC1 25/10/91) mus (Allan Rogers-J.Cohen).*NA*
SUPERDOGS (BBC1 3/11/89) Theme "Powerplay" by MEGABYTE
    on *Thunderbolt (MMG): CDTB 2.049 (CD) THBL 2.049 LP*
SUPERGRAN (T-Tees 20/1/85) Theme (P.Coulter-B.Connolly)
    BILLY CONNOLLY - *see Coll* 'ITV CHILDREN'S THEMES'
SUPERMARKET SWEEP (ITV 5/9/93) music (Kevin Kitchen).*NA*
SURGICAL SPIRIT (Gran 14/4/89) theme (David Cullen)..*NA*
SURPRISE SURPRISE (LWT 14/10/84) Title song (Kate Robbi
    ns) by CILLA BLACK - *Towerbell (ZC)TVLP 10 deleted*
SURVIVAL (Anglia) *see under* 'MADAGASCAR'/'DESERT SONG'
SURVIVAL CHALLENGE (BBC1 8/1/88) Theme "When The Going
    Gets Tough" (BILLY OCEAN) from 'Jewel Of The Nile'
SURVIVAL GUIDE TO FOOD The (BBC1 30/8/92) theme mus "If
    You Can't Stand The Heat" (Andy Hill-Ian Bairson)
    BUCKS FIZZ 'Greatest Hits' *RCA (BMG): PD 70022 (CD)*
SUTHERLAND'S LAW (BBC1 76) Theme (Hamish MacCunn) ROYAL
    MARINES *(TC)MFP 5789 (Cass/LP)* WELSH GUARDS BAND on
    Grasmere (Taylors): GRALP 13 (LP) GRTC 13 (Cas)
SWEENEY The (Thames 2/1/75) Theme music (Harry South)
    see Collection 'ITV THEMES'
SWEET INSPIRATION (BBC1 6/6/93) music prod.by Bob Prize
    man-Ian Lynn & recorded by Steve Lowe-Ian Tilley.*NA*
SWIMMING (European Championships 93 from Sheffield UK)
    (BBC2 31/7/93) theme "The Lebanon" by HUMAN LEAGUE
    on 'Greatest Hits' *Virgin (Poly): HL(CD)(MC)(MD) 1*

SWORD OF TIPU SULTAN The (C4 7/7/91) music (Naushad).*NA*
SYSTEM 93 (Meridian/EBU Children's Prod/BBC2 25/7/93)
music theme (Harvey Brough-Rex Brough)...........*NA*

TAGGART (Scottish TV began 2/7/85) Music (Mike Moran)
theme "No Mean City" (M.Moran) sung by MAGGIE BELL
theme and music from the series on *Soundtrack Music
(EMI): CDSTM 1 (CD) TCSTM 1 (Cass)*
TAKE ME HOME (BBC1 2/5/89) Theme "The Very Thing" from
'Raintown' composed and performed by DEACON BLUE on
CBS: 450549-2 (CD) 450549-1 (LP) 450549-4 (Cass)
TAKE THE HIGH ROAD (Scotl from 81) Theme (Arthur Blake)
SILLY WIZARD - *Highway: (Celtic Mus) SHY 100 (7"s)*
TAKE THREE WOMEN (BBC2 21/9/82) Theme "Light Flight" by
PENTANGLE-*Trans.Demon (Pinn): TRANDEM(CD) 7 (LP/CD)*
TAKE YOUR PICK (Thames 24/2/92) theme (Des O'Connor).*NA*
TAKEOVER BID (BBC1 26/5/90) theme mus (Ian Wilson-Bruce
Forsyth) sung by BRUCE FORSYTH.................*NA*
TAKING THE FLOOR (BBC1/Alomo 4/3/91) music (Denis King)
see 'LOVEJOY' *Collection*
TALES FROM BORGES (BBC2 18/10/93)m:(Alejandro Masso).*NA*
TALES FROM THE CRYPT (USA HBO TV series) various music
-S/T- *Import (Sil.Screen): 924 462-2 (CD) -4 (Cass)*
TALES FROM THE GOLD MONKEY (USA) theme (Mike Post-Pete
Carpenter) *see Coll* 'FANTASTIC TELEVISION THEMES' &
'TELEVISION MUSIV OF MIKE POST AND PETER CARPENTER
TALES F.T.HOLLYWOOD HILLS(C4 20/2/93) m:(Dick Hyman).*NA*
TALES FROM THE MAP ROOM (Ambrose Video/BBC2 6/5/93)
original music (Andy Roberts)................*NA*
TALES FROM THE POOP DECK (Central/Talkback Prod 7/4/92)
music (Pete Brewis).........................*NA*
TALES OF GOLD (BBC1/Chrysalis) music (Steve Parsons).*NA*
TALES OF THE CITY (C4 28/9/93) orig music (John Keane)
music supervor: Bob Last. *score music not available*
'Tales Of The City' 20 Classic Tracks inspired by
the TV series including "Never Can Say Goodbye" by
GLORIA GAYNOR plus songs by DONNA SUMMER-BEE GEES-
ELTON JOHN-KC & SUNSHINE BAND-LABELLE-WILD CHERRY-
KOOL & GANG-ANDREA TRUE CONNECTION-ISLEY BROS-HOT
CHOCOLATE-EDWIN STARR-BARRY WHITE-JAMES BROWN-JULIE
LONDON-10CC-J.J.CALE-JOHNNY BRISTOL-TAVARES-SOUL SE
SENASTION *Polygram: 516 515-2 (CD) 516 515-4 (Cass)*
TALES OF THE RODENT SHERLOCK HOLMES (BBC1 3/3/90) Music
opening mus."Stroking"/ closing mus."Synchronising"
(M.Nyman) on 'The Kiss And Other Movements' MICHAEL
NYMAN on *EG-Virgin (Poly): EGED(C)(CD) 40 (CD/Cass)*
TALES OF THE TOOTH FAIRIES (BBC1 7/9/93) Music (Gerard
Labady) title song (Jimmy McDonnell-Randy Peterson
Robin Lyons)................................*NA*
TALES OF THE UNEXPECTED (Anglia 79-87) Theme (Ron Grain
er) *see Coll* 'FAVOURITE TV THEMES'/'20 GREAT TV..'
'ITV THEMES'
TALKING HEADS (BBC2 19/4/88 & 10/1/89) Music (George Fe
nton) Orig Cast w: Alan Bennett *BBC: ZBBC 1097 Cass*

TALKING SHOW (C4 9/11/93) music (Robert Lockhart)....*NA*
TALKING TO MYSELF (BBC2 Bristol 30/1/92) theme music
     (Ian Butcher and Andrew Wilson)..................*NA*
TASTES OF WALES (BBC1 8/7/91) mus (Heneghan/Lawson)..*NA*
TAXI (USA 78) Theme "Angela" (Bob James) *see Collection*
     'GREAT TV THEMES VOLUME 4'
TEENAGE DIARIES (BBC2 6/6/92) theme (Richard Attree).*NA*
TEENAGE HEALTH FREAK (C4 21/5/91) mus (Pete Baikie)..*NA*
TELL-TALE HEARTS (BBC1 1/11/92) mus (Philip Appleby).*NA*
     opening theme "The Twelfth Of Never" (J.Livingston-
     P.F.Webster) sung by JOHNNY MATHIS on '16 Most Requ
     ested Songs' *Columbia (Sony):472 047-2(CD) -4(Cass)*
TELLY ADDICTS (BBC1 3/9/85) theme (George Fenton)....*NA*
TENDER IS THE NIGHT (BBC2 23/9/85) Music (Richard R.Ben
     nett) *Coll* 'BEST OF BBC TV THEMES' *deleted*
TENKO (UKGold 6/11/92 orig BBC1 22/10/81) theme music
     (James Harpham)..................................*NA*
TENNIS (Federation Cup 91) (BBC1-24/7/91) Theme "Layla"
     (Eric Clapton) by DEREK & THE DOMINOS on *Polydor:*
     PO 163 (7") PZ 163 (12")POCS 163 (MC) PZCZ 163 (CD)
     see also under 'WIMBLEDON'
TENNIS (US Tennis Open) theme "Something For The Leprec
     haun" (Henry Mancini) JAMES GALWAY *RCA (BMG): 09026*
     61178-2(CD) -4(Cass)   *see also under* 'WIMBLEDON'
TERRY & JULIAN (C4 11/9/92) theme mus (Russell Churney-
     Barb Jungr-Michael Parker) *not available* ALSO USED
     "Durham Town" ROGER WHITTAKER *Old Gold: OG 9589 7"s*
TERRY AND JUNE (UKGold 2/11/92 orig BBC1 78) theme mus
     "Bell Hop" (John Shakespeare)....................*NA*
TERRY WOGAN'S FRIDAY NIGHT (BBC1 2/10/92) title music
     by EMOTIONAL......................................*NA*
TESTAMENT (C4 6/11/88) Theme mus (NIGEL HESS) *see Coll*
     'SCREENS & STAGES'/'20 TOP TV THEMES'
TESTAMENT OF YOUTH (BBC2 4/11/79 re-shown BBC2 3/10/92)
     Theme music (Geoffrey Burgon) *see Coll* 'BRIDESHEAD
     REVISITED AND OTHER MUSIC BY GEOFFREY BURGON'
TEX AVERY CARTOONS (USA/BBC2 Various) Music (Scott Brad
     ley) -S/T- *Milan (RTM-Pinn): 12470-2 (CD) -4 (Cass)*
THACKER (BBC1 20/4/92) music (John Du Prez)..........*NA*
THANK YOUR LUCKY STARS (ATV 60's) Theme music (Peter
     Knight) *see Coll* 'TV CLASSICS VOLUME 3'
THATCHER: The Downing Street Years (BBC1 20/10/93) orig
     music composed and conducted by (Carl Davis).....*NA*
THAT'S HISTORY (Border 9/8/91) Theme 'Concerto For Oboe
     & Strings No.6 op.7'(Albinoni)TV arr:Colin Campbell
THAT'S LIFE (BBC1 1973-93) Signature mus (Dave Lee)..*NA*
THAT'S LOVE (TVS from 19/1/88) Title song "That's Love"
     (Richard Myhill) sung by PAUL JOHNSON............*NA*
THAT'S SHOWBUSINESS (BBC1 11/4/92) theme music (Debbie
     Wiseman) and (BBC1 20/5/89 series Ed Welch)......*NA*
THEATRE SCHOOL (BBC2 31/10/93) mus (Guy Fletcher) song
     "(Don't Put Your Daughter On The Stage) Mrs.Worth
     ington" (Noel Coward) NOEL COWARD 'Classic Record
     ings' *Happy Days (Conif): CDHD(MCHD) 168 (CD/Cass)*

THEIR LORDSHIPS'HOUSE (C4 7/4/86) Theme "Odissea" (Gian
   Reverberi) RONDO VENEZIANO - *Fanfare: CD(ZC)RON 5*
THEM AND US (BBC1 1/7/91) theme music (Craig Charles-
   Ian Ritchie).....................................*NA*
THERE IS MUSIC IN THE AIR (BBC2 6/1/91) theme "Andante"
   from 'Enigma Variations op.36' (Sir Edward Elgar)
THICKER THAN WATER (BBC Wales/BBC1 29/7/93) music score
   (Julian Wastall-Daemion Barry)...................*NA*
THIEBEAUD THE CRUSADER (Int.TV ser) Music sco (Georges
   Delerue) -S/T- *Import (Silva Screen): PCD 114 (CD)*
THING IS..BOREDOM (C4 29/4/92) mus (Steve Beresford).*NA*
THINK OF ENGLAND (BBC1 15/10/91) mus (Rachel Portman)*NA*
THIRD AGE The (BBC2 21/10/93)title mus (Xian Vassie).*NA*
THIRD MAN The (BBC1 20/6/88)(o.59-62) Theme "Harry Lime
   Theme" (A.Karas) ANTON KARAS on *Decca SPA 118 (LP)*
   'Third Man' coll *Decca: 421 264-2 (CD) -4 (Cass)*
THIRD WAVE (C4 16/10/90) Theme "Help" (John Lennon-Paul
   McCartney) Baroque Chamber Orch on 'The Beatles Sea
   sons' *EMI: CDP 746873-2 (CD) (TC)SCX 6708 (Cass/LP)*
THIRTYSOMETHING (USA)(C4 18/1/89) theme (W.G.Snuffy Wal
   den-Stewart Levin) Orig TV -S/T- *Geffen (BMG):*
   GEFB(GEFC) 24413 (CD/Cass) all deleted / *theme on:-*
   'GREAT TV THEMES VOL.4'/'AMERICAN TV THEMES VOL.2'
THIS IS HORROR (USA/John Simmons Prod 89/ITV 2/9/91)
   theme comp & performed by Gary William Friedman..*NA*
THIS IS YOUR LIFE (Thames 68-93) Music (Laurie Johnson)
   see Coll 'ROSE AND THE GUN'/'SOUNDS VISUAL'/'GREAT
   TV THEMES VOLUME 2'/'ITV THEMES'
THIS MORNING (Gran 3/10/88-94) theme (David Pringle).*NA*
THIS WEEK (Thames) Theme "Alla Marcia 3 -Karelia Suite"
   (Sibelius) - Academy of Saint Martin-in-the-Fields
   (Neville Marriner) - *Philips (Poly): 412727-2 (CD)*
THOMAS AND SARAH (LWT 14/1/79) Music (Harry Rabinowitz)
   see Coll 'HIT THEMES 1 - BEST OF BRITISH TV MUSIC'
THOMAS THE TANK ENGINE & FRIENDS (ITV 25/2/92 narrator:
   Michael Angelis. Theme music (Junior Campbell-Mike
   O'Donnell) *MFP (EMI): TCMFP 6104 (Cass)*
THOMPSON (BBC1 10/11/88) Theme "Unsquare Dance" (Dave
   Brubeck) DAVE BRUBECK *Pickwick: ELITE 009CD (CD)*
THORA ON THE STRAIGHT AND NARROW (BBC1 4/7/93) music
   director (Robert Prizeman) with ANGEL VOICES.....*NA*
THORN BIRDS The (USA BBC1 8/1/84) Music (Henry Mancini)
   WB (WEA): 925090-1/-4 (LP/Cas) / Theme also on 'Man
   cini's Greatest Hits' by Cinncinati Pops Orchestra
   (Eric Kunzel) on *Telarc USA (Conif): CD 80183 (CD)*
   'Cathedral' seq.music "Panis Angelicus" (C.Franck)
   St.Philips Choir *BBC: BBCD 692 (CD) ZCF 692 (Cass)*
THREE D (3D) (ITV 25/2/93) title mus (Music Force)...*NA*
THREE OF A KIND (UKGold 2/11/92 orig BBC2 81) theme mus
   (Peter Brewis).....................................*NA*
THREE SEVEN ELEVEN (Gran 17/2/93) m: (Tony McAnaney).*NA*
THREE TENORS CONCERT see 'CARRERAS-DOMINGO-PAVAROTTI'
THROUGH THE KEYHOLE (YTV from 3/4/87) theme music by
   Philip Pope and James Simpson....................*NA*

THUNDERBIRDS! (ATV/ITC 30/9/65-66 reshown BBC2 20/9/91)
Music (Barry Gray) *see Coll:* 'F.A.B.-THUNDERBIRDS'/
'NO STRINGS ATTACHED'/''A-Z OF BRITISH THEMES'/'TV
CLASSICS VOLUME 1'/'ITV THEMES'
THUNDERBIRDS ARE GO! (Film 67) Music score from film &
TV series by BARRY GRAY - *Silva Screen (BMG): FILM
018 (LP) FILMC 018 (Cass) FILMCD 018 (Compact Disc)*
TIGHTS CAMERA ACTION (C4 20/9/92) t.mus (Steve Blake)*NA*
TILL DEATH US DO PART (UKGold 7/11/92 orig BBC1 1972)
theme music (Dennis Wilson)....................*NA*
TILL WE MEET AGAIN (USA) Yorks 27/12/89 Theme "My Life
Will Never Be The Same" (Vladimir Cosma) sung by
MIREILLE MATTHIEU-S/T- *Colosseum(Pinn):XCD1003 (CD)*
TIME BUSTERS (Broadsword for BBC2 17/1/93) theme and
incidental music by BRAVE/STEADY STATE..........*NA*
TIME OF HER LIFE (BBC1 16/5/93) music (Simon Davison)
vocals (Mary Phillips) Music Studio Recordings...*NA*
TIME RIDERS (Thames 16/10/91) music (Debbie Wiseman).*NA*
TIME TO DANCE A (BBC1 12/1/92) mus (Howard Goodall)..*NA*
TIME TUNNEL (USA 66) Theme (John Williams) *see Collect*
'GREATEST SCI-FI HITS VOL.1'/'TELEVISION'S G.HITS2'
TINKER TAILOR SOLDIER SPY (BBC1 10/9/79) Theme "Nunc Di
mittis" (Geoffrey Burgon) Seaford College Chapel Cho
Choir *Grasmere (Tayl): GRALP 14 (LP) GRTC 14 (Cass)*
see Coll 'BRIDESHEAD REVISITED AND OTHER MUSIC'
TIN TIN (France/C4 18/10/92) theme and incidental music
(Ray Parker-Jim Morgan-Tom Szczesniak)..........*NA*
TINY TOON ADVENTURES (USA/Speilberg-ITV-2/9/91) music
composed and performed by BRUCE BROUGHTON........*NA*
TITCHMARSH ON SONG (BBC1 21/6/92)m:(Robert Prizeman).*NA*
TITMUSS REGAINED (Thames 3/9/91) music (Nigel Hess) *see
Collection* 'MAIGRET & OTHER TV THEMES'
TO HAVE AND TO HOLD (LWT 29/8/86) Theme (John Worth) by
CATHERINE STOCK *Coll* 'HIT THEMES 1'/'20 GREAT TV..'
TO PLAY THE KING (BBC1 21/11/93) Music (Jim Parker)..*NA*
TO SERVE THEM ALL MY DAYS (UKGO 12/9/93 orig BBC 10/80)
theme music (Kenyon Emrys-Roberts) *BBC deleted*
TO THE MANOR BORN (UKGold 8/11/92 orig BBC1 30/9/79)
theme music (Ronnie Hazlehurst) *deleted*
TODAY'S GOURMET (USA 91 BBC1 8/6/92) mus (Ed Bogas)..*NA*
TODAY'S THE DAY (BBC2 12/7/93) music (Joe Glasman)...*NA*
TOM ALONE (Canada/BBC1 22/7/93) music (Louis Natale).*NA*
TOMORROW PEOPLE The (Tetra/Thames 18/11/92) Music (Tim
Pitt-Bobby Boughton) Andrew Graham: mus.research.*NA*
TOMORROW PEOPLE The (Thames 30/4/73-79) Music (Dudley
Simpson and Brian Hodson) *see Collection:* 'MAN FROM
U.N.C.L.E. - MUSIC FROM CULT TV CLASSICS'
TOMORROW'S END (Aust/BBC1 13/7/93) m: (Ian Davidson).*NA*
TOMORROW'S WORLD (BBC1) 1991-93 ser.theme (BBC Radiopho
nic Workshop) *unavailable* / 1986-91 theme "Halley's
Comet" (Paul Hart) *Coll* 'Best Of BBCTV Th..'*deleted*
72-80 theme(John Dankworth) *Col* 'On The Air'*deleted*
TONIGHT AT 8.30 (BBC1 14/4/91) theme "If Love Were All"
(Noel Coward) Music Director: Burt Rhodes........*NA*

TONIGHT WITH JONATHAN ROSS (C4 from 5/11/90)theme music
(Steve Nieve) played by STEVE NIEVE & HIS BAND...*NA*
TOP CAT (USA 61/85) Theme (Hoyt Curtin) *see Coll* 'TELEV
ISION'S GREATEST HITS VOLUME 1'
TOP GEAR (BBC2 70's-93) *Opening theme* "Jessica" (ALLMAN
BROTHERS BAND) *see Coll* 'MOODS 2' *Closing theme* "Bl
ue Moves" (Elton John-Bernie Taupin) ELTON JOHN on
Rocket (Poly):   822 818-2 (CD) 822 818-4 (Cass)
TOP OF THE HILL (USA) Theme music (Mike Post) *see Coll*
'AMERICAN TELEVISION THEMES VOLUME 3'
TOP OF THE POPS (BBC1 1/1/64-1994) Theme (3/10/91-1993)
(Tony Gibber-*not available*) (1986-91) "The Wizard"
PAUL HARDCASTLE 'World Of BBC TV Themes' *BBC delet*
(1982-85) "Yellow Pearl" (Midge Ure-Phil Lynott) on
Vertigo: PRICE(PRIMC) 88 (LP/Cass) (1970-76) "Whole
Lotta Love" (Led Zeppelin) CCS *(EMI: CD/Cass)* LED
ZEPPELIN - *Atlantic (WEA): K(2)(4) 40037*
TOP SECRET (ITV 11/8/61-62) Theme "Sucu Sucu" (Laurie
Johnson) *see Coll* 'A-Z OF BRITISH TV THEMES'/'TV
CLASSICS VOL.4'
TORCH The (Czech/BBC1 24/4/92) music (John Moore)....*NA*
TOTS TV (Central 4/1/93) mus (Andrew McCrorie-Shand).*NA*
TOUCH OF FROST A (ITV 6/12/92) music composed/performed
by BARBARA THOMPSON and JON HISEMAN..............*NA*
TOUR DE FRANCE (TSL/C4 8/7/91) theme (Peter Shelley).*NA*
note: earlier ser.theme on *Coll* 'GOLD 18 SPORTING.'
TOUR OF DUTY (USA 87)(ITV 7/11/89) Theme music "Paint
It Black" (M.Jagger-K.Richards) THE ROLLING STONES
'Hot Rocks 1964-71' *London:820140-2 (2CD) 820140-4*
TOWN LIKE ALICE A (TV Australia)(C4 12/4/88 & 16/7/90)
Music score (Bruce Smeaton) TV Soundtrack: *Southern
Cross (Silva Screen): SCCD 1013 (CD)*
TRAFFIK (C4 22/6/89) Theme arr.by Fiacha Trench of part
of Chamber Symph.For Strings Op.110A (Shostakovich)
Chandos (Chandos): CHAN 8357 (CD) ABTD 1120 (Cass)
TRAINER (BBC1 1/9/91) theme "More To Life" (Simon May-
Mike Read) performed by CLIFF RICHARD *EMI: CDEM 205
(CDs) TCEM 205 (Cass) EM 205 (7")* TV -S/T- feat mus
ic from series and KYM MAZELLE "Woman Of The World"
EMI: CDEMC 3601 (CD) TCEMC 3601 (Cass) deleted
TRAVEL UK (Central 9/3/93) music (Kerry Minnear).....*NA*
TRAVELLER'S TALES (C4 1/7/91) music (Hal Lindes).....*NA*
TRAVELLING MAN (Granada 3/9/85) Theme (Duncan Browne &
Sebastian Graham Jones) *see Coll* 'GRANADA STUDIOS'
TRAVELOG (C4 17/11/93) m: (Tolga Kashif-Mark S.Wade).*NA*
TREASURE HOUSES (BBC1 11/9/85)Theme music "Duetto" from
'Apollo' (Stravinsky) *Argo: 411 728-1 (LP) -4(Cass)*
TREATY The (Thames/RTE/ABC 15/1/92) music sco. (Micheal
O'Suilleabhain from album 'Oilean' *Virgin Venture:
CDVE 40 (CD) TCVE 40 (Cass) VE 40 (LP)*
TRIAL AND ERROR (C4 8/4/93) thememusic (Alan Coates &
Kim Goody)...*NA*
TRIALS OF LIFE (BBC1 3/10/90) Mus score (George Fenton)
Prestige (BMG): CDSGP 030 (CD) CASSGP 030 (Cass)

TRIALS OF ROSIE O'NEILL The (ITV 15/2/91 USA 90) theme music "I Wish I Knew" (Carole King) sung by MELISSA MANCHESTER *not available Music score Ron Ramin...NA*
TRIANGLE (BBC1 81) Theme (Johnny Pearson) on 'Themes & Dreams' JOHNNY PEARSON - *President: PRCD 132 (CD)*
TRICKS 'N' TRACKS (BBC1 9/4/92) music (Martin Cook)..*NA*
TROUBLE WITH MEDICINE The (BBC2/13WNET Co-Prod 7/1/93) music (Elizabeth Parker: BBC Radiophon.Workshop).*NA*
TROUBLESHOOTER 2 (BBC2 10/11/92) mus (Michael Nyman).*NA*
TRUCKERS (Thames 10/1/92) music (Colin Towns)........*NA*
TRUE ADVENTURES OF CHRISTOPHER COLUMBUS (BBC2 28/7/92) Original music (Richard Blackford)...............*NA*
TRUE CRIMES (Michael Winner's) (LWT 6/6/92) mus (Southb ank Sound Design/Rick Cassman/Vyv Hope-Scott)....*NA*
TRUE STORIES (YTV 2/4/92) music (Christopher Norton).*NA*
TRULY MADLY DEEPLY (BBC2 Screen Two 1/3/92) music score (Barrington Pheloung *not available*) / other music:- Sonata No.3 in G.Min.BVW 1029 3rd m/ment (J.S.Bach)
TRUMPTON (BBC1 1966) Songs (Freddie Phillips) *see Coll* 'THEMES FROM CHILDREN'S BBC'
TRYING TIMES (USA 87 / BBC2 12/1/92) theme music (James Newton Howard)................................*NA*
TUBE The (C4 Tyne Tees 82-84) Theme "Star Cycle" (JEFF BECK) 'Best Of Beckology' *Epic:471348-2 (CD) -4Cass*
TV HEAVEN (C4/Illumin.8/2/92) music (Alan Lawrence)..*NA*
TV NEWSREEL (BBC 50's) Theme "Girls In Grey" (Charles Williams) *see Coll* 'FAMOUS THEMES REMEMBER THESE'
TV WEEKLY (Meridian 9/9/93) Theme music (Simon May)..*NA*
21 JUMP STREET (USA) theme music (Liam Sternberg) *see Coll* 'AMERICAN TV THEMES VOLUME 1'
TWILIGHT ZONE The (USA 60's) Theme (Bernard Herrmann) *see Coll* 'GREATEST SC-FI HITS VOL 2'
NOTE: New 1986 series theme by Grateful Dead & Merl Saunders *(unavailable)* (Orig theme Marius Constant)
TWIN PEAKS (USA 90)(BBC2-23/10/90) Music score (Angelo Badalamenti) Songs (David Lynch-Angelo Badalamenti) "Falling" sung by JULEE CRUISE 'Music From Twin Pea ks' *W.Bros: 7599 26316-2 (CD) -4 (Cass) see Collec* 'AMERICAN TV THEMES VOL1' see also FILMS & SHOWS
TWO OF US The (LWT 31/10/86)Theme (Rod Argent-Peter Van Hooke) SILSOE *Coll* '20 GREAT TV THEMES'/ITV THEMES'
TWO POINT FOUR CHILDREN (BBC1 3/9/91) theme mus (Howard Goodall)..................................*NA*
TWO SECONDS TO MIDNIGHT (BBC2/Discovery C.6/6/93) music (Nigel Beaham Powell and Bella Russell)..........*NA*
U.F.O. (ATV/ITC 16/9/70-73) Music (Barry Gray) *see Coll* 'F.A.B.-THUNDERBIRDS'
UN-AMERICANS The (BBC2 2/9/92) title m:(Larry Adler).*NA*
UNCLE JACK.(BBC1 1/10/92) music dir (Jonathan Cohen).*NA*
UNDERBELLY (BBC2 17/2/92) theme music (Bill Connor)..*NA*
UNITED (BBC2 6/4/90) Theme "United" (Ken Downing-Robert Halford) JUDAS PRIEST *CBS: CBSCD 32412 (CD) 40-Cass*
UNNATURAL PURSUITS (BBC2/Arts & Ent 7/12/92) original music (Robert Lockhart)......................*NA*

UP AND UNDER (BBC2/20:20 Prod) title song composed & sung by GEORGIE FAME.......................*NA*

UP THE GARDEN PATH (Granada 2/5/90) Theme "Ain't Misbeh avin'" (T.'Fats'Waller-H.Brooks-A.Razaf) TV version arr.Nigel Hess sung by IMELDA STAUNTON *unavailable*

UPPER HAND The (Central 1/5/90) mus (Debbie Wiseman).*NA*

UPSTAIRS DOWNSTAIRS (LWT 70 rep C4-13/11/82) Theme "The Edwardians" (Alexander Faris) *see Coll* 'FAVOURITE TV THEMES'/'HIT THEMES 1'/'20 GREAT TV THEMES'/'GRE AT TV THEMES VOLUME 1'/'ITV THEMES'

US GIRLS (BBC1 27/2/92) theme (Nigel Hess) *see Collect* 'MAIGRET & OTHER TV THEMES'

UTTERLY BRILLIANT (YTV from 5/1/90) Theme music (Adrian Burch-David Whitaker).......................*NA*

V: THE SERIES (USA 84 ITV 2/1/89) Theme music (Dennis McCarthy) *see Coll.* 'FANTASTIC TELEVISION THEMES' Orchestral score by (JOE HARNELL) on *5JAYS (Silva Screen): 5JAYS 001/002 (2CDs)*

VALERIE (USA BBC1 87)Theme "Together Through The Years" (Charles Fox-Stephen Geyer) by ROBERTA FLACK.....*NA*

VALUED OPINION (C4 12/1/92) music (Amanda Alexander).*NA*

VAMPYR The: A Soap Opera (BBC2 29/12/92) Mus (Heinrich Marschner) Lyrics (Charles Hart) BBC Philharmonic Orch (David Parry) with soloists Richard Van Allen Omar Ebrahim-Fiona O'Neill-Philip Salmon & company *Virgin Classics (EMI): VC 759 294-2 (CD)*

VAN DER VALK (ITV 73) Theme "Eye Level" (Jack Trombey) SIMON PARK ORCHESTRA - *Old Gold: OG 9600 (7"s) also* MATT MONRO (vocal) *EMI: EMTV 23 (LP) TC-EMTV 23 (C)*

VANITY FAIR (UKGold 8/11/92 orig BBC1 6/9/87) Theme mus (Nigel Hess) *see Collect* '20 GREAT TV THEMES'

VELVET CLAW The (BBC1 7/9/92) music (Terry Oldfield).*NA*

VENTURERS (BBC2 14/12/87) Music "Canton" (Japan) 'Tin Drum" - *Virgin: CDV 2209 (CD) OVED(C) 158 (LP/Cass)*

VERDICT IS YOURS The (ITV 59) Theme music "Promenade" from 'Pictures At An Exhibition" (Mussorgsky) - BPO (H.Von Karajan) - *DG (Poly): 423214-2 (CD) -4 (Cas)*

VERY BRITISH COUP A (C4 19/6/88) Theme from 'Great Mass in C.Minor" K.427 (Mozart) New Phil Orc (R.Leppard) Ileana Cotrubas-Kiri Te Kanawa-John Alldis Choir on *EMI: CDC 7.47385-2 (CD) EG 290277-1/-4 (LP/Cass)*

VERY JEAN MUIR (Antelope/C4 2/5/93) mus (Paul Reade).*NA*

VERY PECULIAR PRACTICE A (UKGold 4/11/92 orig BBC2 21/5 /86) theme (Dave Greenslade)sung by ELKIE BROOKS.*NA*

VERY POLISH PRACTICE A (BBC2 6/9/92) mus (Carl Davis)*NA*

VET SCHOOL (YTV 7/9/93) music (Julian Scott).........*NA*

VETS IN THE WILD (C4 6/9/93) orig music (Simon Benson and Michael Tauben).........................*NA*

VIC REEVES BIG NIGHT OUT (C4 from 25/5/90) theme music (Mark Narayn) end theme "Mr.Songwriter" sung by VIC REEVES & WONDER STUFF and "Dizzy" (T.Roe-F.Weller) all on 'I Will Cure You' *Sense-Island (Poly): SIGH 2-11 (CD) SIGH 4-11 (Cass) SIGH 1-11 (LP)*

VICTOR AND HUGO (Thames/Cosgrove-Hall 11/9/92) orig mus
ic by Dave Roylance and Bob Galvin.............*NA*
VICTORIA WOOD AS SEEN ON TV (BBC2 1986) Music (Victoria
Wood) 'Victoria Wood Live' *(EMI): (CD)(TC)SCX 6716*
VICTORIAN KITCHEN GARDEN (BBC2 16/9/87) and also the
VICTORIAN FLOWER GARDEN (BBC2 31/10/91) Theme music by
(Paul Reade) PAUL READE & EMMA JOHNSON previously
on *Collection* 'WORLD OF BBCTV THEMES' *now deleted*
VICTORY AT SEA (USA 50's) Music score (Richard Rodgers)
arranged & conducted by Robert Russell Bennett -TV-
-S/T- *RCA Vict (BMG): 09026 60963-2 (CD)* also 'More
Victory At Sea' *RCA Vict (BMG): 09026 60964-2 (CD)*
also Cinncinnati Pops Orch *Telarc USA (Con) CD80175*
VIDEO DIARIES (BBC2 11/5/91) theme (Richard Attree)..*NA*
VIDEO FANTASIES (C4 10/5/92)mus:(The Infinite Wheel).*NA*
VIDEO VIEW (Thames 5/4/90) theme m: (Debbie Wiseman).*NA*
VIETNAM (BBC1 7/88) Theme "Canon In D" (C.Pachelbel) on
Coll 'Themes & Dreams'/'The Classic Experience 1'/
also used "San Francisco" (J.Phillips) SCOTT McKENZ
IE on *Old Gold: OG 9305 (7")* orig score (W.Motzing)
VIEW The (Carlton 11/3/93) music (David Stephens)....*NA*
VIRGINIAN The (USA 68) Theme (Percy Faith) *see Coll* 'GR
EAT WESTERN THEMES'
VIRTUAL MURDER (BBC1 24/7/92) mus (Harry Robertson)..*NA*
VISION THING The (BBC2 6/10/93) mus (Roger Jackson)..*NA*
VISIONS (Thames from 9/4/89)theme mus "Ode To Don Jose"
(Anne Dudley-J.Jeczalik) ART OF NOISE on 'Ambient
Collect' *China-Chrys (Poly): 843 403-2(CD) -4(Cass)*
VISIT The (Carlton/Wilcox-Bulmer Prod 16/11/93) theme
mus "Caribbean Blue" (Enya) by ENYA from 'Shepherd
Moons' *WEA Int (WEA): 9031 75572-2 (CD) -4 (Cass)*
VISIT The (BBC1 12/6/91)Theme "How Where When" based on
'Canon In D.' (Pachelbel) CLEO LAINE & JAMES GALWAY
RCA Red Seal (BMG): RD 83628 (CD only)
VIVE LA DIFFERENCE (Border 14/1/92) theme "Step Into My
World" performed by GLOBETOWN (One-To-One Prod)..*NA*
VOYAGE TO THE BOTTOM OF THE SEA (US:9/64 C4:5/92) theme
(Paul Sawtell) *see Coll* 'TELEVISION'S G.HITS Vol.2'

WAGON TRAIN (USA 57-C4 2/89) Theme (1)"Roll Along Wagon
Train" (Fain-Brooks) *vocal version by* ROBERT HORTON
on 'TV CLASSICS 4' *Castle (BMG): MBSCD 412 (4CDset)*
Theme (2) "Wagons Ho!" (Jerome Moross) GEOFF LOVE
MFP: HR 418109-4 (Cass) Theme (3) "Wagon Train" (H.
Rene-B.Russell)JOHNNY GREGORY *Ditto:DTO 10200* delet
WAITING FOR GOD (BBC1 28/6/90) Theme 'Piano Quintet in
A'("Trout") D.667 (Schubert) Alan Berg Quartet with
Elisabeth Leonskaja-Georg Hortnagel on *HMV: CDC 747
448-2 (CD) -4(Cass) -1(LP)* TV version not available
WALDEN (LWT 29/9/91) theme music (David Arch)........*NA*
WALK ON THE WILD SIDE (BBC1 7/7/92) music (David Lowe &
Simon King)...............................*NA*
WALK THE TALK (BBC1 7/4/91) music (Nigel Beaham-Powell
and Bella Russell)..........................*NA*

WALL OF SILENCE (BBC1/Alamo 17/10/93) music composed
and conducted (Barrington Pheloung)..............*NA*
WALL The - Berlin Wall Concert (C4 21/7/90) featuring:
Roger Waters-Sinead O'Connor-Bob Dylan-Van Morrison
Joni Mitchell-Bryan Adams-Cyndi Lauper-James Galway
and others *Mercury (Poly): 846 611-2 (CD) -4 (Cass)*
WALTONS The (USA 1972-81) Theme (Jerry Goldsmith) *see
Coll* 'TELEVISION'S G.HITS V.3' *and* '4 AMERICA TWO'
WAR AND REMEMBRANCE (ITV (USA) 3/9/89) Music score (Bob
Cobert) spin-off 'Winds Of War' (ITV 9/83) TV -S/T-
TER: TER 1070 (LP)   ZCTER 1070 (Cass) Theme also on
'Victory At Sea' *Telarc (Con):CD80175 (CD) see* Coll
WAR OF THE WORLDS (USA Paramount 1988/ ITV 30/4/93) Mus
(Billy Thorpe) add.music (Larry Brown)...........*NA*
WAR STORIES (BBC2 12/3/92) theme mus (David Stevens).*NA*
WARTIME KITCHEN AND GARDEN The (BBC2 5/11/93) Title
song (Paul Reade) and sung by Mary Carewe -S/T- on
D.Sharp (Pinn): DSHCD 7012 (CD) DSHMC 7012 (Cass)
WATCHING (Granada from 5/7/87) theme "What Does He See
In Me" (Charles Hart) sung by Emma Wray.........*NA*
WATER UNDER THE BRIDGE (BBC2 6/9/93) music (Andrew Wilt
shire) lyrics: Ray Kolle / orchest: Peter Jones..*NA*
WATER WARS (BBC2 1/5/91)theme mus (Elizabeth Parker).*NA*
WATERWAYS (RTE / C4 12/1/93) music (Ronan Hardiman)..*NA*
WATT ON EARTH (BBC1 11/11/91) Music (Richard Attree).*NA*
WAX CRACKS HOLLYWOOD (BBC2 17/10/93) m:(Simon Brint).*NA*
WAY AHEAD The (BBC1 20/1/92) music (Kevin Stoney)....*NA*
WEDNESDAY WEEPIE (Planet 21/C4 20/1/93) song "Love Is A
Many Splendored Thing" (S.Fain-P.F.Webster) by MATT
MONRO 'EMI Years' *EMI: CZ355 (CD) TCEMS 1377 (Cass)*
WEEK IN POLITICS (C4 26/11/89) mus (Debbie Wiseman)..*NA*
WEEKEND WORLD (LWT 87) Theme "Nantucket Sleighride" (Fe
lix Pappalardi-Leslie West) by MOUNTAIN 'Best Of Mo
untain' *Beat Goes On (Pinn): BGO(CD)(LP) 33 (CD/LP)*
WELCOME BACK KOTTER! (USA 75)Theme mus John B.Sebastian
see Coll 'TELEVISION'S GREATEST HITS VOLUME 3'
WE'LL MEET AGAIN (LWT 19/2/82) theme (Denis King) *see*
'LOVEJOY' *Collection*
WESTBEACH (BBC1 10/4/93) music score (David MacKay)..*NA*
WETTER THE BETTER The (8.15 From Manchester) (BBC1-20/4
91) music (Rick Juckes)..........................*NA*
WEXFORD TRILOGY The (Initial Film/TV for BBC2 31/7/93)
orig music (Orlando Gough) music supervisor (Ken
Bolam) "King Of The Renegades" (Billy Roche).....*NA*
WHAT SHALL WE TELL THE CHILDREN (BBC1 3/1/93) theme mus
(Simon Davison)..................................*NA*
WHAT THE PAPERS SAY (BBC2 23/3/90 previous C4-Granada)
Theme "English Dance No.5" from 'Eight English Danc
es' (Malcolm Arnold) Philharmonic Orch (Thomspon) -
Chandos: CHAN 8867 (CD) ABTD 1482 (LP)
WHAT YOU LOOKIN'AT (LWT 17/7/93) title music (Trix Worr
ell-Julian Moore) incidental mus (John Collins)..*NA*
WHAT'S UP DOC (ITV 5/9/92) mus (Mr.Miller-Mr.Porter).*NA*
WHEN IN GERMANY (BBC1 21/7/91) m: (Elizabeth Parker).*NA*

WHEN THE BOAT COMES IN (UKGold 26/1/93 orig BBC 1975)
     theme "Dance To Your Daddy" (trad.arr: David Fansha
     we) sung by ALEX GLASGOW *(BBC REB 236 deleted) also
     by* BENJAMIN LUXON-Bill Crofut 'Two Gentleman Folk'
     on *Telarc (Conifer): CD 84401 (CD) CS 34401 (Cass)*
WHERE IN THE WORLD (C4 18/3/84) Theme "Trains and Boats
     and Plane" (Burt Bacharach-Hal David) THE SHADOWS
     MFP: 41 5630-1 (LP) 41 5630-4 (CS) CDMFP 6002 (CD)
WHERE THERE'S LIFE (Yorkshire TV) Theme "Oxygene Pt.2'
     JEAN MICHEL JARRE - *Polydor (Poly): 800 015-2 (CD)*
WHERE'S WALLY (USA Waldo Film Co.92/ITV 6/1/93) theme
     music (Jeff Barry) music score (Michael Tavera)..*NA*
WHICKER'S WORLD: A TASTE OF SPAIN (BBC1 3/5/92) theme
     music "Newsweek" (Graham de Wilde) *Coll* BEST OF BBC
     TV THEMES *deleted / also used for* 'WHICKER' series
WHICKER'S WORLD (BBC 60s series) theme "West End" (Laur
     ie Johnson) *see Coll* 'TV CLASSICS VOL.4' *(Castle C)*
WHISTLE TEST (BBC2 29/4/86 final ser) Theme 'Sure Beats
     Workin' (Dave Stewart) BEATS WORKIN' *London FFR(X)8
     (7"s/12"s deleted) see also* 'OLD GREY WHISTLE TEST'
WHITE SHADOW The (USA) theme (Mike Post-Pete Carpenter)
     see Coll 'TELEVISION MUSIC OF MIKE POST'
WHITE TRIBE OF AFRICA The (BBC 79 Re-run 86) Theme "Arr
     ival of Van Ryebeck" 'Magnificat' (Marc-Antoine Cha
     rpentier) also used: 'Symphony 1 in D Maj' (Mahler)
WHO CARES (BBC2 11/5/89) Theme "Minuet" 'L'Arlessiene'
     (Bizet) New Philharmonia Orchestra on *Decca (Polyg)
     421632-2 (CD) -4 (Cass) also EMI: CDC 747794-2 (CD)*
WHO PAYS THE FERRYMAN (UKGold 24/4/93 orig BBC1 1977)
     Music (Yannis Markopoulos) *version* 'GREAT TV THEMES
     Vol.3' *Tring (Tayl):TFP 029 (4CD) MCTFP 029 (4Cass)*
WHO'S BLUFFING WHO (BBC1 20/5/91) mus (Alan Gruner)..*NA*
WHOSE LINE IS IT ANYWAY (C4/Hat Trick Pr) from 23/9/88)
     theme music (Phil Pope).........................*NA*
WIDE AWAKE CLUB (TV AM 84) "Wacaday"(J.Wyatt-A.Frechter
     C.Frechter) sung by THE MINI-POPS - *see Collection*
     'CHILDREN'S WORLD OF TV THEMES'
WIDE EYED AND LEGLESS (BBC Scr.One 5/9/93) music (Colin
     Towns *not available*) song "Wide Eyed and Legless"
     comp/sung by ANDY FAIRWEATHER LOW *(A.& M.deleted)*
WIDOWS (Thames 3/4/85) Music (Stanley Myers) theme "No
     Man's Land" (Gerard Kenny) *WEA: YZ38(T) del / also*
     "What Is Life" 'Orfeo' (Gluck) by KATHLEEN FERRIER
WILD INDIA (Bedi Films/North & South Prod/Discovery Cha
     nnel/C4 16/5/93) orig music (Steve Marshall).....*NA*
WILD PALMS (USA 92/BBC2 15/11/93) Theme and incid.music
     (Ryuichi Sakamoto) and songs by ZOMBIES-DON GARDNER
     & DEE DEE FORD-MASON WILLIAMS-FRANKIE VALLI-LOU CHR
     ISTIE TV -S/T- on *Capitol (EMI): CDEST 2204 (CD)*
WILDBUNCH (BBC1 3/4/91) music (Steve Marshall).......*NA*
WILDERNESS EDGE (Granada 8/5/92) title song composed
     and performed by (Steve Martland)................*NA*
WILDLIFE ON ONE (BBC1 6/1/92 series started 1977) theme
     (Martin Kiszko) BBC Radiophonic Workshop.........*NA*

WILDSHOTS (C4 18/11/93) music: Atmosphere Music......*NA*
WILDTRACK (BBC1 8/1/85) Theme "Florida Fantasy" ('Midni
ght Cowboy') JOHN BARRY *see under* FILMS & SHOWS
WILL TO WIN (BBC2 20/9/93) title mus (ZooBee Music)..*NA*
WILLIAM TELL (ITV 89) Music score (Stanislas Syrewicz)
-S/T- *Virgin: CDV 2585 (CD) (TC)V 2585 deleted*
WILLIAM TELL (The Adventures Of) (ITV-58) Title theme
sung by DAVID WHITFIELD on 'Sings Stage And Screen
Favourites' - *Pickwick: PWK 096 (CD) SDTO 2004 (CS)*
WILLO THE WISP (BBC1 81) Theme (Tony Kinsey) *see Collec*
'THEMES FROM CHILDREN'S BBC'
WILLY FOG (BBC1-88)Theme "All Around The World" (Guido
& Maurizio De Angelis) TED MATHER *see Collection*
'THEMES FROM CHILDREN'S BBC'
WIMBLEDON (BBC1/2 annually in June)
Opening theme 1974-94 "Light & Tuneful" (Keith Mans
field) on *Coll* 'FAVOURITE SPORTING THEMES' *Pickwick*
Closing theme "Sporting Occasion" (Arnold Steck) on
'More Famous Themes' *Grasmere (Tayl): (TC)GRALP 20)*
WIN LOSE OR DRAW (Scotland 29/4/91) theme music (Gerard
Langella-Olivier Masselot).....................*NA*
WINDS OF WAR The (ITV 9/83 and 5/85) Music (Bob Cobert)
-S/T- Nurnberg Symp.Orc (Bob Cobert) *TER (Con): TER
1070(LP) ZCTER 1070(Cass) see Coll* 'BIG WAR THEMES'
see also 'WAR AND REMEMBRANCE'
WINJIN' POM The (Central 16/3/91) music (Simon Brint-Ro
ddy Matthews-Richard Vranch).....................*NA*
WINNERS AND LOSERS (ITV Scot 6/3/89) Theme (Craig Armst
rong) Leslie Grantham & Craig Armstrong on *Lismor-
Nightshift (Fast Forward): LINI 001(T) (7"/12")*
WINNING (Diverse/BBC1 27/9/92) mus (Debbie Wiseman)..*NA*
WINTER OLYMPIC GAMES 1992 (BBC1 8/2/92) Theme music
"Pop Looks Bach" (Sam Fonteyn) also used "Chorus Of
The Hebrew Slaves" from 'Nabucco' (Verdi) both on
'GOLD' *Telstar (BMG):TCD 2563 (CD) STAC 2563 (Cass)*
WISEGUY (USA) theme mus (Mike Post) *see Coll* 'AMERICAN
TV THEMES VOL.2'/'TELEVISION MUSIC OF MIKE POST..'
WISH ME LUCK (LWT 8/1/89) Theme (Jim Parker) *see Collec*
'FAVOURITE TV THEMES'/'HIT THEMES 1'/'LOVEJOY'/
WISH YOU WERE HERE (Thames for Central 13 Dec 92) Theme
music "Carnival" (Gordon Giltrap) *not available /*
link music "The Long Road" (MARK KNOPFLER) on -S/T-
'CAL' *Vertigo (Poly): 822 769-2 (CD) VERHC 17(Cass)*
WISHING (Action Time/BBC2 31/10/93) mus (Ernie Wood).*NA*
WITHIN THESE WALLS (LWT 74) theme (Denis King)*see under*
'LOVEJOY' *Collection*
WIZ BANG (BBC1 4/1/92) music (Edizanne).............*NA*
WKRP IN CINCINNATI (USA 78) Theme (Tom Wells) *see Coll*
'TELEVISION'S GREATEST HITS VOLUME 3'
WOLF (USA)(ITV 19/2/92) music score (Artie Kane)....*NA*
WOLF IT! (Scottish ITV 4/11/93) music (Paul K.Joyce).*NA*
WOLVIS FAMILY The (BBC2 4/5/91) music (Patrick Campbell
Lyons and Alex Spyropoulos).....................*NA*
WOMAN NAMED JACKIE A (ITV 6/9/92) m: (Lalo Schifrin).*NA*

WOMAN OF SUBSTANCE A (C4 2/1/85) Theme (Nigel Hess) *see Coll* 'FAVOURITE TV THEMES'/'SCREENS AND STAGES'

WOMBLES The (BBC1 73) Theme and songs (Mike Batt) all on 'Wombling Hits' THE WOMBLES (produced by Mike Batt) - *CBS (CBS): 466118-2 (CD) -1 (LP) -4 (Cass)*

WOMEN'S SOCCER (C4 8/4/90) Theme "Lily Was Here" (Dave Stewart) DAVE STEWART & CANDY DULFER (from film S/T 'Lily Was Here') *RCA -S/T- ZD(ZK) 74233 (CD/Cass)*

WONDER WOMAN (USA 78) Theme (Norman Gimbel-Charles Fox) *see Coll* 'TELEVISION'S GREATEST HITS 3'

WONDER YEARS The (USA C4 20/8/89) Theme "With A Little Help From My Friends" (John Lennon-Paul McCartney) JOE COCKER *Old Gold: OG 9232 (7"s)* TV -S/T- with V. Artists *Atlantic: 756782032-4 (Cass) -2(CD) -1(LP)*

WOODY WOODPECKER (TV Cart.USA) *see Collec* 'TELEVISION'S GREATEST HITS VOLUME 1'

WORD IN YOUR EAR, A (BBC1 19/4/93) mus (Andrew Neve).*NA*

WORD IN YOUR ERA, A (Channel X for BBC1 27/9/92) theme "Mazurka" from 'Coppelia' (Bizet) *many recordings*

WORD The (C4 24/8/90) Theme music (808 STATE)........*NA*

WORK IS A FOUR-LETTER WORD (BBC1 23/2/92) theme music (Simon Davison)...................................*NA*

WORKING MIRACLES (Scottish 2/6/91) mus:(Blair Cowan).*NA*

WORLD ATHLETICS CHAMPIONSHIPS TOKYO 1991 (BBC1 24/8/91) Theme 'World Series' (Keith Mansfield) on Coll *'BBC Sporting Themes' Pickwick: PWKS 648 (CD)* Link music 'Tokyo Melody' (Helmut Zacharius) *(EMI: deleted)*

WORLD BOWLS (BBC) Theme "Me & I"(B.Andersson-B.Ulvaeus) ABBA 'Super Trouper' *Polydor: 800 023-2 -4 (Cass)*

WORLD CHESS CHAMPIONSHIPS (The Times) 1993 from 7/9/93 BBC **theme music:** 'Symphony No.12 in D.minor Op.112' (Shostakovich) by THE ROYAL CONCERTGEBOUW ORCHESTRA (Bernard Haitink) on *Decca (Poly): 417 392-2 (2CDs)* C4 **theme music:** original music by (Paul Mardle)..*NA*

WORLD CHESS (BBC2 8/1986) Theme "Montagues & Capulets" from 'Suite No.2 Romeo & Juliet' (Sergei Prokofiev)

WORLD CUP 1990 (Italia'90) and other FOOTBALL Entries BBC Theme "Nessun Dorma" from 'Turandot' (Puccini) LUCIANO PAVAROTTI - *Decca: PAV 03 (7") CDPAV 03(CD)* 'Essential Pavarotti' *Decca: 417 011-2 (2CD)* and by PLACIDO DOMINGO - *Epic: 656005-7 (7") 'Belcanto Domingo' Teldec (WEA): 242983-2 (CD) -4 (Cass)* also on 'Puccini Arias' *CFP (EMI): CDCFP 4569 (CD) TC-(Cas)* **ITV Theme** "Tutti Al Mondo" (R.Argent-P.V.Hooke) ROD ARGENT and PETER VAN HOOKE on *Weekend (Total-BMG):* Coll.'20 Top TV Themes' *Weekend (BMG): WEEKCD(MC) 3*

WORLD CUP RUGBY 1991 (ITV Sport 3/10/91) Theme mus "The World In Union" music 'Jupiter' (The Planets Suite) (Gustav Holst) words (Charles Skarbek) sung by KIRI TE KANAWA on *Columbia: 657481-7(7") -2(CD) -4(Cass)* ORCHESTRAL VERSION:-Berlin Philharmonic Orch (H.Von Karajan) *DG (Poly): 435 289-2(CD) -4(Cass) -1(LP) also:* 'WORLD IN UNION' Var.arts incl.ENGLAND WORLD CUP SQUAD *Columbia: 469047-2(CD) -4(Cass) -1(LP)*

WORLD DARTS - *see under entry* 'DARTS'
WORLD EQUESTRIAN GAMES (BBC2 27/7/90) Theme music "The
   Healer" (J.L.Hooker-C.Santana) - JOHN LEE HOOKER on
   'The Healer' *Silvertone (Pinn): ORE(CD)(C)(LP) 508*
WORLD IN A GARDEN (C4 22/7/92) music (Phil Nicholas).*NA*
WORLD IN ACTION (Granada 64-92) Theme "Jam For World In
   Action"(Jonathan Weston) *see Coll* 'GRANADA STUDIOS'
WORLD OF HERBS (C4 19/1/90) "A Bunch Of Thyme" (Trad.)
   played by Virginia Astley-Simon Nichol-Paul Samwell
   Smith *unavailable* / FOSTER & ALLEN 'Very Best Of'on
   Ritz: RITZCD 102 (CVD)   RITZC TV1 (Cass)
WORLD SNOOKER (Embassy World Championship) Theme Music
   "Drag Racer" (Douglas Wood) DOUGLAS WOOD GROUP on
   'BBC SPORTING TH.' *deleted* Shot Of The Championship
   "Wicked Game" CHRIS ISAAK *London: LON(X)(CD)(CS)279*
   Other music "These Are The Days Of Our Lives" QUEEN
   from 'Innuendo' QUEEN *EMI: CDPCSD 115 (CD) TC-(Cas)*
   "Going Home" from 'Local Hero' -S/T- MARK KNOPFLER
   see FILMS "Private Investigations" (Mark Knopfler)
   DIRE STRAITS 'Money For Nothing' *Vertigo: 836419-2
   (CD) VERH(C) 64 (Cass) other mus* "The Entertainer"
   (Scott Joplin) from 'The Sting' -S/T- (Marvin Hamli
   SCH) on *(MCA)* "Zorba's Dance" (Mikis Theodorakis)
   from film 'Zorba The Greek' (*see* FILMS) *also used*
   "Standing On The Inside" (N.Sedaka) NEIL SEDAKA on
   Polydor:831 541-2 (CD) add.items used "The Snooker
   Song" sung by CAPTAIN SENSIBLE from 'Hunting Of The
   Snark' *see also* 'POT BLACK'
WRESTLING (ITV Sport 9/4/88) Theme "March of The Toread
   ors" from 'Carmen'(Bizet) *Coll* 'ITV THEMES'
WRITING ON THE LINE (Teliesyn for BBC2 11/1/93)original
   music (John Hardy) mus recorded by (David Shell).*NA*
WUTHERING HEIGHTS (UKGO 14/2/93 orig BBC1 24/9/78) orig
   music (Carl Davis) *EMI International deleted*

YEAR IN PROVENCE, A (BBC1 28/2/93) Music score (Carl Da
   vis) accordion played by Jack Emblow -S/T- on *Silva
   Screen (Con): FILMCD 131 (CD) FILMC 131 (Cass) ALSO
   AVAIL:* SPOKEN WORD 4CASS BOX: *BBC (Pinn): ZBBC 4006*
YEAR OF THE FRENCH (BBC2 10/11/82) Theme (Joseph Horovi
   tz) -S/T- music by PADDY MOLONEY & THE CHIEFTAINS
   and RTE ORCH - *see* Coll 'REEL MUSIC' *(RCA) also on
   Claddagh (Celtic Music): CC 36 (LP)*
YEAR WITH FRED A(BBC2 9/2/87)Theme "Carnival Of Venice"
   (Briccialdi) by JAMES GALWAY *RCA: (PD)(PK)PL 70260*
YEARBOOK (USA/BBC1 11/5/92) orig mus (Michael Bacon).*NA*
YESTERDAY'S DREAMS (Central 15/7/90) Title theme (Alan
   Lisk) sung by Paul Freeman-Judy Loe-Trevor Byfield
   on *Rockin' Pig (Spartan): RPP 71 (7"s) deleted*
YOGI BEAR (USA 60/85) "Yogi Bear Song" (Hoyt Curtin)*see*
   'TELEVISION'S GREATEST HITS VOLUME 1'
YORKSHIRE GLORY (YTV 21/4/91) music score "Yorkshire Gl
   ory-A Symphonic Portrait" (Christopher Gunning) The
   Royal Liverpool Philh Orch -S/T- *(YTV Ent): CD/Cass*

YOU BET! (LWT 10/9/93) theme mus (Jonathan Sorrell)..*NA*
YOU BET YOUR LIFE (Carsey-Werner USA/C4 28/9/92) theme
  (Bill Cosby-Shirley Scott)....................*NA*
YOU GOTTA BE JOKIN' (BBC1 27/4/91) mus (Andy Street).*NA*
YOU ME AND IT (BBC1 28/3/93) m: (Stanislas Syrewicz).*NA*
YOU MUST BE THE HUSBAND (UKGO 9/9/87 orig BBC1 8/9/87)
  "Take Five" (Paul Desmond) arr.Ronnie Hazlehurst.*NA*
  DAVE BRUBECK QUARTET *Pickick: ELITE 009CD (Cd)*
YOU RANG M'LORD (BBC1 from 7/1/90) Theme (Roy Moore-Jim
  my Perry) sung by BOB MONKHOUSE and PAUL SHANE...*NA*
YOUNG AND THE RESTLESS The (USA soap 73)'Nadia's theme'
  (Henry Mancini) JAMES GALWAY - 'James Galway G.Hits
  Vol.2' *RCA (BMG): 09026 61178-2 (CD) -4 (Cass)*
YOUNG DOCTORS The (Australian TV/ITV 80's) theme music
  (King-Ollman) on Coll 'Australian TV Greatest Hits'
  Silva Screen: FILMCD 028 (CD) FILMC 028 (Cass)
YOUNG INDIANA JONES CHRONICLES The (USA TV 92) Music sc
  (Laurence Rosenthal) -S/T- *Varese (Pinn) VSD(VSC)*
  5381 (V.1) VSD(VSC) 5391 (V.2) VSD(VSC) 5401 (V.3)
YOUNG ONES The (UKGold 4/11/92 orig BBC2 9/11/82) music
  (Peter Brewis) *NA - also used* "The Young Ones" (Sid
  epper-Roy Bennett) from 62 Cliff Richard movie)
YOUNG RIDERS The (USA 90/ITV 5/91) Theme (John Debney)
  see Coll 'AMERICAN TELEVISION THEMES VOLUME 3'
YOUR BEST SHOT (BBC1 8/1/93) theme mus (David Arch)..*NA*
YOUR CHEATIN' HEART (BBC1 11/10/90) TV Soundtrack on
  BBC (Pinn): BBCCD 791 (CD) ZCF 791 (Cass) deleted
YOUR LIFE IN THEIR HANDS (BBC2 26/4/91) title music by
  (Paddy Kingsland)...........................*NA*
YOUR NUMBER PLEASE (Tham 29/6/92)m:(Peter Griffiths).*NA*

Z CARS (BBC1 began 2/1/62) Theme "Johnny Todd" (Trad.)
  arr.Bridget Fry JOHNNY KEATING AND THE 'Z' MEN *see*
  Coll 'A-Z OF BRITISH TV THEMES'/'TV CLASSICS VOL.2'
ZOO GANG The (ITV 73) Theme (Paul and Linda McCartney)
  by WINGS - *Parlophone (EMI): R 5997 (7"s)*
ZOO TIME (BBC 50s/60s with Desmond Morris) Theme taken
  from 'Peter And The Wolf' (Prokofiev) *many versions*

for the very latest information why not subscribe to
TELE-TUNES *and have your book updated 3 times a year*
plus access to the telephone database information line

SEE PAGE 249 FOR DETAILS

A.. - *see under next word*
ABOUT LAST NIGHT (86) Music score (Miles Goodman) -S/T-
   EMI Amer (EMI): TCAML 3109 (Cass) CDP 746560-2 (CD)
   Import (Silva Screen): 46550-2 (CD) 46560-4 (Cass)
ABOVE THE LAW (88) Music score (David Michael Frank)
   with 'HARD TO KILL' (89) & 'OUT FOR JUSTICE' (91)
   GNP (Sil.Screen): GNPD 8028 (CD) GNP5-8028 (Cass)
ABSOLUTE BEGINNERS (Film Musical 86) Score (Gil Evans)
   *feat:*David Bowie-Ray Davies-Style Council etc.-S/T-
   reiss *VIP (EMI): CDVIP 112 (CD) TCVIP 112 (Cass)*
   also Highlights on *Virgin: CDV 2386 (CD)*
ABYSS The (Film 89) Music score (Alan Silvestri) -S/T-
   Varese (Pinn): VSC(CD) 5235 (Cass/CD)
ACCIDENTAL TOURIST The (88) Music score (John Williams)
   -S/T- *W.Bros USA Imp (S.Screen): 925 846-2 (CD)*
ACE OF CLUBS (Show 1950) - *see under 'Noel Coward' coll*
ACES - *see 'IRON EAGLE III'*
ACT OF PIRACY / GREAT WHITE The (82) Music scores (Mort
   on Stevens) -S/T- *Prometheus (S.Screen): PCD 111 CD*
ACT The (Show 78) *Original Broadway Cast:* LIZA MINNELLI
   DRG USA (Conifer): (CD)DRG 6101 (CD/LP)
ACTION JACKSON (88) Music artists: Herbie Hancock-Skyy-
   Pointer Sisters-Madam X-Levert-Vanity-Sister Sledge
   -S/T- *Atlantic (WEA): K 790886-2 (CD) -4(Cass)*
ADDAMS FAMILY The (91) Music score (Marc Shaiman) -S/T-
   Capitol (EMI): CDESTU 2161 (CD) TCESTU 2161 (Cass)
   see also Television index
ADVENTURES OF BARON MUNCHAUSEN The (89) Music score by
   (Michael Kamen) with Graunke Symphony Orchest -S/T-
   W.Bros USA Imp (Silva Screen): 925 826-2 (CD)
ADVENTURES OF FORD FAIRLANE The (90) Music score: Yello
   with various arts -S/T- *Elektra (WEA): 7559 60952-2*
   (CD) EKT 74 (LP) EKT 74C (Cass)
ADVENTURES OF HUCK FINN The (93) Music sco (Bill Conti)
   -S/T- *Varese (Pinn): VSD 5418 (CD) VSC 5418 (Cass)*
ADVENTURES OF ROBIN HOOD The (38) Music sco (Erich Wolf
   gang Korngold -S/T- *TER (Conifer): (CD)(ZC)TER 1066*
ADVENTURES OF THE GREAT MOUSE DETECTIVE (91) Music sco
   (Henry Mancini) -S/T- *Varese (Pinn): VSD(VSC) 5359*
AFTER DARK MY SWEET (90) Music score (Maurice Jarre)
   -S/T- *Varese (Pinn): VSC(CD) 5274 (Cass/CD)*
AGAGUK - *see under 'SHADOW OF THE WOLF'*
AGAINST ALL ODDS (84) Mus: Michel Colombier-L.Carlton &
   Phil Collins-Peter Gabriel-Stevie Nicks-Kid Creole-
   -S/T- *Virgin (EMI): CDVIP 121 (CD) TCVIP 121 (Cass)*
AGNES OF GOD (85) Music score (Georges Delerue) -S/T-
   TER (Conifer): ZCTER 1108 (Cass)
AGONY AND THE ECSTASY The (65) Music score (Alex North)
   with 'PRIDE & THE PASSION' (George Antheil) 75mins
   Cloud Nine (S.Screen-Conif): CNS 5001 (CD)
AHEAD OF HIS TIME - *see under 'ZACHARIAH'*
AIN'T MISBEHAVIN' (ORIG BROADWAY CAST 79) Music (Fats
   Waller) with Andre de Shields-Nell Carter-Ken Page
   RCA USA (S.Screen): 2965-2 (2CD) CBK2 2965 (Cass)

AIRPORT (70) Music score (Alfred Newman) -S/T- reissue
Varese (Pinn): VSD 5436 (CD)
AKIRA (Cartoon 91) Music score (Yamashiro Shoji) VIDEO
Manga:IWCV 1001(VHS) -S/T- *Demon (Pinn): DSCD 6(CD)*
ALADDIN (Film 92) Music & Songs (Alan Menken-Howard Ash
man with Tim Rice) -S/T- *Disney-Pickwick (Pickwick)
DISCD 470 (CD) DISMC 470 (Cass)* / also "A Whole New
World" sung by PEABO BRYSON-REGINA BELLE *Columbia
659900-2 (CDs) -4 (Cass) -7 (7"s)*
ALADDIN (Show 59) Songs (Cole Porter) Orig Cast Record:
Cyril Richard-Sal Mineo-Dennis King-Basil Rathbone-
Anna Maria Alberghetti) *Sony Broadway: CD48205 (CD)*
ALAMO The (60) Music score (Dimitri Tiomkin) title song
"Green Leaves Of Summer" (D.Tiomkin-Paul F.Webster)
sung by Brothers Four -S/T- *Varese VSD 5224 (CD)*
also on 'The Epic' coll *(Decca 417845-2 (CD)-4 (CS)*
ALEXANDER NEVSKY (USSR 38) Music sco (Sergei Prokofiev)
New recording - Scottish National Orchestra (Neeme
Jarvi) with Linda Finnie (mezzo-soprano) - *Chandos:
(Chan) CHAN 8584 (CD) ABTD 1275 (Cass)*
ALFIE (66) Music (Sonny Rollins) Title song (Burt Bacha
rach-Hal David) *orig FILM vers.sung by* CHER **deleted**
ELAINE PAIGE on 'Cinema' *Pickwick: PWKS 539 (CD)*
ALICE IN WONDERLAND *(Disney) see* WALT DISNEY FILM INDEX
ALICE IN WONDERLAND (1968 RECORDING now reissued) *feat:*
Karen Dotrice-Kenneth Connor-Beryl Reid-Dorothy Squ
ires-Bruce Forsyth-Fenella Fielding-Tommy Cooper-Pe
ggy Mount-Ian Wallace-Arthur Haynes-Frankie Howerd-
Harry Corbett with Orch & Chorus. (Orig MFP 1267/8)
EMI: CDEMS 1471 (CD) TCEMS 1471 (Cass)
ALICE'S RESTAURANT (69) Songs (Arlo Guthrie) Featuring
Pete Seeger -S/Track- *Reprise (WEA): K 44045 (LP)*
ALIEN (79) Music score (Jerry Goldsmith) -S/T- with The
Nat.Philh.Orc *Silva Screen (Conif): FILMC(CD) 003*
ALIENS (86) Music score (James Horner) -S/T- *Varese USA
(Pinn): VCD 47263 (CD)*
ALIEN 3 (92) Music score (Elliot Goldenthal) -S/T- on
MCA (BMG):MCAD 10629 (CD) MCAC 10629 (Cass deleted)
ALIEN NATION (88) Music score (Joe Harnell) on *5Jays
Imp (Silva Screen): 5JAYS 001/002 (2CDs)*
ALL AMERICAN (ORIG BROADWAY CAST 62) Songs (Charles Str
ouse-Lee Adams) Ray Bolger-Ron Husmann-Fritz Weaver
Eileen Herlie *Sony Broadway (Sony): SK 48216 (CD)*
ALL I WANT FOR CHRISTMAS (91) Music score (Bruce Brough
ton) songs: The COASTERS-LLOYD PRICE-STEPHEN BISHOP
-S/T- *Curb (S.Screen): D2 77533 (CD) D4 77533 (Cas)*
ALL THAT JAZZ (Film Mus.79) Mus.score (Ralph Burns) Var
Arts -S/T- *Casablanca (S.Screen): 822 869-4 (Cass)*
ALLAN QUATERMAIN AND THE LOST CITY OF GOLD (86) Music
score (Michael Linn) *selection also includes Suites
from* 'MANIFESTO' (88- Nicola Piovani) 'MAKING THE
GRADE' (84- Basil Poledouris) 'DOIN' TIME ON PLANET
EARTH' (87- Dana Kaproff) 'SEVEN MAGNIFICENT GLADIA
TORS' (83- Dov Seltzer) *Sil.Screen: SIL 1528-2 (CD)*

ALLEGRO (ORIG BROADWAY CAST 47) Songs (Richard Rodgers-Oscar Hammerstein II) *feat:* John Battles-Annamary Dickie-William Ching-Muriel O'Malley-Roberta Jonay-Lisa Kirk *RCA Victor (BMG): 07863 52758-2 (CD)*

ALMOST AN ANGEL (90) Music score (Maurice Jarre) -S/T- on *Varese (Pinn):VSD 5307 (CD) VSC 5307 (Cass)*

ALPHA AND OMEGA (Gospel Musical Show 86) Music (Adrian Snell) Lyrics (Phil Thompson) *Orig Cast Recording Myrrh Word: MYRR 1210 (LP) MYRC 1210 (Cassette)*

ALWAYS (90) Music score (John Williams) 1990 Royal F.P. -S/T- *MCA USA (S.Screen): MCAD(MCAC) 8036 (CD/Cass)*

AMADEUS (84) Music (W.A.Mozart) Academy Of St.Martin-In The Fields (Neville Marriner) -S/T- on *London (Pol) LONDP(C)6 (Dbl LP/CS) 825 126-2 (CD)* 'MORE AMADEUS' *London: LONC 7 (Cass) 827 267-2 (CD)* BOXED SET on *London: 511126-2 (CD Boxed Set)*

AMBASSADOR The (84) Music sco (Dov Seltzer) on 'Mystery Movie Scores' *Silva Screen (Con): FILMCD 054 (CD)*

AMERICAN FLYERS (86) Music(Lee Ritenour-Greg Mathieson) "Bad Moon Rising" (J.Fogerty) CREEDENCE CLEARWATER REVIVAL *OG 9569 (7") -S/T- GRP (Pinn): GRP(C) 2001*

AMERICAN GIGOLO (80) Music score (Giorgio Moroder)-S/T- *Poly Imp (S.Screen): 841066-2 (CD) 813632-4 (Cass)* "Seduction Love Theme" James Last Orch *Polydor: POLHC 34 (Cass) 831 786-2 (CD)*

AMERICAN GRAFFITI (73) Music soundtrack oldies re-issue on *MCA (BMG): MCLD 19150 (CDx2) MCLC 19150 (Cass)*

AMERICAN ME (92) Music score (Dennis Lambert) + Var.Art -S/T- *Virgin USA (S.Screen): (unconfirmed) (CD)*

AMERICAN NINJA Pts 1-3 (87-88)Music by George S.Clinton -S/T- *Silva Screen (Conifer): FILMCD 057 (CD)*

AN AMERICAN IN PARIS (Film Musical 51) Songs (George Gershwin)Feat Gene Kelly & Cyd Charisse -S/T- *MGM EMI CD(TC)MGM 1 (CD/Cass)* + 'Gigi' -S/T- *all deleted*

AN AMERICAN TAIL (87) Music score (James Horner) song: "Somewhere Out There" (J.Horner-Barry Mann-Cynthia Weill) sung by LINDA RONSTADT & JAMES INGRAM -S/Tr- *MCA USA (S.Screen): MCAD 39096 (CD) MCAC 39096 Cass*

AN AMERICAN TAIL 2: Fieval Goes West (91) Music score (James Horner) -S/T- *MCA: MCAD(MCAC) 10416 (CD/Cas)*

AN ANGEL AT MY TABLE (90) Music score (Don McGlashan) -S/T- *DRG USA (Con): CDSBL 12603 (CD)* also on *Alhambra (Silva Screen): A 8925 (CD)*

AN EVENING WITH ALAN JAY LERNER (ORIG LONDON CAST 87) Song lyrics:Alan Jay Lerner / Music:Frederick Loewe Leonard Bernstein-Burton Lane-Charles Strouse) *Feat* LIZ ROBERTSON-MARTI WEBB-PLACINDO DOMINGO-ELAINE PAIGE and others *First Night (Pinn): OCRCD 12 (2CD)*

AN OFFICER AND A GENTLEMAN (82) Mus sco (Jack Nitzsche) "Up Where We Belong" (Jack Nitzsche-Buffy Saint Marie-Will Jennings) sung JOE COCKER-JENNIFER WARNES -S/T- *Island (Polygram): IMCD 77 (CD)*

ANASTASIA (56) Music score (Alfred Newman) -S/T- reiss *Varese (Pinn): VSD 5422 (CD)*

ANASTASIA: THE MYSTERY OF ANNA - *see also* TV Themes
*Southern Cross (Silva Screen): SCCD 1015 (CD) FILMC
012 (Cass) FILM 012 (LP)*

ANASTASIA AFFAIR The (Musical 90) Music (Rachmaninov)
Lyrics (Robert Wright-George Forrest) Recording on
Bay Cities (Silva Screen): BCD 3025 (CD)

ANCHORS AWEIGH (Film Musical 45) Music (George Stoll)
Songs (Jule Styne-Sammy Cahn) Frank Sinatra & Gene
Kelly -S/T- *Sandy Hook (Derann-Pinn):CDSH 2024 (CD)*

AND THE BAND PLAYS ON (93) Music score (Carter Burwell)
-S/T- *Varese (Pinn): VSD 5449 (CD)*

AND THE SHIP SAILS ON (84) Various classical music incl
"Claire De Lune" (Debussy) over titles | Featuring:
MARIO ZAMPEIRI -S/T- *Milan: A 228 (LP) C 228 (Cass)*

AND THE WORLD GOES ROUND (Musical Tribute Show To compo
sers John Kander & Fred Ebb) Orig BROADWAY Cast on
BMG USA (Silva Screen): 60904-2 (CD) 60904-4 (Cass)

AND YOU THOUGHT YOUR PARENTS WERE WEIRD (91)Music score
(Randy Miller) *Bay Cities (S.Screen): BCD 3020 (CD)*

ANDY WARHOL'S DRACULA and **FRANKENSTEIN** (1974) Music sco
(Claudio Gizzi) -S/T- *Impt (S.Screen): OST 119 (CD)*

ANGEL (USA 83) Music score (Craig Safan) -S/T- *Intrada
USA Imprt (Silva Screen-Koch): MAF 7051D (CD)*

ANGEL AND THE SOLDIER BOY The (89) Music by (CLANNAD)
-S/T- *RCA (BMG): PD(PL)(PK) 74328 (CD/LP/Cass)*

ANGEL HEART (87) Music score (Trevor Jones) -S/T- on
Island (Poly) IMCD 76 (CD) ICM(ILPM) 2025 (Cass/LP)

ANGST (86) Electronic Music score (Klaus Schulze) -S/T-
Thunderbolt-Magnum (MMG): CDTB(THBL) 2.027 (CD/LP)

ANIMAL HOUSE - *see under* 'National Lampoon's...'

ANNIE (FILM MUSICAL 82) Songs (Charles Strouse & Martin
Charnin) feat: Albert Finney-Aileen Quinn-Carol Bur
nett -S/T- reiss: *Sony: 467608-2(CD) -4(Cass)*

ANNIE (ORIG ORIGINAL CAST 77) *Columb USA (Silva Screen)
CK 34712 (CD) JST 34712 (Cass)*

ANNIE GET YOUR GUN (ORIG BROADWAY CAST 46) Songs(Irving
Berlin)with Ethel Merman-Bruce Yarnell-Benay Venuta
Jerry Orbach on *RCA Victor (BMG): RD 81124 (CD)*

ANNIE GET YOUR GUN (FILM MUSICAL 50) with Betty Hutton
Howard Keel -S/T- *MCA: MCL(C) 1660 (LP/Cas) deleted*

ANNIE GET YOUR GUN (1950's *unreleased recording*) feat:
JUDY GARLAND *Sandy Hook (Derann/Pinn):CSH 2053 Cass*

ANNIE GET YOUR GUN (LIVE) Songs (Irving Berlin) *featur:*
MARY MARTIN-JOHN RAITT *EMI Angel: ZDM 764765-2 (CD)*

ANNIE GET YOUR GUN (NEW LONDON CAST 86) featuring SUZI
QUATRO *First Night: CASTCD 4 (CD) CASTC 4 (Cass)*

ANNIE GET YOUR GUN (STUDIO 90) *feat* Kim Criswell-Thomas
Hampson-Jason Graae-Rebecca Luker-Ambrosian Chorus-
London Sinfonia (John McGlinn) *EMI: CD(TC)ANNIE 1*

ANOTHER 48 HOURS (90) Music score (James Horner) & trac
ks by Hank Williams-Michael Williams-Lamont Dozier-
-S/T- *Polydor (Polyg) 846872-2 -4 -1   all deleted*

ANOTHER TIME ANOTHER PLACE (83) Music sco (John McLeod-
Corrado Sfogli)·-S/T- *TER (Conif):STER 12007 (12"s)*

ANTARCTICA (83) Music score (Vangelis) -S/T- *Polydor UK 815732-1 (LP) 815732-4 (Cass) 815732-2 (CD)* see also *Coll* 'SYNTHESIZER MEGA-HITS'

ANTHONY ADVERSE (36) Music sc (Erich Wolfgang Korngold) -S/T- reissue *Varese (Pinn-S.Screen): VSD 5285 (CD)*

ANTONY AND CLEOPATRA (72)Music score (John Scott) Royal Philharmonic Orch (Scott) Symphonic score on *John Scott Records (Silva Screen): JSCDC 114 (CD)*

ANYONE CAN WHISTLE (ORIG BROADWAY CAST) Songs (Stephen Sondheim) *with* Angela Lansbury-Lee Remick & Company *CBS USA (S.Screen): CK 02480 (CD) JST 02480 (Cass)*

ANYTHING GOES (ORIG LONDON CAST 89) Songs (Cole Porter) feat: Elaine Paige-Bernard Cribbins-Howard McGillin *1st Night (Pinn): CASTCD 18 (CD) CAST(C) 18 (LP/CS)*

ANYTHING GOES (ORIG BROADWAY CAST 88) feat Patti Lupone Howard McGillin *RCA (BMG): RD(RK) 87769 (CD/Cass)*

ANYTHING GOES (STUDIO RECORDING 89) Songs (Cole Porter) Feat: Frederica Von Stade-Kim Criswell-Cris Groenen daal-Jack Gilford-LSO-Ambrosian Chor.(John McGlinn) *EMI: CDC 749848-2 (CD) EL 749848-1 (LP) -4 (Cass)*

ANYTHING GOES (REVIVAL LONDON CAST 69) feat: Marian Mon tgomery & James Kenney *TER (Conifer): TER 1080 (LP)*

ANYTHING GOES (REVIVAL BROADWAY CAST 62) Songs (Cole Po rter) *Imp (S.Screen): EK 15100 (CD)*

APARTMENT ZERO (89) Music score (Elia Cmiral) -S/T- on *Filmtrax (S.Screen): MOMCD 120 (CD) MOMC 120 (Cass)*

APOCALYPSE NOW (79) Music score (Carmine Coppola) also includes 'Die Walkure' (Wagner) -S/T- *W.Bros (WEA): K.960826-2 (CD) / Elektra (S.Screen): 90001-2 (2CD)*

APPLE TREE The (ORIG BROADWAY CAST 66) Mus (Jerry Bock) Lyr (Sheldon Harnick) *with* Barbara Harris-Larry Bly den-Alan Alda-Carmen Alvarez-Robert Klein) on *Sony Broadway (Sony Mus): CD 48209 (CD)*

APPOINTMENT WITH DEATH (88) Music score (Pino Donaggio) 'Mystery Movie Scores' *S.Screen (Con): FILMCD 054*

APRES LA GUERRE (After The War) Music score (Jurgen Kni eper) -S/T- *Milan (S.Screen): CDCH 386 (CD)*

APRES L'AMOUR (92-France) Music score (Yves Simon)-S/T- *Import (Silva Screen): 31026 (CD)*

ARACHNOPHOBIA (90) Music score (Trevor Jones) -S/T- on *Hollywood (Pinn): HWDCD 1 (CD) HWDMC(LP) 1 (Cas/LP)*

ARCADIANS The (ORIG LONDON CAST STUDIO RECORDING 1969) Music (Lionel Monckton-Howard Talbot) Lyr (Arthur Wimperis) *feat* June Bronhill-Michael Burgess-Andy Cole-Ann Howard-Jon Pertwee-John McCarthy Singers *EMI Angel (EMI): CDANGEL 1 (CD)*

ARE YOU LONESOME TONIGHT (ORIG LONDON CAST 85) Play by Alan Bleasdale / Elvis Presley songs perf by MARTIN SHAW-SIMON BOWMAN *First Night (Pinn): CASTC1 (Cass)*

ARISTOCATS The - see **WALT DISNEY FILM INDEX**

ARIZONA DREAM (93) Music score (Goran Bregovich) -S/T- *Vertigo (Poly): 512 112-2 (CD) 512 112 -4 (Cass)*

ARMY OF DARKNESS (92) Music score (Joe Lo Duca) -S/T- *Varese (Pinn): VSD 5411 (CD) VSC 5411 (Cass)*

ARNOLD (Coll) Music from films of Arnold Schwarzenegger
Varese USA (Pinn): VSD 5398 (CD) VSC 5398 (Cass)
AROUND THE WORLD IN 80 DAYS (56) Music score (Victor Yo
ung) -S/T- *MCA USA (S.Screen) MCAD 31164 (CD)*
ARRIVAL (91) Music score (Richard Band) -S/T- *Intrada
(Koch): MAF 7032CD (CD)*
ARTHUR (80)Theme song 'Best That You Can Do' (Burt Bach
rach-C.B.Sager-C.Cross-P.Allen) sung by CHRISTOPHER
CROSS on *Old Gold (Pinn): OG 9935 (7"s)*
ARTICLE 99 (91) Music score (Danny Elfman) -S/T- *Varese
(Pinn): VSD(VSC) 5352 (CD/Cass) also* 'EVIL DEAD 2'
AS YOU LIKE IT (36) Music score (William Walton) New
Recording by Academy of St.Martin-in-the-Fields
(Neville Marriner) also music from 'Hamlet' (48) on
Chandos (Chandos): CHAN 8842 (CD) ABTD 1461 (Cass)
ASHES AND DIAMONDS (54-Andrzej Wajda) Music on 'Andrez
Wajda Trilogy' on *TER (Conifer): TER 1053 (LP)*
ASPECTS OF LOVE (ORIG LONDON CAST 89) Music (Andrew Llo
yd Webber) Lyrics (Don Black-Charles Hart) featur:-
Michael Ball-Ann Crumb-Diana Morrison-Kevin Colson
Polydor: 841 126-2 (CD) -4 (Cass)
ASPECTS OF LOVE (SHOWS COLLECTION Studio Recording 93)
featuring: PAUL JONES-STEPHANIE LAWRENCE-DAVE WILLE
TTS-FIONA HENDLEY-CARL WAYNE-WEST END CONCERT ORCH.
plus music from 'PHANTOM OF THE OPERA'
Pickwick Shows: PWKS 4164 (CD) PWKMC 4164 (Cass)
see also Coll 'ROYAL PHILHARMONIC ORCH PLAY SUITES'
ASSASSIN The: Point Of No Return (92) Music score (Hans
Zimmer) -S/T- *Milan (Pinn): 14302-2 (CD) -4 (Cass)*
ASSASSINS (ORIG USA CAST 91) Songs (Stephen Sondheim)
William Parry-Terence Mann-Greg Germann and Company
RCA Victor (BMG): RD 60737 (CD) RK 60737 (Cass)
ASSAULT ON PRECINCT 13 (76) Music sco (John Carpenter)
see Collection 'ASSAULT ON PRECINCT 13'
ASSAULT The (86) - *see under* 'CRY IN THE DARK'
ASSISSI UNDERGROUND The (85) *see under* 'HANNA'S WAR'
AT PLAY IN THE FIELDS OF THE LORD (91) Music (Zbigniew
Preisner) -S/T- *Fantasy USA (S.Screen): unconfirmed*
AT THE DROP OF A HAT (Musical Revue 58 Fortune Theatre)
featuring MICHAEL FLANDERS and DONALD SWANN on
EMI: CDP 797465-2 (CD) / **AT THE DROP OF ANOTHER HAT**
(Musical Revue 60 Haymarket) feat: MICHAEL FLANDERS
-DONALD SWANN *EMI: CDP 797466-2 (CD) ECC (2Cass)*
ATLANTIC CITY (81) Music score (Michel Legrand) -S/T-
DRG USA Import (Silva Screen) DRG(C) 6104 (LP/Cass)
ATLANTIS (91) Music score (Eric Serra) -S/T- *Virgin Imp
(Silva Screen): 30867 (CD) 50867 (Cass)*
ATTACK AND RETREAT (Italiani Brava Gente) Film Music Sc
(Armando Trovajoli) *ALSO* 'THE CAMP FOLLOWERS' (LE
SOLDATESSE) Film Music Score (Mario Nascimbene) on
Import (Silva Screen): OST 112 (CD)
ATTACK ON THE IRON COAST (67) Music (Gerard Schurmann)
'Coastal Command' *S.Screen (BMG): FILM(C)(CD) 072*
see also Coll 'HORRORS OF THE BLACK MUSEUM'

AUNTIE DANIELLE ('Tatie Danielle') (Fr.90) Music score
(Gabriel Yared) -S/T- *Impt (S.Screen): 30761-2 (CD)*
AVALON (90) Music score (Randy Newman) -S/T- on *Warner
Bros Imp (S.Screen): 926 437-2 (CD) 926 437-4 (Cas)*
A.W.O.L. (90) Music score (John Scott) -S/T- on *Intrada
USA (Silva Screen): MAF 7011D (CD)*
AY CARMELA (91) Music score (Alejandro Masso) -S/T- on
Milan (Silva Screen): CDCH 557 (CD) C 557 (Cass)

BABE (92) Music score (Elmer Bernstein) -S/T- Import on
MCA (S.Screen): MCAD 10576 (CD) MCAC 10576 (Cass)
BABES IN ARMS (39) Songs (Richard Rodgers-Lorenz Hart)
-S/T- with JUDY GARLANDO-MICKEY ROONEY *New World
(Harmonia Mundi): NW 386-2 (CD) NW 386-4 (Cass)*
BABETTE'S FEAST (88) Music score (Per Norgard) -S/T-
Milan Fra (Silva Screen) A.333 (LP) CDCH 333 (CD)
BABY (ORIG BROADWAY CAST 83) Mus (David Shire) Lyrics
(Richard Maltby Jnr) *feat:* Liz Callaway-Beth Fowler
James Congdon-Todd Graff *TER (Con): CDTER 1089 (CD)*
BABY OF MACON The (93) Classical music by MONTEVERDI-
CORELLI-TALLIS-BACH-CLAMER-FRESCOBALDI etc. -S/T-
Koch International (Koch): 34014-2 (CD)
BABY THE RAIN MUST FALL (64) Music score (Elmer Bernste
in) with 'The Caretakers' (63-E.Bernstein) -S/T- on
Mainstream USA (Koch Int): MDCD 603 (CD)
BACK TO THE FUTURE (85) Music score (Alan Silvestri)
-S/T- *MCA (BMG) MCLD 19151 (CD) MCLC 19151 (Cass)*
BACK TO THE FUTURE 2 (89) Music (Alan Silvestri) -S/T-
MCA (BMG): MCGC 6072 (Cass) deleted
BACK TO THE FUTURE 3 (90) Music (Alan Silvestri) -S/T-
Varese (Pinn): VSD 5272 (CD) VSC 5272 (Cass)
BACKDRAFT (91) Mus: (Hans Zimmer) Songs:(Bruce Hornsby)
by -S/T- *Milan (S.Screen-Pinn): (CDCH)(C) 807*
BAD AND THE BEAUTIFUL The (52) Music sco (David Raskin)
selection on *RCA Vic (BMG): GD(GK) 81490 (CD/Cass)*
BAD INFLUENCE (88) Music score (Trevor Jones) -S/T- on
Mango Island: CIDM(MLPS)(MCT) 1067 (CD/LP/Cass)
BAGDAD CAFE (88) Music (B.Telson-P.Adlon-O.Ebner-L.Brue
hr-Bach) Theme "Calling You" sung by JEVETTA STEELE
-S/T- *Island: CID 5718 (CD) ISTA(IC) 18 (LP/Cass)*
BAKER'S WIFE The (ORIG LONDON CAST 89) Songs (Stephen
Schwartz) featuring Sharon Lee Hill *TER (Conifer):
CD2TER 1175 (2CD) ZCTED 1175 (2Cass)*
BAKER'S WIFE The (ORIG USA CAST)with Paul Sorvino-Patti
Lupone: *TakeHomeTunes (USA(S.Screen) THT 772 (LP)*
BALLROOM (ORIG BROADWAY CAST) Music (Billy Goldenberg)
Lyr (Alan & Marilyn Bergman) *Sony Broadway: CD35762*
BAMBI - *see* WALT DISNEY FILM INDEX
BAND OF ANGELS (57) Music score (Max Steiner) -S/T- on
W.Bros USA Import (Silva Screen): LXCD 3 (CD)
BANDOLERO (68) Music score (Jerry Goldsmith) -S/T- on
Edel Germany (Silva Screen) TCS 1001-2 (CD)
BARAKA (93) Music score (Michael Stearns) -S/T- on
Milan (Pinn): 15306-2 (CD)

BARBARIANS The (Film) Music score (Pino Donaggio) -S/T-
Intrada Import (Silva Screen): MAF 7008D (CD)

BARNUM (ORIG LONDON CAST 81) Songs (Cy Coleman-Michael
Stewart) with MICHAEL CRAWFORD-Deborah Grant *Chrysa
lis: CDL 1348 (LP) ZCDL 1348 (Cass)* deleted

BARNUM (ORIG BROADWAY CAST 84) with JIM DALE *Columbia
Imp. (Silva Screen): CK 36576 (CD) JST 36576 (Cass)*

BARON BLOOD (72) Music score (Les Baxter) -S/T- *also in
cludes* 'BLACK SUNDAY' (60) Music (Les Baxter) on
Bay Cities (Silva Screen): BCD 3034 (CD)

BARRY LYNDON (75) Various classical music -S/T- reissue
Sony France (Discov): SK 61684 (CD) ST 61684 (Cass)
additional mus (Paddy Moloney) The Chieftains *SEE
Coll* 'Reel Music'

BASHVILLE (ORIG LONDON CAST 84) Songs (Denis King-Benny
Green) Peter Woodward-Christina Collier-Donal Pelm
ar-Douglas Hodge *TER (Con): (ZC)TER 1072 (Cass/LP)*

BASIC INSTINCT (92) Music score (Jerry Goldsmith) -S/T-
Varese (Pinn): VSD(VSC) 5360 (CD/Cass) note: disco
number (NOT on -ST-) "Rave The Rhythm" CHANNEL X on
Beat Box (APT): BB 025 (12"s)

BASIL THE GREAT MOUSE DETECTIVE see *WALT DISNEY FILM IN
DEX page 304*

BASKET CASE 2 (88) Music score (Joe Renzetti) -S/T- on
Silva Screen (Total-BMG): FILMCD 073 (CD) also inc:
-S/T- 'FRANKENHOOKER' (88) music by Joe Rezetti

BAT 21 (88) Music score (Christopher Young)-S/T- *Varese
(Pinn): VSC 5202 (Cass) VSD 5202 (CD)*

BATMAN (89) *Songs* composed and sung by Prince on -S/T-
W.Bros (WEA): K.925936-2 (CD) WX 281(C) (LP/Cass)

BATMAN (89) *Music score* only (Danny Elfman) -S/T- *Warn
er (WEA): 925977-2 (CD)*

BATMAN (2) RETURNS (92) Music score (Danny Elfman)-S/T-
Warner (WEA): 759 92697-2 (CD) 759 92697-4 (Cass)

BATTERIES NOT INCLUDED (88) Music score (James Horner)
-S/T- *MCA USA (S.Screen) MCAD 6225 (CD)*

BATTLE OF ALGIERS The (Italy-65) Music sc: (Ennio Morri
cone) -S/T- includes 'Massacre In Rome' (Italy-73)
Italian import (Silva Screen): OST 105 (CD)

BATTLE OF BRITAIN (69) Mus (Ron Goodwin-William Walton)
Academy of St.Martin-in-the-Fields (N.Marriner) and
'Escape me Never'/'Three Sisters'/'Spitfire Prelude
and Fuge'/'Wartime Sketchbook *Chandos:CHAN 8870(CD)
ABTD 1485 (Cass)* see also *Collect* 'BIG WAR THEMES'

BATTLE OF NERETVA The (71) Music score:Bernard Herrmann
London Philharmonic Orchestra (B.Herrmann) -S/T- on
Southern Cross Imp (Silva Screen): SCCD 5005 (CD)

BATTLESTAR GALACTICA (78) Music sco (Stu Phillips) Los
Angeles Phil.Orch *Import (S.Screen): TCS 104.2 (CD)*

BEACHES (89) Bette Midler (songs by Cole Porter-Randy
Newman etc.)"Wind Beneath My Wings" (Henley-Silbar)
-S/T- *Atlantic (WEA): K.781933-2 (CD) .-4 (Cass)*

BEAR The (89) Music score (Phillipe Sarde) -S/T- on
Ariola (Silva Screen): 841 584-2 (CD) -4 (Cass)

BEAST The (88) Music (Mark Isham) -S/T- *A.& M.USA Impt.*
(S.Screen): SP3919 (LP) A&MCS 3919 (CS) CD3919 (CD)
BEASTMASTER 2 (91) Music score (Robert Folk) -S/T- on
Intrada USA (Koch Int): MAFCD 7019 (CD)
BEAT GIRL (60) Music score (John Barry) Featuring: Adam
Faith-John Barry Seven + 4-Shirley Anne Field -S/T-
Play It Again (Silva Screen): PLAY 001 (CD) also
contains John Barry's 1961 "Stringbeat" album
BEAUTIFUL GIRL LIKE ME, A (72-'Belle Fille..') Music sc
(Georges Delerue) see COLL 'TRUFFAUT & DELERUE ON'
BEAUTY AND THE BEAST (92) Music score (Alan Menken) and
Songs "Beauty and the Beast"/"Belle"/"Be Our Guest"
(Alan Menken-Howard Ashman) sung by CELINE DION-PEA
BO BRYSON -S/T- *Disney (Pickwick): DST(CD)(MC) 458*
BEAUTY AND THE BEAST (76) Music (Ron Goodwin) *see under*
Coll 'Drake 400' *(Chandos) LBRD 001 (LP) LBTD 001CS*
BED AND BREAKFAST (92) Music score (David Shire) -S/T-
Varese (Pinn): VSD(VSC) (-) (CD/Cass)
BEDFORD INCIDENT see Coll 'HORRORS OF THE BLACK MUSEUM'
BEDKNOBS AND BROOMSTICKS - see **WALT DISNEY FILM INDEX**
BEETHOVEN (92) Music score (Randy Edelman) -S/T- *MCA*
(BMG): MCAD 10593 (CD) MCAC 10593 (Cass deleted)
BEETLEJUICE (88) Music score (Danny Elfman) -S/T- score
re-issue import: *Geffen (S.Screen): GED 24202 (CD)*
originally *Elektra (WEA): K 924202-2 (CD) -4 (Cass)*
BEGGAR'S OPERA The (LIGHT OPERA by John Gay) dig.record
ing feat: Warren Mitchell-Michael Hordern-Joan Suth
erland-Kiri Te Kanawa-Angela Lansbury-Stafford Dean
Alfred Marks-James Morris-Regina Resnik & National
Phil.Orch (Richard Bonynge) *Decca: 430 066-2 (2CDs)*
BELLE OF NEW YORK The (Film Musical 52) Music (Adolph
Deutsch) Songs (Harry Warren-Johnny Mercer) Featur
Fred Astaire-Vera Ellen-Alice Pearce-Gale Robbins-
MGM USA Imp (Silva Screen): AK 47701 (CD) AT 47701
BELLS ARE RINGING (ORIG BROADWAY CAST 56) Judy Holliday
Col (Silva Screen): CK 02006 (CD) JST 02006 (Cass)
BELLS ARE RINGING (FILM MUSICAL 60) Music (Jule Styne)
Lyrics (B.Comden-A.Green) -S/T- feat: Judy Holliday
Dean Martin - *Capitol USA (Silva Screen) 92060 (CD)*
BELLY OF AN ARCHITECT (87) Music score (Wim Mertens)
-S/T- *Crepuscule (APT): TWI 8132 (CD)* also on
Factory (Pinn): FACD 195 (CD)
BEN HUR (59) Music (Miklos Rosza) Orig score + unissued
material *MGM Imp (Silva Screen): A2K 47020 (2CDs)*
Nat.Phil Orch *Decca:417849-2* see 'My Kind Of Music'
ALSO 'Choral Pieces from BEN HUR' Collec 'MIKLOS RO
ZSA FILM MUSIC V.1' *Prometheus (S.Scr): PCD 122 (CD)*
BEN-HUR (silent 25) New score (Carl Davis) -S/T-
Silva Screen (BMG): FILMC(CD) 043 (Cass/CD)
BENNY AND JOON (93) music score (Rachel Portman) -S/T-
*Milan (Pinn): 15168-2 (CD) 15168-4 (Cass) also from
Silva Screen on 35644-2 (CD) 35644-4 (Cass)*
BERLIN BLUES (88) Music songs (Lalo Schifrin) sung by
Julia Migenes -S/T- *Milan (S.Screen): CDCH 357 (CD)*

BERNADETTE (MUSICAL 90) Songs (Gwyn & Maureen Hughes)
at *Dominion London 21/6/90* with Natalie Wright) on
Sunbelt (Dress Circle): SRSCD 001 (ltd edition CD)
BEST FOOT FORWARD (ORIG OFF-BROADWAY CAST 63) Songs
(Hugh Martin-Ralph Blane) *feat* LIZA MINNELLI-RONALD
CHRISTOPHER WALKEN & Co. *DRG USA (Pinn) CD15003 (CD)*
BEST LITTLE WHOREHOUSE IN TEXAS (82) Music (Patrick Wil
liams) Songs (Carol Hall) featuring DOLLY PARTON
-S/T- *MCA USA (Silva Screen): MCAD 31007 (CD)*
BEST OF THE BEST (89) Music score (Paul Gilman) Various
Artists -S/T- *FM Revolver (BMG): FMOVILP 144 (LP)*
BEST OF THE BEST 2 (92) Music sco (David Michael Frank)
+ songs -S/T- *Impt (Silva Screen): CIN 22012 (CD)*
BEST SHOT 'Hoosiers' (87) Music (Jerry Goldsmith) -S/T-
TER (Silva Screen): CDTER 1141 (CD)
BEST YEARS OF OUR LIVES (46) Music sc (Hugo Friedhofer)
-S/T- *Preamble USA Impt (S.Screen): PRCD 1779 (CD)*
BETJEMAN (Musical Project 87) Music (Mike Read) Lyrics
from poetry of Sir John Betjeman "Myfanwy" sung by
David Essex on 'Greatest Hits' *Mercury: 510308-2 CD*
BETRAYED (88) Music score (Bill Conti) -S/T- *TER (Silva
Screen): CDTER 1163 (CD)*
BETTY BLUE (86) Music score (Gabriel Yared) -S/T- on
Virgin: (TC)V 2396 (Cass/LP) CDV 2396 (CD)
BEVERLY HILLBILLIES The (93) Various Music / Songs on
Impt (Silva Screen): 66313-2 (CD) 66313-4 (Cass)
see also TELEVISION SECTION for 1960's series
BEVERLY HILLS COP 1 (85) Music score:Harold Faltermeyer
Songs Glenn Frey-Pointer Sisters & others -S/T- on
MCA (BMG): MCLD 19087 (CD) MCLC 19087 (Cass)
BEYOND THE FRINGE (REVUE 1961 Fortune Theatre London)
featuring PETER COOK-DUDLEY MOORE-ALAN BENNETT-JONA
THAN MILLER-PAXTON WHITEHEAD and The Company - *EMI
CDECC 1 (CDx2) ECC 1 (2Cass)*
BEYOND THE FRINGE (ORIG BROADWAY CAST 1962) feat: PETER
COOK-DUDLEY MOORE-ALAN BENNETT and JONATHAN MILLER
EMI Angel (EMI): ZDM 764771-2 (CD)
BEYOND THE LAW (68) Music score (Riz Ortolani) c/w 'DAY
OF ANGER' (69) -S/T- *Impt (S.Screen): OST 110 (CD)*
BIBLE The (66) Music score (Toshiro Mayuzumi) Score on
Import (Silva Screen): OST 115 (CD) LEGENDCD 7 (CD)
BIENVENUE A BORD (France 90) - *see* 'WELCOME ABOARD'
BIG BLUE The (88) Music score (Eric Serra) -S/T- *Virgin
CDV 2541 (CD) (TC)V 2541 (Cass/LP) MDV 2541 (MiniD)*
VOL.1 *30145 (CD) 50145 (Cass)* VOL.2 *30667 (CD) 506
67 (Cass)* / COMPLETE *30193 (2CDs) 40065 (2Cass)*
BIG CHILL The (84) Music: Marvin Gaye-Temptations-Four
Tops etc. -S/T-*Motown (Poly): 530017-2(CD) -4(Cass)*
BIG COUNTRY The (58) Music score (Jerome Moross) New Di
gital Recording - Philharmonia Orch - *Silva Screen
Screen (Con): FILM(C)(CD)(DT) 030 (LP/Cass/CD/DAT)*
BIG EASY The (87) Music score (Brad Fiedel) Featuring:
Dixie Cups (Iko Iko) Aaron Neville & other artists
-S/T- *Island ISTA 14 (LP) ICT 14 (Cas) IMCD 31 (CD)*

BIG RIVER (ORIG BROADWAY CAST 85) Songs (Roger Miller)
MCA USA (S.Screen): MCAD 6147 (CD) MCAC 6147 (Cass)
BIG SLEEP The (46) Music (Max Steiner) *see collection*
'Classic Film Scores For Humphrey Bogart'
BIG TROUBLE IN LITTLE CHINA (86) Music score (John Carp
enter) Title music performed by the Coupe De Villes
-S/T- *Demon/Enigma (Pinn): DSCS 2 (Cas) DSCD 2 (CD)*
-S/T- *Silva Screen (Conifer): FILMC 008 (Cass)*
BILITIS (77) Music (Francis Lai) -S/T- *Editions 23 Fra.*
(S.Screen) 80034-2 (CD) -4 (Cass) Theme version by:
Gheorge Zamfir *Knight (Castle-BMG): KNCD 11005 (CD)*
BILL AND TED'S BOGUS JOURNEY (91) Mus sc (David Newman)
-S/T- *Interscope (WEA): 756791725-2 (CD) 4(Cass)*
BILL AND TED'S EXCELLENT ADVENTURE (90) Various Artists
A.& M. (Poly): 39-3915-2 (CD) 39-3915-4 (Cass)
BILLY (ORIG LONDON CAST 74) Music (John Barry) Lyrics
(Don Black)*with* Michael Crawford-Avis Bunnage-Billy
Boyle-Elaine Paige etc. *Sony: 472818-2(CD) -4(Cass)*
BILLY BATHGATE (91) Music score (Mark Isham) -S/T- Impt
Milan (S.Screen-Pinn): 262 495 (CD) 412 495 (Cass)
BINGO! (91) Music score (Richard Gibbs) -S/T-*Bay Cities*
(Silva Screen): BCD 3019 (CD)
BIRD (88) Music score (Lennie Niehaus) featuring music
of Charlie Parker -S/T- *CBS 461002-2 (CD) -4 (Cass)*
CHARLIE PARKER (49) on *Polydor 837176-2(CD)-4(Cass)*
BIRD ON A WIRE (90) Music score (Hans Zimmer)title song
'Bird On A Wire' sung by Neville Brothers on *A & M*
(Poly): AM(Y)(CD) 568 (7"s/12"s/CDsingle) no -S/T-
BIRD WITH THE CRYSTAL PLUMAGE The (69) Music score (Enn
io Morricone) -S/T- also inclu. 'Four Flies On Grey
Velvet'*Cinevox Italy (S.Screen): CDCIA 5087 (CD)*
BIRDY (85) Music (Peter Gabriel) -S/T- *Charisma-Virgin*
(Poly): CASCD 1167 (CD) OVEDC 283 (Cass)
BIRTH OF A NATION (D.W.Griffith) New Recording of Orig
1915 Score (Joseph Carl Breil) on *CBS USA Import*
(Silva Screen): LXCD 701 (CD)
BITTER SWEET (Musical Show 88) Songs (Noel Coward) New
Sadlers Wells Opera & Valerie Masterson *TER (Con:)*
TER2 1160 (2LP) ZCTED 1160 (CSx2) CDTER2 1160 (2CD)
BITTER SWEET (Musical Show 29) *see Collect* 'NOEL'
BLACK HOLE The - *see* WALT DISNEY FILM INDEX
BLACK ORPHEUS (58) Music sco (Luis Bonfa-Antonio Carlos
Jobim) -S/T- *Verve (S.Screen): 830783-2(CD) -4(Cas)*
BLACK RAIN (89) Music score (Hans Zimmer) plus UB 40-
Iggy Pop-Soul II Soul-Gregg Allman-Ryiuchi Sakamoto
Virgin: CDV 2607 (CD) OVEDC 363 (Cass)
BLACK ROBE (91) Music score (Georges Delerue) -S/T- on
Varese (Pinn): VSD 5349 (CD) VSC 5349 (Cass)
BLACK SUNDAY (60) Music score (Les Baxter) -S/T- *includ*
es 'BARON BLOOD' (72) Music score (Les Baxter) on
Bay Cities (Silva Screen): BCD 3034 (CD)
BLACKBEARD'S GHOST - *see* WALT DISNEY FILM INDEX
BLADE RUNNER (82) Music (Vangelis) New American Orchest
(Jack Elliott) *Full Moon: K 99262 (LP) K4 99262 (C)*

BLAZE (89) Music score (Bennie Wallace) tracks by Fats
    Domino-Hank Williams-Randy Newman etc. -S/T- *A.& M.*
    Imp (Silva Screen): CDA 3932-2 (CD)
BLIND DATE (87) Music score (Henry Mancini) -S/T- on
    Silva Screen (Conifer): FILMC(CD) 016 (Cass/CD)
BLITZ ! (ORIG LONDON CAST 61) Songs (Lionel Bart) Inclu
    ding Vera Lynn and add.songs *HMV (EMI): CZ461 (CD)*
BLOOD AND SAND (41) Music score (Alfred Newman) Stanley
    Black - *Decca (Poly): 417850-2 (CD) -4 (Cass)*
BLOOD BROTHERS (ORIG LONDON CAST 88) Songs (Willy Russe
    ll) KIKI DEE *1st Night (Pinn):CASTC(CD)17 (Cass/CD)*
BLOOD IN BLOOD OUT (93) Music score (Bill Conti) -S/T-
    Varese (Pinn): VSD 5396 (CD) VSC 5396 (Cass)
BLOODMOON (Australian Film) Music score (Brian May)
    -S/T- *OneMone: IMICD 1006 (CD)*
BLOODSPORT (89) Music score (Paul Hertzog) -S/T- *Silva*
    Screen (Con): FILMCD 055 (CD) see also 'KICKBOXER'
BLOOMER GIRL (ORIG BROADWAY CAST 44) Music (Harold Arl
    en) Lyrics (E.Y.Harburg)*MCA USA Imp (Silva Screen)*
    MCAD 10522 (CD) MCAC 10522 (Cass)
BLUE (93) Music score (Simon Fisher Turner + Var.Arts.
    -S/T- *Mute (Pinn): CDSTUMM 49 (CD)*
BLUE HAWAII (Film Musical 61) Elvis Presley -S/T- *RCA:*
    NL/NK/ND 83683 (LP/Cas/CD) see 'Elvis P.Film Index'
BLUE LAGOON The (80) Music score (Basil Poledouris)
    -S/T- *Silva Screen: SCCD 1018 (CD)*
BLUE PLANET / THE DREAM IS ALIVE (Imax Films) Music by
    Micky Erbe 'Space Suite' *(S.Screen): CDC 1010 (CD)*
BLUE SKIES (Film Musical 46) Songs (Irving Berlin) Fred
    Astaire-Bing Crosby-Joan Caulfield-Billy De Wolfe
    -S/T- *Sandy Hook USA (Derann-Pinn): CDSH 2095 (CD)*
BLUE VELVET (87) Music score (Angelo Badalamenti) -S/T-
    TER (Sil.Screen): CDTER 1127 (CD) ZCTER 1127 (Cass)
BLUES BROTHERS (80) Featuring: Ray Charles-James Brown-
    Aretha Franklin-Cab Calloway-Blues Brothers -S/Trk-
    Atlantic: K 50715 (LP) K4 50715 (Cas) K2 50715 (CD)
    756781471-5 (DCC)
BLUES IN THE NIGHT (ORIG DONMAR WAREHOUSE THEATRE PRD).
    With Carol Woods-Debby Bishop-Maria Friedman-Clarke
    Peters - *First Night (Pinn): SCENE(C)(CD) 9*
BOAT The (Film 82-TV BBC2 21/10/84) Music (Klaus Doldin
    ger) -S/T- *Warner Bros (WEA): K 58366 (LP only)*
BOCCACCIO '70 (62) Music score (Nino Rota with Armando
    Trovaioli-Piero Umiliani) "Soldi Soldi Soldi" sung
    by Sophia Loren *Italian Imp (S.Screen): OST 116(CD)*
BODIES REST AND MOTION (93) Mus sc (Michael Convertino)
    -S/T- *WB Import (S.Screen): 924 506-2 (CD) -4(Cass)*
BODY BAGS (93) Music score (John Carpenter-Jim Lang)
    -S/T- *Varese (Pinn): VSD 5448 (CD)*
BODY DOUBLE (84) Music score (Pino Donaggio) *see COLLEC*
    'HORROR AND SCIENCE FICTION FILM MUSIC'
BODY HEAT (81) Musi sc (John Barry) *see Coll* 'MOVIEOLA'
BODY OF EVIDENCE (92) Music score (Graeme Revell) -S/T-
    SCORE on *Milan (Pinn): 12720-2 (CD) 12720-4 (Cass)*

BODY PARTS (91) Music score (Loek Dikker) -S/T- *Varese (Pinn): VSC 5337 (Cass) VSD 5337 (CD)*

BODY The (70) Music (Roger Waters-Ron Geesin) -S/T- on *Fame (MFP-EMI): CDFA 3299 (CD) TCFA 3299 (Cass-)*

BODYGUARD (92) Songs by WHITNEY HOUSTON-LISA STANSFIELD JOE COCKER-SASS JORDAN-CURTIS STIGERS-KENNY G-AARON NEVILLE-S.O.U.L.SYSTEM -S/T-*Arista (BMG): 07822 186 992 (CD) 07822 186 994 (Cass) 07822 186 991 (LP)*

BODYWORK (LIGHT OPERA MUSICAL 88) Music-Lyrics (Richard Stilgoe) featuring *The National Youth Music Theatre* with Lonnie Donegan-Chas & Dave and Jake Thackray *1st Night (Pinn): CASTCD 15 (CD) CAST(C) 15 (LP/CS)*

BOLERO (84) Music score (Peter Bernstein) -S/T- incl: Elmer Bernstein previously unreleased material *cond* Christopher Palmer *Prometheus (S.Scr): PCD 124 (CD)*

BONFIRE OF VANITIES (91) Music score (Dave Grusin)-S/T- on *Atlantic USA (S.Screen): 782177-2 (CD) -4 (Cass)*

BOOMERANG (92) Feat:BABYFACE feat TONI BRAXTON & Others -S/T- *Arista (BMG): 73008 26006-20 (CD) -44 (Cass)*

BORN FREE (65) Mus sco (John Barry) title song (J.Barry Don Black) orig sung by MATT MONRO *Coll 'MOVIEOLA'*

BOSTONIANS The (84) Music score (Richard Robbins) -S/T- *Audiotrax: (deleted) see Coll 'MERCHANT-IVORY 25th'*

BOUND BY HONOR (93) Various arts including SANTANA-WAR-RICK JAMES-THE SCREAM-ISLEY BROTHERS-JIMI HENDRIX songs on *Hollywood Rec.(Silva Screen): 61478-2 (CD)*

BOY WHO GREW TOO FAST The (OPERA) Music &Libretto (Gian Carlo'Menotti) Royal Opera House Orch/Chorus (David Syrus) - *TER (Con): (CD)(ZC)TER 1125 (CD/Cass/LP)*

BOYFRIEND The (REVIVAL LONDON CAST 84) *Featuring* Anna Quayle-Derek Waring-Peter Bayliss-Jane Wellman *TER (Silva Screen):ZCTER 1095 (Cas) CDTER 1095 (CD)*

BOYFRIEND The (ORIG BROADWAY CAST 54)with JULIE ANDREWS *RCA (BMG): GD(GK) 60056 (CD/Cass)*

BOYS FROM SYRACUSE The (OFF-BROADWAY REVIVAL CAST 63) Songs (Richard Rodgers-Lorenz Hart) *Angel (EMI): ZDM 764695-2 (CD)*

BOYS FROM SYRACUSE The (USA STUDIO RECORDING 53) *feat:* Portia Nelson-Jack Cassidy-Bibi Osterwald-Holly Ha rris-Stanley Prager *Sony Broadway: SK 53329 (CD)*

BOYZ 'N' THE HOOD (91) Music sc. (Stanley Clarke) -S/T- *Qwest (WEA): 759926643-2 (CD) -4 (Cass) -1 LP)*

BRAZIL (85) Music score (Michael Kamen) -S/T- *Milan/RTM (Pinn): 11125-2 (CD) 11125-4 (Cass)*

BREAKFAST AT TIFFANY'S (61) Music score (Henry Mancini) song "Moon River" (Lyrics: Johnny Mercer) -S/T- on *RCA: ND 89905 (CD) see collection* 'PINK PANTHER...'

BREAKFAST CLUB The (85) Music sco (Keith Forsey) songs: Simple Minds-Wang Chung-Karlo De Vito-Jesse Johnson -S/T- *A.& M. (Poly): CDMID 179 (CD) AMC 5045 (Cass)*

BREAKING GLASS (80) Music (Hazel O'Connor) -S/T- re-iss ue: *A.& M.(Poly): CDMID 124 (CD) CMID 124 (Cass)*

BREAKING THE RULES (92) Music score (-) Various Artists -S/T- *Varese (Pinn): VSD 5386 (CD) VSC 5386 (Cass)*

BRIDE OF FRANKENSTEIN The (35) Music sco (Franz Waxman)
New Digital Recording with the Westminster Philharm
onic Orchest (Kenneth Alwyn) *also* THE INVISIBLE RAY
(35 Franz Waxman) *Sil.Screen (Con): FILMCD 135 (CD)*
see Coll 'Sunset Boulevard' RCA: RD 87017 (CD)
BRIDE OF THE RE-ANIMATOR (90) Music sco (Richard Band)
+'RE-ANIMATOR' -S/T- *S.Screen (Con) FILMCD 082 (CD)*
BRIDGE ON THE RIVER KWAI (57) Music score (Malcolm Arn
old) Suite played by LONDON SYMPHONY ORCH (Richard
Hickox) on *Chandos: 9100 (CD) ABTD 1600 (Cass)*
"Colonel Bogey" (Sir Kenneth Alford) *see Collect*
'BIG WAR THEMES'/'GUNS OF NAVARONE'
BRIDGE The (-) Music score (Richard G.Mitchell) -S/T-
Demon (Pinn): DSCD 5 (CD) DSCASS 5 (Cass)
BRIDGE TOO FAR A (77) Music (John Addison) Theme by The
Grenadier Guards 'The Guards' *MFP (EMI) CC 247 (CD)*
BRIEF ENCOUNTER (54) Music: 2nd movement from 'Piano
Concerto No.2 in C min' Op.18 (Rachmaninov) version
Philips: 412 738-1/-4 (LP/Cas) see also Coll 'Class
ic Movie Music' Vol.1' *note:* Eric Carmen's 1976 hit
"All By Myself" also based on it *(Old Gold:OG 9122)*
BRIGADOON (BROADWAY CAST RECORD) Songs (Lerner-Loewe)
Featur: David Brooks-Marion Bell-Pamela Britton-Lee
Sullivan - *RCA Victor (BMG): GD(GK) 81001 (CD/Cass)*
BRIGADOON (ORIG LONDON CAST 88) Songs (Alan Jay Lerner-
Frederick Loewe) *1st Night (Pinn): CAST(C)(CD) 16*
BRIGADOON (STUDIO RECORDING 91) Ambrosian Chorus & Lond
on Sinfonietta (John McGlynn)-Brent Barrett-Rebecca
Luker-Judy Kaye-John Mark Ainsley *EMI: CDC 754481-2*
BRIGHT ANGEL (90) Music score (Christopher Young) -S/T-
Intrada USA (Silva Screen): MAF 7014D (CD)
BRIGHT LIGHTS BIG CITY (88) Music: Prince-Donald Fagen-
Narada-Bryan Ferry-M/A/R/R/S-New Order-Depeche Mode
enni Hall -S/T- *W.Bros(WEA): K925688-2(CD) -4(Cass)*
BRILLIANT THE DINOSAUR (MUSICAL 93) Songs (Richard Stil
goe) *narrated by* Christopher Timothy on *Alchemy*
(Pinn): PBAU 102CD (CD) PBAU 102C (Cass)
BRIMSTONE AND TREACLE (82) Music: Sting-Police-Squeeze
Go Go's -S/T- *A.& M.(Poly): CAM 64915 (Cass)*
BRING ON THE NIGHT (86) Music by STING on 'Bring On The
Night' *A.& M. (Poly): BRIND 1 (2CD) BRINC 1 (2Cass)*
BROOD The (79) *see under* 'DEAD RINGERS'
BRUTE FORCE (47) Music score (Miklos Rozsa) selection
on 'LUST FOR LIFE' *Varese (Pinn): VSD 5405 (CD)*
BUBBLING BROWN SUGAR (ORIG LONDON CAST 77)Var composers
feat: Billy Daniels-Helen Gelzer-Lon Satton-Elaine
Delmar-Stephanie Lawrence-Clarke Peters-MiquelBrown
C.Augins-Amii Stewart *DRG (Con): CDSBL 13106 (CDx2)*
BUCCANEER The (58) Music score (Elmer Bernstein) -S/T-
Varese (Silva Screen): VSD 5214 (CD)
BUDDY (ORIG LONDON CAST 89) Paul Hipp-Gareth Marks-Enzo
Squillino *1st Night (Pinn): QUEUEC (CD) 1 (Cass/CD)*
BUDDY'S SONG (90) Featur: Chesney Hawkes-Roger Daltrey
-S/T- *Chrysalis (EMI): CCD21 (CD) ZDD21 (Cass)*

BUFFY THE VAMPIRE SLAYER (92) Mus (Carter Burwell) +V/A
    (Songs) *Columbia (SM):472 076-2(CD) -4(Cass) -1(LP)*
BUGSY (91) Mus.sc (Ennio Morricone) Songs:Johnny Mercer
    Peggy Lee-Jo Stafford -S/T- *Epic (Sony Music): 469
    371-2 (CD) 469371-4 (Cass) (all deleted 8/93)*
BUGSY MALONE (76) Music and songs (Paul Williams) -S/T-
    Polydor: 2442 142 (LP) deleted
BULL DURHAM (88) Music score (Michael Convertino)
    EMI USA (S.Screen): 90586-4 (Cass)
BULLET FOR THE GENERAl, A (aka 'Quien Sabe') (67) Music
    (Luis Bacalov) -S/T- *Alhambra (S.Scre): A.8932 (CD)*
BURNING SECRET (89) Music score (Hans Zimmer) *see Coll*
    'FILM MUSIC OF HANS ZIMMER'
BURNING The (80) Music score (Rick Wakeman) -S/T- on
    Charisma: CLASS 12 (LP) CASMC 111 (Cassette)
BUSTER (88) Music score (Anne Dudley) with PHIL COLLINS
    -S/T- *Virgin (EMI): CDV 2544 (CD) OVEDC 398 (Cass)*
BUTCH CASSIDY & THE SUNDANCE KID (69) Music score (Burt
    Bacharach) Song "Raindrops Keep Falling on My Head"
    Lyrics (Hal David) sung by B.J.Thomas -S/T- *Import
    A.& M.(Silv.Screen): CD 3159 (CD) CS 3159 (Cass)*
BUTTERFLY (81) Music score (Ennio Morricone) -S/T- on
    import on *Prometheus (Silva Screen): PCD 108 (CD)*
BUTTERFLY BALL The (Film Musical 74) Music score (Roger
    Glover) - Roger Glover & Friends -S/T- *Connoisseur
    (Pinn): VSOPCD 139 (CD) VSOLP(MC) 139 (Dbl LP/Cass)*
BY THE BEAUTIFUL SEA (ORIG BROADWAY CAST 54) Songs by
    (Arthur Schwartz-Herbert & Dorothy Fields) *featur:*
    SHIRLEY BOOTH-WILBUR EVANS-DAVID BURNS *EMI Angel
    (EMI): ZDM 764889-2 (CD)*
BYE BYE BIRDIE (ORIG BROADWAY CAST 60) Music (Charles
    Strouse) Lyrics (Lee Adams) Dick Van Dyke & Company
    CBS USA (S.Screen): CK 02025 (CD) JST 02025 (Cass)
BYE BYE BIRDIE (FILM MUSICAL 63) featur: DICK VAN DYKE
    -S/T- *Import (Silva Screen): 1081-2 (CD)*

CABARET (FILM MUSICAL 72) Songs (John Kander-Fred Ebb)
    Liza Minnelli -S/T- *MCA (BMG): MCLD(MCLC) 19088*
CABARET (NEW LONDON CAST 86) with Wayne Sleep-Vivienne
    Martin-Caroline Clare-Grazina Frame-Kelly Hunter-Os
    car Quitak & Co. *First Night (Pinn): OCRCD 10 (CD)*
CABARET (ORIG BROADWAY CAST 66) Songs (John Kander-Fred
    Ebb) *CBS (S.Screen) CK 03040(CD) JST 03040 (Cass)*
CABIN IN THE SKY (ORIG NEW YORK CAST 64) Songs (Vernon
    Duke-John Latouche-Ted Fetter) *featuring:* LE NOIRE
    LEISTER-MIDDLETON *EMI Angel: ZDM 764892-2 (CD)*
CABIRIA (57-Italy) - *see under* 'LA STRADA'
CABOBLANCO (80) Music score (Jerry Goldsmith) -S/T- on
    Prometheus Imp (Silva Screen): PCD 127 (CD)
CAINE MUTINY The (54) Music (Max Steiner) *see* collect
    'Classic Film Scores For Humphrey Bogart'
CAL (84) Music score (Mark Knopfler) -S/T- *Vertigo-Poly
    VERH 17 (LP) VERHC 17 (CS) 822 769-2 (CD) see also*
    'Screenplaying' *collection*

CALAMITY JANE (FILM MUSICAL 53) Songs (Sammy Fain-Paul
Francis Webster) Featuring Doris Day -S/T- on *Sony:
467610-2 (CD) -4(Cass)* also featuring -S/T- songs
from *'Pajama Game The'* with Doris Day (Film 57)
CALL ME MADAM (ORIG BROADWAY CAST 50) Songs (Irving Ber
lin) with Ethel Merman-Dick Haymes *MCA USA Import
(Silva Screen): MCAD 10521 (CD) MCAC 10521 (Cass)*
CALL ME MADAM (ORIG LONDON CAST 52) Billie Worth-Anton
Brook-Shani Wallis-Jeff Warren *TER: ZCTER 1062 (CS)*
CAMELOT (FILM MUSICAL 67) Songs (Alan Jay Lerner-Freder
ick Loewe) Featur: Richard Harris-Vanessa Redgrave
-S/T- *W.Bros Imp (S.Screen): 3102-2 (CD) -4 (Cass)*
CAMELOT (ORIG BROADWAY CAST 61) Julie Andrews-Richard
Burton-Robert Goulet-Roddy McDowell *CBS UK(40)70009
(Cass/LP)+CBS USA (Silva S) CK(JST) 32602 (CD/Cass)*
CAMELOT (ORIG LONDON CAST 64) with Laurence Harvey-Eliz
abeth Larner-Nicky Henson-Josephine Gordon-Kit Will
iams-Barry Kent *1st Night (Pinn): OCR(C) 4 (LP/Cas)*
CAMELOT (REVIVAL LONDON CAST 82) Featur: Richard Harris
Fiona Fullerton *TER (Con/S.Screen): CD(ZC)TER 1030*
CAMILLE CLAUDEL (89) Music score (Gabriel Yared) -S/T-
Virgin Fr.(S.Screen) 30673(CD) 50673 (Cass)
CAMP FOLLOWERS The - *see* **'ATTACK AND RETREAT'**
CAN-CAN (FILM MUSICAL 67) Songs (Cole Porter) Featuring
Frank Sinatra-Shirley MacLaine-Maurice Chevalier-Lo
ius Jourdan -S/T- *Capitol USA (S.Screen): 91248-2CD*
CAN-CAN (ORIG BROADWAY CAST 53) Songs (Cole Porter)
feat: GWEN VERDON-LILO-PETER COOKSON-HANS CONREID-
ERIK RHODES *Angel (EMI): ZDM 764664-2 (CD)*
CANDIDE (ORIG BROADWAY CAST 56) *feat:* Barbara Cook-Max
Adrian-Robert Rounseville-Irra Petina-William Olvis
Louis Edmonds-C.Bain *Sony Broadway: SK 48017 (CD)*
CANDIDE (MUSICAL OPERA 88) Music by Leonard Bernstein
Lyrics by Richard Wilbur with additional lyrics by
Stephen Sondheim and John Latouche - **Scottish Opera
Cast Recording (April 88)** prod by John Yap *TER Prod
(Con): TER 1156(LP) ZCTER 1156(Cass) CDTER 1156(CD)*
CANDIDE (MUSICAL OPERA 91) **Studio Recording** featuring
Jerry Hadley-June Anderson-Christa Ludwig-Adolph Gr
een-Nicolai Gedda-Della Jones-Hurt Ollmann & L.S.O.
(Bernstein) *DG (Poly): 429734-2 (2CDs) -4 (2Cass)*
CANDLESHOE (77) Music score (Ron Goodwin) *see under*
Collections - 'Drake 400' (Ron Goodwin Orchestra)
CAPE FEAR (91) Music score (Elmer Bernstein: re-orchest
ration of Bernard Herrmann's original 1962 score)
-S/T- *MCA: MCAD(MCAC) 10463 (CD/Cass) all deleted*
CAPRICORN ONE (78) Music score (Jerry Goldsmith) -S/T-
so containing music from 'OUTLAND') on *GNP USA
(Silva Screen): GNPD 8035 (CD) GNP-5 8035 (Cass)*
CAPTAIN HORATIO HORNBLOWER (51) Mus sco (Robert Farnon)
Suite from the film featur: The Royal Philharmonic
Orch (R.Farnon) *Reference Recordings: RR 47CD (CD)*
CAPTIVE (86) Music sco (Michael Berkley-The Edge) -S/T-
Virgin: CDV 2401 (CD)

CARD The (ORIG LONDON CAST 73) Songs (Tony Hatch-Jackie Trent) with Jim Dale-Millicent Martin-Joan Hickson Marti Webb-Eleanor Bron-Alan Norburn-John Savident *First Night (Con): OCRC(CD) 5 (Cass/CD)*

CARDINAL The (63) Music score (Jerome Moross) -S/T- on *Preamble USA (Silva Screen): PRCD 1778 (CD)*

CARETAKERS The (63) Music score (Elmer Bernstein) with 'Baby The Rain Must Fall' (64-E.Bernstein) -S/T- on *Mainstream USA (Koch Int): MDCD 603 (CD)*

CARLITO'S WAY (93) Music score (Patrick Doyle) -S/T- on *Varese (Pinn): VSD 5463 (CD) VSC 5463 (Cass)*

CARMEN (FILM MUSICAL 84) Music (Bizet) with Placido Domingo-Julia Migenes Johnson -S/T- *Erato: NUM 75113 (3 LP set) MCE 75113 (3 Cass) ECD 88037 (3 CD set)*

CARMEN (OPERA by Bizet) *with* Marilyn Horne as Carmen *DG (Poly): 427 440-2 (3CD's)*

CARMEN JONES (FILM MUSICAL 54) (Bizet-Hammerstein) feat Marilyn Horne-Pearl Bailey-LaVern Hutchinson-Marvin Hayes-Olga James-Bernice Peterson-Brock Peters-Joe Crawford. -S/T- *RCA Vic: GD(GK) 81881 (CD/Cass)*

CARMEN JONES (ORIG LONDON CAST 91) Music (Bizet) Lyrics (O.Hammerstein II) Dir:Simon Callow with Wilhelmina Fernandez-Sharon Benson-Damon Evans-Michael Austin-Gregg Baker-Karen Parks-Clive Rowe-Danny John Jules Carolyn Sebron-Wendy Brown: *EMI: (CD)(TC)JONES 1*

CARNIVAL (61 ORIG BROADWAY CAST) with Kay Ballard *Impt (Silva Screen): 837 195-2 (CD)*

CAROUSEL (FILM MUSICAL 56) (R.Rodgers & O.Hammerstein) Gordon McRae-Shirley Jones-Gene Nelson-Rod Steiger -S/T- Reissue *EMI Angel: ZDM 764 692-2 (CD)*

CAROUSEL (ORIG LONDON CAST 93) with JOANNA RIDING-KATRINA MURPHY & Comp. *1st Night (Pinn): CAST(CD)(C) 40*

CAROUSEL (SHOWS COLLECTION 93) *featuring:* DAVE WILLETTS CLAIRE MOORE-SU POLLARD-IAN WALLACE-LINDA HIBBERD *Pickwick Shows: PWKS 4144 (CD) PWKMC 4144 (Cass)*

CAROUSEL (ORIG BROADWAY CAST 45) with Jan Clayton-John Raitt-Jean Darling-Chris Johnson *MCA (BMG): MCLD 19152 (CD) MCLC 19152 (Cass)*

CAROUSEL (REVIVAL BROADWAY CAST 1965) with JOHN RAITT *Import (Silva Screen): 6395-2 (CD)*

CARTOUCHE (61) Music score (Georges Delerue) -S/T- on a *French Import Prometheus (S.Screen): PCD 104 (CD)*

CASABLANCA (43) Music sco (Max Steiner) Songs: "As Time Goes By" (Hubert Hupfeld) "It Had To Be You" (Isham Jones-Gus Kahn) -S/T- with music and dialogue *Impt (Arabesque): FCBAK 4400 (CD picture disc)* see also Collection 'Classic Scores For Humphrey Bogart'

CASINO ROYALE (67) Music score (Burt Bacharach) -S/T- *Varese USA (Pinn) VSD(VSC) 5265 (CD/Cass)*

CASSANDRA CROSSING The (77) Music sc: (Jerry Goldsmith) feat song "I'm Still On My Way" sung by Ann Turkel -S/T- *Citadel USA Imp (Silva Screen): OST 102 (CD)*

CAST A GIANT SHADOW (66) Music score (Elmer Bernstein) -S/T- *EMI MGM: CDMGM 11 (CD)* with -S/T- 'EXODUS'*del*

CAT PEOPLE (82) Music score Giorgio Moroder feat: DAVID
BOWIE -S/T- *MCA USA (S.Screen): MCAD 1498 (CD)*
CATS (ORIG LONDON CAST 81) Songs (Andrew Lloyd Webber
Trevor Nunn-T.S.Eliott) with Elaine Paige & Company
Polydor: CATXC 001 (Double Cass) and 817 810-2 (CD)
'Highlights' 839415-2(CD) -1(LP) -4(Cass) -5 (DCC)
see also Coll 'ROYAL PHILHARMONIC ORCH PLAY SUITES'
CELEBRATION (Musical 60)Songs: Harvey Schmidt-Tom Jones
Or.Broadway Cast *Bay Cities (S.Screen):BCD 3015(CD)*
CELL BLOCK 4 (92) Music details to be confirmed -S/T-
MCA (BMG): MCD(MCC) 10758 (CD/Cass)
CEMETARY CLUB The (93) Music score (Elmer Bernstein)
-S/T- *Varese (Pinn): VSD 5412 (CD) VSC 5412 (Cass)*
CHAIRMAN The (69) Music sc: (Jerry Goldsmith) -S/T- inc
'Ransom' (75) *Silva Screen (Conif): FILMCD 081 (CD)*
CHALLENGE The (ORIG L.CAST) *TER (Koch):TERCD 1201 (2CD)*
CHAMPIONS The (84) Music score (Carl Davis) -S/T-*Island*
deleted "Sometimes" Elaine Paige see *Coll* 'Cinema'
CHANT OF JIMMIE BLACKSMITH (78) Music score (Bruce Smea
ton) 'Music From Great Australian Films' (collect.)
DRG USA (Con): SBLC 12582 (Cass) CDSBL 12582 (CD)
CHAPLIN (92) Music sco (John Barry) -S/T- *Epic (Sony M)*
472 602-2 (CD) 472 602-4 (Cass) see *Coll* 'MOVIEOLA'
CHARADE (64) Music score (Henry Mancini) see *Collection*
'Mancini's Gr.Hits' (*Telarc*) & 'Third Man' (*Decca*)
-S/T- *Import (Silva Screen): 2755-2 (CD)*
CHARIOTS OF FIRE (81) Music score (Vangelis) -S/T- on
Polydor (Polyg): POLDC (Cass) 800 020-2 (CD)
CHARLIE GIRL (NEW LONDON CAST 86) Songs (David Heneker
John Taylor) with Paul Nicholas-Cyd Charisse-Mark
Wynter-Dora Bryan-Nicholas Parsons-Karen Davies-
Lisa Hull-C.P.Henry *1st Night (Pinn): OCRCD 9 (CD)*
CHASE The (66) Music score (John Barry) -S/T- *Import*
Varese (Silva Screen): VSD 5229 (CD)
CHATEAU DE MA MERE (90) *see under* 'GLORY OF MY FATHER'
CHESS (86) **Chess Pieces: The Best Of Chess** *feat:* ELAINE
PAIGE-BARBARA DICKSON-MURRAY HEAD-TOMMY KORBERG-DEN
IS QUILLEY-BJORN SKIFS-LONDON SYMPHONY ORCH-AMBROSI
AN SINGERS *RCA (BMG): 74321 15120-2 (CD) -4 (Cass)*
CHEYENNE AUTUMN (64) Music score (Alex North) -S/T- Imp
CBS (USA) Silva Screen: LXCD 2 (CD)
CHICAGO (ORIG BROADWAY CAST 75) Songs (John Kander-Fred
Ebb) *with* Gwen Verdon-Chita Rivera and Jerry Orbach
Bay Cities USA (Silva Screen): BCD 3003 (CD)
CHICAGO BLUES (Film 'Blues' Documentary) Muddy Waters &
J.B.Hutto-Junior Wells-Mighty Joe Young-Koko Taylor
Johnnie Young etc - *Red Lightnin': RL 0055 (2LP)*
CHILDREN OF A LESSER GOD (86)Theme "Largo Ma Mon Tanto"
2nd m/m 'Concerto D.Min For Violins' (Bach) / Music
score (Michael Convertino) -S/T- *GNP (Silva Screen)*
GNPD(GNP5)(GNPS)8007 (CD/Cass/LP) theme Coll 'Class
ics 2'/'Weekend Classics' *others* "Jump For My Love"
(Pointer Sisters)"I'll Take You There" (Staple Sing
ers) "I've Been Loving You Too Long" (Otis Redding)

CHILDREN OF EDEN (ORIG LONDON CAST 91) Songs by Stephen Schwartz feat: Ken Page-Martin Smith-Shezwae Powell Kevin Colson-Frances Ruffelle-Earlene Bentley on *London (Polyg): 828 234-2(CD) -4(2Cass)*

CHILDEN OF THE CORN 2: The Final Sacrifice (92) Music score (Daniel Licht) -S/T- *Bay Cities (S.Screen) BCD 3039 (CD)*

CHILDREN OF THE NIGHT (91) Music score (Daniel Licht) -S/T- *Bay Cities (Silva Screen): BCD 3017 (CD)*

CHILDREN'S THIEF The (Film Italy) Music score (Franco Piersanti) -S/T- contains mus from 'ON MY OWN'(92) -S/T- *OST (Silva Screen): OST 117 (CD)*

CHILDS PLAY (88) Music score (Joe Renzetti) -S/T- *Impt Milan (Silva Screen): CDCH 382 (CD) C 382 (Cass)*

CHINA 9 LIBERTY 37 (78) Music sco (Pino Donaggio) -S/T- *Import (Silva Screen): PCD 117 (CD)*

CHITTY CHITTY BANG BANG (68) Music and songs (Richard & Robert Sherman) -S/T- *UA (EMI): SLS 50408 (deleted)*

CHORUS LINE A (ORIGINAL BROADWAY CAST 75) *Columbia Imp (Silva Screen): CK 33581 (CD) JST 33581 (Cass)*

CHRISTINE (84) Music score (John Carpenter) -S/T- feat John Carpenter's original music only on import *Varese (Pinn): VS(C)(CD) 5240 (LP/Cass/CD)*

CHRISTOPHER COLUMBUS (49) Music score: Sir Arthur Bliss Music from film and from 'Seven Waves Away' (56) on *Marco Polo (Harmonia Mundi): 8223315 (CD)*

CHRISTOPHER COLUMBUS: THE DISCOVERY (92) Music score (Cliff Eidelman) -S/T- *Varese (Pinn): VSD(VSC) 5389*

CINDERELLA (Disney 50) see **WALT DISNEY FILM INDEX**

CINDERELLA (MUSICAL SHOW 57) with JULIE ANDREWS *Col.USA (Silva Screen): CK 02005 (CD) JST 02005 (Cass)*

CINDERELLA (ORIG LONDON CAST 59) Songs (Richard Rodgers O.Hammerstein) with Tommy Steele *TER: TER 1045 (LP)*

CINEMA PARADISO (90) Music score (Ennio Morricone)-S/T- *DRG (Pinn): CDSBL 12598 (CD) SBLC 12598 (Cass)*

CINERAMA SOUTH SEAS ADVENTURE (1958) Music score (Alex North) *Import (Silva Screen): LXCD 2 (CD)*

CITIZEN KANE (41) Music score (Bernard Herrmann) New recording (complete score) by Australian Philharmonic Orchestra (Tony Bremner) with Rosamund Illing *5th Continent (S.Screen): PRCD 1788 (CD)* main theme on coll 'Citizen Kane' *Decca: 417 852-2(CD)-4(Cass)*

CITY LIGHTS (1931) Original Music composed by Charlie Chaplin. New recording reconstructed from the orig manuscripts. City Lights Orch conductor: Carl Davis *Silva Screen (Conifer): FILM(C)(CD) 078 (CD/Cass)* see also Coll 'CHARLIE'

CITY OF ANGELS (ORIG BROADWAY CAST 90) Songs Cy Coleman *Sony Broadway (Sony Music): 466714-2 (CD) -4 (Cass)*

CITY OF JOY (92) Music score (Ennio Morricone) -S/T- *Epic Import (Silva Screen): EK 52750 (CD)*

CITY SLICKERS (91) Music score (Marc Shaiman) -S/T- on *Varese (Pinn): VSC 5321 (Cass) VSD 5321 (CD)*

CLAMBAKE (67) - see 'Elvis Presley Film Index'

CLASS ACTION (91) Music score (James Horner) -S/T- on
   Varese USA (Pinn): VSD 5303 (CD) VSC 5303 (Cass)
CLEOPATRA (63) Music score (Alex North) theme on Collec
   'The Epic' *Decca (Poly): 417 845-2 (CD) -4 (Cass)*
CLIFFHANGER (93) Mus score (Trevor Jones) Song "Do You
   Need Some" (Matt Mercado) by TIMEBOMB -S/T- *Scotti*
   Bros (Polyg): 514 455-2 (CD) 514 455-4 (Cass)
CLOCKWORK ORANGE A (71) Electronic music score by (Walt
   er 'Wendy' Carlos) V.Classical Pieces -S/T- *Warner*
   Bros (WEA): K 446127 (Cass) K2 46127 (CD)
CLOSE ENCOUNTERS OF THE THIRD KIND (77) Music score by
   John Williams -Nat.Phil.Orch on *RCA: RCD 13650 (CD)*
   -S/T- *Varese (Pinn-S.Screen) VSD(VSC) 5275 (CD/Cas)*
   also on Arista USA: AL 9500 (LP) ACB6 8365 (Cass)
   also on -S/T- Alhambra (S.Screen/Pinn): A.8915 CD
CLOSER THAN EVER (ORIG BROADWAY CAST 89) Songs (David
   Shire-Richard Maltby) *Import (Silva Screen):60399-2*
   (2CD's) 60399-4 (2Cass)
CLOSET LAND (91) Music score (Richard Einhorn).......*NA*
COASTAL COMMAND (42) Music score (Vaughan Williams)
   see Coll 'Classic British Film Music' *Silva Screen*
COBRA (86) Music score (Sylvester Levay)"Feel The Heat"
   sung by Jean Beauvoir -S/T- *CBS: CDCBS 70297 (CD)*
   also on Imp (Sil.Screen): 75239-2(CD) -4(Cass)
COBRA VERDE (88) Music score (Popol Vuh) -S/T- *Milan Fr*
   (Silva Screen): C.353 (Cass) CD.353 (CD)
COCKTAIL (88) Music score (J.Peter Robinson) -S/T- on
   Elektra (WEA): EKT 54(C) (LP/Cass) 960806-2 (CD)
COCOON (85) Music score (James Horner) Featur: Michael
   Sembello -S/T- *Polydor (Polyg): 827 041-2 (CD)*
COCOON 2 'The Return' (89) Music score (James Horner)
   -S/T- *Varese (Pinn): VSD(VSC) 5211 (CD/Cass)*
COLD FEET (89) Music score (Tom Bahler) -S/T- Import on
   Varese USA (Pinn): VSD 5231 (CD) VSC 5231 (Cass)
COLD HEAVEN (92) Music score (Stanley Myers) Suite on
   Intrada (S.Screen): MAF 7048D (CD) also includes
   Suite from film 'TRUSTING BEATRICE' (S.Myers)
COLLECTOR The (65) Music score (Maurice Jarre) -S/T- on
   Mainstream USA (Koch Int): MDCD 606 (CD)
COLOR OF MONEY The (86) Music (Robbie Robertson)+ songs
   -S/T- *MCA USA Imp (Silva Screen): MCAD 6189 (CD)*
COLOR PURPLE The (86) Music score (Quincy Jones) Songs
   Tata Vega -S/T- *Qwest Impt (Silva Screen): 925389-2*
   (CD) 925389-4 (Cass)
COLORS (88) Title song: Ice T - featuring Various Arts
   - S/T- *Warner Bros.(WEA): K925713-4 (Cass) -2 (CD)*
COMA (78) Music score (Jerry Goldsmith) -S/T-*Bay Cities*
   (Silva Screen): BCD 3027 (CD)
COMANCHEROS The (61) *see under* 'True Grit'
COME SEE THE PARADISE (90) Music score (Randy Edelman)
   -S/T- *Milan (S.Screen): CDCH 614(CD) C.614 (Cass)*
COME TOGETHER AGAIN (GOSPEL MUSICAL 86) Songs (Jimmy &
   Carol Owens) Feat: Pat Boone-Terry Talbot-Anne Herr
   ing-Jamie Owens Collins - *Oak: OAKR(C) 3006 (LP/CS)*

COMFORT AND JOY (84) Music score (Mark Knopfler) Theme
only on *Vertigo (Poly): DSTR 712 (12"s) no -S/T-*
COMMANDO - see COLL 'UNIVERSAL SOLDIER'
COMMITMENTS The (91) *Covers* of soul track hits by Otis
Redding-Wilson Pickett-Aretha Franklin-Percy Sledge
-S/T- *MCA: MCAD 10286 (CD) MCA(C) 10286 (LP/Cass) &
MCAX 10286 (DCC)* / ORIG ARTISTS on 'SOUL CLASSICS'
Atlantic (WEA) 7567 91813-2 (CD) 756791813-4 (Cass)
COMMITMENTS 2 (92) Second Album of Songs from the film
including "Hard To Handle"/"Show Me"/"Too Many Fish
In The Sea"/"Nowhere To Run" plus 7 new tracks *MCA:
MCAD 10506 (CD) MCAC 10506 (Cass) MCAX 10506 (DCC)*
COMPANY (ORIG BROADWAY CAST 70) Songs: Stephen Sondheim
Col (Silva Screen): CK 03550 (CD) JST 03550 (Cass)
COMPANY BUSINESS (91) Music score (Michael Kamen) -S/T-
Alhambra Germany (Silva Screen): CDA 8931 (CD) also
on *Intrada (Silva Screen): MAF 7013D (CD)*
COMPANY OF WOLVES The (84) Music (George Fenton) -S/T-
TER (Conifer): (CD)(ZC)TER 1094 (CD/Cass/LP)
CONAN THE BARBARIAN (81) Music score (Basil Poledouris)
*USA CD containing an extra 20mins of previously unr
eleased material Varese (S.Screen): VSD 5390 (CD)*
CONAN THE DESTROYER (83) Music score (Basil Poledouris)
Varese (S.Screen): VSD 5392 (CD)
CONCIERGE The (93) Music score (Bruce Broughton) -S/T-
USA Imp (S.Screen): 924 515-2 (CD) 924 515-4 (Cass)
CONE OF SILENCE see COLL 'HORRORS OF THE BLACK MUSEUM'
CONEHEADS The (93) Var.artists inc: ANDY BELL & k.d.lang
MORTEN HARKET (A-Ha)-RED HOT CHILLI PEPPERS-BARENAK
ED LADIES etc -S/T- *WB (WEA): 9362 45345-2 (CD) -4*
CONFESSIONS OF A POLICE CAPTAIN (71-Italy) *see under*
'IN THE GRIP OF THE SPIDER'
CONFIDENTIALLY YOURS (83 'Vivement Dimanche') Music sco
(Georges Delerue) *see coll* 'TRUFFAUT & DELERUE'
CONNECTION The (Film 61) Music (Freddie Redd-Jackie Mc
Lean) -S/T- *Boplicity (Ace): BOP 4 (LP)*
CONQUEST OF THE AIR (38) Music score (Sir Arthur Bliss)
see Coll 'Classic British Film Music'*(Silva Screen)*
CONSENTING ADULTS (92) Music sco (Michael Small) -S/T-
Milan (Pinn): 12479-2 (CD) 12479-4 (Cass)
CONVERSATION PIECE (Musical Show 34) - *see under* 'Noel
Coward The Great Shows' collection *(EMI Retrospect)*
COOK THE THIEF HIS WIFE AND HER LOVER The (89) Music Sc
(Michael Nyman) -S/T- *Virgin: (CD)(TC) VE 53*
see Collect 'Nyman-Greenaway Soundtracks' (Virgin)
COOL WORLD (92) Music score (Mark Isham) -S/T- *Varese
(Pinn): VSD(VSC) 5382 (CD/Cass)* Songs (Var.Arts) on
W.Bros (WEA): 9362 45078-2 (CD) -4 (Cass) -1 (LP)
COSI COME SEI (Stay The Way You Are) (Ital) Music score
(Ennio Morricone)-S/T-*Prometheus (S.Scr):PCD115(CD)*
COTTON CLUB The (85) Music score (John Barry) -S/T- on
reissued on Geffen USA (Sil.Screen): GEF 24062 (CD)
also on Giants Of Jazz (Counterpoint):CD 53022 (CD)
see also Coll 'MOVIEOLA'

COUNT OF LUXEMBOURG The (OPERETTA) Music (Franz Lehar) English lyr (Eric Mascwitz) *New Sadlers Wells Cast* English Highlights *TER (Koch): CD(ZC)TER 1050*

COUNTESS FROM HONG KONG A (67) Music score (Charles Chaplin) - *see Coll* 'CHARLIE'

COUNTESS MARITZA (OPERETTA) Mus (Emerich Kallmann) English lyrics (Nigel Douglas) *New Sadlers Wells Cast* Highlights in English *TER (Koch) (CD)(ZC)TER 1051*

COURIER The (88) Music score Declan McManus (Elvis Costello) Songs: U2-Something Happens-Hothouse Flowers-Lord John White-Aslan-Too Much For The White Man-Cry Before Dawn -S/T- *Virgin (Poly): CDV 2517 (CD)*

COURTESANS OF BOMBAY (Film India) Music Zubaida Khanam *see* Collections 'Merchant-Ivory 25th Anniversary'

CRADLE WILL ROCK The (ORIG CAST 1985) Songs (Marc Blitzstein) *TER (Koch): TERCD 1105 (CD)*

CRASH AND BURN (91) Music score (Richard Band) -S/T- on *Intrada (Koch): MAF 7033CD (CD)*

CRAZY FOR YOU (ORIG LONDON CAST 93) Songs (George & Ira Gershwin) *feat:* RUTHIE HENSHALL-KIRBY WARD & Comp. *First Night (Pinn): CASTCD 37 (CD) CASTC 37 (Cass)*

CRAZY FOR YOU (ORIG BROADWAY CAST 92) Songs (George and Ira Gershwin) on *EMI: CDC 754618-2 (CD)*

CRIMES OF PASSION (84) Music score (Rick Wakeman) Songs "It's A Lovely Life" (theme) (R.Wakeman-N.Gimbel) "Dangerous Woman" (Bell-Crumley) sung by MAGGIE BELL -S/T- *President (Rio/Target): RWCD 3(CD) RWK 3(Cass)*

CRIMES OF THE HEART (87) Music score (Georges Delerue) -S/T- *TER (Conif):TER 1130 (LP) CTV 81298 (CS)*

CRISSCROSS (91) Music score (Trevor Jones)-S/T- *Intrada USA (Koch/Silva Screen): MAFCD 7021 (CD)*

CRITTERS 2:The Main Course (88) Music score (Nicholas Pike) -S/T- *Intrada (S.Screen): MAF 7045D (CD)*

CROCODILE DUNDEE (86) Music score (Peter Best) Mental As Anything "Live It Up" -S/T- *Silva Screen (Conif) FILM 009 (LP) FILMC 009 (Cass) FILMCD 009 (CD)*

CROSSING DELANCEY (88) Music score (Paul Chihara) -S/T- *Varese (Pinn) VSC(CD) 5201 (CD/Cass)*

CROSSING The (90) Music score (Martin Armiger) Songs by The Proclaimers-Tin Machine-Kate Cerebano -S/T- on *Chrysalis: CCD1826 (CD) (ZCHR1826 Cass/LP deleted)*

CROSSING THE LINE (91) Music sco (Ennio Morricone)-S/T- *Varese (Pinn): VSD 5326 (CD) VSC 5326 (Cass)*

CRY BABY (89) Music score (Patrick Williams) -S/T- on *MCA: DMCG 6089 (CD) / MCGC 6089 (Cass) deleted*

CRY IN THE DARK A (88) Music score (Bruce Smeaton) *also* Suites from 'The Assault' (mus: Jurriaan Andriessen) 'The Rosegarden' (Egisto Macchi) 'The Naked Cage' (Christopher L.Stone) *Silva Screen: SIL 1527-2 (CD)*

CRYING GAME The (92) Music sco (Anne Dudley) Song "The Crying Game" (Geoff Stevens) -S/T- feat Var.Artists *Polydor: 517024-2 (CD) -4 (Cass) -1 (LP)*

CURLY SUE (91) Music score (Georges Delerue)-S/T- *Giant -WBros (WEA): 759924439-2 (CD) 759924439-4 (Cass)*

CYBORG (89) Music score (Kevin Bassinson) -S/T- *Silva Screen (BMG): FILMCD 050 (CD)* see *also* 'KICKBOXER'
CYRANO DE BEGERAC (90) Music score (Jean-Claude Petit) -S/T- *Enteleky (Pinn): ETKY 310 (CD)(C)(LP)* -S/T- *DRG (S.Screen): CDSBL 12602 (CD) SBLC 12602*

DA (89) Music score (Elmer Bernstein) -S/T- *Varese USA (Pinn) VS(VSC)(VSD) 5244 (LP/Cas/CD)*+'MY LEFT FOOT'
DAD (89) Music score (James Horner) -S/T- *MCA USA (Silva Screen): MCAD 6359 (CD) MCAC 6359 (Cass)*
DADDY NOSTALGIA (90) Music score (Antoine Duhamel-Ron Carter) Ron Carter-Jimmy Rowles-Philippe Catherine -S/T- *(Silva Screen): 467134-2 (CD)*
DAMAGE (93) Music score (Zbigniew Preisner) -S/T- on *Varese (Pinn): VSD 5406 (CD) VSC 5406 (Cass)*
DAMES AT SEA (ORIG UK TOURING CAST 89) Music (Jim Wise) Lyrics (George Haimsohn-Robin Miller) Featuring: Brian Cant-Sandra Dickinson-Josephine Blake *TER (Conif): CDTER 1169 (CD) (ZC)TER 1169 (Cass/LP)*
DAMES AT SEA (ORIG BROADWAY CAST 68) feat Bernadette Peters-David Christmas-Tamara Long-Steve Elmore-Sally Stark-Joseph R.Scicari *Sony Broadway: SK 48214 (CD)*
DAMIEN: OMEN 2 (78) Music score (Jerry Goldsmith) -S/T- *Silva Screen (Conif): FILMC(CD) 002 (Cass/CD)*
DAMBUSTERS The (55) Music score (Eric Coates) see Coll: 'BIG WAR THEMES' (coll- *MFP HR 8140 Cass*)
DAMN YANKEES (FILM MUSICAL 58) Songs (Richard Adler-Jerry Ross) -S/T- *RCA Austr (S.Screen): 1047-2 (CD)* -4
DAMN YANKEES (ORIG BROADWAY CAST 55) Songs (Richard Adler-Jerry Ross) *with* Gwen Verdon *RCA (BMG): GD 83948 (CD) GK 83948 (Cass)*
DAMNED The (69) Music score (Maurice Jarre) -S/T- *Alhamra Germany (Silva Screen): A.8920 (CD)*
DANCE A LITTLE CLOSER (Musical) Music (Charles Strouse) Lyrics (Alan Jay Lerner) *Original Broadway Cast* on *TER (Conif): CDTER 1174 (CD) ZCTER 1174 (Cass)*
DANCES WITH WOLVES (90) Music score (John Barry) -S/T- *Epic (Sony): 467591-2(CD) -4(Cass) -1(LP)* / "John Dunbar's Theme" *Epic: 656796-7"-12"-2(cd)-4(cass)* see *Collect* 'BEST OF KEVIN COSTNER'/'MOVIEOLA'
DANCIN' THRU THE DARK (90) Music (Willy Russell) + V/A -S/T- *Jive (BMG): CHIP 92 (CD) HIP(C) 92 (LP/Cass)*
DANGEROUS LIAISONS (88) Music Score (George Fenton) -S/T- *Virgin: CDV 2583 (CD) OVEDC 365 (Cass)*
DANGEROUS MOONLIGHT (41) Theme mus 'Warsaw Concerto' by Richard Addinsell see *Collection* 'Warsaw Concerrto'
DANZON (92) Music of DANZONERA DIMAS-PEREZ BROTHERS on *Milan (Pinn): 412470 (Cass) 262 470 (CD)*
DARK HALF The (92) Music score (Christopher Young)-S/T- *Varese (Pinn): VSD 5340 (CD) VSC 5340 (Cass)*
DARK STAR (74) Music (John Carpenter) -S/T- *Varese USA (Pinn): VSD 5327 (CD)*
DARKMAN (90) Music score (Danny Elfman) -S/T- *Impt. MCA USA (Sil.Screen): MCAD 10094 (CD) MCAC 10094 (Cass)*

DAVE (93) Music score (James Newton Howard) -S/T- on
  Warner Imp (Silva Screen): 925 510-2 (CD) -4 (Cass)
DAVID AND LISA (62) Music score (Mark Lawrence) with
  'A Patch Of Blue' (65-Jerry Goldsmith) -S/T on
  Mainstream USA (Koch Int): MDCD 607 (CD)
DAVY CROCKETT (55) Theme song "Ballad Of Davy Crockett"
  (Tom BLackburn-George Bruns) sung by FESS PARKER
  on 'Americana' *Columbia (SM): 468121-2(CD) -4(Cass)*
DAWN OF THE DEAD (Film) - *see* 'Zombies' *(UK Title)*
DAY AFTER HALLOWEEN The (79) Music score (Brian May) &
  HARLEQUIN (80) (Brian May) -S/T- *Australian Import*
  (Silva Screen): 1MI 1010 (CD)
DAY FOR NIGHT (73-'La Nuit Americain') Mus sco (Georges
  Delerue)*see COLL* 'TRUFFAUT & DELERUE ON THE SCREEN'
DAY OF ANGER (69) Music score (Riz Ortolani)c/w 'BEYOND
  THE LAW' (68) -S/T- *Impt (S.Screen): OST 110 (CD)*
DAY THE EARTH STOOD STILL The (51) Music (Bernard Herrm
  ann) Symphonic Suite (Nat.Philha.Orch-Fred Steiner)
  'The Kentuckian' *Preamble USA (S.Screen): PRCD 1777*
DAYS OF HOPE (Musical 91) Songs (Howard Goodall) Orig.
  London Cast *TER (Conifer): (CD)ZCTER 1183 (CD/Cass)*
DAYS OF THUNDER (90) Music score (Hans Zimmer) and feat
  "Show Me Heaven" by Maria McKee and other artists
  -S/T- *Epic (Sony M): 467159-2 (CD) -4(Cass)*
DAYS OF WINE AND ROSES The (62) - *see under* collections
  'Mancini's Greatest Hits' *(Telarc-Conifer)*
DEAD AGAIN (91) Music score (Patrick Doyle)-S/T- *Varese*
  (Pinn-S.Screen): VSD(VSC) 5339 (CD/Cass)
DEAD MEN DON'T WEAR PLAID (81) Music sco (Miklos Rozsa)
  -S/T- *Prometheus (Silva Screen): PCD 126 (CD)*
DEAD POETS SOCIETY (89) Music score (Maurice Jarre)
  -S/T- *Milan (S.Screen): CDCH 558 (CD) C.558 (Cass)*
  incl: 'THE YEAR OF LIVING DANGEROUSLY' (M.Jarre)
DEAD RINGERS (88) Music score (Howard Shore) with music
  from 'SCANNERS' (80) and 'The BROOD' (79) music by
  Howard Shore on *Silva Screen (Con): FILMCD 115 (CD)*
DEAD SOLID PERFECT (91) Music score by Tangerine Dream
  -S/T- *Silva Screen (Conifer): FILMCD 079 (CD)*
DEAD The (88) Music score (Alex North) -S/T- Import on
  Varese USA Import (Silva Screen) STV 81341 (LP) CTV
  81341 (Cass) VCD 47341 (Compact Disc)
DEADLOCK aka 'WEDLOCK' (91) Music score (Richard Gibbs)
  -S/T- *Silva Screen (Conifer): FILCD 086 (CD)*
DEADLY CARE (92)Music (Edgar Froese-Christopher Franke)
  TANGERINE DREAM -S/T- *S.Screen (Con):FILMCD 121(CD)*
DEAR WORLD (ORIG BROADWAY CAST 69) Songs (Jerry Herman)
  feat: Angela Lansbury-Milo O'Shea-Jane Connell-Carm
  en Matthews *Sony Broadway (Sony Mus): SK 48220 (CD)*
DEATH BECOMES HER (92) Music sco (Alan Silvestri) -S/T-
  Varese (Pinn): VSD 5375 (CD) VSC 5375 (Cass)
DEATH BEFORE DISHONOUR (87) Music sco (Brian May) -S/T-
  Prometheus (Silva Screen): PCD 118 (CD)
DEATH IN BRUNSWICK (91) Music score (Philip Judd) -S/T-
  Alhambra Germany Impt. (Silva Screen): A.8933 (CD)

DEATH IN VENICE (71) Music (Gustav Mahler) from Symphon
ies numbers 3 & 5 (music dir: Franco Mannio) -S/T-
Sony France (Discov): SK 70097 (CD) ST 70097 (Cass)

DEATH OF A SOLDIER (87) Music score (Allen Zavod) feat:
Big Bands Of The 40's -S/T- *DRG USA: SBL 12001 (LP)*

DEATH ON THE NILE (78) Music score (Nino Rota) -S/T- on
Cloud Nine (S.Screen): CNS 5007 (CD) also contains
'MURDER ON THE ORIENT EXPRESS (74) (R.R.Bennett)

DEATH RIDES A HORSE (69) Music score (Ennio Morricone)
-S/T- also inc.'A PISTOL FOR RINGO' and 'THE RETURN
OF RINGO' *Import (Silva Screen): OST 107 (CD)*

DEATH WARRANT (90) - *see under* 'KICKBOXER'

DEATH WISH (74) Mus sco (Herbie Hancock) *selection also
includes* 'DEATH WISH 4' (87-John Bisharat-Val McCal
lum) 'TEN TO MIDNIGHT' (84-Robert O Ragland) 'MURPH
Y'S LAW' (86-Marc Donahue-Val McCallum) 'TOUGH GUYS
DON'T DANCE' (87-Angelo Badalamenti) 'X-RAY' (80-Ar
lon Ober) *Silva Screen: 1529-2 (CD)*

DEEP BLUES (92) Blues music: JACK JOHNSON-R.L.BURNSIDE-
JNR.KIMBROUGH-FRANK FROST-JESSE MAE HEMPHILL-ROOSEV
ELT B.BARNES-LONNIE PITCHFORD-JACK OWENS-BUD SPIRES
-S/T-*Anxious-E.West (WEA):4509 91981-2(CD) -4(Cass)*

DEEP COVER (92) Music score (Michel Colombier) -S/T- *fe
at var.arts Epic (Sony M): 471669-2 (CD) -4(Cass)*

DEEP IN MY HEART (FILM MUSICAL 54) Music of Sigmund Rom
berg feat Gene Kelly-Rosemary Clooney-Howard Keel-
Ann Miller-Vic Damone-Jane Powell -S/T- *MGM Import
(Silva Screen): AK 47703 (CD) AT 47703 (Cass)*

DEEP STAR SIX (89) Music score (Harry Manfredini) -S/T-
Intrada (Silva Screen): MAF 7004D (CD)

DEERHUNTER The (78) Music score inc 'Cavatina' (Stanley
Myers) *-S/T- Capitol (S.Screen) 92058-2(CD) -4(Cas)*
'Cavatina' played by John Williams

DEF-CON 4 (85) Music sc: (Christopher Young) -S/T- also
includes Music from "Avenging Angel" (85) "Torment"
(85) "The Telephone" (88) Music (Christopher Young)
on *Intrada USA (Sil.Screen): MAF 7010D (CD) ALSO ON
Geffen (WEA): 759926049-2 (CD) -4 (Cass) -1 (LP)*

DEFENDING YOUR LIFE (91) Music score (Michael Gore) and
song "Something's Coming" (Sondheim-Bernstein) sung
by Barbra Streisand -S/T- *Columbia Impt (S.Screen):
CK 47836(CD) CT 47836 (Cass)* SEE 'HOLLYWOOD DREAMS'

DELICATESSEN (91) Music score (Carlos D'Alessio) -S/T-
Polydor: 839 345-2 (CD) 839 345-4 (Cass)

DELINQUENTS (89) Music score (Miles Goodman) -S/T- *PWL
(Pinn): HF(C)11 (Cass/LP) HFCD11 (CD) all deleted*

DELIVERANCE (72) Music (Eric Weissberg) "Duelling Banj
os" feat Steve Mandell on *Old Gold: OG 9574 (7"s)*
-S/T- *Warner Bros.(WEA): K (2)(4)46214 (CD/Cass/LP)*

DELTA FORCE (86) Music score (Alan Silvestri) -S/T- on
Milan Frace (Silva Screen): CDCH 290 (CD) includes
'KING SOLOMAN'S MINES' film music

DELTA FORCE II: THE Columbian (90) Music sco (Frederick
Talgorn) -S/T- *Alhambra (Pinn): A.8921 (CD)*

DELUSION (91) Music score (Barry Adamson) *MUTE: IONIC 4 (LP) IONIC 4C (Cass) IONIC 4CD (CD)*

DEMOLITION MAN (93) Music sco (Elliot Goldenthal) -S/T- *Varese (Pinn): VSD 5447 (CD) VSC 5447 (Cass)*

DENNIS THE MENACE (92) Music score (Jerry Goldsmith) -S/T- *WB USA Imp (S.Screen):925 514-2 (CD) -4(Cass)*

DESERT SONG The (MUSICAL) Songs (Sigmund Romberg) with Gordon MacRae & Dorothy Kirsten + music from 'New Moon'/'The Student Prince' *HMV (EMI): CDM 769052-2*

DESERT SONG The (MUSICAL) with Mario Lanza on *RCA (BMG) GD(GK)(GL)60048 (CD/Cass/LP)* with 'Student Prince'

DESPERATE HOURS (90)Music score (David Mansfield) -S/T- *Varese (Pinn): VSD(VSC) 5284 (CD/Cass)*

DESEPERATELY SEEKING SUSAN (85) Music (Thomas Newman) score only with 'Making Mr.Right' (Film 87) on Impt *Varese USA: CTV 81320 (CS) VCD 47291 (CD)*

DESTRY RIDES AGAIN (ORIG LONDON CAST 79) Songs (Harold Rome)featuring Jill Gascoine and Co. / Recording on *TER (Conifer): TER 1034 (LP) ZCTER 1034 (Cass)*

DEUX ANGLAISES ET LE CONTINENT *SEE 'Two English Girls'*

DEVIL IN THE FLESH (47) Music score (Philipe Sarde) and WE OF THE NEVER NEVER (82) (Peter Best) -S/T- on *Australian Import (Silva Screen): 1MICD 1012 (CD)*

DEVIL'S TOOTHPICK The (92) Documentary Brazilian/USA Film with music by GILBERTO GIL-BILLY COBHAM-KENIA-LARRY CORYELL-DONALD HARRISON-TED ROSENTHAL etc. *CTI-Kudu (New Note-Pinn): CTI 10122 (CD)*

DIAMOND SKULLS (89) Music (Hans Zimmer) *see Collection* 'Film Music Of Hans Zimmer'

DIAMONDS ARE FOREVER - *see* JAMES BOND FILM INDEX

DICK TRACY (90) Music score (Danny Elfman) Orig Songs (Stephen Sondheim) -S/T- *Warner Bros: 759926264-2 (CD) 759926264-4 (Cas) 759926264-1 (LP)*

DIE HARD 2: DIE HARDER (89) Music score (Michael Kamen) -S/T- *Varese (Pinn): VSC(CD) 5273 (Cass/CD)*

DIEN BIEN PHU (92-France) Music score (Georges Delerue) -S/T- *Import (Silva Screen): 513 289-2 (CD)*

DIGGSTOWN (92) Music score (James Newton Howard) -S/T- *Varese (Pinn): VSD 5379 (CD) VSC 5379 (Cass)*

DINER (82) Music score (Bruce Brody) -S/T- *Warner Bros USA (S.Screen): 60107-2 (CD) 60107-4 (Cass)*

DINGO (91) Music by Miles Davis & Michel Legrand -S/T- *Warner Bros (WEA): 759926438-2 (CD) -4 (Cass)*

DIRTY DANCING (87) Music score (John Morris) + Var Arts S/T- *RCA: BL 86408 (LP) BK 86408 (CS) BD 86408 (CD)* 'More Dirty Dancing' -S/T- *BD(BK)86965 (CD/Cass)* *'Live' music RCA (BMG): PK 90336 (Cass)*

DIRTY WEEKEND (93) Music sco (David Fanshawe) NATIONAL P.ORCH -S/T- (SCORE)*Silva Scr (Con): FILMCD 140(CD)* (SONGS) *V.Arts Columbia (SM) 474808-2(CD) -4 (Cass)*

DISTINGUISHED GENTLEMAN (92) Music sco (Randy Edelman) -S/T- *Varese (Pinn): VSD 5402 (CD) VSC 5402 (Cass)*

DIVA (82) Music sc (Vladimir Cosa) Feat Wilhelmina Fernandez -S/T-*DRG USA (Con):CDCH 061(CD) C120061 (Cas)*

DIVORCE ME DARLING (ORIG LONDON CAST 65) Songs by Sandy Wilson with Jenny Wren-Geoffrey Hibbert and Company *TER (Conifer): TER 1077 (LP) ZCTER 1077 (Cass)*

DO I HEAR A WALTZ (ORIG BROADWAY CAST 65) Mus (Richard Rodgers) Lyr(Stephen Sondheim) *with* Elizabeth Allen Sergio Franchi-Carol Bruce-Madeline Sherwood-Stuart Damon-Jack Manning-Juliene Marie-Fleury D'Antonakis *Sony Broadway (Sony M): CD 48206 (CD)*

DO RE MI (ORIG LONDON CAST 61) Songs (Jule Styne-Bette Comden-Adolph Green) *with* Max Bygraves-Steve Arlen-Maggie Fitzgibbon *TER (Con): (ZC)TER 1075 (Cass/LP)*

DO THE RIGHT THING (89) M.Score (Alex Steyermark) Feat music: Steel Pulse-Perri-Take 6-Lorri Perri-Gerald Alston-Keith John-Al Jarreau-Ruben Blades -S/T- on *Motown: ZD(ZL)(ZK) 72665 (CD/LP/Cass) all deleted*

DOC HOLLYWOOD (91) Music score (Carter Burwell) -S/T-*Varese (Pinn): VSD 5332 (CD) VSC 5332 (Cass)*

DOCTOR GIGGLES (92) Music score (Brian May) -S/T- (SCORE) *Intrada (Koch): MAF 7043CD (CD)* -S/T- (SONGS) *Victor USA: cat.no to be confirmed*

DOCTOR JEKYLL & MR HYDE (41) Music (Franz Waxman) *see* Collections 'Omen The: 50 Years Of Classic...'

DOCTOR JEKYLL & SISTER HYDE (71) Music (David Whitaker) *see* Collections 'Omen The: 50 Years Of...'

DOCTOR NO - *see* **JAMES BOND FILM INDEX**

DOCTOR ZHIVAGO (65) Music score (Maurice Jarre) -S/T-*MGM (EMI): CDMGM 3 (CD) TCMGM 3 (Cass)*also includes music from 'Ryan's Daughter' (Maurice Jarre)

DOIN' TIME ON PLANET EARTH *see under* 'ALLAN QUATERMAIN'

DON'T LOOK NOW (73) Music by Pino Donaggio -S/T- on *TER Conifer): CDTER 1007 (CD) ZCTER 1007 (Cass)*

DOORS The (91) Music score (Budd Carr) Original songs Jim Morrison & The Doors -S/T- *Elektra (WEA): 7599 61047-2 (CD) EKT 85C (Cass) EKT 85 (LP)*

DOUBLE IMPACT (91) Music score (Arthur Kempel) -S/T- on *S.Screen (Con): FILCD 110 (CD) see* 'KICKBOXER'

DOUBLE LIFE OF VERONIKA The (91) Music score (Zbigniew Preisner) Choral music by Van Den Budenmayer -S/T-*Impt (Silva Screen): SID 001 (CD)*

DOUBLE TROUBLE (67) Elvis Presley (24th film) *RCA (BMG) NL 82564 (LP) see also* 'Elvis Presley Film Index'

DOWN TO THE SEA IN SHIPS (48) Music score Alfred Newman Symphonic Suite - Nat.Phil.Orch.(Fred Steiner) 'The Kentuckian'- *Preamble USA (S.Screen) PRCD 1777 (CD)*

DR. *see under* 'DOCTOR'

DRACULA (92) Music sco (Wojciech Kilar) -S/T- *featuring* "Love Song For A Vampire" performed by ANNIE LENNOX *Columbia (Sony): 472746-2 (CD) 472746-4 (Cass)*

DRACULA (79 Frank Langella) Music score (John Williams) -S/T- *Varese (Pinn): VSD(VSC) 5250 (CD/Cass)*

DRACULA (73) Music score (Robert Cobert) theme music *see Collection* 'VAMPIRE CIRCUS'

DRACULA *see* COLLECTIONS 'HORROR OF DRACULA'

DRACULA PRINCE OF DARKNESS *see* COLL 'HORROR OF DRACULA'

DRAGON: THE BRUCE LEE STORY (93) Mus sc.(Randy Edelman)
-S/T- *MCA (BMG): MCAD(MCAC) 10827 (CD/Cass)*
DRAGONSLAYER (81) Music score (Alex North) -S/T- on
5th Continent Music (Silva Screen): SCSECD 3 (CD)
DRAUGHTSMAN'S CONTRACT The (83) Music (Michael Nyman)
-S/T- *Charisma (Virgin-Poly): CAS(MC)(CD) 1158*
see Collect 'Nyman-Greenaway Soundtracks' *(Virgin)*
DREAM DEMON (88) Music (Bill Nelson) Theme on 'Duplex'
Cocteau (Pinn): CDJCD 22(CD) TCJCD 22(Cass) JCD 22
DREAM IS ALIVE The - see 'BLUE PLANET'
DREAM OF OLWEN The - see 'WHILE I LIVE'
DRIVING MISS DAISY (89) Music score (Hans Zimmer) songs
Eartha Kitt-Louis Armstrong -S/T- *Varese (Pinn):*
VSD(VS)(VSC) 5246 (CD/LP/Cass)
DROWNING BY NUMBERS (88) Music score (Michael Nyman)
-S/T- *Venture (Virg-Poly): (CD)(TC)VE 23 (CD/CS/LP)*
see Collect 'Nyman-Greenaway Soundtracks' *(Virgin)*
DRUGSTORE COWBOY (89) Music score (Elliot Goldenthal)
+ Abbey Lincoln-Bobby Goldsboro-Jackie De Shannon-
Desmond Dekker etc. -S/T- *RCA (BMG): BD(BK) 83077*
DUCK YOU SUCKER! (aka 'A FISTFUL OF DYNAMITE' 72) Music
(Ennio Morricone)-S/T- *Alhambra (Pinn): A.8917 (CD)*
DUCKTAILS - THE MOVIE - see WALT DISNEY FILM INDEX
DUDES (88) Music score (Charles Bernstein) -S/T- *MCA*
(BMG): MCF(C) 3419 (LP/Cass) MCAD 6212 (CD)
DUEL OF HEARTS A (TVM 88) Music score (Laurie Johnson)
Theme only see *Collections* 'ROSE AND THE GUN The'
DULCIMA (Film 71) Music score (Johnny Douglas) Theme by
Johnny Douglas Strings 'On Screen' *Dulcima (Taylors*
T.Blood): DLCD 110 (CD) DLCT 110 (Cass)
DUMBO - see WALT DISNEY FILM INDEX
DUNE (84) Music score (Brian Eno & Toto) -S/T- re-issue
Imprt (Silva Screen): TCS 103.2 (CD)
DUST DEVIL (92) Music sco (Simon Boswell) -S/T- *Varese*
(Pinn): VSD 5395 (CD) VSC 5395 (Cass)
DUTCH (91) Music (various artists) -S/T- *Varese (Pinn):*
VSD 5336 (CD) VSC 5336 (Cass)
DYING YOUNG (91)Music score (James Newton Howard) theme
by Kenny G. *Arista (BMG): 114 592 (7") 664592 (CDs)*
-S/T- *Arista: 261952 (CD) 411952 (Cass) 211952 (LP)*

EAGLE HAS LANDED The (76) Music sc (Lalo Schifrin) also
music from 'FOUR MUSKETEERS'(74) 'VOYAGE OF THE DAM
NED' (76) (Schifrin) *Legend (S.Screen): LXCD 5 (CD)*
EARTH GIRLS ARE EASY (89) Mus: Jesus & Mary Chain-Depec
he Mode-Julie Brown -S/T- *W.Bros K.925835-4 (Cass)*
EARTHQUAKE (74) Music score (John Williams) -S/T- reiss
ue: *Varese USA (Pinn) VSD 5262 (CD) VSC 5262 (Cass)*
EAST OF EDEN (55) Music sco (Leonard Rosenman) complete
score +music from 'GIANT' & 'REBEL WITHOUT A CAUSE'
Import (Silva Screen): CIN 2206-2 (CD) -4 (Cass)
EASTER PARADE (FILM MUSICAL 48) Songs (Irving Berlin)
Fred Astaire-Judy Garland -S/T- *MGM (EMI): (CD)(TC)*
MGM 4 (LP/Cass) + -S/T-'Singin'In The Rain' *deleted*

EASY RIDER (69) Music: Steppenwolf-Electric Prunes-Jimi
   Hendrix Experience-Byrds-Roger McGuinn+others -S/T-
   MCA (BMG): MCLD 19153 (CD) MCLC 19153 (Cass)
EDUCATING RITA (83) Music score (David Hentschel) -S/T-
   reissue *C5 (Pinn): C5CD 587 (CD)*
EDWARD II (91) Music score (Simon Fisher Turner) -S/T-
   Mute (Pinn): IONIC 8CD (CD) IONIC 8LP (LP)
EDWARD SCISSORHANDS (90) Music score (Danny Elfman)
   -S/T- *MCA USA (S.Screen): MCAD(MCAC) 10133 (CD/Cas)*
EDWIN DROOD (MUSICAL SHOW 86) *see* 'Mystery Of Edwin D.'
EGYPTIAN The (54) Music score (Bernard Herrmann-Alfred
   Newman) -S/T- with Hollywood Symphony Orchestra on
   Colosseum (Pinn): VSD 5258 (CD) VSC 5258 (Cas)
EIGER SANCTION The (75) Music sco (John Williams) -S/T-
   reissue *Varese (Pinn): VSD 5277 (CD) VSC 5277 (Cas)*
84 CHARING CROSS ROAD (87) Music score (George Fenton)
   -S/T- *TER (Conif): TER 1129 (LP) ZCTER 1129 (CS)*
EL AMOR BRUJU (FILM BALLET 86)'Love The Magician'/'Love
   Bewitched' (Manuel De Falla) Nat.Orch of Spain (Jes
   us Lopez-Lobos) Rocio Jurado -S/T- *EMI:CDC 747586-2*
EL CID (61) Music score (Miklos Rozsa) -S/T- *MGM (EMI):*
   (EMI): CDMGM 5 (CD)
EL DORADO (88) Music score (Alejandro Masso) -S/T- Impt
   Milan (S.Screen) C.342 (Cas) CDCH 342 (CD)
EL GRECO (64) Music score (Ennio Morricone) with 'Giord
   ano Bruno' *Impt (Silva Screen): OST 111 (CD)*
ELECTRIC DREAMS (84) Mus (Giorgio Moroder-Philip Oakey)
   -S/T- *Virgin: CDV 2318 (CD) OVED(C) 242*
ELECTRIC HORSEMAN The (79) Music score (Dave Grusin) +
   Willie Nelson -S/T- *Columb (S.Screen): CK 36327 CD*
ELEGIES For Angels Punks and Raging Queens (ORIG LONDON
   CAST 93) *First Night (Pinn): CAST(CD)(C)35 (CD/Cas)*
ELEPHANT MAN The (80) Theme 'Adagio' (Samuel Barber)
   see Coll 'CLASSICS OF THE SILVER SCREEN'/'FAVOURITE
   MOVIE CLASSICS'/'FILM CLASSICS'
ELIZABETH AND ESSEX (39) Mus (Erich Wolfgang Korngold)
   New rec:CARL DAVIS & Munich S.O.*Milan: 873 122 (CD)*
ELVIRA MADIGAN (87) mus 'Piano Con.No.21'K.467'(Mozart)
   see Collect 'CLASSICS OF THE SILVER SCREEN'
ELVIS PRESLEY NBC TV SPECIAL (68) Featur ELVIS PRESLEY
   -S/T- *RCA (BMG): ND 83894 (CD) NK 83894 (Cass)*
EMMANUELLE (74) Music score (Pierre Bachelet-Herve Roy)
   -S/T- *Silva Screen (Conifer): FILMCD 058 (CD)*
EMPIRE OF THE SUN (87) Music score (John Williams)-S/T-
   WBros (S.Screen) 925 668-2 (CD) 925 668-4 (Cass)
EMPIRE STRIKES BACK The (Star Wars II) (81) Music score
   (John Williams) -S/T- *Varese (Pinn): VSD(VSC) 5353*
   see also under 'STAR WARS 2'
ENCHANTED APRIL (91) Music (Richard Rodney Bennett)
   Bay Cities (Silva Screen): BCD 3035(CD)
ENEMIES A LOVE STORY (90) Music score (Maurice Jarre)
   -S/T- *Varese (Pinn): VS(VSC)(VSD) 5253 (LP/Cass/CD)*
ENEMY MINE (86) Music (Maurice Jarre) -S/T- *Varese Impt*
   (Pinn): VCD 47249 (CD) / TER (Con): TER 1112 LP

EQUINOXE (92) Music by Various Artists -S/T- *Varese*
   (Pinn): VSD 5424 (CD) VSC 5424 (Cass)
ERASERHEAD (78) Music score (David Lynch & Alan Splet)
   -S/T- *A&M USA (Silva Screen): CD 70027 (CD)*
ESCAPE FROM NEW YORK (81) Music score (John Carpenter-
   Alan Howarth) -S/T- *Varese (Pinn): VCD 47224 (CD)*
ESCAPE ME NEVER (35) Music score (William Walton) Suite
   Chandos: CHAN 8870 (CD) ABTD 1485 (Cass)
ESCAPE ME NEVER (47) Music sco: Erich Wolfgang Korngold
   Theme on 'Warsaw Concerto' coll *(Decca 421261-2/-4)*
E.T. (82) Music score (John Williams) -S/T- *MCA (BMG):*
   MCLD 19021 (CD) MCLC 19021 (Cass)
EUROPA EUROPA (91) Music score (Zbigniew Preisner)-S/T-
   also inc.music from 'OLIVIER OLIVIER' (Zbigniew Pre
   isner) *DRG (Pinn): DRGCD 12606(CD) DRGMC 12606(Cas)*
EUROPEANS The (79) Music score (Richard Robbins) *see*
   Collections 'Merchant-Ivory 25th Anniversary'
EVEN COWGIRLS GET THE BLUES (93) Music and songs (k.d.
   lang)-S/T- *Sire-WB (WEA): 9362 45433-2(CD) -4(Cass)*
EVERLASTING SECRET FAMILY The (87) Music (Tony Bremner)
   -S/T- *Southern Cross (Silva Screen) SCCD 1020 (CD)*
EVERYBODY'S ALL AMERICAN (88) -S/T- *Capitol (S.Screen):*
   C11G 91184 (LP) C41G 91184 (Cass) C21Z 91184 (CD)
EVIL DEAD (85) Music score (Joe Lo Duca) -S/T- *Varese*
   (Pinn): VSD 5362 (CD)
EVIL DEAD 2 (87) Music score (Joe Lo Duca) -S/T- *TER*
   (Conifer): CDTER 1142 (CD)
EVIL DEAD 3 (Army Of Darkness) (92) Music (Joe Lo Duca)
   -S/T- *Varese (Pinn): VSD 5411 (CD) VSC 5411 (Cass)*
EVITA (STUDIO RECORDING 76) with Julie Covington etc.
   MCA (BMG): (D)MCX(C) 503 (CD/LP/Cass)
EVITA (ORIG BROADWAY CAST) *MCA (BMG): MCDW 453 (2LP)*
EVITA (ORIG LONDON CAST 78) Songs (Andrew Lloyd Webber
   Tim Rice) *with* Elaine Paige-David Essex and Company
   MCA (BMG): MCGC 3527 (Cass) DMCG 3527 (CD)
EXCALIBER (81) Orig Music score (Trevor Jones) other
   music includes "Carmina Burana" (Carl Orff)*no -S/T-*
EXIT (Film) Music score (Tangerine Dream) -S/T- *Virgin*
   (Poly): CDV 2212 (CD) OVEDC 166 (Cass)
EXODUS (60) Music score (Ernest Gold) -S/T- on *EMI:*
   MGM: CDMGM 11 (CD) inc -S/T- 'Cast A Giant Shadow'
EXORCIST 2 The Heretic (77) Music sco (Ennio Morricone)
   see Collections 'Omen The: 50 Years Of Classic...'
EXPERIENCE (Rock Film 68) Jimi Hendrix Experience feat:
   Jimi Hendrix-Noel Redding-Mitch Mitchell -S/T- *Bull*
   dog (Presid): BDL 4002 (Vol.1-LP) BDL 4003 (Vol.2)
   BDC 4002 (Vol.1-Cass) BDC 4003 (Vol.2-Cass)
EXPLORERS The (85) Music score (Jerry Goldsmith) Import
   -S/T- *Varese USA (Pinn): VSD 5261 (CD)*
EXTREME PREJUDICE (87) Music (Jerry Goldsmith -S/T- on
   Silva Screen (Con): FILMC(CD) 011 (Cass/CD)
EYES OF LAURA MARS The (78) Music sco (Artie Kane) Love
   Theme'The Prisoner' (Karen Lawrence-John Desautels)
   Elaine Paige -*see* Coll 'Cinema' (-S/T-*CBS deleted*)

FABULOUS BAKER BOYS The (89) Music score (Dave Grusin)
-S/T- *GRP USA (Mov.Boulev): GRP 2002-2(CD)-4(Cass)*
FALL OF THE ROMAN EMPIRE The (64) Music score (Dimitri
Tiomkin) *Varese (S.Screen): VSD 5228 (CD)* / music
from ORIG -S/T- *Cloud Nine (S.Screen): ACN 7016(CD)*
FALLEN IDOL (48) Music score (William Alwyn) Suite from
film played by London Symphony Orchestra (Richard
Hickox) on *Chandos: CHAN 9243 (CD) ABTD 1606 (Cass)*
FALLING FROM GRACE (92) Various Artists: -S/T- on
Mercury (Poly): 512 004-2 (CD) -4 (Cass)
FALLING IN LOVE (85) Music score(Dave Grusin) Selection
by Dave Grusin *GRP USA (Pinn): GRPA(D) 9018 (LP/CD)*
FAME (FILM MUSICAL 80) Mus (Michael Gore-Dean Pitchford
& others) Irene Cara - *Old Gold OG 9595 (7"s)* -S/T-
*Polydor SPELP(MC) 82(LP/Cass) 800 034-2(CD) deleted
see also under 'TV THEMES' section*
FANDANGO (85) Music score (Alan Silvestri)on Collection
'BEST OF KEVIN COSTNER' *Silva Screen (Conif):FILMCD
104 (CD) FIMC 104 (Cass) - see also collections*
FANTASIA (Disney 40) featur: The Philadelphia Orchestra
(Leopold Stowkowski) -S/T- (digitally remastered in
1990) - *Buena Vista (Pickwick): DSTCD 452D (2CD)
DSTMC 452MC (2Cass) - see* WALT DISNEY FILM INDEX
FANTASTICKS The (ORIG BROADWAY CAST 60) Songs (Harvey
Schmidt-Tom Jones) w: Jerry Orbach-Rita Gardner-Ken
neth Nelson *TER (Con): ZCTER 1099 (Cass) CDTER 1099*
JAPAN TOUR CAST RECORD *DRG (Pinn) DRGCD 19005 (CD)*
FANTOZZI (Italian) and IL SECONDO TRAGICO FANTOZZI Mus
(Franco Bixio-Fabio Frizzi-Vince Tempera) *Cinevox
Italy Imp (Silva Screen): CDCIA 5096 (CD)*
FAR AND AWAY (92) Music score (John Williams) also feat
The Chieftains and ENYA ("Book Of Days") -S/T- on
MCA (BMG): MCAD 10628 (CD) MCAC 10628 (Cass)
FAR FROM THE MADDING CROWD (67) Mus sco (Richard Rodney
Bennett) vocals: Julie Christie-Terence Stamp-Isla
Cameron-Trevor Lucas. flute: James Galway *Impt (Sil
va Screen): AK 47023-2 (CD) AT 47023-4 (Cass)*
FARAWAY SO CLOSE (93) Music sco (Laurent Petigand) with
Various Artists: NICK CAVE-U2-LOU REED-SIMON BONNEY
HOUSE OF LOVE-JANE SIBERRY-LAURIE ANDERSON -S/T- on
EMI: CDEMC 3660(CD) (TC)EMC 3660(Cass) EMC 3660(LP)
FAREWELL MY LOVELY (75) Music sco (David Shire) Select.
Bay Cities (S.Screen):BCD 3021 (CD) BCC 3021 (Cass)
FAREWELL TO MY CONCUBINE (93) Music score (Zhao Jiping)
-S/T- *Varese (Pinn): VSD 5454 (CD)*
FAREWELL TO THE KING (89)Music score (Basil Poledouris)
-S/T- *Milan Fr. (Silva Screen): CDCH 375 (CD) C.375*
FAST BREAK (79) Music score (David Shire) Selection on
Bay Cities (S.Screen):BCD 3021 (CD) BCC 3021 (Cass)
FATAL ATTRACTION (87) Music score (Maurice Jarre) -S/T-
on *GNP USA (Silva Screen) GNPD 8011 (CD) GNP-5 8011
(Cass) other music:* 'Madam Butterfly' (Puccini)
FATAL BEAUTY (88) Music score (Harold Faltermeyer)-S/T-
Atlantic (WEA): K.781809-2 (CD) K.781809-4 (Cass)

FATHER CHRISTMAS (C4-25/12/91) Music (Mike Hewer) perf
  Phoenix Chamber Orch (Julian Bigg) narrated by Mel
  Smith -S/T- *Columbia 469475-2 (CD) -4(Cass) -1(LP)*
FATHER OF THE BRIDE (91) Music score (Alan Silvestri)
  -S/T- *Varese (Pinn): VSD 5348 (CD) VSC 5348 (Cass)*
FEAR IN THE NIGHT (72) Music score (John McCabe) *see*
  Coll 'Omen The: 50 Years Of Classic Horror Movies'
FEARLESS (93) Music score (Maurice Jarre) -S/T- Import
  (Silva Screen): 79334-2 (CD) 79334-4 (Cass)
FEDS (88) Music score & songs (Randy Edelmen) -S/T- on
  GNP (S.Screen) GNPS(C) 8014 (LP/Cas) GNPD 8014 (CD)
FERNGULLY: LAST RAINFOREST (91) Mus sc.(Alan Silvestri)
  Songs: TIM CURRY-RAFFI-SHEENA EASTON-ELTON JOHN etc
  -S/T- (SONGS) *MCA (BMG): MCAD 10567 (CD) Cass delet*
  -S/T- (SCORE) *MCA (Silva Screen): MCAD 10619 (CD)*
FERRY CROSS THE MERSEY (Film Musical 64) Feat Gerry and
  The Pacemakers-Cilla Black-Fourmost -S/T- (reissue)
  Beat Goes On (Pinn): BGOLP 10 (LP)
FEW GOOD MEN A (92) Music score (Marc Shaiman & Hummie
  Mann) -S/T- with Var.Arts includ: BIG MAMA THORNTON
  Columbia (Sony): 472926-2 (CD) 472929-4 (Cass)
FIDDLER ON THE ROOF (FILM MUSICAL 71) feat Topol -S/T-
  U.Artists (S.Screen): 46091-2 (CD) 46091-4 (Cass)
FIDDLER ON THE ROOF (ORIG BROADWAY CAST 64) Songs (Bock
  Harnick) *with* Zero Mostel-Maria Karnilova-Beatrice
  Arthur-Julia Migenes *RCA (BMG) RD 87060 CD also on*
  Silva Screen Import: RCD1 7060 (CD)
FIDDLER ON THE ROOF (ORIG LONDON CAST 67) *with* Topol-Mi
  riam Karlin-Linda Garner-Paul Whitsun Jones *Columb*
  (Silva Screen): CK 30742 (CD) JST 30742 (Cass)
FIELD OF DREAMS (89) Music score (James Horner) -S/T-
  RCA Novus (Silva Screen): 3060-2 (CD) 3060-4 (Cas)
  see Collect 'BEST OF KEVIN COSTNER'
FIELD OF HONOR (86) Music score (Roy Budd) -S/T- includ
  'SECRET OF THE ICE CAVE' (89) music: Robert Esty)
  Silva Screen: SIL 1502-2 (CD)
FIELD The (90) Music score (Elmer Bernstein) -S/T- on
  Varese (Pinn): VSD 5292 (CD) VSC 5292 (Cass)
55 DAYS AT PEKING (61) Music score (Dimitri Tiomkin)
  -S/T- *Varese USA (Silva Screen-Pinn): VSD 5233 (CD)*
FINAL ANALYSIS (91) Music score (George Fenton) -S/T-
  Varese (Pinn): VSD(VSC) 5356 (CD/Cass)
FINAL CONFLICT The (85) Music score (Jerry Goldsmith)
  -S/T- *Varese USA (Silva Screen-Pin): STV 81272 (LP)*
  CTV 81272 (CS) and Colosseum (Pinn): VCD 47242 (CD)
FINIAN'S RAINBOW (ORIGINAL BROADWAY CAST 47) Songs (Bur
  ton Lane-E.Y.Harburg) *Columbia (S.Screen): CK 04062*
  (CD) JST 04062 (Cass)
FINIAN'S RAINBOW (REVIVAL BROADWAY CAST 60) with Jeanne
  Carson *(Silva Screen): 1057-2 (CD) 1057-4 (Cass)*
FIORELLO (ORIG BROADWAY CAST 59) Songs (Jerry Bock-Shel
  don Harnick) *featuring:* TOM BOSLEY-PATRICIA WILSON-
  ELLEN HANLEY-HOWARD DA SILVA-MARK DAWSON *EMI Angel*
  (EMI): ZDM 565 023-2 (CD)

FIRE IN THE SKY (92) Music score (Mark Isham) -S.T- on
    Varese (Pinn): VSD 5417 (CD) VSC 5417 (Cass)
FIRESTARTER (84) Music (TANGERINE DREAM) -S/T- reissue
    MCA (BMG): MCLD 19154 (CD) MCLC 19154 (Cass)
FIREWALKER (87) Music score (Gary Chang) -S/T- Import
    Varese USA (Silva Screen): STV 81303 (LP) deleted
FIRM The (93) Music score (Dave Grusin) -S/T-*GRP USA
    New Note-MCA (BMG): GRM 20072 (CD)*
FIRST BLOOD (82) Music score (Jerry Goldsmith) vocal by
    Dan Hill -S/T- *TER: TER 1038 (LP) / Intrada (Silva
    Screen): FMT 8001D (CD)* - see also under 'RAMBO'
FIRST GREAT TRAIN ROBBERY (78) *see under* 'WILD ROVERS'
FIRST MEN IN THE MOON The (UK-64) Music score (Laurie
    Johnson) *Cloud Nine (S.Screen-Conif): ACN 7015 (CD)*
    see Collections 'ROSE AND THE GUN The'
FIRST OF THE FEW (42) Music score inc "Spitfire Prelude
    and Fugue"(William Walton) L.P.Orch (Sir A.Boult)
    HMV: ED 2911129-4 (Cass) with 'Things To Come'
FISH CALLED WANDA A (88) Music sco (John Du Prez) -S/T-
    Milan (S.Screen):A.376(LP) C.376(Cass) CDCH 376(CD)
FISHER KING The (91) Music score (George Fenton) -S/T-
    artists include Harry Nilsson-Brenda Lee-Chill Rob.G
    MCA (BMG): MCAD 10249 (CD) MCAC 10249 (Cass)
FISTFUL OF DOLLARS A (64) Music score (Ennio Morricone)
    see under 'For A Few Dollars More'
FISTFUL OF DYNAMITE A - *see* 'DUCK YOU SUCKER!'
FITZCARALDO (82) Music score (Popol Vuh) -S/T- Import
    Sync-Pulse (Rough Trade-Cartel): ZYX 20017 (LP)
FIVE CORNERS (88) Music sco (James Newton Howard) -S/T-
    Varese (Movie Boulevard) VCD 81354 (CD)
FIVE GUYS NAMED MOE (ORIG LONDON CAST 91) Song & Dance
    Review celebrating the music & work of Louis Jordan
    writer: Clarke Peters / choreography: Charles Augin
    music dir: Chapman Roberts featuring Clarke Peters
    First Night (Pinn): CAST(C)(CD) 23 / 'Five Guys Nam
    ed Moe' (Louis Jordan) *MCA: DMCL 1718 (CD)* LOUIS JO
    RDAN & TYMPANY 5 *Bandstand (H.Mundi):BDCD 1531 (CD)*
FIVE HEARTBEATS The (91) Various Artists -S/T- *Virgin
    Movie Music (Poly): CDVMM 4 (CD) TCVMM 4 (Cass)*
FLAHOOLEY (ORIG BROADWAY CAST) *feat:* BARBARA COOK-YMA
    SUMAC-Marilyn Ross-Jerome Courtland and Company
    Angel (EMI): ZDM 764764-2 (CD)
FLAME IN MY HEART A (88) Music used "Chaconne In D.Min"
    'Partitas for solo violin' BVW 1002 (J.S.Bach)
FLASH GORDON (80) Music & Songs (Queen) -S/T- on *EMI
    (EMI): (TC)ATAK 26 (Cass/LP) CZ 100 (CD)*
FLASHDANCE (83) Music sco (Giorgio Moroder) song (Irene
    Cara) -S/T-*Casablanca: 811 492-2(CD) PRIMC 111(Cas)*
FLASHPOINT (85) Music score (Tangerine Dream) -S/T- on
    Heavy Metal: HMILP(MC) 29 (LP/Cass) HMIXD 29 (CD)
FLESH AND BONE (93) Music score (Thomas Newman) -S/T-
    Varese (Pinn): VSD 5460 (CD)
FLETCH (85) Music sco (Harold Faltermeyer) + Stephanie
    Mills-Kim Wilde-Dan Hartman etc. *MCA: DMCF 3284(CD)*

FLORA THE RED MENACE (ORIG BROADWAY CAST 65) Songs by
(John Kander-Fred Ebb) *feat:* Liza Minnelli-Mary Lou
ise Wilson-Cathryn Damon-Robert Kaye-Stephanie Hill
James Cresson & Com *RCA Victor (BMG): GD 60821 (CD)*
FLORA THE RED MENACE (OFF BROADWAY CAST 87) *TER (Con):*
ZCTER 1159 (Cass) CDTER 1159 (CD)
FLORADORA (ORIG LONDON CAST 1899) Music (Leslie Stuart)
Lyrics (Ernest Boyd-Jones &Paul Rubens) Louis Bradf
field-Kate Cutler-Ada Reeve-Syney Barraclough on
Pearl(Harmonia Mundi): OPALCD 9835 (CD)
FLOWER DRUM SONG The (ORIG BROADWAY CAST 58) Songs (R.R
odgers-O.Hammerstein II) *Col (S.Screen): CK 02009*
(CD) JST 02009 (Cass)
FLOWER DRUM SONG The (ORIG LONDON CAST 60) (R.Rodgers-
O.Hammerstein) with Yama Saki-George Pastell-Ida Sh
epley-Kevin Scott *TER (Con) TER 1060(LP) ZCTER 1060*
FLOWERS IN THE ATTIC (88) Music sc: (Christopher Young)
-S/T- on *Intrada USA (Silva Screen): MAF 7009D (CD)*
FLY The (86) Music score (Howard Shore) London Philharm
Orch -S/T- *TER: (ZC)TER 1120 (LP/CS)*
FOG The (79) Music score (John Carpenter) -S/T- Import
Colosseum (Pinn): CST 8002 (LP) VCD 47267 (CD)
FOLLIES (ORIG BROADWAY CAST 71) Songs(Stephen Sondheim)
feat: ALEXIS SMITH-GENE NELSON-DOROTHY COLLINS-JOHN
McMARTIN-YVONNE DE CARLO *Angel(EMI):ZDM 764666-2 CD*
FOLLIES (ORIG LONDON CAST 87) with Julia McKenzie-Diana
Rigg-Daniel Massey-David Healey-Dolores Gray *First*
Night (Pinn) ENCORECD 3 (CD) ENCOREC 3 (Cass)
FOLLIES (LIVE NEW RECORDING 85) also featur 'Stavisky'
(S.Sondheim) *RCA Red Seal (BMG): RD 87128 (2CD's)*
FOLLIES (REVIVAL USA LINCOLN CENTER CAST 85) Barbara Co
ok-George Hearn-Mandy Patinkin-Lee Remick-Elaine St
ritch-Carol Burnett & New York Philharmonic Orchest
RCA (BMG) BL 87128 (LP) BK 87128 (CS) BD 87128 (CD)
FOLLOW THE FLEET (FILM MUSICAL 36) featur: Fred Astaire
see Coll 'Top Hat White Tie and Tails' *(Saville)*
FOOLS OF FORTUNE (90) Music score (Hans 7immer) -S/T-
Milan (Silva Screen): CDCH 334 (CD) C 334 (Cass)
FOOTLOOSE (Rock Film 84) Music (Kenny Loggins) featur:
Bonnie Tyler "Holding Out For A Hero" / also music
from Deneice Williams-Shalamar-Ann Wilson-Mike Reno
Karla Bonoff-Moving Pictures-Sammy Hagar-K.Loggins
-S/T- *CBS: CBS 463000-2 (CD) 463000-4 (Cass) -1(LP)*
FOR A FEW DOLLARS MORE (65) Music score Ennio Morricone
-S/T- *RCA Camden: CDS 1052 (LP)* includes music from
'A Fistful Of Dollars' (64) / also on import:
RCA Germany: NL 70391 (LP) NK 70391 (Cass) see also
'Good The Bad And The Ugly' (Ennio Morricone 1966)
FOR LOVE OR MONEY - see under 'CONCIERGE, The'
FOR THE BOYS (91) Music score (Dave Grusin) with BETTE
MIDLER -S/T- *Atlantic (WEA): 75678239-2(CD)-4(Cass)*
FOR WHOM THE BELL TOLLS (43) Music score (Victor Young)
-S/T- *Dunhill USA (S.Screen) STZ 112 (CD)*
FOR YOUR EYES ONLY - *see* JAMES BOND FILM INDEX

FORBIDDEN PLANET (54) Music score: Louis & Bebe Barron
    -S/T- *GNP USA Imp (Silva Screen): PRD 001 (CD)*
FORBIDDEN PLANET (89) Music score (Danny Elfman) -S/T-
    Varese (Pinn): VSD 5268 (CD) VSC 5268 (Cass)
FORBIDDEN WORLD (82) - see under 'MUTANT'
FORCE TEN FROM NAVARONE (78) Music score (Ron Goodwin)
    Chandos (Chandos): LBRD 001 (LP) LBTD 001 (Cass)
FOREVER AMBER (47) Music score (David Raksin) Selection
    on 'Laura' *RCA Victor (BMG): GD(GK) 81490 (CD/Cass)*
FOREVER KNIGHT (USA 92) Music score (Fred Mollin)
    see Collection 'VAMPIRE CIRCUS'
FOREVER PLAID (ORIG LONDON CAST RECORDING 93) American
    Hit Musical with songs from the 50's/60's *featuring:*
    STAN CHANDLER-DAVID ENGEL-LARRY RABEN-GUY STROMAN &
    Company on *First Night (Pinn):CAST(C)(CD) 33*
FOREVER YOUNG (92) Music score (Jerry Goldsmith) -S/T-
    USA Impt (Silva Screen): WA 24482-2 (CD) -4 (Cass)
FORT SAGANNE (France) Music score (Phillipe Sarde)-S/T-
    Import (Silva Screen): CDFMC 9 (CD)
FORTY SECOND STREET (REVIVAL BROADWAY CAST 82) Songs(Al
    Dubin-Harry Warren) *with* Danny Carroll-Jerry Orbach
    Tammy Grimes-LeeRoy Reames-Wanda Richert-Carol Cook
    RCA: BL 83891 (LP) BK (C) BD (CD)
FOUR FLIES ON GREY VELVET (71) Music score (Ennio Morri
    cone) with THE BIRD WITH THE CRYSTAL PLUMAGE (69)
    (E.Morricone)-S/T- *Cinevox (S.Screen) CDCIAK 5087CD*
FOUR IN THE MORNING (65) Music score (John Barry) -S/T-
    Play It Again (Silva Screen): PLAY 002 (CD)   .
FOUR MUSKETEERS The (74) Music score (Lalo Schifrin)
    Suite *(S.Screen): LXCD 5(CD)*+'The Eagle Has Landed'
1492: CONQUEST OF PARADISE (92) Music score VANGELIS
    -S/T-*East West (WEA):4509 91014-2 (CD) WX 497C Cass*
FOX AND THE HOUND The - *see* WALT DISNEY FILM INDEX
FRANCES (82) Music sco (John Barry) *see Coll* 'MOVIEOLA'
FRANKENHOOKER (88) Music score (Joe Renzetti)+ -S/T- to
    'Basket Case 2' (88) *S.Screen (Con) FILMCD 073 (CD)*
FRANKIE AND JOHNNY (66) see ELVIS PRESLEY FILM INDEX
FRANKIE AND JOHNNY (91) Music sco (Marvin Hamlisch) and
    songs: Doobie Bros-Golden Earring-Rickie Lee Jones-
    -S/T- *CURB (Sony M):469 485-2 (CD) 469 485-4 (Cass)*
FRANTIC (88) Music score (Ennio Morricone) & featuring
    Simply Red -S/T- *Elektra (WEA): K 7559 60782-2 (CD)*
FRAUDS (92) Music (Guy Cross) -S/T- *Mushroom (Tot-BMG)*
    PTR 003 (CD)
FREDDIE AS F.R.O.7 (92) Music (David Dundas-Rick Wentwo
    rth) Lyr: (Don Black-David Ashton-Jan Acevski) song
    "I'll Keep Your Dreams Alive" sung by GEORGE BENSON
    PATTI AUSTIN - *AAMI (BMG): AMMI 101 (7") 12AMMI 101*
    (12") CDAMMI 101 (CDs) MCAMMI 101 (Cass) -S/T- on
    Music Club Int (TBD): FRO7 CD1 (CD) FRO7 MC1 (Cass)
FREDDIE'S DEAD: THE FINAL NIGHTMARE (A NIGHTMARE ON ELM
    STREET 6)(91) Music (Brian May) -S/T- *Metal Blade*
    (Pinn): CDZZORRO 33 (CD) ZORRO 33 (LP) / IMPORT on
    Varese (Pinn): VS(VSC)(VSCD) 5333 (LP/Cass/CD)

FREE WILLY (93) Music sco (Basil Poledouris) Song "Will
You Be There" composed and sung by MICHAEL JACKSON
Also feat NEW KIDS ON THE BLOCK-3T-FUNKY POETS-SWV
-S/T- *MJJ (Sony Music): 474 264-2 (CD) -4 (Cass)*
FREEJACK (91) Jesus Jones-Jesus & Mary Chain-Scorpions-
-S/T- *Morgan Creek (Poly): 513 105-2 (CD) -4 (Cass)*
FRENCH LIEUTENANT'S WOMAN The (81) Music (Carl Davis) +
'Adagio' Sonata in D.K576 (Mozart) John Lill (pno)
-S/T- on *DRG USA (Conifer) CDRG 6108 (CD)*
FREUDIANA (MUSICAL CONCEPT ALBUM 90) with Eric Woolfson
Leo Sayer-Graham Dye-Flying Pickets-Eric Stewart-Ki
ki Dee-Frankie Howerd-Gary Howard-John Miles-Chris
Rainbow-Marti Webb -*EMI: CDEN 5012 (CD)*
FRIDAY THE 13TH (Film 80) Music sco (Harry Manfredini)
-S/T- *Import (Silva Screen): CDFMC 10 (CD)*
see COLLECT 'HORROR AND SCIENCE FICTION FILM MUSIC'
FRIED GREEN TOMATOES (92) Music score (Thomas Newman)
also feat: Paul Young-Patti La Belle-Grayson Hugh-
Taylor Dayne-S/T- *MCA: MCAD 10461 (CD)*
FRIGHT NIGHT (85) Music score (Brad Fiedel) selection
see Collection 'VAMPIRE CIRCUS'
FRIGHTENED CITY The (61) Theme music (Norrie Paramor)
Shadows on 'In the 60s' *MFP (EMI): CDMFP 6076 (CD)*
FROG DREAMING (Austral) Mus (Brian May) *also* 'The WILD
DUCK'* (Simon Walker) *S.Cross (S.Scr) SCCD 1019(CD)*
FROM RUSSIA WITH LOVE - *see* JAMES BOND FILM INDEX
FRUIT MACHINE (88) Music (Hans Zimmer) *see Collection*
'FILM MUSIC OF HANS ZIMMER'
FUGITIVE The (93) Music score (James Newton Howard)
-S/T- *Elektra (WEA): 7599 61592-2 (CD)*
FULL METAL JACKET (87) Songs by various artists
-S/T- *Warner Bros (WEA): 925 613-2(CD) -4(Cass)*
FUN IN ACAPULCO (63) *feat:* ELVIS PRESLEY -S/T- reissue
with 'It Happened At The World's Fair' (63) on *RCA
(BMG): 74321 13431-4 (Cass) 74321 13431-2 (CD)*
FUNNY FACE (FILM MUSICAL 56) (G./I.Gershwin) with Fred
Astaire-Audrey Hepburn-S/T- *DRG USA: CDS 15001 (CD)*
FUNNY GIRL (ORIG BROADWAY CAST 64) Songs (Jule Styne-
Bob Merrill) *feat:* BARBRA STREISAND-JEAN STAPLETON-
SYD.CHAPLIN-KAY MEDFORD *EMI Angel:ZDM 764661-2 (CD)*
FUNNY LADY (FILM MUSICAL 75)Songs: John Kander-Fred Ebb
Featuring: Barbra Streisand -S/T- *Bay Cities USA
Import (Silva Screen): BCD 3006 (CD)*
FUNNY THING HAPPENED ON THE WAY TO THE THEATRE, A (ORIG
LONDON CAST 1963) Music & Lyrics (Stephen Sondheim)
feat FRANKIE HOWERD-ISLA BLAIR-KENNETH CONNOR-JOHN
RYE-JON PERTWEE-MON.EDDIE GRAY-LEON GREENE & Comp.
EMI Angel (EMI): CDANGEL 3 (CD)
FUNNY THING HAPPENED ON THE WAY TO THE FORUM, A (ORIG
BROADWAY CAST 1962) Songs (Stephen Sondheim) feat:
Zero Mostel-John Carradine-Jack Gilford-Raymond Wal
burn-David Burns *EMI Angel (EMI): ZDM 764770-2 (CD)*
FURY The (78) Music score (John Williams) LONDON S.ORCH
-S/T- import on *Alhambra (Pinn): A.8914 (CD)*

GADFLY The (55) Music Suite Op.97A (Dim.Shostakovich)
   -S/T- USSR Symph Orch (Emin Khachaturian) *CFP (EMI)*
   CFP 4463-1 (LP) -4 (Cass) CDCFP 4463 (CD)
GALLIPOLI (Film) Music inc: 'Pearl Fishers' (Bizet) 'Ce
   ntone Di Sonata No.3' (Paganini) 'Adagio'(Albinoni)
   see Coll 'Music From Great Australian Films' *(DRG)*
GAMBLE The (91) Music sc: (Pino Donaggio) -S/T- *Italian
   Import (Silva Screen): OST 106 (CD)*
GAMBLER The (ORIG LONDON CAST 86) Songs/Sketches (Peter
   Brewis-Bob Goody-Mel Smith) *with* Mel Smith *First Ni
   ght (Pinn): SCENE 3 (LP) SCENEC 3 (Cass)*
GAME OF DEATH (79) Music score (John Barry) c/w NIGHT
   GAMES (80-John Barry) *Silva Screen: FILMCD 123 (CD)*
GANG'S ALL HERE The (FILM MUSICAL 43) Songs (Leo Robin-
   Harry Warren) Alice Faye-Benny Goodman-Carmen Miran
   da -S/T- *Sandy Hook USA (Derann-Pinn):CDSH 2009(CD)*
GARDEN The (91) Music score (Simon Fisher Turner) -S/T-
   Ionic (Pinn): IONIC 5C (Cass) IONIC 5CD (CD)
GAS FOOD AND LODGING (92) Music score (Barry Adamson &
   V.Arts) *Ionic (RTM/Pinn): IONIC 9(C)(CD) (Cass/CD)*
GAY LIFE The (ORIG BROADWAY CAST 61) Songs (Arthur Schw
   artz-Howard Dietz) *feat* BARBARA COOK-Walter Chiari
   and Company *Angel (EMI): ZDM 764763-2 (CD)*
GENERATION,A (56-Andrzej Wajda) Mus: Andrzej Markowski
   on coll 'Andrez Wajda Trilogy' *TER (Con) TER 1053LP*
GENESIS (86) Music score (Ravi Shankar) -S/T- Import on
   Milan France: A.287 (LP) C.287 (Cass) CDCH.287 (CD)
GENTLEMEN PREFER BLONDES (ORIG BROADWAY CAST 49) *feat:*
   Carol Channing-Yvonene Adair-Jack McCauley-Eric
   Brotherson *Sony Broadway (Sony Mus): SK 48013 (CD)*
GENTLEMEN PREFER BLONDES (ORIG LONDON CAST 62) *featur:*
   Dora Bryan-Anne Hart-Donald Stewart-Robin Palmer on
   TER (Conif): TER 1059 (LP) ZCTER 1059 (Cass)
GETTYSBURG (93) Music score (Randy Edelman) -S/T- *Impt
   (Silva Screen): 35654-2 (CD) 35654-4 (Cass)*
GHOST (90) Music score (Maurice Jarre) feat "Unchained
   Melody" (Alex North-Hy Zaret) - Righteous Brothers
   -S/T- *Milan (S.Screen): CDCH 620(CD) C.620(Cass)*
GHOST IN MONTE CARLO A (TVM 90) Music (Laurie Johnson)
   'Grand Waltz' *see Collection* 'ROSE AND THE GUN The'
GHOST STORY (90) Music score (Phillipe Sarde) -S/T- on
   Varese (Pinn): VSD 5259 (CD) VSC 5259 (Cass)
GHOSTBUSTERS (84) Music score (Elmer Bernstein) Title
   song: Ray Parker Jnr. feat songs by Various Artists
   -S/T- *Arista (BMG) 258720 (CD) 408720 (Cas deleted)*
GHOSTS OF THE CIVIL DEAD (91) Music sco (Nick Cave-Bli
   xa Bargoed-Mick Harvey) -S/T- *Mute (RTM/Pinn):-(CD)*
G.I.BLUES (60) Featuring ELVIS PRESLEY -S/T- *RCA (BMG):
   ND 83735 (CD) NK 83735 (Cass)*
GIANT (56) Music sco (Dimitri Tiompkin) complete score+
   music from 'EAST OF EDEN' & 'REBEL WITHOUT A CAUSE'
   Import (Silva Screen): CIN 2206-2 (CD) -4 (Cass)
GIGI (FILM MUSICAL 58) Songs (Alan Jay Lerner-Frederick
   Loewe) Featuring Leslie Caron and Maurice Chevalier

-S/T- *MGM(EMI): CDMGM 1 (CD) TCMGM 1 (Cass) deleted*
inc -S/T- music to 'An American In Paris' (Film 51)
GIGI (ORIG LONDON CAST 85)*with* Sian Phillips-Beryl Reid
Amanda Waring-Jean Pierre Aumont-Geoffrey Burridge-
John Aaron *First Night (Pinn): OCRCD 7 (CD)*
GILBERT & SULLIVAN OVERTURES (LIGHT OPERA) The Pro Arte
Orchestra (Sir M.Sargent) - *Classics For Pleasure
(EMI): CDCFP 4529 (CD) TCCFP 4529 (Cas) CFP 4529 LP*
GINGER ALE AFTERNOON (89) Music score by Willie Dixon
-S/T- *Varese (Pinn): VSD 5234 (CD) VSC 5234 (Cass)*
GINGER AND FRED (86) Songs (Irving Berlin) Music score
(Nicola Piovani) -S/T- *Milan (S.Screen) CDFMC 4(CD)*
GIRL CAN'T HELP IT The (56) Rock'n'Roll songs by Little
Richard-Eddie Fontaine-Gene Vincent-Eddie Cochran-
Ray Anthony-The Treniers-Fats Domino-Platters-Nino
Tempo-Julie London-Johnny Olenn *EMI: CDGO 2037 (CD)*
GIRL HAPPY (65) *feat:* ELVIS PRESLEY *reiss* -S/T- with
'Harum Scarum' *RCA (BMG):74321 13433-2(CD) -4(Cas)*
GIRL WHO CAME TO SUPPER The (ORIG CAST RECORDING) Songs
(Noel Coward) *with* Jose Ferrer-Florence Henderson
Sony Broadway (Sony Music): CD 48210 (CD)
GIRLS GIRLS GIRLS (62) ELVIS PRESLEY *reissue* -S/T- with
'Kid Galahad' (62) *RCA: 74321 13430-2 (CD) -4(Cass)*
GIVE MY REGARDS TO BROAD STREET (84) Songs (P.McCartney
J.Lennon) -S/T- *EMI:CDP 746043-2(CD) TCPCTC 2(Cass)*
GLADIATOR (92) Music score (Brad Fiedel) with V.Artists
-S/T-*Columbia (Sony M): 471 364-2 (CD) -4 (Cass)*
GLASS MENAGERIE (88) Music score (Henry Mancini) -S/T-
MCA: MCF 3414 (LP) MCFC 3414 (Cass) MCAD 6222 (CD)
GLASS MOUNTAIN The (49) Music score (Nino Rota) 'LEGEND
OF THE GLASS MOUNTAIN' (Nino Rota) by MANTOVANI ORC
Horatio Nelson (TBD):CDSIV 6128 (CD) SIV 1128(Cass)
GLENN MILLER STORY The (54) Univesal Studio Orchestra
-S/T- *MCA (BMG): MCLD 19025 (CD) MCLC 19025 (Cass)*
GLENGARRY GLEN ROSS (91) Music sc (James Newton Howard)
-S/T- *Elektra Imp (S.Screen): 961384-2(CD) -4(Cass)*
GLORY (89) Music score (James Horner) with Boys Choir
Of Harlem -S/T- *Virgin: CDV(TCV)V 2614 (CD/Cass/LP)*
GLORY OF MY FATHER (LA GLOIRE DE MON PERE)(90) Music by
(Vladimir Cosma) + 'MY MOTHER'S CASTLE' (CHATEAU DE
MA MERE)(90) -S/T-*Imp (S.Scr) 50050(CD) 40050(Cass)*
GO BETWEEN The (70) Music score (Michel Legrand) -S/T-
CBS: CBS 73886 (LP) with 'Umbrellas Of Cherbourg'
GO INTO YOUR DANCE (FILM MUSICAL 35) Songs (Al Dubin-Ha
rry Warren) Feat: Al Jolson -S/T- *Sandy Hook (Deran
n Trax): CDSH 2030 (CD)* with 'Wonder Bar'(34) -S/T-
GOBLIN MARKET (ORIG OFF BROADWAY CAST 87) Songs (Polly
Penn) Christina Rossetti fairy tale *feat* Terry Klau
sner-Anne Morrison *TER (Con):(CD)(ZC)TER 1144*
GODFATHER The (72) Music score (Nino Rota) -S/T- *MCA
(BMG): MCLD(MCLC) 19022 (CD/Cas)* / SUITE: *Silva
Screen (BMG): FILM(C)(CD) 032 (LP/Cass/CD)*
GODFATHER II (74) Music score (Nino Rota) -S/T- *MCA USA
(Silva Screen): MCAD 10232 (CD) MCAC 10232 (Cass)*

GODFATHER III (91) Music score (Carmine Coppola) Theme
(Nino Rota) vocal: Harry Connick Jnr -S/T- on *Epic*
(Sony): 467 813-2 (CD) -4 (Cass)
SEE ALSO UNDER COLLECTIONS: 'GODFATHER SUITE The'
GODSPELL (STUDIO RECORDING 93) Songs (Stephen Schwartz)
Feat: John Barrowman-Claire Burt-Jacqueline Dankwo
rth-Ruthie Henshall-Glyn Kerslake-Paul Manuel-Clive
Rowe-Elizabeth Sastre-Samantha Shaw-Darren Day
TER (Koch): CDTER 1204 (CD) ZCTER 1204 (Cass)
GODSPELL (ORIG BROADWAY CAST 71) *feat:* David Haskell-La
mar Alford-Johanne Jonas-Robin Lamont-Sonia Manzano
Jeffrey Mylett-Stephen Nathan and Company *Orig Cast
Ariola (S.Screen): ARCD 8304 (CD) ACB6 8304 (Cass)*
GODSPELL (FILM -S/T- 1973) *Feat:* Victor Garber-David Ha
skell-Jerry Sroka-Lynne Thigpen-Robin Lamont *-S/T-
Ariola (S.Screen): ARCD 8304 (CD) ACB6 8304 (Cass)*
GOLDEN BOY (ORIG BROADWAY CAST 59) Songs (Charles Stro
use-Lee Adams) *feat:* SAMMY DAVIS JNR.-BILLY DANIELS
PAUL WAYNE-KENNETH TOBEY-TED BENIADES-LOUIS GOSSETT
EMI Angel (EMI): ZDM 565 024-2 (CD)
GOLDFINGER - see JAMES BOND FILM INDEX
GOLDILOCKS (ORIG BROADWAY CAST 58) Music (Leroy Anders
on) Lyrics (Joan Ford-Walter & Jean Kerr) *featur:*
Don Ameche-Elaine Stritch-Russell Nype-Pat Stanley
Sony Broadway (Sony): SK 48222 (CD)
GONDOLIERS The (OPERETTA) (Gilbert & Sullivan)
PRO-ARTE ORCHEST (Malcolm Sargent) and GLYNDEBOURNE
FESTIVAL CHOIR Soloists: Geraint Evans-Alexander Yo
ung-Owen Brannigan-R.Lewis *EMI: CMS 764394-2 (2CDs)*
GONDOLIERS The (OPERETTA) (Gilbert & Sullivan) *New
Sadlers Wells Opera - TER (Con): TER2 1162 (Dbl LP)
ZCTED 1162 (Doublplay Cass) CDTER2 1162 (Dbl CDisc)*
GONDOLIERS The - *D'Oyly Carte Opera Company* - New Symph
Orch (I.Godfrey) *London (Poly): 425 177-2 (CDx2)*
GONE WITH THE WIND (39) Music score (Max Steiner) -S/T-
with addition.unissued items *Import (Silva Screen):
9676-2 (CD) 9676-4 (Cass)*inc.oher MAX STEINER *music*
National Philharmonic Orchestra (Charles Gerhardt)
RCA Red Seal (BMG): GD 80452 (CD) GK 80452 (Cass)
GOOD COMPANIONS (ORIG LONDON CAST 74) Songs (Andre Prev
in-Johnny Mercer) *with* John Mills-Judi Dench-Marti
Webb-Chris Gable *DRG USA (Conifer): DS 15020 (LP)*
GOOD GOLLY MISS MOLLY (MUSICAL 91) Bob Eaton's Rock'n'
Roll Musical (ARTS THEATRE) *recording unconfirmed*
GOOD MORNING BABYLON (87) Music score (Nicola Piovani)
-S/T- *Milan (S.Screen): CDFMC 300 (CD)*
GOOD MORNING VIETNAM (88) Music score (Alan Mason) and
Var.Arts -S/T- *A.& M: CDMID 163(CD) CMID 163(Cass)*
GOOD ROCKIN'TONITE (ORIG LONDON CAST 92) *JACK GOOD'S* no
stalgic look back at the 50's *with* Philip Bird-Tim
Whitnall-Gavin Stanley-Joe Brown and Company on
First Night (Pinn): CASTC(CD)26 (Cass/CD)
GOOD SON The (93) Music score (Elmer Bernstein) -S/T-
FOX Impt (Silva Screen): FOX 11013-2 (CD) -4 (Cass)

GOOD THE BAD & THE UGLY The (66) Music: Ennio Morricone
     -S/T- *Liberty Import (Silva Screen): 46408-2 (CD)*
     Theme also on *Old Gold: OG 9604 (7"s)*
GOODFELLAS The (90) Music score (Christopher Brooks)
     Song "Roses Are Red" (Al Byron-Paul Evans) sung by
     Bobby Vinton -S/T- *Atlantic (WEA): 756782152-2 (CD)*
     756 782 152-4 (Cass) 756 782 152-1 (LP)
GORILLAS IN THE MIST (88) Music score (Maurice Jarre)
     -S/T- *MCA USA (S.Screen) MCAC(MCAD) 6255 (Cass/CD)*
GORKY PARK (83) Music score (James Horner) -S/T- reiss:
     Varese (Pinn): VCD 47260 (CD)
GOTHIC (87) Music (Thomas Dolby) feat Screaming Lord
     Byron (Tim Spall) -S/T- *Virgin: CDV 2417*
GRADUATE The (67) Songs by Paul Simon & Art Garfunkel
     -S/T- *40-32359 (Cass) CD 32359 (CD)*
GRAFFITI BRIDGE (90) Music (Prince) -S/T- *Paisley Park*
     WB (WEA): 759927493-2 (CD) WX(C) 361 (LP/Cass)
GRAND CANYON (92) Music score (James Newton Howard)
     -S/T- *Milan (Pinn): 262493 (CD) 412493 (Cass)*
GRAND HOTEL (BROADWAY CAST RECORDING) with John Wylie-
     Henry Grossman-Willm Ryall-David Elledge and Comp.
     RCA Vic (BMG): 09026 61327-2(CD) -4 (Cass) -5 (DCC)
GRAND PRIX (66) Mus (Maurice Jarre) *see* RYAN'S DAUGHTER
GRANPA (Film Car C4/31/12/89) Music (Howard Blake) with
     Sarah Brightman and Peter Ustinov -S/T- on *Columbia*
     (Sony Music) CDHB 1 (CD) HBC 1 (Cass) HB 1 (LP)
GREASE (ORIG LONDON CAST 93) Orig songs by (Jim Jacobs
     -Warren Casey) and additional songs by (Barry,Robin
     & Maurice Gibb-John Farrar-Louis St.Louis-S.Simon)
     featuring CRAIG McLACHLAN-DEBBIE GIBSON-VOYD EVANS
     & Comp. *Epic (Sony): 474 632-2(CD) -4(Cass) -1(LP)*
GREASE (FILM MUSICAL 78) Songs (Var) feat:John Travolta
     Olivia Newton-John-Frankie Valli-Stockard Channing-
     Frankie Avalon-Sha Na Na etc. -S/T- *Polydor: (Poly)*
     817 998-2 (CD) 817 998-4 (Cass) 817 998-5 (DCC)
GREASE (ORIG BROADWAY CAST 72) *Import (Silva Screen)*
     827 548-2 (CD) 827 548-4 (Cass)
GREASE (SHOWS COLL.Studio Recording 1993) *featur:* CARL
     WAYNE and MICHAELA STRACHAN *Pickwick Shows Collect*
     PWKS 4176 (CD) PWKMC 4176 (Cass)
GREAT BALLS OF FIRE (89) Music score (Jack Baran-Jim Mc
     Bride) Film Biopic of Jerry Lee Lewis -S/T- on
     Polydor (Poly): 839 516-2 (CD) -4 (Cass)
GREAT CARUSO The (50) Sung by Mario Lanza on *RCA Gold*
     Seal (BMG): GD(GK)(GL) 60049 (CD/Cass/LP)
GREAT DICTATOR (40) Mus (Charles Chaplin)*Coll* 'CHARLIE'
GREAT ESCAPE The (62) Music sco (Elmer Bernstein) -S/T-
     Intrada USA (Koch Int): MAFCD 7025 (CD)
     see Collect.'BIG WAR THEMES' and 'GUNS OF NAVARONE'
GREAT OUTDOORS The (88) Music score (Thomas Newman)
     -S/T- *Atlantic (WEA): K 781859-1(LP) -4(Cas) -2(CD)*
GREAT ROCK AND ROLL SWINDLE (80) Music (Sex Pistols)
     -S/T- full *Virgin (EMI): TCVD 2510(2Cass) CDVD 2510*
     (2CDs) highlights: *OVED 234 (LP) OVEDC 234 (Cass)*

GREAT TRAIN ROBBERY (FIRST) - *see under* 'WILD ROVERS'
GREAT WHITE The - *see* 'ACT OF PIRACY'
GREATEST STORY EVER TOLD The (65) Music sco (Alfed New
    man) -S/T- + 'King of Kings' *EMI CDMGM25(CD) delet*
GREEN BERETS The (68) Music score (Miklos Rozsa) 'Big
    War Themes' coll *(MFP: HR 8140 Dblplay Cass)*
GREEN CARD (91) Music score (Hans Zimmer) -S/T- *Varese*
    (Pinn): VSD 5309 (CD) VSC 5309 (Cass) VS 5309 (LP)
GREMLINS (84) Music sco (Jerry Goldsmith) "Out Out" (Pe
    ter Gabriel) *Geffen Imp (S.Screen): GED 24044 (CD)*
GREMLINS 2 'The New Batch' (90) Music (Jerry Goldsmith)
    -S/T- *Varese (Pinn-S.Screen): VSD(VSC) 5269*
GREY FOX The (82) Music (Paddy Moloney) SEE Collections
    'REEL MUSIC' (Filmscore Music by Paddy Moloney) and
    Michael Conway Baker (Import) *DRG USA: (CD)SL 9515*
GRIFTERS The (90) Music score (Elmer Bernstein) -S/T-
    Varese (Pinn-S.Screen): VSD(VSC) 5290 (CD/Cass)
GRIND (ORIG BROADWAY CAST 85) Songs (Larry Grossman-Ell
    en Fitzhugh) *with* Ben Vereen-Leilani Jones and Comp
    TER (Conifer): (CD)(ZC)TER 1103 (CD/Cass/LP)
GROUNDHOG DAYS (92) Music score (George Fenton) -S/T-
    Epic (Sony Music): 473647-2 (CD) -4 (Cass) -1 (LP)
GUILTY BY SUSPICION (91) Music sc (James Newton Howard)
    -S/T- *Varese (Pinn): VSD(VSC) 5310 (CD/Cass)*
GUNMAN (93) music score (-) -S/T- *MCA (BMG): MCD 10708*
    (CD) MCC 10708 (Cass)
GUNS FOR SAN SEBASTIAN (68) Music sco (Ennio Morricone)
    -S/T- also inc 'HANG 'EM HIGH' (Dominic Frontiere)
    USA Imp (Silva Screen): AK(AT) 47705 (CD/Cass)
GUNS OF NAVARONE The (61) Music score (Dimitri Tiomkin)
    -S/T- *Varese (Pinn-S.Screen) VSD 5236 (CD)*
    see also Coll 'Guns Of Navarone' *Decca: 417853-2/4*
GURU The (India 69) Music score (Ustad Vilayat Khan)
    see Collections 'Merchant-Ivory 25th Anniversary'
GUYS AND DOLLS (FILM MUSICAL 55) Songs (Frank Loesser)
    MCA (BMG): MCLD 19155 (CD) MCLC 19155 (Cass)
GUYS & DOLLS (ORIG BROADWAY CAST 50) *with* Robert Alda
    Viviene Blaine-Stubby Kaye on *MCA USA (Sil.Screen):*
    MCAD 10301 (CD) MCAC 10301 (Cass)
GUYS AND DOLLS (NEW BROADWAY CAST 91)Walter Bobbie-John
    Carpenter-Steve Ryan-Ernie Sabella-Herschel Sparber
    Ruth Williamson *RCA: 09026 61317-2 (CD) -5 (DCC)*
GUYS AND DOLLS (REVIVAL LONDON N.THEATRE CAST 82) Songs
    (Frank Loesser) *feat:* Ian Charleson-Julie Covington
    David Healy-Bob Hoskins-Julia McKenzie and Company
    reissued on MFP (EMI): CD(TC)MFP 5978 (CD/Cass)
GYPSY (ORIG LONDON CAST 73) Songs (Jules Styne-Stephen
    Sondheim) *with* Angela Lansbury-Debbie Bowen-Judy Ca
    nnon-Zan Charisse-Barrie Ingham on *RCA Import (Sil.*
    Screen): 60571-2 (CD) 60571-4 (Cass)
GYPSY (ORIG BROADWAY CAST 59) *with* Ethel Merman *Columb*
    (Silva Screen): CK 32607 (CD) JST 32607 (Cass)
GYPSY (REVIVAL BROADWAY CAST 90) *with* Tyne Daly *Elektra*
    Nonesuch Imp (Silva Screen): 79239-2 (CD) -4 (Cass)

HAIR (ORIG LONDON CAST 93) *with*PAUL HIPP-JOHN BARROWMAN
  SINITTA-PEPSI LAWRIE DEMACQUE-ANDREE BERNARD-FELICE
  ARENA-PAUL J.MEDFORD *EMI: CD(TC)EMC 3663 (CD/Cass)*
HAIR (ORIG LONDON CAST 68) *with* Paul Nicholas-Vince Edw
  ards-Oliver Tobias *Polydor 519 973-2 (CD) -4 (Cass)*
HAIR (ORIG BROADWAY CAST 68) Songs (Galt McDermott-Jero
  me Ragni-James Rado) *feat:* Steve Curry-Ronald Dyson
  Sally Eaton-Leata Galloway-Paul Jabara-Diane Keaton
  Melba Moore *RCA Victor (BMG): BD(BK) 89667 (CD/Cas)*
HAIR (FILM MUSICAL 79) Songs(Galt McDermot-Jerome Ragni
  James Rado) -S/T- *RCA (S.Screen):3274-2(CD)-4(Cass)*
HAIRDRESSER'S HUSBAND (91) Music score (Michael Nyman)
  -S/T- *Japanese Import through Movie Boulevard Leeds*
HALF A SIXPENCE (ORIG LONDON CAST 63) Songs (David Hene
  ker) *with* Tommy Steele *Deram (Poly): 820 589-2 (CD)*
HALF MOON STREET (86) Music score (Richard Harvey) Impt
  -S/T- *Milan Fr (S.Screen) A.282 (LP)*
HALLELUJAH BABY! (ORIG BROADWAY CAST 67) Music (Jule St
  yne) Lyrics (Betty Comden-Adolph Green) *featuring:-*
  Leslie Uggams-Robert Hooks-Allen Case-Justin McDono
  ugh-Lillian Hayman & Co *Sony Broadway:SK 48218 (CD)*
HALLOWEEN 1 (78) Music score (John Carpenter) -S/T- Imp
  Varese USA (Pinn): VCD 47230 (CD) CTV
  81176 (Cass) STV 81176 (LP) /Colosseum CL 0008 (LP)
HALLOWEEN 2 (81) Music score (John Carpenter) -S/T- Imp
  Varese (Pinn): VCD 47152 (CD) CTV 81152(Cass)
HALLOWEEN 3 (83) Music (Alan Howarth-J.Carpenter) -S/T-
  Varese (Pinn): VSD(VSC) 5243 (CD/Cass)
HALLOWEEN 4 (88) Music score (Alan Howarth) -S/T- Imprt
  Varese (Pinn: VSC 5205 (Cass) VSD 5205 (CD)
HALLOWEEN 5 (89) Music score (Alan Howarth) -S/T- Imprt
  Varese (Pinn): VS(C) 5239 (LP/Cass) VSD 5239 CD
HAMLET (48) Music score (William Walton) inc.music from
  'As You Like It' *Chandos (Chandos): CHAN 8842 (CD)*
HAMLET (90) Music score (Ennio Morricone) -S/T- *Virgin*
  (Polyg): CDVMM 3 (CD)
HAND THAT ROCKS THE CRADLE (91) Mus sco (Graeme Revell)
  -S/T- *Hollywood (S.Screen): HR 61304.2(CD) -4(Cass)*
HANDFUL OF DUST A (88) Music score (George Fenton) on
  -S/T- *Ocean Disque: LPLTD 071 (LP) CDLTD 071 (CD)*
  MCLTD 071 (Cass) / also on DRG USA (Silva Screen)
HANDMAID'S TALE The (90) Music score (Ryuichi Sakamoto)
  -S/T- *GNP (S.Screen): GNPD 8020(CD) GNP-5 8020(Cas)*
HANG 'EM HIGH (67) Music score (Dominic Frontiere) on
  -S/T- also inc: 'Guns Fo San Sebastian' (Ennio Morr
  icone) *Imp (S.Screen): AK 47705 (CD) AT 47705 (Cas)*
HANGIN'WITH THE HOMEBOYS (91) Music (Rap) artists incl:
  2Live Crew-Snap-Stevie B-Poison Clan-Beat Goes Bang
  -S/T- *Musidisc (APT):108832 (CD) 108664 (Cass)*
HANNAH 1939 (ORIG USA CAST) Songs (Bob Merrill)
  TER (Conifer): CDTER 1192 (CD) ZCTER 1192 (Cass)
HANNAH AND HER SISTERS (86) Music:Count Basie Orchestra
  Harry James Orch-Bobby Short etc. -ST- *MCA (BMG):*
  IMCAC 6190 (Cass) / MCA USA (S.Screen) MCAD 6190 CD

HANNA'S WAR (88) Music score (Dov Seltzer) with 'ASSISI
UNDERGROUND The (85) (Dov Seltzer) on *Silva Screen
(Conif): FILMCD 094 (CD)*
HANS CHRISTIAN ANDERSEN (52) Songs (Frank Loesser) sung
by DANNY KAYE on 'Very Best Of Danny Kaye' collect.
MCA (BMG): MCLD 19049 (CD) MCLC 19049 (Cass)
HAPPIEST MILLIONAIRE The - see WALT DISNEY FILM INDEX
HAPPY TIME (ORIG BROADWAY CAST 68) Songs (John Kander-
Fred Ebb) *with* Robert Goulet *Import (Silva Screen):
61016-2 (CD) 61016-4 (Cass)*
HARD BOILED (93) music score (Michael Gibbs) -S/T- on
Ionic-Mute (RTM-Pinn): IONIC 11CD (CD)
HARD DAY'S NIGHT A (64) Songs (John Lennon-Paul McCartn
ey) The Beatles & George Martin -S/T-*Parlophone EMI
PCS 3058 (LP) TCPCS 3058 (Cass) CDP 746437-2 (CD)*
HARD TARGET (93) Music score (Graeme Revell) -S/T- on
Varese (Pinn): VSD 5445 (CD) VSC 5445 (Cass)
HARD TO HOLD (83) Songs (Rick Springfield) -S/T- on
RCA: BL 84935 (LP) BK 84935 (Cass) BD 84935 (CD)
HARD TO KILL (89) Music score (David Michael Frank)
with 'ABOVE THE LAW' (88) & 'OUT FOR JUSTICE' (91)
GNP (Sil.Screen): GNPD 8028 (CD) GNP5-8028 (Cass)
HARD WAY The (91) Music score (Arthur B.Rubinstein)
Title song by LL Cool J on *Def Jam (Sony)* -S/T- on
Varese (Pinn-S.Screen): VSC(CD) 5315 (Cass/CD)
HARDER THEY COME The (71) Music & songs (Jimmy Cliff)
-S/T- *Mango Island: RRCD 11 (CD) RRCT 11 (Cass)*
HARDWARE (90) Music score (Simon Boswell) + tracks
by Public Image Ltd and Luciano Pavarotti -S/T- on
*Varese USA (Pinn-S.Screen): VSD(VSC) 5283 (CD/Cass)
Milan (Silva Screeb) CDCH 627 (CD) C.627 (Cass)*
see *Coll* 'HORROR AND SCIENCE FICTION FILM MUSIC'
HARLEQUIN (80) Music score (Brian May) with DAY AFTER
HALLOWEEN *OneMone IMICD 1010 (CD)*
HARLEY DAVIDSON AND THE MARLBORO MAN (91) Music score
(Basil Poledouris) -S/T- *Mercury (unconfirmed)*
HAROLD LLOYD'S WORLD OF COMEDY (62) Music sco: (Walter
Scharf) Brussels SO *Bay Cities (S.Scr): BCD 3016 CD*
HARUM SCARUM (63) ELVIS PRESLEY *reissued* -S/T- with
'Girl Happy' (65) *RCA: 74321 13433-2 (CD) -4 (Cass)*
HATARI (62) Music score (Henry Mancini) -S/T- on *RCA Im
(Silva Screen): 2559-2 (CD)*
HAUNTED SUMMER (89) Music score (Christopher Young)
-S/T- *Silva Screen: FILM(CD) 037 (CD)*
HAVANA (90) Music score (Dave Grusin) -S/T- on *GRP USA
(S.Screen): GRP 2003-2 (CD) GRP 2003-4 (Ca)* deleted
HAWKS (88) Music Score (John Cameron) songs: Barry Gibb
"Childhood Days" sung by BARRY GIBB -S/T- record on
Polydor (Poly):POLD(C) 5234 (LP/Cass) 837264-2 (CD)
HAZARD OF HEARTS A (TVM 87) Music sco (Laurie Johnson)
'Serena' *see Coll* 'ROSE AND THE GUN The'
HEAD (68) Music (The Monkees) Songs (Carole King-Gerry
Goffin-Nilsson-Toni Stern-Tommy Boyce & Bobby Hart)
-S/T- *Lightning (Grapevine/Polyg): LIGCD 5001 (CD)*

HEAR MY SONG (91) Music sco (John Altman) Josef Locke's voice sung in the film by Vernon Midgley. -S/T- on *Big Screen (WEA): 759924456-2 (CD) -4 (Cass)* - Orig inal **JOSEF LOCKE** recordings are on 'Hear My Song' (Best Of) *EMI (EMI):CDGO 2034 (CD) TCGO 2034 (Cass)*

HEART CONDITION (90) Music score (Patrick Leonard) and song "Have A Heart" sung by Bonnie Raitt from 'Nick Of Time' *Capitol: (CD)(TC)EST 2095 (CD/Cass/LP)*

HEART OF MIDNIGHT (88) Music score (Yanni) -S/T- *South ern Cross (Silva Screen): SSD 1003 (CD)*

HEARTS AND SOULS (93) Music score (Marc Shaiman) *feat:* songs by FRANKIE VALLI-STEPHEN BISHOP-RAY CHARLES-B.B.KING etc. -S/T- *MCA USA (S.Screen): MCAD 10919 (CD) MCAC 10919 (Cass)*

HEAT AND DUST (82) Music score (Richard Robbins) -S/T- *TER (Con): TER 1032 (LP) see 'Merchant-Ivory' (col)*

HEATHERS (89) Music score (David Newman) -S/T- Import *Varese (S.Screen): VSD 5223 (CD) VS(C) 5223 (LP/CS)*

HELEN MORGAN STORY The (Film 57) feat GOGI GRANT *Import (Silva Screen): 1030-2 (CD) 1030-4 (Cass)*

HELL CAN BE HEAVEN (ORIG LONDON CAST 83)Songs (Hereward Kaye) *TER (Conifer): 1068 (LP) ZCTER 1068 (Cas)*

HELLO AGAIN (88) Music score (William Goldstein) -S/T- *Cinedisc (Silva Screen) CDC 1003 (CD)*

HELLO DOLLY (FILM MUSICAL 69) *featur* Barbra Streisand -S/T- *Casablanca (S.Screen):810368-4 (Cass)*

HELLO DOLLY (ORIG BROADWAY CAST 64)Songs (Jerry Herman) *feat* Mary Martin-Loring Smith-Mark Alden-Marilyn Lo vell *RCA Vict (BMG): GD 83814 (CD) GK 83814 (Cass)*

HELLO DOLLY (BROADWAY MUSICAL 67) *featur:* Pearl Bailey Cab Calloway on *RCA Victor (BMG): GD 81147 (CD)*

HELLRAISER (87) Music score (Christopher Young) -S/T- *Silva Screen (Conif): FILMCD 021 (CD)*

HELLRAISER 2 'Hellbound' (88) Music score (Chris.Young) -S/T- *GNP (S.Screen): GNP(C)(D) 8015 (LP/Cass/CD)*

HELLRAISER III 'Hell On Earth'(92) Music (Randy Miller) -S/T- (SCORE) *GNP (S.Screen): GNPD 8233 (CD) GNP5 8233 (Cass)* (SONGS) *S.Screen: 480007-2(CD) -4(Cass)*

HELP (65) Songs (John Lennon-Paul McCartney)with George Martin / The Beatles -S/T- *Parlophone (EMI): PCS 3071 (LP) TC-PCS 3071 (Cass) CDP 746439-2 (CD)*

HENRY AND JUNE (90) Music score (Alan Splet) with selec tion by Rose & Philip Kaufman) -S/T- on *Varese Impt (Pinn-Silva Screen): VSD 5294 (CD) VSC 5294 (Cass)*

HENRY PORTRAIT OF A SERIAL KILLER (90) Music sco (John McNaughton-Ken Hale) -S/T- *QDK (SRD):EFA 11910 (CD)*

HENRY V (89) Music score (Patrick Doyle) C.B.S.O.(Simon Rattle) -S/T- *EMI:CDC(EL)749919-2(CD)-4(Cass)-1(LP)*

HERE'S LOVE (ORIG BROADWAY CAST 63) Songs (Meredith Wil lson) *feat* Laurence Naismith-Craig Stevens-Valerie Lee-Fred GWynne-Janis Page *Sony Broadway CD48204 CD*

HERO (92) Music (George Fenton) "Heart Of A Hero" sung by LUTHER VANDROSS & Los Angeles Children's Chorus -S/T- *Epic (Sony): 472331-2 (CD) -4 (Cass) -1 (LP)*

HERO AND THE TERROR (88) Music score (David Frank)-S/T-
Cinedisc (Silva Screen): EDL 2508-2 (CD)
HERO'S The / HERO'S 2 (Return) see Television Section
HIDER IN THE HOUSE (89) Music score (Christopher Young)
-S/T- Intrada USA (Silva Screen): MAF 7007D (CD)
HIGH HEELS (92) Music score (Ryuichi Sakamoto) -S/T- on
Import (Silva Screen):510855.2 (CD) 510855.4 (Cass)
HIGH NOON (52) Song "Do Not Forsake Me" (Ned Washington
Dimitri Tiomkin) Tex Ritter Bear Family: BFX 15126
(LP) Frankie Laine - Warwick: WW2014(4) (LP/Cass)
HIGH ROAD TO CHINA (84) Music score (John Barry) -S/T-
Silva Screen: SCSCE CD2 (CD)
HIGH SOCIETY (FILM MUSICAL 56) Songs (Cole Porter) Bing
Crosby-Gene Kelly-Frank Sinatra-Grace Kelly-Celeste
Holme -S/T- Capitol (EMI): TC-SLCT 6116 (Cass)
HIGH SPIRITS (88) Music score (George Fenton) -S/T- on
GNP (S.Screen) GNPD 8016 (CD) GNPS(5) 8016 (LP/Cas)
HIGH SPIRITS (ORIG LONDON CAST 64) Songs (Tim Gray-Hugh
Martin) feat Cicely Courtneidge-Dennis Quilley-Jack
Waters-Marti Stevens DRG (Conif): CDSBL 13107 (CD)
HIGHLANDER (86) Music score (Michael Kamen) Songs by
by Queen (6 from 'A Kind Of Magic' inc. title track
Parlophone: (TC)EU 3509 (Cas/LP) CDP 746267-2 (CD)
HIGHLANDER 2: The Quickening (91) Music score (Stewart
Copeland) -S/T- Bronze (WEA): 9031 73657-2 (CD) and
BWX2C (Cass) BWX2 (LP)
HINDENBURG The (75) Music score (David Shire) Selection
Bay Cities (S.Screen):BCD 3021 (CD) BCC 3021 (Cass)
HIRED MAN The (ORIG LONDON CAST 84) Songs (Howard Gooda
11) Book by Melvyn Bragg Orig London Cast 1st Night
(Con): SCENE 10 (LP) SCENEC 10 (Cass)
HIRED MAN The (IN CONCERT CAST RECORDING) Songs (Howard
Goodall) (Cancer Relief Macmillan Fund)
TER (Conifer): CDTER2 1189 (2CD) ZCTED 1189 (Cass)
HISTORY OF MR.POLLY (49) Music sc (William Alwyn) Suite
from film played by London Symphony Orch (Richard
Hickox) on Chandos: CHAN 9243 (CD) ABTD 1606 (Cass)
HITCHER The (86) Music score (Mark Isham) -S/T- Silva
Screen: SSD 1002 (CD)
HMS PINAFORE (OPERETTA) (Gilbert & Sullivan) PRO-ARTE
ORCH (Malcolm Sargent) GLYNDEBOURNE FESTIVAL CHOIR
George Baker-John Cameron-Richard Lewis-Owen Branni
gan with 'TRIAL BY JURY' EMI: CMS 764397-2 (2CDs)
HMS PINAFORE (1930 recording) featuring GEORGE BAKER-
HENRY A.LYTTON-ELSIE GRIFFIN and LIGHT OPERA ORCHES
(Sir M.Sargent) Pro-Arte (Sil.Screen): CDD 597 (CD)
HMS PINAFORE (Musical Operetta 87) (Gilbert & Sullivan)
New Sadlers Wells Opera Cast - TER: TER2 1150 (Doub
le LP) ZCTED 1150 (Dbl Cass) CDTER2 1150 (Dbl CD)
HMS PINAFORE - D'Oyly Carte Opera Company -New Symphony
Orch (I.Godfrey) London (Poly): 414 283-2 (CDx2)
HOBSON'S CHOICE (53) Music score (Malcolm Arnold) Suite
'Film Music' London Symphony Orchestra (Richard Hic
kox) Chandos: CHAN 9100 (CD) ABTD 1600 (Cass)

HOFFA (92) Music score (David Newman) -S/T- on *Fox Impt (Silva Screen): FOX 11001-2 (CD) FOX 11001-4 (Cass)*
HOME ALONE (90) Music score (John Williams) -S/T- on *Columbia (Sony): MK 46595 (CD)*
HOME ALONE 2 (92) Var.arts: BETTE MIDLER-DARLENE LOVE-LITTLE STEPHEN & E.ST.BAND-WAS NOT WAS-ALAN JACKSON ATLANTIC STARR-TLC -S/T- *Arista (BMG): 07822 11000-21 (CD) 07822 11000-45 (Cass)*
HOME MOVIES (79) Music score (Pino Donaggio) *see* coll: 'Music From the Films Of Brian De Palma' - *Milan Fr (S.Screen) A.384 (LP) C.384 (CS) CDCH 384 (CD)* also with music from 'Blow Out'/'Carrie' & 'Body Double'
HOME OF THE BRAVE (87) Featuring Laurie Anderson -S/T- *WEA: 925400-4 (CS) 925400-2 (CD)*
HOMEBOY (88) Music score (Eric Clapton-Michael Kamen) -S/T- *Virgin: CDV 2574 (CD) OVEDC 364 (Cass)*
HOMER AND EDDIE (90) Music:Richie Havens-Billy Burnette -S/T- *Milan Fr (S.Screen): CDCH 630 (CD) C630 (Cas)*
HOMEWARD BOUND (93) Music score (Bruce Broughton) -S/T- *Intrada (Silva Screen): MAF 7041D (CD)*
HOMME ET UNE FEMME Un - *see under* 'MAN & A WOMAN, A'
HONEY I BLEW UP THE KIDS (92) Music score (Bruce Broughton) -S/T- *Intrada (Koch/S.Screen): MAFCD 7030 (CD)*
HONEYMOON IN VEGAS (92) Music sco (David Newman) -S/T- *Epic (Sony Music): 471925-2 (CD) -4 (Cass) -1 (LP)*
HOOK (91) Music score (John Williams) -S/T- *Epic (Sony Music) 469 349-2 (CD) -4 (Cass) (all deleted 8/93)*
HOOSIERS (87) - *see under* 'Best Shot' (UK Title)
HOPE AND GLORY (87) Music score (Peter Martin) -S/T- on *TER (Conif): (ZC)TER 1147 (Cass/LP) VCD 47290 (CD)*
HORROR OF DRACULA *see COLLECTIONS* 'HORROR OF DRACULA'
HORRORS OF THE BLACK MUSEUM - *see under* COLLECTIONS
HORS LA VIE () Music score (Nicola Piovani) -S/T- *Milan (Pinn): CDCH 541 (CD)*
HOT MILLIONS (68) Music score (Laurie Johnson) suite of three pieces *see Collections* 'ROSE AND THE GUN The'
HOT SHOTS (91) Music score (Sylvester Levay) -S/T- on *Varese (Pinn-S.Screen): VSD(VSC) 5338 (CD/Cass)*
HOT SHOTS 2 (93) Music score (Basil Poledouris) -S/T- *Varese (Pinn): VSD 5426 (CD) VSC 5426 (Cass)*
HOT SPOT The (91) Music sco (Jack Nitzsche) + John Lee Hooker-Miles Davis-TajMahal-Roy Rogers-Tim Drummond -S/T- *Antilles (Poly): ANCD 8755(CD) ANC 8755(Cass)*
HOUR OF THE GUN (67) Music score(Jerry Goldsmith) -S/T- *Intrada (Koch/Silva Screen): MAFCD 7020 (CD)*
HOUSEHOLDER The (62) Music score unconfirmed *see under* collections 'Merchant-Ivory 25th Anniversary'
HOW GREEN WAS MY VALLEY (41) Music sco (Alfred Newman) -S/T- *Fox (Silva Screen): FOX 11008 (CD)*
HOW THE WEST WAS WON (62) Music score (Alfred Newman) also inc -S/T- to 'The Big Country' (58) (J.Moross) -S/T- *EMI MGM: (CD)(TC)MGM 12 (CD/Cass)*
New recording featuring complete 'Main Title' theme *Impt (Silva Screen): AK47024-2(CD) AT 47024-4(Cass)*

HOW TO GET AHEAD IN ADVERTISING (89) Music score (David
Dundas-Rick Wentworth) -S/T- *Silva Screen (Conifer)
FILM(C)(CD) 041 (LP/Cass/CD)* CD inc: 'Withnail & I'
HOW TO MAKE LOVE TO A NEGRO..(89) Music score (Manu Dib
ango) "On Vit De Femmes" sung by Claude Dubois
-S/T- *Milan (S.Screen): CDCH 513 (CD) C 513 (Cass)*
HOW TO SUCCEED IN BUSINESS WITHOUT REALLY TRYING (ORIG
BROADWAY CAST 61) Songs (Frank Loesser) feat Robert
Morse-Rudy Vallee-Bonnie Scott-Virginia Martin etc
RCA (Silva Screen): 60352-2(CD) -4(Cass)
HOWARDS END (92) Music score (Richard Robbins) -S/T- on
Nimbus (Nimbus): NI 5339 (CD) NC 5339 (Cass)
HUDSON HAWK (91) Music sco (Michael Kamen-Robert Kraft)
Songs: Bing Crosby-James Brown-Snap /Theme by Bruce
Willis) by Dr.John-S/T-*Varese (Pinn): VSC(VSD) 5323*
HUMANOID The (79) Music score (Ennio Morricone) -S/T-
incl.music from 'NIGHTMARE CASTLE' (65-E.Morricone)
Italian Imp (Silva Screen): OST 118 (CD)
HUMORESQUE (47) Music score (Franz Waxman) Violin solos
Isaac Stern /select.on *Varese (Pinn): VSD 5257 (CD)*
HUNDRA (Film -) Music score (Ennio Morricone) -S/T- imp
ort - *Prometheus (Silva Screen): PCD 107 (CD)*
HUNGER The (82) Music score:Michael Rubini-Denny Jaeger
+music "Lakme" (Delibes) "Solo Cello Suites" (Bach)
-S/T- *Milan France (Silva Screen): CDCH 004 (CD)*
see COLL 'HORROR AND SCIENCE FICTION FILM MUSIC'
also "The Flower Duet" from 'Lakme'(Delibes)version
by LESLEY GARRETT *see Collection* 'VAMPIRE CIRCUS'
HUNT FOR RED OCTOBER The (89) Music sco (Basil Poledour
is) -S/T- *MCA USA (Pinn): MCAD(MCAC) 6428 (CD/Cass)*
HUNTING OF THE SNARK The (ORIG LONDON CAST 91) Songs by
(Mike Batt) Kenny Everett-David McCallum-Veronica
Hart-John Partridge *1ST Night (Pinn):CAST(C)(CD) 24*
HYPERSPACE (Film) Music score (Don Davis) on *Prometheus
(S.Screen): PCD 120 (CD)* also contains SUITE FROM
TV SERIES *'Beauty And The Beast'*

I AIM AT THE STARS (60) Music score (Laurie Johnson)
Theme only *see Collections* 'ROSE AND THE GUN The'
I DO I DO (ORIG BROADWAY CAST 66) Mus (Harvey Schmidt)
Lyrics (Tom Jones) *feat* Robert Preston & Company
RCA (Silva Screen): 1128-2 (CD) 1128-4 (Cass)
I LOVE MY WIFE (ORIG BROADWAY CAS) Songs (Cy Coleman-Mi
chael Stewart) *DRG (Conif): CDRG 6109 (CD)*
I LOVE YOU PERFECT (TVM 89) Music score (Yanni) -S/T-
Silva Screen (Conif): FILMCD 122 (CD)
I REMEMBER MAMA (MUSICAL SHOW 85) Songs Richard Rodgers
Martin Charnin) *World premiere cast recording* with
Sally Anne Howes-George Hearn-Ann Morrison-Sian Phi
llips-Gay Soper-George S.Irving-Patricia Routeledge
TER: TER 1102 (LP) ZCTER 1102 (Cas) CDTER 1102 (CD)
I WANT TO BE A ACTOR LADY (Hits From Early Musical Come
dies) CINCINNATI UNIVERSITY SINGERS & THEATRE ORCH
New World USA (Harmonia Mundi): 80221-2 (CD)

I WANT TO LIVE (58) Music score (John Mandel) featuring
   Gerry Mulligan-Shelly Manne -S/T- *Affinity: AFF 188*
ICE CASTLES (78) Music score (Marvin Hamlisch) -S/T- on
   Arista (S.Screen): ARCD 8317 (CD) ACB6 8317 (Cass)
ICEMAN (84) Music score (Bruce Smeaton) -S/T- *Southern*
   Cross (Silva Screen): SCCD 1006 (CD)
IF LOOKS COULD KILL (91) Var.arts -S/T- *MCA USA (Silva*
   Screen): MCAD 10240 (CD) MCAC 10240 (Cass)
IF THEY COULD SEE ME NOW (ORIG LONDON CAST 84) *with*
   Tim Curry-Michael Hordern-Alan Jay Lerner-Sian Phil
   lips-Virginia McKenna-Joan Plowright-Christopher
   Reeve-Liz Robertson *TER (Conif): TERX 1087 (2 LP)*
IGNATIO (Film) Music (Vangelis) -S/T- *813 042-2 (CD)*
IL SECONDO TRAGICO FANTOZZI - *see under* 'FANTOZZI'
IMAGINE - THE MOVIE (88) Music (John Lennon) -S/T- *Parl*
   ophone (EMI):(TC)PCSP 722 (2LP/Cass) CDPCSP 722(CD)
IN A SHALLOW GRAVE (88) Music score (Jonathan Sheffer)
   -S/T- *Varese Imp (S.Screen-TER) STV 81359 (LP)*
IN LIKE FLINT - *see under* 'Our Man Flint'
IN LOVE AND WAR (58) Music score (Hugo Friedhofer) Symp
   honic Suite - National Philh.Orch (Fred Steiner) on
   'The Kentuckian' *Preamble (S.Screen) PRCD 1777 (CD)*
IN THE GRIP OF THE SPIDER (*aka* WEB OF THE SPIDER)(72)
   Music score (Riz Ortolani) also inc 'CONFESSIONS OF
   A POLICE CAPTAIN' (71-Italy) (Riz Ortloani) *Import*
   OST (Silva Screen): OST 114 (CD)
IN THE LINE OF DUTY (TV) Music sco (Mark Snow) TV -S/T-
   Intrada (Koch Int): MAFCD 7034 (CD)
IN THE LINE OF FIRE (93) Music score (Ennio Morricone)
   -S/T- *Epic (Sony Music): 474 285-2 (CD) -4 (Cass)*
INCHON (81) Music score (Jerry Goldsmith) -S/T- *Fantasy*
   (Silva Screen): FMT 8002D (CD)
INDECENT PROPOSAL (92) Music score (John Barry) -S/T-
   MCA (BMG): MCD 10863 (CD) MCC 10863 (Cass)
INDIANA JONES & THE LAST CRUSADE (89) Music score (John
   Williams) -S/T- *W.Bros (WEA):K.925883-2(CD) -4(Cas)*
INDIANA JONES & THE TEMPLE OF DOOM (84) Music sco (John
   Williams)-S/T-*Poly (S.Scr):TCS 102.2 (CD) 821 592-4*
INDOCHINE (INDOCHINA) (92) Music score (Patrick Doyle)
   -S/T- *Warner Bros (WEA): 903177338-2 (CD)* also on
   Varese (S.Screen): VSD(VSC) 5397 (CD/Cass)
INFERNO (80) Music score (Keith Emerson) -S/T- *Cinevox*
   Italy (S.Screen): CDCIA 5022 (CD) CIAK 75022 (Cass)
INFORMER The (35) *see under* 'STREETCAR NAMED DESIRE A'
INN OF THE SIXTH HAPPINESS The (58) Mus score (Malcolm
   Arnold) Suite on 'Film Music' London Symphony Orch
   (R.Hicox) *Chandos: CHAN 9100 (CD) ABTD 1600 (Cass)*
INNER CIRCLE The (91) Music sco (Edward Artemyev) -S/T-
   Milan (Pinn/S.Screen): 262494 (CD) 412494 (Cass)
INNERSPACE (87) Music sco (Jerry Goldsmith) songs: Rod
   Stewart etc. *Geffen Imp (S.Screen): GED 24161 (CD)*
INS AND THE OUTS The (Uns Et Les Autres Les)(France 81)
   Music score (Francis Lai/Michel Legrand/Ravel)-S/T-
   Editions 23 (S.Screen): 80043-2 (CD) 80042-4 (Cass)

INTO THE WEST (93) Music score (Patrick Doyle) arrang:
(Fiachra Trench) -S/T- *SBK (Silva Screen): SBK 890
49-2 (CD) SBK 89049-4 (Cass)*

INTO THE WOODS (ORIG BROADWAY CAST 88) Songs (Stephen
Sondheim) *with* Bernadette Peters-Chip Zein & Comp
RCA (BMG) BD 86796 (CD)

INTO THE WOODS (ORIG LONDON CAST 90) *feat:* Imelda Staun
ton-Julia McKenzie-Jacqueline Dankworth-Ann Howard
RCA Victor (BMG): RD(RK) 60752 (CD/Cass)

INTOLERANCE (Film Silent 1916 D.W.Griffiths) New Score
by Carl Davis played by Luxembourg Symphony Orchest
(Carl Davis): *Prometheus (S.Screen): PCD 105 (CD)*

INVADE MY PRIVACY (ORIG LONDON CAST) A Musical celebra
tion of FRAN LANDESMAN *TER (Koch): TERCD 1202 (CD)*

INVASION USA (85) Music score (Jay Chattaway) -S/T- Imp
Milan France (S.Screen): A.285 (LP) C.285 (Cass)

INVESTIGATION OF A CITIZEN ABOVE SUSPICION (70) Music
score (Ennio Morricone) -S/T- with IL GIOCATTOLO
Cinevox Italy (Silva Screen): CDCIA 5086 (CD)

INVISIBLE RAY The (35) Music score (Franz Waxman)
Westminster Phil Orch (Kenneth Alwyn) *also* BRIDE OF
FRANKENSTEIN (Waxman) *S.Screen (Con):FILMCD 135(CD)*

IOLANTHE (OPERETTA) (Gilbert & Sullivan)
PRO-ARTE ORCHEST (Malcolm Sargent) and GLYNDEBOURNE
FESTIVAL CHOIR Soloists: George Baker-Ian Wallace-
Alex.Young-Owen Brannigan *EMI: CMS 764400-2 (2CDs)*

IOLANTHE (OPERETTA)(Gilbert & Sullivan) *D'Oyly Carte Op
era Comp.* & New Symphony Orch Of London (I.Godrey)
London (Poly): 414 145-2 (CDx2) 414 145-4 (Cass)

IRENE (BROADWAY REVIVAL CAST 73) Songs (Various) *featur*
Debbie Reynolds-Patsy Kelly-George S.Irving & Comp.
Sony Broadway (Sony Mus): CD 32266 (CD)

IRMA LA DOUCE (ORIG BROADWAY CAST 60) Music (Marguerite
Monnot) Lyrics (David Heneker-Monty Norman) *feat:*
Elizabeth Seal-Keith Michell-Clive Revill-Elliot Go
uld-George S.Irving *Sony Broadway: SK 48018 (CD)*

IRON AND SILK (91) Music score (Michael Gibbs) -S/T- on
Ionic (RTM/Pinn): IONIC 7C (Cass) IONIC 7CD (CD)

IRON EAGLE III (ACES) (91) Music sco (Harry Manfredini)
-S/T- *Intrada USA (Koch Int): MAFCD 7022 (CD)*

IS PARIS BURNING (66) Music score (Maurice Jarre) with
110 piece Symphony Orchestra with 12 pianos - Impt
Varese (Silva Screen): VSD 5222 (CD only)

ISLANDS IN THE STREAM (76) Music score: Jerry Goldsmith
-S/T- *Intrada USA (Silva Screen): RVF 6003D (CD)*

IT HAPPENED AT THE WORLD'S FAIR (63) *feat:*ELVIS PRESLEY
reissued -S/T- with 'Fun In Acapulco' (63) on *RCA
(BMG): 74321 13431-2 (CD) 74321 13431-4 (Cass)*

IT'S A BIRD IT'S A PLANE IT'S SUPERMAN! (ORIG BROADWAY
CAST 66) Songs (Charles Strouse-Lee Adams) *feat* Bob
Holiday-Jack Cassidy-Patricia Maran-Linda Lavin-Mic
hael O'Sullivan *Sony Broadway (Sony): CD 48027 (CD)*

IT'S ALIVE 2 'It Lives Again' (78) Music score (Bernard
Herrmann) -S/T- *Silva Screen (Con): FILMCD 074 (CD)*

IVAN THE TERRIBLE (43) Music (Prokofiev) New Recording
with Philharmonia Orchestra (Neeme Jarvi) and Linda
Finnie (mezzo-sop) Nikita Storojev (bass-bar) on
Chandos (Chandos): CHAN 8977 (CD) ABTD 1566 (Cass)
new record: Philharmonic Orch (Riccardo Muti) and
Ambrosian Chorus (John McCarthy) with Irina Arkhipo
va-Boris Morgunov-Anatoly Mokrenko *EMI Studio (EMI)
CDM 769584-2 (CD) EG 769584-4 (Cass)*

J'AI TUE RASPPOUTINE (-) Music score (Andre Hossein)
-S/T- *Alhambra (Pinn): A.8929 (CD)*
JACOB'S LADDER (90) Music score (Maurice Jarre) -S/T-
Varese (Pinn): VSD(VSC) 5291 (CD/Cass)
JAILHOUSE ROCK (57) *see* 'Elvis Presley Film Index'
JAMBON JAMBON (92) Music sco (Nicola Piovani) -S/T- on
Milan (Pinn): 873139 (CD)
JAMES BOND FILMS - *see under* **'JAMES BOND FILM INDEX'**
JANE EYRE (43) Music score (Bernard Hermann) -S/T- with
'LAURA' (David Raksin) *Fox (S.Screen) FOX 11006(CD)*
JASON AND THE ARGONAUTS (63) Music score (Bernard Herrm
ann) National Philharmonic Orch (Bernard Herrmann)
see Coll 'Classic Fantasy Film Scores' *(Cloud Nine)*
JAWS (75) Music score (John Williams) -S/T- *MCA USA Imp
(Silva Screen): MCAC 1660 (Cass)*
JAWS 2 (78) Music score (John Williams) -S/T- *Varese Im
(Pinn): VSD 5328 (CD) VSC 5328 (Cass)*
JAZZ SINGER The (80) Featuring: Neil Diamond -S/T- on
*Capitol: EAST 12120 (LP) TC- (CS) CDP 746026-2 (CD)
MDEAST 12120 (MD) DCCEAST 12120 (DCC)*
JEAN DE FLORETTE (87) Music score (Jean-Claude Petit)
main theme adap.from "La Forza Del Destino" (Verdi)
Orchestra De Paris with Toots Thielemans on *Milan
(Pinn) CDCH 241 (CD)* + MANON DE SOURSES -S/T-
JEKYLL AND HYDE (MUSICAL 90) Music (Frank Wildhorn) &
Lyrics (Leslie Bricusse) *Highlights with* Linda Eder
Colm Wilkinson - *RCA: BD(BL)(BK) 74446 deleted*
JELLY'S LAST JAM (ORIG BROADWAY CAST 92) Music (Jelly
Roll Morton) *feat:* GREGORY HINES and Company USA
Imp (Silva Screen): 510 846-2 (CD) 510 846-4 (Cass)
JENNIFER EIGHT (92) Music sco (Christopher Young) -S/T-
USA Imp (Silva Screen): 66120-2 (CD) 66120-4 (Cass)
JERRY'S GIRLS (ORIG BROADWAY CAST 84) Songs (Jerry Herm
an) *feat:* Carol Channing-Leslie Uggams *TER (Conif):
CDTER 21093 (2CD) ZCTER 21093 (2Cass)*
JESUS CHRIST SUPERSTAR (FILM MUSICAL 73) Songs (A.L.Web
ber-T.Rice) Yvonne Elliman-Ted Neely-Carl Anderson-
Barry Dennen -S/T- *MCA (BMG): MCXC 502 (2Cass)*
JESUS CHRIST SUPERSTAR (ORIG LONDON CAST 72) *featuring:*
Paul Nicholas-Dana Gillespie-Paul Jabara & Company
MCA (BMG): MCFC 2503 (Cass)
JESUS CHRIST SUPERSTAR (STUDIO RECORDING 72) *featuring:*
Murray Head-Ian Gillan-Yvonne Elliman-Paul Davis-Ba
Barry Dennen-Mike D'Abo-Paul Raven and others *MCA
(BMG): MCXC 501 (2Cass) DMCX 501 (CD)*

JEWEL OF THE NILE The (86) Music (Jack Nitzsche) "When
    The Going Gets..." Billy Ocean -S/T- *Jive deleted*
JFK (92) Music score (John Williams) -S/T- *Elektra*
    (WEA): 755961293-2 (CD) 755961293-4 (Cass) see also
    Collection 'BEST OF KEVIN COSTNER'
JIT - THE MOVIE (91 Film Afrika) Music (Var.arts) -S/T-
    Earthworks/Virgin: CD EWV 23 (CD) TCEWV 23 (Cass)
JOHNNY GUITAR (53) Music score (Victor Young) -S/T- on
    Varese (Pinn): VSD 5377 (CD)
JOHNNY HANDSOME (89) Music score (Ry Cooder) -S/T- on
    WEA (WEA): K925996-2 (CD) WX 307 (LP) WX 307C (Cas)
JOHNNY JOHNSON (STUDIO CAST 55) Songs (Kurt Weill) *Impt*
    (Silva Screen): 831384-2 (CD) 831384-4 (Cass)
JONATHAN LIVINGSTON SEAGULL (73) Music by Neil Diamond
    -S/T- re-issue on *Sony: 467607-2(CD) -4(Cas) -1(LP)*
JOSEPH & THE AMAZING TECHNICOLOR DREAMCOAT (ORIG LONDON
    CAST 91) Songs (Tim Rice-Andrew Lloyd Webber) *featu*
    ring Jason Donovan (June 91) Phillip Schofield (92)
    Polydor-Really Useful (Poly):511 130-2(CD) -4(Cass)
    (Jason Donovan & Company) *also available* "Any Dream
    Will Do"/"Close Every Door To Me"/"Pharaoh's Story"
    (Phillip Schofield) *Poly: RUR(CD)(CS)11(7"/CDs/Cas)*
JOSEPH & THE AMAZING TECHNICOLOR DREAMCOAT (ORIG LONDON
    CAST 73) *MCA (BMG): MCLD 19023(CD) MCLC 19023(Cass)*
JOSEPH AND THE AMAZING TECHNICOLOR DREAMCOAT (MUSICAL)
    Paul Jones-Tim Rice-Gordon Waller-Mike Sammes-Geoff
    Love Orch - *CFP (EMI): CC 242 (CD) HR 8200 (Cass)*
    see also Coll 'ROYAL PHILHARMONIC ORCH PLAY SUITES'
JOSEPH & THE AMAZING TECHNICOLOUR DREAMCOAT(SHOWS COLL)
    Pickwick: PWKS 4163 (CD) PWKMC 4163 (Cass)
    see COLLECTIONS for full details
JOSH AND SAM (93) Music score (Thomas Newman) -S/T- on
    Varese (Pinn): VSD 5432 (CD) VSC 5432 (Cass)
JOUR DE FETE (France 48) Music score (Jean Yatove)-S/T-
    details see under 'MON ONCLE' *entry*
JOURNEY THROUGH THE PAST (73) Music (Neil Young) -S/T-
    Reprise USA: WEA 64015 (2LPs) + Buffalo Springfield
JUDGEMENT NIGHT (93) V.Artists -S/T- including SONIC
    YOUTH & CYPRESS HILL-BIOHAZARD & ONYX-LIVING COLOUR
    & RUN DMC etc.*Epic (SM): 474 183-2 (CD) -4 (Cass)*
JUICE (92) Music score (Hank Shocklee & The Bomb Squad)
    -S/T-inc Naughty By Nature-Erik B.& Rakim-Big Daddy
    Kane-Salt'n'Pepa *MCAD 10462 (CD) note:Cass deleted*
JULES ET JIM (61) Music score (Georges Delerue) -S/T-
    Prometheus (Silva Screen): PCD 103 (CD only)
JULIA (77) Music score (Georges Delerue) -S/T- Import
    DRG USA DRG 9514 (LP) c/w 'Return Of Martin Guerre'
JULIET OF THE SPIRITS (65) Music score (Nino Rota) on
    Collection 'Fellini-Rota' *see Coll*
JUNGLE BOOK The (Disney 67) Songs (Richard & Robert She
    rman) performed by PHIL HARRIS-LOUIS PRIMA-STERLING
    HOLLOWAY -S/T- *Disney-Pickwick: DSMCDSE 457 (CD spe*
    cial edition) DSMCCSE 457 (Cass special edit) ALSO
    PDC 305 (Children's Collect.Cass spoken word/songs)

JUNGLE FEVER (91) Music & songs (Stevie Wonder) "If She Breaks Your Heart" sung by Kimberly Brewer -S/T- on *Polydor: 530000-2 (CD) 530000-4 (Cass) 530000-1(LP)*

JURASSIC PARK (93) Music score (John Williams) -S/T- on *MCA (BMG): MCD 10859(CD) MCC 10859(Cass)* Theme also on *MCA: MCSTD 1927 (CDs) MCSC 1927 (Cass)*

JUST LIKE A WOMAN (92) Music sco (Michael Storey) songs ELVIS PRESLEY-LATIN TOUCH-EURYTHMICS & ARETHA FRANK LIN-COLIN BLUNSTONE -S/T- *RCA (BMG): 74321 11070-20 (CD) 74321 11070-44 (Cass)*

K2 (91) Music score (Hans Zimmer) -S/T- *Varese (Pinn): VSD 5354 (CD) VSC 5354 (Cass)*

KAFKA (91) Music score (Cliff Martinez) -S/T- on *Import (Silva Screen): 92095.2 (CD) 92095.4 (Cass)*

KANAL (58-Andrzej Wajda) Music score (Jan Krenz) on col lect 'Andrez Wajda Trilogy' *TER (Conif) TER 1053LP*

KAPO see 'ROSOLINO PARTNO SOLDAO'

KARATE KID The (84) Music (various artists): Survivor-Flirts-Shandi-Jan & Dean-Paul Davis-Comuter-Gang Of Four -S/T- *Casablanca: (S.Screen): 822213-4 (Cass)*

KEEPER OF THE CITY (91) Music score (Leonard Rosenman) Utah Symph Orch -S/T- *Intrada USA (Koch) MAFCD 7024*

KENTUCKIAN The (55) Music score (Bernard Herrmann) collection on *Silva Screen PRCD 1777 (CD)*

KERN GOES TO HOLLYWOOD (ORIG LONDON CAST 85) Songs by Jerome Kern-Dorothy Fields and others *featuring* ELAINE DELMAR-DAVID KERNAN-ELISABETH WELCH-LIZ ROBE TSON *First Night (Pinn): OCRCD 6014 (CD)* note: for full track listing see Collections section

KEY LARGO (48) Music score (Max Steiner) *see* 'Classic Film Scores For Humphrey Bogart' National Phil Orch

KICKBOXER (89) Music score (Paul Hertzog) + songs/music from 'BLOODSPORT'(87) 'CYBORG' (89-Kevin Bassinson) 'DEATH WARRANT' (90) 'DOUBLE IMPACT' (91-Arthur Kem pel) *Silva Screen (Con): FILM(C)(CD) 103 (Cass/CD)*

KID GALAHAD (62) *featuring* ELVIS PRESLEY *reissued* -S/T- with 'Girls Girls Girls' (62) on *RCA (BMG): 74321 13430-2 (CD) 74321 13430-4 (Cass)*

KIDS ARE ALRIGHT The (Documentary Film Of THE WHO) Mus: (Pete Townshend & others) *BMG Video: 74321 10087-30*

KILLERS The (46) Music score (Miklos Rozsa)selection on 'LUST FOR LIFE' *Varese (Pinn): VSD 5405 (CD)*

KILLING FIELDS The (84) Music score (Michael Oldfield) -S/T- *Virgin: OVEDC 183 (Cass) CDV 2328 (CD)*

KINDERGARTEN COP (90) Music score (Randy Edelman) -S/T- *Varese (Pinn-S.Screen): VSD(VSC) 5305 (CD/Cass)*

KING (ORIG LONDON CAST 90) Music (Richard Blackford) Ly rics (Maya Angelou) *with* Simon Estes-Cynthia Haymon *Decca (Poly): 425 212-2 (CD) -4 (Cass)*

KING AND I (FILM MUSICAL 56) Songs: Rodgers-Hammerstein Yul Brynner-Deborah Kerr (sung by Marni Nixon) Rita Moreno-Terry Saunders -S/T- **reissue** *EMI Broadway Cl assics: EG 764 693-2 (CD)*

KING AND I (ORIG BROADWAY CAST 51) *feat:* Yul Brynner-Ge
rtrude Lawrence-Doretta Morrow-Larry Douglas & Comp
MCA (BMG): MCLD 19156 (CD) MCLC 19156 (Cas)

KING AND I (ORIG LONDON CAST 53) *with:* Herbert Lom-Vale
rie Hobson - *DRG USA (Conifer): DS 15014 (LP)*

KING AND I The (USA STUDIO RECORDING 64) *feat:* BARBARA
COOK-THEODORE BIKEL-JEANETTE SCOVOTTI-ANITA DARIAN
DANIEL FERRO *Sony Broadway (Sony M): SK 53328 (CD)*

KING AND I (REVIVAL BROADWAY CAST 77) *with:* Yul Brynner
Constance Towers *RCA Red Seal (BMG): RD 82610 (CD)*

KING AND I The (STUDIO RECORDING 92) *with* Julie Andrews
Ben Kingsley-Lea Salonga-Peabo Bryson-Marilyn Horne
Roger Moore-Martin Sheen-Hollywood Bowl Symph Orche
stra conducted by John Mauceri *Philips: 438 007-2
(CD) -4(Cass) -5 (DCC) -1 (LP)*

KING CREOLE (58) Featuring ELVIS PRESLEY -S/T- *RCA Vict
(BMG): ND 83733 (CD) NK 83733 (Cass)*
see Elvis Presley Film Index

KING IN NEW YORK A (57) Music score (Charles Chaplin)
see Collect 'CHARLIE'

KING KONG (33) Music score (Max Steiner) New recording
of orig score National Philharm Orch (Fred Steiner)
Silva Screen Import: LXCD 10 (CD) / see Coll 'Omen'

KING OF KINGS (61) Music sco (Miklos Rozsa) orig -S/T-
Import (Silva Screen): AK 52424 (CD) Also available
Symphonic Suite on 'MIKLOS ROZSA FILM MUSIC VOL.1'
Prometheus (Silva Screen): PCD 122 (CD)

KING OF THE HILL (93) Music sco (Cliff Martinez) -S/T-
Varese (Pinn): VSD 5425 (CD)

KING OF THE WIND (89) Music score (John Scott) -S/T- on
JOS Records (Silva Screen): JSCD 109 (CD)

KING SOLOMON'S MINES (85) Music score (Jerry Goldsmith)
-S/T- *Intrada USA (S.Screen): FMT 8005D (CD)*
-S/T- *Spi Milan (S.Screen):A.259 (LP) C.259 (Cass)*

KINGS GO FORTH (58) Music score (Elmer Bernstein) also
inc -S/T- to SOME CAME RUNNING (58-Elmer Bernstein)
Cloud Nine/Silva Prod (Conif): CNS 5004 (CD)

KINGS ROW (42) Music score (Erich Wolfgang Korngold)
N.P.O. on *Varese USA (Silva Screen): VCD 47203 (CD)*

KING'S STORY A (65) Music score (Ivor Slaney) Narrator:
(Orson Welles) -S/T- *DRG (Silv.Screen: SL 5185 (LP)*

KISMET (USA STUDIO RECORDING 92) *featur:* Samuel Ramey-
Julia Minges-Jerry Hadley-Mandy Patinkin-Dom DeLui
se-Ruth Ann Swenson *Sony Broadway: SK 46638 (CD)*

KISMET (ORIG BROADWAY CAST 53) with Alfred Drake
Columbia (S.Screen): CK 32605 (CD) JST 32605 (Cass)

KISMET (STUDIO RECORDING 90)*feat:* Valerie Masterson-Don
ald Maxwell-David Rendall-Rosemary Ashe-Bonaventura
Bottone Richard Van Allan-Judy Kaye-Philharmonia Or
chestra *TER (Conifer): CDTER2-1170 (2CD) TER2-1170
(2LP) ZCTED 1170 (Cass)*

KISS ME KATE (ROYAL SHAKESPEARE CO.CAST 87) *with:* Paul
Jones-Tim Flavin-Fiona Hendley and Company
1st Night (Pinn): CAST 10 (LP) CASTC 10 (Cass)

KISS ME KATE (ORIG BROADWAY CAST 48) Songs(Cole Porter)
    feat: LISA KIRK-PATRICIA MORISON-ALFRED DRAKE-HARRY
    CLARK-HAROLD LANG *EMI Angel (EMI):ZDM 764760-2 (CD)*
KISS ME KATE (STUDIO RECORDING 91) *feat:*Josephine Barst
    ow-Thomas Hampson-Kim Criswell-George Dvorsky & Co.
    EMI: CDS 754 033-2 (2CDs) EX 754 033-4 (2 Cass)
KISS OF THE SPIDER WOMAN (ORIG LONDON CAST 92) *featur:*
    CHITA RIVERA-BRENT CARVER-ANTHONY CRIVELLO & Comp:
    First Night (Pinn): SCOREC(CD) 37 (Cass/CD single)
    Cast Album: *First Night: CASTC(CD) 30 (Cass/CD)*
KISSIN' COUSINS (64) *see* Elvis Presley Film Index
KNACK The (65) Music score (John Barry) -S/T- Import on
    MCA USA (S.Screen): MCA 25109 (LP) MCAC 25109 (Cas)
    KEN MACKINTOSH OR 'Mac's Back' *President: PLCD 532*
KNIGHT MOVES (92) Music score (Anne Dudley) -S/T- *Milan*
    (Pinn): 262 753 (CD) 412 753 (Cass)
KNIGHTS OF THE ROUND TABLE (53) Music score (Miklos Roz
    sa) MGM Studio Orch (Muir Mathieson)Orig Film Score
    Varese (Pinn): VCD 47269 (CD) STV 81128 (LP)
KONGA - *see under Coll* 'HORRORS OF THE BLACK MUSEUM'
KOYAANISQATSI (82) Music score (Philip Glass) -S/T- on
    Antilles (Island-Poly): IMCD 98 or ANCD 8707 (CD)
KRAMER V KRAMER (79) Music includes 'Concerto in G.Maj'
    for two mandolins, strings and organ (Vivaldi) plus
    'Concerto in C.Maj' for mandolins, strings and harp
    sichord (Vivaldi) 'Sonata in D.Maj' for trumpet, st
    rings & continuo (Purcell) music from orig -S/T- on
    Sony Fr.(Discovery): SK 73945(CD) ST 73945 (Cass)
KRULL (83) Music score (James Horner) London S.O. -S/T-
    ltd edit.release feat LSO (70min inc.30m of unreleas
    ed music) *Southern Cross (S.Screen): SCSE CD 4 (CD)*
KUFFS (91) Music sco (Harold Faltermeyer) song "I Don't
    Want To Live Without You" by GREGG TRIPP on *EMI:*
    (CD)EMI 230 (CDs/7") -S/T- Milan (Pinn):101512 (CD)
KWAMINA (ORIG BROADWAY CAST 61) *featuring* ROBERT GUILLA
    UME-SALLY ANN HOWES *EMI Angel: ZDM 764891-2 (CD)*

L.627 (92) Music score (Philippe Sarde) -S/T- recording
    Milan (Pinn): 873131 (CD)
L'AMANT *see* 'LOVER The'
L'ATALANTE (Film) Music score (Maurice Jaubert) *also*
    contains score from **ZERO DE CONDUITE** (M.Jaubert) on
    Milan (Pinn): CDCH 0274 (CD)
LA BALANCE (84) Music score (Roland Bocquet) -S/T- Impt
    Milan France (Silva Screen): A.188 (LP)
LA BAMBA (87) Music sco (Miles Goodman-Carlos Santana)
    feat Los Lobos -S/T- *Slash-London: 828 058-2 (CD)*
    Orig Ritchie Valens songs on *ACE: CDCHD 953 (CD)*
LA CAGE AUX FOLLES (ORIG BROADWAY CAST 83) Songs (Jerry
    Herman) *with* George Hearn-Gene Barry & Company
    RCA (BMG):BL 84824 (LP) BK 84824 (CS) BD 84824 (CD)
LA CALIFFA (-) Music score (Ennio Morricone) -S/T- on
    Alhambra (Pinn): A.8928 (CD) deleted
LA DAME AUX CAMELIAS *see* 'LADY OF THE CAMELIAS'

LA DERNIER METRO *see* 'LAST METRO The'
LA DONNA DELLA DOMENICA /LA MOGLIE PIU BELLA (It.films)
   Music score (Ennio Morricone) -S/T- *Impt Prometheus*
   (Silva Screen): PCDC 119 (CD)
LA FEMME D'A COTE *see* 'WOMAN NEXT DOOR The'
LA FEMME DE MON POTE 'My Best Friends Girl' (82) Music
   (J.J.Cale) -S/T- *Mercury France Imp: 814 401-1 (LP)*
LA FETE SAUVAGE (Film) Music score (Vangelis) -S/T- on
   Polydor France (SILva Screen): 823 756-2 (CD)
LA GLOIRE DE MON PERE - *see under* 'GLORY OF MY FATHER'
LA REVOLUTION FRANCAISE 1789-1794 (Musical 90) Original
   Paris Cast on *First Night (Pinn): OCR(C)(CD) 6*
LA SIRENE DU MISSISSIPI (91) Music score (Antoine Duham
   el) -S/T- *Milan (Pinn): 873 084 (CD)*
LA STRADA (54-Italy) Music score (Nino Rota) also incl:
   'NIGHTS OF CABIRIA The' (57-Italy) (Nino Rota) on
   Legend (Silva Screen): LEGEND CD 7 (CD)
LA TRAVIATA (FILM OPERA 83) Music (Verdi) Feat: Placido
   Domingo -S/T- *W.Bros: 250072-1 (Dbl LP) -4 (Dbl CS)*
LABYRINTH (86) Music score (Trevor Jones-David Bowie)
   -S/T- *EMI Amer: (S.Screen): 46312-2 (CD) -4 (Cass)*
LADY AND THE HIGHWAYMAN The (TVM 1989) Music sc (Laurie
   Johnson) *see Collections* 'ROSE AND THE GUN The'
LADY AND THE TRAMP - *see* WALT DISNEY FILM INDEX
LADY BE GOOD (ORIG BROADWAY CAST) Songs (George and Ira
   Gershwin) *Elektra Nonesuch (WEA): 7559 79308-2 / -4*
LADY CAROLINE LAMB (72) Music sc Richard Rodney Bennett
   Sil.Screen (Con): FILM(FILMC) 019 (LP/Cass) deleted
LADY IN THE DARK (MUSICAL 41)Songs (K.Weill-I.Gershwin)
   feat GERTRUDE LAWRENCE *AEI (S.Screen):AEICD 003(CD)*
LADY OF THE CAMELIAS (La Dame Aux Camelias)(81) Music s
   Ennio Morricone-S/T-*Prometheus (S.Scr): PCD 116(CD)*
LADY SINGS THE BLUES The (72) Music sc (Michel Legrand)
   Songs of Billie Holiday sung by DIANA ROSS -S/T- on
   re-issued on Motown-Polydor (Poly): 530 135-2 (2CD)
LADY SINGS THE BLUES (MUSICAL 89) *Birmingham Inter.Jazz
   Festival Production* - Val Wiseman as Billie Holiday
   with Digby Fairweather-Roy Williams-Al Gay and Comp
   Big Bear (Conifer): BEAR(CD)(MC) 33 (LP/CD/Cass)
LADYKILLERS The (55) Music score (Tristam Cary) theme
   'Minuet No.5 In E.String Quintet Op.11'(Boccherini)
LAND BEFORE TIME The (88) Music score (James Horner)
   and Diana Ross -S/T- *MCA (S.Screen) MCAD 6266 (CD)*
LAND OF SMILES The (OPERETTA) Songs (Franz Lehar-Ludwig
   Herzer-Fritz Lohner Beda) **Highlights in French** with
   songs from 'THE MERRY WIDOW' and other works on
   EMI Belle Epoque (EMI): CZS 767 872-2 (2CD)
LAND RAIDERS (69) Music score (Bruno Nicolai) -S/T- on
   Prometheus (Silva Screen): PCD 128 (CD)
LAND WITHOUT MUSIC (FILM OPERETTA 36) Music score Oscar
   Strauss and featuring songs sung by Richard Tauber
   -S/T- excerpts on *Pearl (H.Mundi): GEMM 263 (LP)*
LARKRISE TO CANDLEFORD (NAT.THEATRE STAGE PROD.1978)
   Music (Albion Band) *Charisma/Virg: CDSCD 4020 (CD)*

LASSITER (84) Mus (Ken Thorne) -S/T- TER: TER 1092 (LP)
LAST ACTION HERO (93) Music score (Michael Kamen) with
   songs by AC/DC-ALICE IN CHAINS-MEGADETH-QUEENSRYCHE
   AEROSMITH-ANTHRAX-DEF LEPPARD-FISHBONE-TESLA etc.
   -S/T- *Columbia (Sony): 473990-2(CD) -4(Cass) -1(LP)*
LAST BUTTERFLY The (90) Music score (Alex North) -S/T-
   Varese imp (Pinn-S.Screen): VSD(VSC) 5287 (CD/Cass)
LAST DAYS OF CHEZ NOUS (92) Music sco (Paul Grabowsky)
   -S/T- *DRG USA (Pinn): DRGCD 12607 (CD)*
LAST EMPEROR The (88) Music ((David Byrne-Ryiuchi Sakam
   oto-Cong Su) -S/T- *Virgin: CDV 2485 (CD) OVEDC 366*
LAST EXIT TO BROOKLYN (89) Music score (Mark Knopfler)
   -S/T- *Vertigo (Poly): 838 725-2(CD) -4(Cass) see*
   also 'Screenplaying' *Collection*
LAST METRO The (80) + 'THE WOMAN NEXT DOOR' (81) Music
   score (Georges Delerue) -S/T- *Imp Prometheus (Silva*
   Screen): PCD 113 (CD) see COLL 'TRUFFAUT & DELERUE'
LAST OF ENGLAND The (87) Music sc (Simon Fisher Turner)
   Song "Skye Boat Song" sung by Marianne Faithfull
   -S/T- *Mute: IONIC 1 (LP) CDIONIC 1 (CD)*
LAST OF THE MOHICANS (92) Music sco (Trevor Jones-Randy
   Edelman) -S/T- *Morgan Creek (Poly): 517 497-2 (CD)*
   517 497-4 (Cass)
LAST PICTURE SHOW The (71) Music & Songs (var.artists)
   -S/T- *CBS USA (Silva Screen): CK 31143 (CD)*
LAST STARFIGHTER The (84) Music sco (Craig Safan) -S/T-
   Import (Silva Screen): LXE 705 (CD) deleted
LAST TEMPTATION OF CHRIST (88) Music sc (Peter Gabriel)
   -S/T- 'Passion' *Real World (Virgin): RWCD 1 (CD)*
   RWMC 1 (Cass) RWLP 1 (LP) RWMD 1 (Mini-D)
LAST WALTZ The (78) Bob Dylan-Ron Wood-Joni Mitchell-N.
   Diamond-Emmy Lou Harris-Dr.John-Neil Young-Van Morr
   ison-Eric Clapton -S/T- *W.Bros: K(4)66076 (2Cas/LP)*
LAURA (44) Music score (David Raksin) -S/T- recording
   with 'JANE EYRE' (43-B.Herrmann) *Fox (S.Screen):*
   FOX 11006 (CD) / also LAURA + 'Forever Amber' and
   'Bad & T.Beautiful' *RCA (BMG):GD(GK) 81490(CD/Cass)*
LAUREL & HARDY (SONGS & DIALOGUE) - *SEE Collections*
LAWRENCE OF ARABIA (62) Music score (Maurice Jarre)
   -S/T- *PRT (BMG): PYL(M) 6040 (LP/Cass) /* see 'Epic'
   Silva Screen (Conifer):FILM(C)(CD)036 (LP/Cass/CD)
LE BAL (82 France) Music score (Vladimir Cosma) -S/T-
   Import (Silva Screen): 76.078 (Cass)
LE CHATEAU DE MA MERE - *see under* 'GLORY OF MY FATHER'
LE PROFESSIONAL (Film Fr) Music score (Ennio Morricone)
   -S/T- *RCA (Silva Screen): 250 434-2 (CD)*
LEAGUE OF THEIR OWN A (92) Music sco (Hans Zimmer) plus
   V.Arts -S/T- *Columbia (Sony): 472056-2(CD) -4(Cass)*
LEAP OF FAITH (92) Music score (Cliff Eidelman) -S/T-
   MCA (BMG): MCD 10671 (CD) MCC 10671 (Cass)
LEAVE IT TO JANE (REV.BROADWAY CAST 59) (Jerome Kern-
   P.G.Wodehouse-G.Bolton) *DRG (Pinn): CDS 15017 (CD)*
LEAVING OF LIVERPOOL The (Australian Film) Music score
   (Peter Best)-S/T-*OneMone (S.Screen):IMICD 1019 (CD)*

LEGEND (86) *note: this film can be heard with two -S/T-*
   Mus *(1)* JERRY GOLDSMITH Lyrics (John Bettis) -S/T-
   Silva Screen (Conifer): FILMCD 045 *(CD)* / Mus *(2)*
   TANGERINE DREAM *MCA USA (S.Screen):MCAC 6165 (Cass)*
LEGEND OF THE GLASS MOUNTAIN - see 'GLASS MOUNTAIN The'
LEGEND OF THE LONE RANGER The (81) Music (John Barry)
   -S/T- *MCA USA (S.Screen):* MCA(C) *1564 (LP/Cass)*
LEGS DIAMOND (ORIG BROADWAY CAST 88)Songs (Peter Allen)
   with Peter Allen-Julie Wilson and supporting Comp
   RCA USA (S.Screen): 7983-2 *(CD)* -1 *(LP)* -4 *(Cass)*
LEON THE PIG FARMER (92) Music score (John Murphy-David
   Hughes) Songs by Thomas Lang & The Band -S/T- *EMI:*
   CDSTY 1 (CD) TCSTY 1 (Cass)
LEPRECHAUN (93) Music score (Kevin Kiner) -S/T- *Intrada*
   (Koch): MAFCD 7050CD *(CD)*
LES MISERABLES (MUSICAL SHOW 85) Music (Alain Boublil-
   Claude Michel Schonberg) English lyrics (Herbert Kr
   etzmer) *Orig London Cast:* Patti Lupone - *1st Night:*
   ENCORE 1 *(Dbl LP)* ENCORE C1 *(Db C)* ENCORE CD1 *(CD)*
   also available: Original French Cast Recording on
   First Night (Pinn): DOCRCD 1 *(2CD)* DOCRC 1 *(2Cass)*
   'Les Miserables-Complete Symphonic Recordings' Lond
   on Philh Orch with **UK and USA Casts** on *First Night*
   (Pinn): MIZ 1 *(4LP's)* MIZC1 *(3 CS)* MIZCD 1 *(3 CD's)*
   Five Outstanding Performances From Les Miserables:
   First Night (Pinn): SCOREL 17 *(LP)* Highlights from
   Int.Cast Record: *TER (Con):* CAST(C)(CD)20 *(Cass/CD)*
LES MISERABLES (MANCHESTER 92 CAST RECORDING) on *First*
   Night (Pinn): SCORECD 34 *(CDep)*
LES MISERABLES (SHOWS COLL.Studio Recording 93) *featur:*
   DAVE WILLETTS-CLAIRE MOORE & West End Concert Orch
   Pickwick Shows: PWKS 4175 *(CD)* PWKMC 4175 *(Cass)*
   see also Coll 'ROYAL PHILHARMONIC ORCH PLAY SUITES'
LES UNS ET LES AUTRES - see under 'INS AND THE OUTS'
LET IT BE (70) Songs (John Lennon-Paul McCartney) -S/T-
   Parlophone: (TC)PCS 7096 *(Cass/LP)* CDP 746447-2*(CD)*
LETHAL WEAPON 3 (92) Mus (Michael Kamen-Eric Clapton-Da
   vid Sanborn) -S/T- *WEA:* 759926 989-2 *(CD)* -4*(Cass)*
LET'S GET LOST (92) Music score (Chet Baker) Chet Baker
   Novus-RCA (BMG) PD(PK)(PL)83054 *(CD/Cass/LP)*
LET'S MAKE LOVE (60) Songs (S.Cahn-J.Van Huesen) featur
   MARILYN MONROE *Import (S.Screen):* 838984-2 *(CD)*
LEVIATHAN (89) Music score (Jerry Goldsmith) -S/T- on
   Vases (Pinn): VCD 5226 *(CD)* VSC 5226 *(Cass)*
LICENCE TO KILL - *see* JAMES BOND FILM INDEX
LIEBESTRAUM (91) Music score (Mike Figgis) and tracks
   by Earl Bostic & His Orch and Bennie Moiseiwitsch
   -S/T- *Virgin (Poly):* CDV 2682 *(CD)* TCV 2682 *(Cass)*
LIFEFORCE (85) Music score (Henry Mancini) London Symph
   Orchestra -S/T- *(Silva Screen):* CDFMC 256 *(CD)*
LIGHT AT THE EDGE OF THE WORLD The (71) Music sc (Piero
   Piccione) -S/T- *Alhambra (Pinn):A.8934 (CD) deleted*
LIGHTHORSEMEN The (87) Music score (Mario Millo) -S/T-
   Australian Imp.(Silva Screen): 1MICD 1009 *(CD)*

LILI (FILM MUSICAL 52) Music score by Bronislau Kaper &
    Songs by Bob Merrill / Feat Leslie Caron-Mel Ferrer
    also inc -S/T- from '7 Brides For 7 Brothers' -S/T-
    MGM (EMI): CD(TC)(LP)MGM 9 (CD/Cass/LP) all deleted
LILIES OF THE FIELD (63) Music score (Jerry Goldsmith)
    -S/T- *Tsunami Imp (Silva Screen): TSU 0101 (CD)*
LILY WAS HERE (90) Title music (Dave Stewart) performed
    by Dave Stewart & Candy Dulfer (sax)- Anxious (BMG)
    -S/T- *Anxious (BMG): ZD(ZK)(ZL) 74233 (deleted)*
LIMELIGHT (52) Music score (Charles Chaplin)
    see Collect 'CHARLIE'
LINGUINI INCIDENT The (92) Music score (Thomas Newman)
    -S/T- *Varese (Pinn): VSD 5372 (CD) VSC 5372 (Cass)*
LION IN WINTER The (68) Music score (John Barry) *Varese
    (S.Screen): VSD 5217 (CD)*
LION OF THE DESERT (81) Music score (Maurice Jarre)
    London Symph Orch *Sil.Screen (BMG): FILMCD 060 (CD)*
    also inc music from 'The Message' (77) (Jarre)
LIONHEART (87) Music score (Jerry Goldsmith) -S/T- on
    Varese (Pinn): VCD 47282 (CD-V1) VCD 47288 (CD-V2)
LIONHEART (90) - *see* '*A.W.O.L.*'
LIPSTICK (76) Music score (Michel Polnareff) -S/T- Impt
    (Silva Screen): 466994-2 (CD)
LITTLE MAN TATE (91) Music score (Mark Isham) -S/T- on
    Varese (Pinn): VSD 5343 (CD) VSC 5343 (Cass)
LITTLE MARY SUNSHINE (ORIG LONDON CAST 62) Songs (Rick
    Besoyan) *feat:* Ed Bishop-Joyce Blair-Erik Chitty-Te
    rence Cooper-Bernard Cribbins-Anna Dawson-Patricia
    Routledge-Gita Denise. Philip Martell (mus direct)
    DRG (Conifer): CDSBL 13108 (CD)
LITTLE MARY SUNSHINE ORIG OFF-BROADWAY CAST 1959) Songs
    (Rick Besoyan) featuring: Eileen Brennan-John McMar
    tin-William Graham-ElMarie Wendel and Company on
    EMI Angel (EMI): ZDM 764774-2 (CD)
LITTLE ME (ORIG LONDON CAST 64) Songs (Cy Coleman-Carol
    yn Leigh)*feat:* BRUCE FORSYTH-AVRIL ANGERS-EILEEN GO
    URLAY-DAVID H.TATE *DRG USA (Pinn): DRGCD 13111 (CD)*
LITTLE ME (ORIG BROADWAY CAST 62) Songs (Cy Coleman-Car
    olyn Leigh) *feat:* Sid Caesar-Virginia Martin-Nancy
    andrews-Mort Marshall-Peter Turgeon-Mickey Deems-
    Joey Faye *RCA Victor (BMG): 09026 61482-2 (CD)*
LITTLE MERMAID The (Disney Cartoon Film 89) Music (Alan
    Menken) Songs (Alan Menken-Howard Ashman) -S/T- on
    Disney (Pickwick): DSTCD 451 (CD) DSTMC 451 (Cass)
LITTLE NEMO Adventures In Slumberland (92) Music/Songs
    (Richard and Robert Sherman) -S/T- *Buena Vista/Disn
    ey USA Impt: catalogue number to be confirmed*
LITTLE NIGHT MUSIC A (NEW DIGITAL RECORDING) Songs (Ste
    phen Sondheim) Sian Phillips-Susan Hampshire-Elisab
    eth Welch arranged & conducted by John Owen Edwards
    TER (Conifer-S.Screen): CDTER(ZCTER) 1179 (CD/Cass)
LITTLE NIGHT MUSIC A (ORIG LONDON CAST 75) Songs (Steph
    en Sondheim) Jean Simmons-Hermoine Gingold-Joss Ack
    land: *RCA (Silva Screen) 5090-2 (CD) 5090-4 (Cass)*

LITTLE NIGHT MUSIC A (ORIG BROADWAY CAST 73)*with* Glynis
Johns *CBS USA (S.Scr): CK 32265(CD) JST 32265(Cass)*
LITTLE ROMANCE A (79) Music score (Georges Delerue)
-S/T- *Varese (Pinn): VSD 5367 (CD)*
LITTLE SHOP OF HORRORS (FILM MUSICAL 87) Songs (Alan Me
nkin-Howard Ashman) Orig Film score (Miles Goodman)
-S/T- *Geffen: 924 125-4(Cass) -2(CD) all deleted*
LITTLE SHOP OF HORRORS (ORIG BROADWAY CAST) with Ellen
Greene-Lee Wilkof-Hy Anzell-Frank Luz *Geffen Import
(Silva Screen): GF 2020 (CD)*
LITTLE TRAMP (STUDIO RECORD 92) Songs (David Pomeranz)
feat Richard Harris-Petula Clark-Lea Salonga-Mel Sm
ith-Mel Brooks-Treat Williams-Peter Duncan on *WEA:
4509 91387-2 (CD) 4509 91387-4 (Cass)*
LIVE AND LET DIE (73) *see* JAMES BOND FILM INDEX
LIVE FOR LIFE (Vivre Pour Vivre) (67) Music score (Fran
cis Lai) -S/T- *Musidisc France (Pinn): 10129-2 (CD)
-4 (Cass)* / plus 'A Man & A Woman' (66) -S/T-
LIVING DAYLIGHTS The - *see* JAMES BOND FILM INDEX
LOCAL HERO (82) Music sco (Mark Knopfler) -S/T- *Vertigo
(Poly) 811 038-2 (CD) see also* 'Screenplaying' Coll
LOCK UP YOUR DAUGHTERS (ORIG LONDON CAST 59) Songs (Lio
nel Bart-Laurie Johnson) *with* Hy Hazel and Company
TER (Conifer): TER 1049 (LP) ZCTER 1049 (Cass)
LOGAN'S RUN (76) Music score (Jerry Goldsmith) -S/T- on
Bay Cities (Silva Screen): BCD 3024 (CD)
LOLA (82) Music (Peer Raben) -S/T- *DRG USA (Sil.Screen)
SL 9508 (LP)* also with 'Veronika Voss' (Film 82)
LOLITA (62) Music score (Nelson Riddle) -S/T- Import on
MCA USA (Silva Screen): MCA(C) 39067 (LP/Cass)
LONG ARM The - *see* Coll 'HORRORS OF THE BLACK MUSEUM'
LONG GOOD FRIDAY The (80) Music score (Francis Monkman)
feat Kevin Peek-Tristram Fry-Herbie Flowers (SKY)
-S/T- *Silva Screen (Con) FILM(C)(CD) 020 (LP/CS/CD)*
LONG WALK HOME (91) Music score (George Fenton) -S/T-
Varese: (Pinn): VSD 5304 (CD) VSC 5304 (Cass)
LONGEST DAY The (62) Music score (Paul Anka) *see* Collec
'BIG WAR THEMES' / 'GUNS OF NAVARONE' etc.
LORCA AND THE OUTLAWS (86) Music (Tony Banks) Marillion
Fish-Jim Diamond-Toyah -S/T- *Charisma: CASCD 1173CD*
LORD OF THE FLIES (90) Music score (Philippe Sarde)
London Symphony Orch & The Trinity Boys Choir -S/T-
Silva Screen (Conifer): FILMC(CD) 067 (Cass/CD)
LORD OF THE RINGS The (78 Car) Music (Leonard Rosenman)
-S/T- *Fantasy/Intrada (Koch Int): FMTCD 8003 (CD)*
LORENZO'S OIL (92) Classical mus.soundtrack supervised
by Christine Woodruff on *MCA (BMG): MCD 10782 (CD)*
LOST BOYS The (87) Music score (Thomas Newman) -S/T- on
Atlantic (WEA): 781767-2 (CD) -4(Cass)
LOST CONTINENT The *see* 'HORRORS OF THE BLACK MUSEUM'
LOST EMPIRE The (Film) Music score (Alan Howarth) -S/T-
Silva Screen (Con): FILMCD 068 (CD) + 'Retribution'
LOST IN THE STARS (ORIG BROADWAY CAST 49) Music (Kurt
Weill) Lyr (Maxwell Anderson) *feat:* Todd Duncan-Les

lie Banks-Warren Coleman-Inez Matthews-Frank Roane-
MCA USA (S.Scr): MCAD 10302 (CD) MCAC 10302 (Cass)
LOST IN YONKERS (92) Music score (Elmer Bernstein)
 -S/T- *Varese (Pinn): VSD 5419 (CD) VSC 5419 (Cass)*
LOVE AND DEATH (Film 75) Director: Woody Allen / Music
 score taken from Lieutenant Kiji Suite (Prokofiev)
LOVE FIELD (91) Music score (Jerry Goldsmith) -S/T- on
 Varese (Pinn): VSD 5316 (CD) VSC 5316 (Cass)
LOVE ME OR LEAVE ME (55) Musical Biopic of RUTH ETTING
 featuring DORIS DAY Songs (Sammy Cahn-Nicholas Brod
 zsky-Walter Donaldson-Gus Kahn-Irving Berlin etc.)
 -S/T- on *CBS-Sony (Japanese Import): 32DP 913 (CD)*
LOVE POTION NUMBER 9 (92) Title song (Jerry Lieber-Mike
 Stoller) orig The Clovers (59) / The Searchers on
 'Best Of' *Pickwick: PWKS 4076 (CD)* -S/T *unconfirmed*
LOVE STORY (70) Music score (Francis Lai) -S/T- *MCA
 (BMG): MCLD 19157 (CD) MCLC 19157 (Cass)*
LOVE YOU 'TIL TUESDAY (69) C4 14/2/88 Music (David Bow
 ie) DAVID BOWIE -S/T- *Pickwick: PWKS 4131P (CD)*
LOVERS The (L'Amant) (Fr91) Music score (Gabriel Yared)
 -S/T- *Circa / Virgin (Poly): CDVMM 9 (CD)* and *Impt
 Import (Silva Screen): 30948 (CD) 50948 (Cass)*
LOVESPELL (79) Music (Paddy Moloney) The Chieftains SEE
 'REEL MUSIC' (Collections)
LOVING YOU (FILM MUSICAL 57) E.Presley *RCA: ND(NK)(NL)
 81515 (CD/Cass/LP)* see ELVIS PRESLEY FILM INDEX
LUNATIC The (91) Music score (Wally Badarou) songs by:
 Aswad-Shabba Ranks-Toots &Maytals-Black Uhuru-Arrow
 Burning Flames-J.C.Lodge -S/T- *Mango-Island (Rio-Po
 ly): CIDM 1086 (CD) MCT 1086 (Cass) MLPS 1086 (LP)*
LUST FOR LIFE (56) Music score (Miklos Rosza) -S/T- on
 Varese (Pinn): VSD 5405 (CD)

M.BUTTERFLY (93) Music score (Howard Shore) -S/T- on
 Varese (Pinn): VSD 5435 (CD)
MacARTHUR (77) Music score (Jerry Goldsmith) -S/T- Impt
 Varese (Pinn): VSD 5260 (CD) VSC 5260 (Cass)
MACBETH (FILM OPERA 86) Music (Verdi) Dir:Claude D'Anna
 feat:Leon Nucci-Shirley Verrett-Samuel Ramsey -S/T-
 Decca 417 525-1 (LP) 417 525-4 (CS) 417 525-2 (CD)
MACHINE GUN McCAIN (70) Music score (Ennio Morricone)
 -S/T- *Alhambra (Pinn): A.8922 (CD)* deleted
MACK AND MABEL (ORIG BROADWAY CAST 74) Songs (Jerry Her
 man) *with* ROBERT PRESTON-BERNADETTE PETERS & Comp
 MCA (BMG): MCLD 19089 (CD) MCLC 19089 (Cass)
MACK AND MABEL (NEW IN CONCERT RECORDING) (Var.Artists)
 1st Night (Pinn): CASTC 13 (Cass) CASTCD 1 (CD)
MACK THE KNIFE (89)Songs (Kurt Weill-B.Brecht) Raul Jul
 ia-Richard Harris-Julia Migenes-Roger Daltrey-Julie
 Walters-S/T-*Col (S.Screen): MK(SMT) 45630 (CD/Cass)*
MAD DOG AND GLORY (92) Music score (Elmer Bernstein)
 -S/T- *Varese (Pinn): VSD 5415 (CD) VSC 5415 (Cass)*
MAD MAX (79) Music score (Brian May) -S/T- Import on
 Varese (Pinn-S.Scr): STV 81144 (LP) VCD 47144 (CD)

MAD MAX 2 (81) Music score (Brian May) -S/T- TER (Con):
     TER 1016 (LP) Varese (Pinn) VCD 47262 (CD)
MAD MAX 3 'Beyond Thunderdome' (85) Music Maurice Jarre
     -S/T- *Capitol: EJ 240380-1(LP)-4(Cass) deleted*
MADAME SOUSATZKA (88) Music score (Gerald Gouriet)-S/T-
     Varese (Pinn): VSD(VSC) 5204(CD/Cass)
MADE IN AMERICA (92) V.Arts including: Ephraim Lewis-
     Gloria Estefan-Del The Funky HomoSapien-Keith Sweat
     & Silk-Lisa Fischer and other artists -S/T- *Elektra
     (WEA): 7559 61498-2 (CD) 7559 61498-4 (Cass)*
MADE IN HEAVEN (88) Music (Mark Isham) + Var.Artists
     -S/T- *Elektra (Silva Screen): 960 729-2/-4 deleted*
MAGDALENE (88) Music score (Cliff Eidelman) -S/T- on
     Intrada (Koch/S.Screen): MFCD 7029 (CD)
MAGGIE MAY (ORIG LONDON CAST 64)Songs (Lionel Bart)
     with Rachel Roberts *TER:(ZC)TER 1046 (Cas/LP)*
MAGIC CHRISTIAN The (70) Music score (Ken Thorne) Songs
     by BADFINGER on 'Magic Christian Music' *Apple (EMI)
     CDSAPCOR 12 (CD) TCSAPCOR 12 (Cass) SAPCOR 12 (LP)*
MAGIC RIDDLE The (91 Animated) Music score (-) -S/T- on
     Alhambra (Pinn): A.8937 (CD) MCA 8937 (Cass)
MAGIC TOYSHOP The (87) Music score (Bill Connor) "Jonat
     hon's Song" sung by James Rainbird -S/T- TER (Con):
     TER 1138 (LP) ZCTER 1138 (Cass) STER 012 (7")
MAGICAL MYSTERY TOUR (67) Featur music by The Beatles
     -S/T- *Parlophone (EMI): PCTC 255 (LP) TC-PCS 3077
     (Cass) CD-PCTC 255 (CD) SMMT 1 (2 x 7" singles)*
MAGNIFICENT AMBERSONS The (42) Music (Bernard Herrmann)
     -S/T- *5th Continent (Silva Screen): PRCD 1783 (CD)*
MAGNIFICENT 7 The (60) Music score (Elmer Bernstein)
     -S/T- *Liberty EMI: EG 260581-1/-4 (LP/Cass) deleted*
MAHATMA AND THE MAD BOY (Film India) Music: Vivaldi etc
     see Collections 'Merchant-Ivory 25th Anniversary'
MAJOR BARBARA (41) Music score (Sir William Walton) New
     Recording by Academy Of St.Martin-In-The Fields
     (Sir Neville Marriner) *Chandos: CHAN 8841 (CD) ABTD
     1460 (Cass)* + Music from 'Richard III' & 'Macbeth'
MAJOR LEAGUE (89) Music score (James Newton Howard)
     -S/T- *Motown (BMG): ZD/ZL/ZK 74277 (CD/LP/Cass)*
MAKING MR.RIGHT (87) Music (Thomas Newman-Chaz Jankel)
     -S/T- *Varese (S.Screen): STV(CTV) 81320 (LP/Cass)
     VCD 47291 (CD)* + music 'Desperately Seeking Susan'
MAKING THE GRADE (84) - *see under* 'ALLAN QUATERMAIN'
MALCOLM (86) Music (Penguin Cafe Orchestra) on albums:-
     'Penguin Cafe Orchestra' EG-Virgin: EGED 11 (CD)
     'Music From The P.C.O.' EGED 27 'Broadcasting From
     Home' EGED 38) - all available on CD Album and Cass
MALCOLM X (92) Music score (Terence Blanchard) 3 -S/T-:
     **Var.Arts: W.Bros (WEA): 9362 45130-2 (CD) -4(Cass)
     Music sco: Columbia (Sony): 472806-2 (CD) -4 (Cass)
     Speeches & Dialogue from 1972 film documentary by
     Malcolm X: QWest/WB (WEA): 9362 45157-2 (CD)**
MALICE (93) Music score (Jerry Goldsmith) -S/T- issued
     Varese (Pinn): VSD 5442 (CD)

MALTA G.C. (42) Music score (Arnold Bax) Royal Philharm
   Orch (Kenneth Alwyn) *Cloud Nine (Con):ACN 7012 (CD)*
MAMBO KINGS The (92) Music by various artists -S/T- on
   Elektra (WEA): 755961 240-2 (CD) 755961 240-4 (Cas)
   also available 'MAMBO KINGS PLAY SONGS OF LOVE' *BBC*
   (Pinn): ZBBC 1275 (Cass) / 'MAMBO KINGS' (V.Arts)
   Taylor-Movie Play: MPV 5524 (CD) MPV 4-5524 (Cass)
MAME (ORIG BROADWAY CAST 66) Songs (Jerry Herman) *with*
   Angela Lansbury and Company *CBS USA (Silva Screen)*
   CK 03000 (CD) JST 03000 (Cass)
MAN AND A WOMAN A 'Un Homme Et Une Femme' (Fr.66) Music
   score (Francis Lai) -S/T- *Musidisc (Pinn): 10129-2*
   (CD) -4 (Cass) + 'Live For Life' (Film 67)
MAN BITES DOG (Fr.92) Music score (Jean-Marc Chenut)
   -S/T- *Milan (Pinn): 87314-2 (CD)*
MAN CALLED NOON A (-) Music score (Luis Bacalov) -S/T-
   Alhambra (Silva Screen): A.8935 (CD)
MAN OF LA MANCHA (ORIG LONDON CAST 65) Songs (Mitch Lei
   gh-Joe Darion) *feat* Keith Michell and Company
   MCA USA (Silva Screen): MCAD 31065 (CD)
MAN OF LA MANCHA (ORIG FRENCH CAST) "L'Homme De La Manc
   ha") *with* Jacques Brel-Joan Diener and Company on
   import *(Silva Screen): 839 586-2 (CD)*
MAN TROUBLE (91) Music score (Georges Delerue) -S/T- on
   Varese (Pinn): VSD 5369 (CD) VSC 5369 (Cass)
MAN WHO MISTOOK HIS WIFE FOR A HAT (87) Music (Michael
   Nyman) -S/T- *Columbia (Sony):CD44669 (CD) 40-(Cass)*
MAN WHO WOULD BE KING The (75) Music sc (Maurice Jarre)
   Nat.Philh.Orch *Bay Cities (S.Screen): BCD 3007 (CD)*
MAN WITH THE GOLDEN GUN The *see* JAMES BOND FILM INDEX
MAN WITHOUT A FACE The (93) Music score (James Horner)
   -S/T- *Impt (Silva Screen): 518 244-2 (CD) -4 (Cass)*
MANHATTAN (79) Music score (George Gershwin) -S/T- on
   CBS 73875 (LP) MK 36020 (CD)
MANIFESTO (88) - *see under* 'ALLAN QUATERMAIN'
MANNAJA / TEDEUM (Italian Spaghetti Westerns) Mus score
   (G.& M.DeAngelis) *Import (S.Screen): OST 1212 (CD)*
MANON DES SOURCES (87) Music score (Jean-Claude Petit)
   -S/T- *Milan Fr. (S.Screen) CDCH 241 (CD)*
   CD also inc music from 'JEAN DE FLORETTE' (Film 87)
MARIA'S LOVERS (84) Music score (Gary S.Renal) plus 40s
   Hits with V.Arts -S/T- *MILAN (Pinn): CDEMC 363 (CD)*
MARRIED TO THE MOB (89) Music (Gary Goetzman-Sharon Boy
   le) -S/T- with David Byrne *(WEA) K 925763-2 (CD)*
MARRY ME A LITTLE (ORIG USA CAST 81) Songs (Stephen Son
   dheim) *with* Suzanne Henry-Craig Lucas and E.Martin
   Perry (pno) *RCA (Silva Screen): 7142-2(CD) -4(Cass)*
MARRYING MAN The - *see* 'TOO HOT TO HANDLE'
MARY POPPINS (64) Songs (Richard & Robert Sherman) sung
   by JULIE ANDREWS-DICK VAN DYKE-DAVID TOMLINSON etc
   -S/T- *Disney (Pickwick): DSMCD(DSMMC) 459 (CD/Cass)*
   see - WALT DISNEY FILM INDEX
MARY QUEEN OF SCOTS (71) Music score (John Barry)
        see Coll 'MOVIEOLA'

MASADA (Film-BBC2 3/9/86) Music score (Jerry Goldsmith)
-S/T- *Varese (Pinn): VSD(VSC) 5249 (CD/Cass)*
M*A*S*H (70) Music score (Johnny Mandel & Mike Altman)
-S/T- *Import (S.Screen): PST 32753 (Cass)*
MASSACRE IN ROME (Italy-73) Music sc: (Ennio Morricone)
-S/T- includes 'The Battle Of Algiers' (Italy-65)
Italian import (Silva Screen): OST 105 (CD)
MASTERS OF THE UNIVERSE (87) Music score (Bill Conti)
-S/T- *Silva Screen (Conifer): FILMCD 095 (CD)*
MATINEE (92) Music score (Jerry Goldsmith) -S/T- score
Varese (Pinn): VSD 5408 (CD) VSC 5408 (Cass)
MAURICE (87) Orig music score by Richard Robbins -S/T-
RCA (BMG): BL 86618 (LP) BD 86618 (CD)
see also Collect 'Merchant-Ivory 25th Anniversary'
MAX AND HELEN (91) Music sco: (Christopher Young) -S/T-
Bay Cities (Silva Screen): BCD 3014 (CD)
MAYRIG (92) Music score (Jean-Claude Petit) -S/T- on
Milan (Silva Screen): 752001 (CD)
ME AND JULIET (ORIG BROADWAY CAST 53) Songs (Richard Ro
dgers-Oscar Hammerstein II) *featuring* Isabel Bigley
Bill Hayes-Barbara Carroll Trio-Ray Walston-Shirley
MacLaine-Mark Dawson-Joan McCracken-Arthur Maxwell-
George S.Irving *RCA Vict (BMG): 09026 61480-2 (CD)*
ME AND MY GIRL (ORIG LONDON CAST 85) Songs (Noel Gay-Do
uglas Furber) *with* ROBERT LINDSAY-EMMA THOMPSON-FRA
NK THORNTON and Company *EMI: CDP 746393-2 (CD)*
ME AND MY GIRL (ORIG BROADWAY CAST 87) *with* Robert Lind
say-Maryann Plunkett and Company on *TER (Conifer):-*
TER 1145 (LP) ZCTER 1145 (Cass) CDTER 1145 (CD)
ME AND MY GIRL (SHOWS COLLECTION-STUDIO REC) *feat* DAVID
KERNAN-JACQI SCOTT-TRACEY COLLIER & MASTER SINGERS
on *Pickwick Shows: PWKS 4143 (CD) PWKMC 4143 (Cass)*
MEDAL OF HONOR (91) Music score (Richard Stone and Mark
Watters) on *Prometheus (Silva Screen): PCD 106 (CD)*
MEDICINE MAN (92) Music score (Jerry Goldsmith) -S/T-
Varese (Pinn): VSD 5350 (CD) VSC 5350 (Cass)
MEET ME IN ST.LOUIS (ORIG BROADWAY CAST 90) Songs (Hugh
Martin-Ralph Blane) at Gershwin Theatre)
DRG USA (Conif): CDSBL 19002 (CD) SBLC 19002 (Cass)
MEETING VENUS (91) Music (Wagner) incid score (Rachel
Portman) -S/T-feat KIRI TE KANAWA & RENE KOLLO with
'Tannhauser' *Teldec (WEA): 229246336-2 (CD)* -4 *Cass*
MELANCHOLIA (89) Music score (Simon Fisher Turner)-S/T-
Silva Screen (Conifer): FILMCD 061 (CD)
MEMED MY HAWK (84) Music score (Manos Hadjidakis) -S/T-
TER (Conif): TER 1088 (LP) ZCTER 1088 (Cass)
MEMOIRS OF AN INVISIBLE MAN (92) Music score (Shirley
Walker) -S/T- *Varese (Pinn):VSD(VSC) 5355 (CD/Cass)*
MEMPHIS BELLE (90) Music score (George Fenton) -S/T- Im
Varese (Pinn): VSD(VSC) 5293 (CD/Cass)
"Danny Boy" by Mark Williamson on: *VS 52937 (7"s)*
MEN AT WORK (90) Music score (Stewart Copeland) songs:
Ziggy Marley-UB 40-Black Uhuru etc. -S/T- *Import*
(Silva Screen): 79025-2 (CD) -4 (Cass)

MENACE II SOCIETY (92) Music: QDII -S/T- on *Jive (BMG)*
   CHIP 137 (CD) HIPC 137 (Cass)
MERMAIDS (90) Music score (Jack Nitzsche) + Var.Artists
   -S/T- *Epic (Sony): 467874-2 (CD) -4(Cass)*
MERRILY WE ROLL ALONG (ORIG CAST 81) Songs (Stephen Son
   dheim) *RCA (S.Screen): RCD1 5840(CD) CBK1 4917(Cas)*
MERRY CHRISTMAS MR.LAWRENCE (83) Music Ryuichi Sakamoto
   David Sylvian)-S/T- *Virgin: CDV 2276 (CD) OVEDC 237*
MERRY WIDOW The (MUSICAL OPERETTA 86) Songs (Franz Leh
   ar) New Sadlers Wells Cast: *TER (Koch): (CD)(ZC)TER
   1111 (CD/Cass/LP)* / Highlights + songs from 'Land
   Of Smiles' on *EMI Belle Epoque: CZS 767 872-2 (2CD)*
MESSAGE The (aka MOHAMMED MESSENGER OF GOD) (77) Music
   score (Maurice Jarre) Royal P.Orch on *Silva Screen
   (Con): FILMCD 060 (CD)* + music 'Lion Of The Desert'
METELLO (Italy 60's) Music score (Ennio Morricone)-S/T-
   Import (Silva Screen): OST 103 (CD)
METROPOLIS (ORIG LONDON CAST 88) Music (Joe Brooks) Lyr
   ics (Joe Brooks-Dusty Hughes) *with* Brian Blessed-Ju
   dy Kuhn-Graham Bickley-Jonathan Adams and Company
   TER (Coni) CDTER2 1168 (CDx2) ZCTER2 1168 (2Cass)
MICKEY'S CHRISTMAS CAROL - *see* WALT DISNEY FILM INDEX
MIDNIGHT COWBOY (69) Music sc (John Barry) "Everybody's
   Talkin" Nilsson-S/T-*Liberty (EMI): CDP 748409-2(CD)*
   see Coll 'MOVIEOLA'
MIDNIGHT EXPRESS (78) Music: Giorgio Moroder -S/T- on
   Casablanca PRICE 91 (LP) PRIMC 91 (C) 824206-2 (CD)
MIDNIGHT RUN (88) Music score (Danny Elfman) -S/T- Impt
   MCA USA (S.Screen): MCAC(MCAD) 6250 (Cass/CD)
MIGHTY QUINN The (89) Music score (Anne Dudley) plus 19
   songs (V.Arts) -S/T- *A.& M: 393924-2(CD) -4(Cass)*
MIKADO The (OPERETTA - Gilbert and Sullivan) SADLER'S
   WELLS OPERA ORCH & CHORUS (Alex.Faris) John Holmes
   John Wakefield-Clive Revill-Denis Dowling-John Hedd
   le Nash-Marion Studholme-Patricia Kern-Dorothy Nash
   Classics FP (EMI): CDCFPD(TCCPFD) 4730 (2CDs/2Cass)
MIKADO The (OPERETTA) (Gilbert & Sullivan)
   PRO-ARTE ORCHEST (Malcolm Sargent) and GLYNDEBOURNE
   FESTIVAL CHOIR Soloists: Owen Brannigan-Richard Lew
   is-Geraint Evans-Ian Wallace *EMI:CMS 764403-2 (2CD)*
MIKADO The (OPERETTA-Gilbert & Sullivan) New 1989 recor
   ding - *D'Oyly Carte Opera Company* (Jonathan Miller)
   TER (Con): CDTER2(ZCTED(TER2) 1178 (2CD/Cass/2LP)
MIKADO The (MUSICAL OPERETTA 86) (Gilbert & Sullivan)
   Highlights feat *National Opera Company* - *TER: TER
   1121 (LP) ZCTER 1121 (CS) CDTER 1121 (CD)*
MIKADO The - *D'Oyly Carte Opera Company* - Royal Philhar
   Orch (R.Nash) - *London (Poly): 425 190-2 (CDx2)*
MIKADO (1936 RECORDING) featuring: DEREK OLDHAM-SYDNEY
   GRANVILLE-DARRELL FANCOURT and Symphony Orchestra
   (Isidore Godfrey) *Pro-Arte (S.Screen):CDD 3416 (CD)*
MILAGRO BEANFIELD WAR The (88) Music score: Dave Grusin
   Suite from film on 'Migration' (Dave Grusin) - *GRP
   USA (Poly): GRP 9592-2 (CD) -1 (LP) -4 (Cass)*

MILLER'S CROSSING (90) Music score (Carter Burwell)
-S/T- *Varese USA (Pinn): VSD(VSC) 5288 (CD/Cass)*
"Danny Boy" by Mark Williamson *Varese VS 52937 (7")*
MISERY (Stephen King's) (90) Music score (Marc Shaiman)
-S/T- *Bay Cities (S.Screen): BCD(BCC) 3011 (CD/Cas)*
MISHIMA 'A Life. In Four Chapters' (85) Music by Philip
Glass -S/T- *Elektra Nonesuch (WEA): 7559 79113-2 CD*
MISS LIBERTY (ORIG BROADWAY CAST 49) Songs (Irving Berl
in)*feat:* Eddie Albert-Allyn McLerie-Mary McCarty-C.
Dingle-Maria Karnilova *Sony Broadway: SK 48015 (CD)*
MISS SAIGON (ORIG LONDON CAST 89) *with* Lea Salonga-Jona
than Pryce-Simon Bowman-Peter Polycarpou & Company
Highlights: First Night (Pinn): CAST(C)(CD) 38
Full Recording: First Night (Pinn): ENCORE(C)(CD) 5
Symphonic Suites: CASTCD 39 (CD) CASTC 39 (Cass)
see also Coll 'ROYAL PHILHARMONIC ORCH PLAY SUITES'
MISSA LUBA (AFRICAN MASS) - Kenyan Folk Melodies By The
Muungano National Choir directed by Boniface Mganga
Philips (Poly): 426 836-2 (CD) -4 (Cass) -1 (LP)
MISSING (82) Music score (Vangelis) available versions
Vangelis on 'Themes' *Polydor: 839518-2 (CD) -4(Cas)*
Shadows on 'Diamonds' *Pickwick: PWKS 4018P (CD)*
Elaine Paige (vocal) 'Cinema' *Pickwick: PWKS 545 CD*
MISSING IN ACTION (Parts 1-3) (Films 1984/85/88) Music
scores (Jay Chattaway-Brian May) -S/T- *Silva Screen*
(Total-BMG): FILMCD 056 (CD)
MISSION The (86) Music sco (Ennio Morricone)-S/T-*Virgin*
(TC)V 2402 (Cass/LP) CDV 2402 (CD) MDV 2402 (MiniD)
MISSISSIPPI BURNING (88) Music score (Trevor Jones)
-S/T- *Antilles-Island (Poly): AN(C)(CD) 8745*
MISSISSIPPI MASALA (91) Music sco (L.Subramanian) -S/T-
with Var.Arts *First Night (Pinn): CASTCD 27(CD) +*
Imp(Silva Screen):JRS 35809.2(CD) JRS 35809.4(Cass)
MO' BETTER BLUES (90) Music score (Bill Lee) featuring:
B.Marsalis - *CBS: 467160-2 (CD) -4 (Cass)*
MO' MONEY (92) Various artists -S/T- *Perspective/A & M*
(Polyg): 361004-2 (CD) 361004-4 (Cass) -1 (LP)
MOBSTERS (91) Music score (Michael Small) -S/T- *Varese*
(Pinn-S.Screen): VSD 5334 (CD) VSC 5334 (Cass)
MOBY DICK (ORIG LONDON CAST 92) Songs (Robert Longdon-
Hereward Kaye) *with* TONY MONOPOLY-HOPE AUGUSTUS-THE
RESA KARTEL & Co *First Night (Pinn): DICKCD 1 (CD)*
HIGHLIGHTS on *First Night:SCORECD 35 (5 track CD)*
MODERN TIMES (36) Music score (Charles Chaplin)
see Collect 'CHARLIE'
MODERNS The (88) Music score (Mark Isham) Songs Charlel
ie Couture -S/T- *Virgin: CDV 2530 (CD)*
MOLL FLANDERS (ORIG LONDON CAST 93) Songs (George Stil
es-Paul Leigh) *featuring* JOSIE LAWRENCE and ANGELA
RICHARDS and Co.*First Night (Pinn): CASTCD 36 (CD)*
MOLLY MAGUIRES The (70) Music score (Henry Mancini)
-S/T- *Bay Cities (Silva Screen): BCD 3029 (CD)*
MOM AND DAD SAVE THE WORLD (92) Music score (Jerry Gold
smith) -S/T- *Varese (Pinn): VSD(VSC) 5385 (CD/Cass)*

MON ONCLE (Film France 56) Music score (Alain Romains)
    -S/T- excerpts *Philips (S.Screen): 836 983-2 (CD)*
    includes 'Jour De Fete'/'Monsieur Hulot's Holiday'
MONSIEUR HULOT'S HOLIDAY (Film France 53) Music (Alain
    Romains) -S/T- *details see under* 'MON ONCLE' entry
MONSIEUR VERDOUX (47) Music score (Charles Chaplin)
    see Collect 'CHARLIE'
MONTY PYTHON AND THE HOLY GRAIL (75) Music (Neil Innes)
    -S/T- *Charisma: CASCD 1103 (CD) CHC(MC) 17 (LP/Cas)*
MOON 44 (90) Music score (Joel Goldsmith) -S/T- *Silva
    Screen (Conifer): FILMCD 075 (CD)*
MOON IN THE GUTTER The (83) Music score (Gabriel Yared)
    -S/T- *DRG USA: (Silva Screen): CDFMC 2 (CD)*
MOONRAKER - *see* **JAMES BOND FILM INDEX**
MOONSTRUCK (87) Music score (Dick Hyman) -S/T- *Capitol
    EMI: EST 2060 (LP) TC-EST 2060 (Cass) all deleted*
MOONWALKER (88) Music score (Bruce Broughton) Songs by
    Michael Jackson on "Bad" *Epic: 450290-2(CD)-4(Cas)*
    Suite from 'Moonwalker' (Bruce Broughton) on "Fanta
    stic Journey" *Telarc (Conifer): CD 80231 (CD)*
MORE (69) Music score (Pink Floyd) -S/T- Columbia (EMI)
    SCX 6346 (LP) TC-SCX 6346 (Cass) CDP 746386-2 (CD)
MOSES: THE LAWGIVER (TVM mini-ser 75)Music score (Ennio
    Morricone) -S/T- *OST (Silva Screen): OST 113 (2CD)*
MOSQUITO COAST The (87) Music score (Maurice Jarre) inc
    song by Byron Lee & The Dragonaires -S/T- on *London
    (Silva Screen): FCD 21005-2 (CD)*
MOST HAPPY FELLA The (ORIG BROADWAY CAST 56) Songs (Fr
    ank Loesser) *feat:* Robert Weede-Jo Sullivan-Susan
    Johnson-Art Lund-Shorty Long-Mona Paulee *Sony Broa
    dway (Sony Music): SK 48010 (CD)*
MOST HAPPY FELLA The (NEW BROADWAY CAST 91)Songs (Frank
    Loesser) *with* Spiro Malas-Sophie Hayden-Claudia Cat
    tania-Buddy Crutchfield-Tad Ingram-Liz Larson-Charl
    es Pistone-Mark Lotito-Bill Nabel-Scott Waara & Com
    RCA Victor (BMG): 09026 61294-23 (CD)
MOTHER LODE (82) Music score (Ken Wannberg) -S/T- *also
    contains score from* 'The Philadelphia Experiment'
    Prometheus (Silva Screen): PCD 121 (CD)
MOUNTAINS OF THE MOON (89) Music score (Michael Small)
    -S/T- *Polygram Im (S.Screen): 843013-2(-4) (CD/Cas)*
MOVE OVER DARLING (63) Title song (T.Melcher-H.Kanter-J
    Lubin) Doris Day 'Portrait' *Stylus (CD/CASS/LP)*
MOVIEOLA - Music (John Barry) *see Coll* 'MOVIEOLA'
MR.& MRS.BRIDGE (90) Music score (Richard Robbins) with
    Tommy Dorsey/GlennMiller/Dinah Shore/Lena Horne etc
    -S/T- on *RCA Imp (Silva Screen): 83100-2 (CD)*
MR.BASEBALL (92) Music score (Jerry Goldsmith) -S/T- on
    Varese (Pinn): VSD 5383 (CD) VSC 5383 (Cass)
MR.CINDERS (REVIVAL LONDON CAST 83) Songs (Vivian Ellis
    Richard Myers-Clifford Grey-Leo Robin) *with* Graham
    Hoadly-Andrea Kealy-Dennis Lawson-Diana Martin-Chri
    stina Matthews-Steven Pacey / Michael Reed (md) on
    TER (Koch): CDTER 1069 (CD): ZCTER 1069 (Cass)

MR.DESTINY (90) Music score (David Newman) -S/T- Import
Varese (Pinn-S.Screen): VSD(VSC) 5299 (CD/Cass)
MR.HORN (79) Music score (Jerry Fielding) -S/T- also co
ntains score to 'CHATO'S LAND' (71- Jerry Fielding)
Bay Cities (Sil.Screen): cat.number to be confirmed
MR.PRESIDENT (ORIG BROADWAY CAST 62) Songs (Irving Berl
in) *feat:* Robert Ryan-Nanette Fabray-Anita Gillette
Jack Haskell *Sony Broadway (Sony M): SK 48212 (CD)*
MR.SATURDAY NIGHT (92) Music score (Marc Shaiman) -S/T-
Milan (Pinn): 12468-2 (CD) 12468-4 (Cass)
MR.WONDERFUL (ORIG BROADWAY CAST 56) Songs (Jerry Bock-
George Weiss-Larry Holfencor) *with* Sammy Davis Jnr.
MCA USA (S.Screen): MCAD 10303(CD) MCAC 10303(Cass)
MUCH ADO ABOUT NOTHING (93) Music score (Patrick Doyle)
-S/T- *Epic (Sony M): MOOCD 30 (CD) MOODC 30 (Cass)*
MUPPET CHRISTMAS CAROL The (92) Music score (Miles Good
man) Songs (Paul Williams) -S/T-*Arista (BMG): 74321
12194-26 (CD) 74321 12194-40 (Cass)*
MURDER ON THE ORIENT EXPRESS (74) Music score (Richard
Rodney Bennett) -S/T- on *Cloud Nine (S.Screen): CNS
5007 (CD)* also with 'DEATH ON THE NILE' (78) (Rota)
MURPHY'S LAW (86) - *see under* 'DEATH WISH'
MUSIC BOX (89) Music score (Philippe Sarde) -S/T- Imprt
Varese (Pinn): VS(VSC)(VSD) 5248 (LP/Cass/CD)
MUSIC MAN The (FILM MUSICAL 62) Songs (Meredith Wilson)
Feat: Robert Preston and Shirley Jones -S/T- *Warner
Bros USA (Silva Screen) 1459-2 (CD) M5 1459 (Cass)*
MUSIC MAN The (ORIG BROADWAY CAST 58) *with* Robert Prest
on-Barbara Cook *Import (Silva Screen): 46633-2 (CD)*
MUSIC TEACHER The (90) -S/T- Operatic and Classical Mus
on *President (Taylors): PCOM(PTLC) 1109 (CD/Cass)*
MUTANT (82) Music score (Richard Band) perf.by National
Philharmonic Orch *Intrada (S.Screen):MAF 7052D (CD)*
MY BEAUTIFUL LAUNDERETTE (85) Music score Stanley Myers
(selection)+'Sammy & Rosie Get Laid''Wish You Were
Here'- *Milan (S.Screen) C.369 (Cass) CDCH.369 (CD)*
MY BEST FRIENDS GIRL - *see* 'La Femme De Mon Pote'
MY BRILLIANT CAREER (Austr 79) Theme music adapted from
'Scenes From Childhood'/'Piano Quartet E.Flat' (Sch
umann) *see* Coll 'Music From Great Australian Films'
MY COUSIN VINNY (91) Music score (Randy Edelman) -S/T-
Varese (Pinn): VSD 5364 (CD) VSC 5364 (Cass)
MY GIRL (92) Music score (James Newton Howard) -S/T-
-S/T- *Epic (Sony M): 469213-2 (CD) -4 (Cass) -1(LP)*
MY HEROES HAVE ALWAYS BEEN COWBOYS (91) Music sc (James
Horner) -S/T- *RCA USA (S.Screen) 2388-2 (CD) -4(CS)*
MY FAIR LADY (FILM MUSICAL 64) Songs (Alan Jay Lerner &
Frederick Loewe) Rex Harrison-Audrey Hepburn (sung
by Marni Nixon)-S/T-*CBS 40-32043 (Cass) CBSCD 70000*
MY FAIR LADY (ORIG LONDON CAST 58) *with* Rex Harrison-
Julie Andrews-Stanley Holloway and Company *Columbia
(Silva Screen): CK 02105 (CD) 02105 (Cass)*
MY FAIR LADY (ORIG BROADWAY CAST 56) *with* Julie Andrews
R.Harrison *CBS (S.Screen): CK(JST) 05090 (CD/Cass)*

MY FAIR LADY (STUDIO RECORDING 87) *with:* Kiri Te Kanawa
Jeremy Irons-Warren Mitchell-John Gielgud & others
Decca: MFL 1 (LP) MFLC 1 (Cass) 421 200-2 (CD)

MY FAVORITE YEAR (ORIG USA CAST 92) Songs (Flaherty-Ahr
ens) *feat:* Tim Curry-Evan Pappas-Josh Mostel-Andrea
Martin-Lainie Kazan-Tom Mardirosian-Lannyl Stephens
Ethan Phillips..*RCA Victor (BMG):09026 61617-2 (CD)*

MY FUNNY VALENTINE (NEW DIGITAL RECORDING) Songs (Richa
rd Rodgers-Lorenz Hart) *feat:* Frederica Von Stade &
London Symph Orch & Ambrosian Chorus (John McGlinn)
EMI: CDC 754071-2 (CD) EL 754071-4 (Cass) -1 (LP)

MY LEFT FOOT (89) Music score (Elmer Bernstein) -S/T-
Varese USA (Pinn): VS(C)(D) 5244 (LP/Cass/CD)

MY LIFE AS A DOG (Sweden-85) Music sc. (Bjoern Isfaelt)
see under Collect.'Best Of Scandinavian Film Music'

MY MOTHER'S CASTLE (90) *see* 'GLORY OF MY FATHER'

MY NAME IS NOBODY (74) Music score (Ennio Morricone)
-S/T- *Alhambra (Pinn): A.8918 (CD) deleted*

MY RIFLE MY PONY AND ME A Collection of Music and Songs
from *WESTERN Films:see Collections* for full details

MY STEPMOTHER IS AN ALIEN (89) Music (Alan Silvestri) +
music Siren-Marrs-Cameo-Dan Ackroyd-Animotion-Ivan
Neville -S/T-*Poly: 837 798-2(CD)-4(Cas) all deleted*

MYSTERIOUS ISLAND (61) Mus sco (Bernard Herrmann) -S/T-
Stereo release *Cloud Nine (S.Screen): ACN 7017 (CD)*

MYSTERY TRAIN (89) Songs: John Lurie-Elvis Presley-Roy
Orbison-Junior Parker-Rufus Thomas-Otis Redding-Bar
Kays -S/T- *Milan France (S.Screen): CDCH(A)(C) 509*

NAILS (92) Music score (Bill Conti) -S/T- *Varese (Pinn)
VSD 5384 (CD) VSC 5384 (Cass)*

NAKED CAGE The (85) - *see under* 'CRY IN THE DARK, A'

NAKED CITY The (48) Music sco (Miklos Rozsa) selection
on 'LUST FOR LIFE' *Varese (Pinn): VSD 5405 (CD)*

NAKED GUN 2 1/2 (91) Music score (Ira Newborn) -S/T-
Varese (Pinn): VSD 5351 (CD) VSC 5351 (Cass)

NAKED LUNCH The (92) Music sco (Howard Shore & Ornette
Coleman)-S/T- *Milan (Pinn):262732(CD) 412732(Cass)*

NAME OF THE ROSE (87) Music score (James Horner) -S/T-
Import (S.Screen): 30046 (CD)

NAPOLEON (Silent Film 27) Music score composed 1982 by
Carl Davis - SCO (Davis) *CFP (EMI): CDCFP 4542 (CD)*

NATIONAL LAMPOON'S ANIMAL HOUSE (78) Score (Elmer Berns
tein) songs John Belushi-Sam Cooke-Bobby Lewis-Paul
and Paula-Chris Montez-Stephen Bishop -S/T- *MCA BMG
MCLD 19086 (CD) MCLC: 19086 (Cass)*

NATURAL The (84) Music score (Randy Newman) -S/T- Imprt
W.Bros USA (Silva Screen) 925116-2 -4 (CD/Cass)

NAVIGATOR The (88) Music score (Davood A.Tabrizi) -S/T-
Silva Screen (Conifer: FILMCD 039 (CD)

NAVY SEALS (91) Music score (Sylvester Levay) -S/T- on
Atlantic (WEA): 7567 82125-2 (CD) -4(Cass)

NEAR DARK (88) Music score (Tangerine Dream) -S/T- Impt
Silva Screen (Con): FILM(C)(CD) 026 (LP/ Cass/CD)

NEEDFUL THINGS (93) Music score (Patrick Doyle) -S/T-
   Varese (Pinn): VSD 5438 (CD) VSC 5438 (Cass)
NETCHAIEV EST DE RETOUR (HAS RETURNED) (90) Music score
   (Claude Bolling) -S/T- *Milan (S.Screen): CDCH 801CD*
NEVER CRY WOLF (83) Music (Mark Isham) *see* 'Mrs.Soffel'
NEVER SAY NEVER AGAIN - *see* **JAMES BOND FILM INDEX**
NEW JACK CITY (91) Music score (Michel Colombier) + V/A
   -S/T- *Giant: 759 7599-24409-2(CD)-4(Cass)-1(LP)*
NEW MOON (MUSICAL) Songs (Sigmund Romberg) feat Gordon
   MacRae & Dorothy Kirsten - *see under* 'Desert Song'
NEW YORK NEW YORK (77) Title song: John Kander-Fred Ebb
   Feat: Liza Minnelli-Georgie Auld-Diahanne Abbott &
   Larry Kent-Robert de Niro-Mary Kay Place-R.Burns Or
   -S/T- *Liberty (Silva Screen): 46090-2 (CD) -4(Cass)*
NEW YORK STORIES (89) Music score (Carmine Coppola)
   -S/T- *Geffen (WEA): 960 857-2 (CD) -4 (Cas) -1 (LP)*
NEWSIES (Disney 92) Music score (Alan Menken) -S/T- on
   Disney-BV (Silva Screen): DIS 60832 (CD)
NICHOLAS NICKLEBY Life & Adventures ORIG LONDON CAST 82
   Songs (Stephen Oliver) *with* Royal Shakespeare Comp
   TER (Con) TER 1029 (LP) ZCTER 1029 (Cass)
NICK & NORA (ORIG BROADWAY CAST 91) Music (Charles Stro
   use) Lyrics (Richard Maltby Jnr) *TER (Conif): CDTER
   1191 (CD) ZCTER 1191 (Cass)*
NIGHT OF THE GENERALS (66) Music score (Maurice Jarre)
   -S/T- *Fantasy/Intrada (Silva Sc): FM 8004D (CD)*
NIGHT ON EARTH (92) Music score (Tom Waits) Songs (Tom
   Waits-Kathleen Brennan) -S/T- *Island Import (Silva
   Screen): 510929-2 (CD) 510929-4 (Cass)*
NIGHTBREED (90) Music Score (Danny Elfman) -S/T- MCA
   USA (S.Screen) MCAD 8037 (CD) MCAC 8037 (Cass)
NIGHTCROSSING (87) Music score (Jerry Goldsmith) -S/T-
   Intrada USA (Silva Screen) RVF 6004D (CD)
NIGHTGAMES (80) Music score (John Barry) c/w GAME OF DE
   ATH (79-John Barry) *S.Screen (Con): FILMCD 123 (CD)*
NIGHTINGALE (ORIG LONDON CAST 82) Songs Charles Strouse
   with Sarah Brightman-Gordon Sandison-Susannah Fello
   ws and Company *TER: TER 1031 (LP) ZCTED 1031 (Cass)*
NIGHTMARE CAFE (91) Music by various artists -S/T- on
   Varese (Pinn): VSD 5363 (CD) VSC 5363 (Cass)
NIGHTMARE CASTLE (65) - *see under* 'HUMANOID,The'
NIGHTMARE ON ELM STREET (85) Music (Charles Bernstein)
   -S/T- *Varese USA (Pinn): STV(CTV) 81236*
NIGHTMARE ON ELM STREET 2 Freddie's Revenge (86) Music
   score (Christopher Young) -S/T- *Varese USA (Pinn):
   STV(CTV) 81275 (LP/ Cas) VCD 47275 (CD)*
NIGHTMARE ON ELM STREET 3 Dream Warriors (87) Music
   score (Angelo Badalamenti) -S/T- *TER (Conifer):
   (ZC)TER 1143 (CS/LP) VCD 47293 (CD)*
NIGHTMARE ON ELM STREET 4 (88) Music score: Craig Safan
   Chrysalis (CCD)(Z)CHR 1673 (CD/Cass/LP) all deleted
NIGHTMARE ON ELM STREET 5 Dream Child (89) Music score
   (Jay Ferguson) -S/T- *Jive (BMG): CHIP 87(CD) HIP(C)
   87 (LP/Cass) and Varese USA (Pinn): VS(C)(D) 5238*

NIGHTMARE ON ELM STREET 6 Freddie's Dead: The Final
   Nightmare (91) Music (Brian May) -S/T- *Metal Blade*
   (Pinn): CDZZORRO 33 (CD) ZORRO 33 (LP) / IMPORT on
   Varese (Pinn): VS(VSC)(VSCD) 5333 (LP/Cass/CD)
NIGHTSUN (90) Music score (Nicola Piovani) -S/T- Import
   Milan (Silva Screen): CDCH 605 (CD)
NIKITA (89) Music score (Eric Serra) -S/T- on *Virgin*
   (Poly): CDVMM 2 (CD) TCVMM 2 (Cass)
NINE (ORIG LONDON CONCERT CAST 92) Songs (Maury Yeston)
   feat: Jonathan Pryce-Elaine Paige and Company
   TER (Conifer): CDTER 1193 (CD) ZCTER 1193 (Cass)
NINE (ORIG AUSTRALIAN CAST 91) Songs (Maury Yeston)*with*
   John Diedrich-Maria Mercedes-Peta Toppano-Jackie Re
   es-Gerda Nicholson-Caroline Gillmer: *TER (Conifer):*
   CDTER 1190 (CD) ZCTER 1190 (Cass)
9 TO 5 (Film-TV) Music: Dolly Parton on *RCA Camden: CDS*
   (CAM) 1225 (LP/Cas) and on RCA (BMG): ND 84830 (CD)
9½ WEEKS (86) Music score (Jack Nitzsche) -S/T- *Capitol*
   (Silva Screen): 46722-2 (CD)
1941 (79) Music score (John Williams) -S/T- *Alhambra Im*
   (Silva Screen-Pinn): A.8913 (CD)
1984 (84) Music composed & performed (Eurythmics) -S/T-
   Virgin: CDV 1984 (CD) OVEDC 207 (Cass)
NO MAN'S LAND (88) Music score (Basil Poledouris) -S/T-
   Varese USA STV 81352 (LP) CTV 81352 (Cass)
NO NO NANNETTE (REVIVAL CAST 71 with Ruby Keeler) Songs
   (Vincent Youmans-Otto Harbach-Irving Caesar) *Columb*
   (Silva Screen): CK 30563 (CD) JST 30563 (Cass)
NO STRINGS (ORIG BROADWAY CAST 62) Songs (Richard Rodge
   rs) *feat:*RICHARD KILEY-DIAHANN CARROLL-POLLY ROWLES
   NOELLE ADAM *Angel (EMI): ZDM 764694-2 (CD)*
NO WAY OUT (88) Music score (Maurice Jarre) -S/T- also
   inc.'The Year Of Living Dangerously' (81) *TER (Con)*
   CDTER 1149 (CD) see Collect 'BEST OF KEVIN COSTNER'
NOEL AND GERTIE (ORIG LONDON CAST 86) Songs Noel Coward
   with Lewis Flander-Patricia Hodge and Company
   TER (Conif): TER 1117 (LP) ZCTER 1117 (Cass)
NORMA RAE (79) Music score (David Shire) Selection on
   Bay Cities (S.Screen):BCD 3021 (CD) BCC 3021 (Cass)
NORTH BY NORTHWEST (59) Music score (Bernard Herrmann)
   -S/T- on *Varese (Pinn): VCD 47205 (CD)* 'North By
   Northwest' London Studio Symph Orc (Laurie Johnson)
   Milan: CCH 022 (C) CDCH 022 (CD) c/w 'PSYCHO'
NOT QUITE JERUSALEM (85) Music score (Rondo Veneziano)
   -S/T- *Fanfare (Mainline): RON 4 (LP) ZCRON 4 (Cass)*
NOT WITHOUT MY DAUGHTER (91) Music Sc (Jerry Goldsmith)
   -S/T- on *Silva Screen (Conifer): FILM(C)(CD) 091*
NOTHING BUT TROUBLE (91) Music score (Michael Kamen) +
   Songs -S/T- *WB USA (S.Screen):926491-2(CD) -4(Cass)*
NOTORIOUS (46) Music score (Roy Webb) - *on* Collec 'Four
   Alfred Hitchcock Films' *TER: (ZC)TER 1109 (Cass/LP)*
NOW VOYAGER! (42) *see under* 'STREETCAR NAMED DESIRE A'
NUNS STORY The (59) Music score (Franz Waxman) -S/T-
   Imprt (Silva Screen): STZ 114 (CD)

NUNSENSE (ORIG LONDON CAST 87) Songs (Dan Goggin) *feat:*
Honor Blackman-Anna Sharkey-Louise Gold and Company
TER (Coifer): TER 1132 (LP) ZCTER 1132 (Cass)
NUNSENSE (ORIG OFF-BROADWAY CAST 86) *feat:* Christine An
derson-Semina de Laurentis-Marilyn Farina-Edwina Le
wis-Suzi Winston *DRG (S.Screen) SBLC 12589 (Cass)*
NUNSENSE 2 (ORIG CAST RECORDING) details unconfirmed
DRG USA (Pinn): DRGCD 12608 (CD) DRGMC 12608 (Cass)
NUTS (88) Music score (Barbra Streisand) -S/T- on *CBS*
(Sony Music): CBS 651 3796-1 (mini album)
NYMPH ERRANT (MUSICAL Cole Porter) *World Premiere Recor*
ding with Stephen Hill Singers/Orch cond: Donald Pi
ppin-David Firman) Cast: Elisabeth Welch-Andrea McA
rdle-Lorna Dallas-Maureen McGovern-Virginia McKenna
Fiona Fullerton-Derek Waring-Larry Kert-KayeBallard
Patricia Hodge on *EMI: CDC 764079-2(CD) EL 754079-4*

O PIONEERS! (91) Music score (Bruce Broughton) -S/T- on
Intrada USA (Koch Int): MAFCD 7023 (CD)
OBJECTIVE BURMA! (44) Music score (Franz Waxman) see
'Sunset Boulevard' coll - *RCA: RD 87017 (CD)*
OCEANO - *see under* 'The ROVER'
OCCHIO ALLA PENNA (-) Music score (Ennio Morricone)
-S/T- *Alhambra (Pinn): A.8916 (CD)*
OCTOPUSSY - *see* JAMES BOND FILM INDEX
ODD MAN OUT (46) Music score (William Alwyn) Suite from
film played by London Symphony Orchestra (Richard
Hickox) on *Chandos: CHAN 9243 (CD) ABTD 1606 (Cass)*
ODDS AGAINST TOMORROW (59) Jazz music score: John Lewis
with M.J.Q.-Bill Evans-Milt Jackson-Jim Hall -S/T-
Columbia Import (Silva Screen): AK 47836 (CD)
OF MICE AND MEN (92) Music score (Mark Isham) -S/T- on
Varese (Pinn): VSCD 5371 (CD) VSC 5371 (Cass)
OFF THE WALL (REVUE-MUSICAL 91) Songs (Don Black-Geoff
Stephens) A New Revuesical with Mark McGann-Maria
Friedman-Claire Moore-Teddy Kempner on *First Night*
(Pinn): SCENECD 20 (CD) SCENEC 20 (Cass)
OH! WHAT A LOVELY WAR (ORIG LONDON CAST 63) Var.Songs
feat: Avis Bunnage-Fanny Carby-John Gower-Myfanwy
Jenn-Colin Kembal-Brian Murphy-Victor Spinetti etc
TER (Conifer): TER 1043 (LP) ZCTER 1043 (Cass)
OKLAHOMA (FILM MUSICAL 55) Songs (Richard Rodgers-Oscar
Hammerstein II) GORDON MacRAE-SHIRLEY JONES-GLORIA
GRAHAM-ROD STEIGER-GENE NELSON-CHARLOTTE GREENWOOD
-S/T- *EMI Broadway Classics: EG 764 691-2 (CD)*
OKLAHOMA (ORIG BROADWAY CAST 43) *Theatre Guild Producti*
on with Alfred Drake-Joan Roberts-Celeste Holme-Lee
Dixon *MCA (BMG): MCLD(MCLC) 19026 (CD/Cass)*
OKLAHOMA (USA STUDIO RECORDING 52) *feat:* NELSON EDDY-
Virginia Haskins-Kaye Ballard-Portia Nelson-Lee
Cass-David Atkinson-Wilton Clary-David Morris on
Sony Broadway (Sony Music): SK 53326 (CD)
OKLAHOMA (BROADWAY CAST RECORDING)*with* Laurence Guttard
Christine Andreas-Mary Wickes *RCA(BMG):RD 83572(CD)*

OLD BOYFRIENDS (79) Music score (David Shire) Selection
   Bay Cities (S.Screen):BCD 3021 (CD) BCC 3021 (Cass)
OLD GRINGO (89) Music score (Lee Holdridge) -S/T- on
   GNP USA (S.Screen) GNPD 8017 (CD) GNP5 8017(Cass)
OLD MAN AND THE SEA The (58) Music score (Dimitri Tiomk
   in) -S/T- *Varese USA (S.Screen): VSD 5232 (CD)*
OLD MAN OF LOCHNAGAR The (MUSICAL SHOW 86) Music (David
   Wood) From a story by H.R.H.Prince Charles with Ian
   Loughlan as the old man - *1st Night: SCENEC 5 (Cas)*
OLIVER! (FILM MUSICAL 68) Songs (Lionel Bart)feat Harry
   Secombe-Ron Moody-Shani Wallis-Jack Wild -S/T- on
   RCA (BMG) ND 90311 (CD) NK 90311 (Cass)
OLIVER! (NEW RECORDING 91) *feat:* Josephine Barstow-Juli
   an Forsythe-Sheila Hancock-Stuart Kale-Richard Van
   Allan-NSO (John Owen Edwards) *TER: CD(ZC) TER 1184*
OLIVER! (LONDON STUDIO RECORDING 62) *feat:* STANLEY HOLL
   OWAY-ALMA COGAN *EMI Angel (EMI): ZDM 764890-2 (CD)*
OLIVER! (ORIG LONDON CAST 60) *with* Ron Moody-Georgia Br
   own-Paul Whitsun Jones-Hope Jackman-Danny Sewell
   Deram (Poly): 820 590-2 (CD deleted) -4 (Cass)
OLIVER! (ORIG BROADWAY CAST 63) *with* Clive Revill and
   Georgia Brown *RCA (BMG):GD 84113(CD) GK 84113(Cass)*
OLIVER AND CO (89) Music (J.A.C.Redford) songs by V/A
   see WALT DISNEY FILM INDEX
OLIVER TWIST (48) Music sco (Arnold Bax) Royal Philharm
   onic Orch (K.Alwyn) *Cloud Nine (Con): ACN 7012 (CD)*
OLIVIER OLIVIER (91) Music sco (Zbigniew Preisner) incl
   'EUROPA EUROPA' -S/T- *DRG (Pinn): DRG(CD)(MC) 12606*
OLYMPUS ON MY MIND (ORIG USA CAST 86) Music (Grant Stur
   iale) Lyr (Barry Harman) *TER (Con): ZCTER 1131 (CS)*
OMEN The (76) Music sco (Jerry Goldsmith) -S/T- *Varese*
   (Pinn):VSD(VSC) 5281 (CD/Cass) and 'O Fortuna' from
   "Carmina Burana" (Carl Orff) *see Coll* 'OMEN'
OMEN II 'Damien' (78) Music score (Jerry Goldsmith)
   -S/T- *Sil.Screen: FILMCD 002 (CD) FILMC 002 (Cass)*
OMEN III 'Final Conflict' (81) Music (Jerry Goldsmith)
   -S/T- *Varese (Pinn-S.Scr): VSD(VSC) 5282 (CD/Cass)*
OMEN IV The Awakening' (91) Music score (Jonathan Sheff
   fer) -S/T- *Varese (Pinn-S.Screen):VS(VSC)(VSD) 5318*
ON A CLEAR DAY YOU CAN SEE FOREVER (70) Music (Burton
   Lane) Lyrics (Alan Jay Lerner)feat BARBRA STREISAND
   -S/T- *Columbia Imp (S.Screen): A.20716 (CD)*
ON GOLDEN POND (81) Music score (Dave Grusin)-S/T- with
   dialogue *MCA Imp (Silva Screen): MCAC 1497 (Cass)*
ON HER MAJESTY'S SECRET SERVICE *see* JAMES BOND FILM IND
ON MY OWN (92) Music (Franco Piersanti) -S/T- *Import*
   (Silva Screen): OST 117(CD) with 'CHILDREN'S THIEF'
ON THE TOWN (ORIG BROADWAY CAST 44) Music (Leonard Bern
   stein) Lyrics (Bette Comden and Adolph Green) *on*
   CBS USA (S.Screen): CK(JST) 02038 (CD/Cass)
ON THE TWENTIETH CENTURY (ORIG BROADWAY CAST 78) Songs
   (Cy Coleman-Betty Comden-Adoph Green)*feat:* Madeline
   Kahn-John Cullum-Imogene Coca-Kevin Kline-Georg.Coe
   Dean Dittman-Judy Kaye *Sony Broadway: SK 35330 (CD)*

ON YOUR TOES (REVIVAL BROADWAY CAST 83) Songs (Richard
    Rodgers-Lorenz Hart) *TER (Conifer): TER2 1063 (2LP)*
    ZCTED 1063 (Dblplay Cass) CDTER 1063 (CD)
ONCE AROUND (91) Music score (James Horner) -S/T- on
    Varese (Pinn): VSD 5308 (CD) VSC 5308 (Cass)
ONCE ON THIS ISLAND (ORIG BROADWAY CAST 90) Songs (Lynn
    Ahrens and Stephen Flaherty) *RCA Imp (Silva Screen)*
    60595-2 (CD) 60595-4 (Cass)
ONCE UPON A FOREST (92) Music sco (James Horner) -S/T-
    Import (Silva Screen): 66286-2 (CD) 66286-4 (Cass)
ONCE UPON A TIME IN AMERICA (84) Music: Ennio Morricone
    -S/T- *Mercury: MERH(C) 45 (LP/Cass) 822 334-2 (CD)*
ONCE UPON A TIME IN THE WEST(69) Music: Ennio Morricone
    -S/T- *RCA (Silva Screen): 4736-2 (CD) 4736-4 (Cass)*
ONE AGAINST THE WIND (92) Music score (Lee Holdridge)
    -S/T- *Intrada (S.Screen): MAF 7039D (CD)*
ONE FLEW OVER THE CUCKOO'S NEST (75) Music score (Jack
    Nitzsche) -S/T- *Fantasy (Sil.Screen): FCD 4531 (CD)*
ONE FROM THE HEART (82) Music/Songs (Tom Waits-Crystal
    Gayle) -S/T- reissue *Sony 467609-2/-4/-1(CD/CS/LP)*
101 DALMATIONS - *see under* WALT DISNEY FILM INDEX
110 IN THE SHADE (ORIG BROADWAY CAST 63) Songs (Harvey
    Schmidt-Tom Jones) *feat:* Robert Horton-Inga Swenson
    Stephen Douglass-Will Geer-Lesley A.Warren and Comp
    RCA Victor (BMG): GD 81085 (CD) GK 81085 (Cass)
ONE TRICK PONY (80) Music (Paul Simon) -S/T- *Warn.Bros*
    (WEA): K4-56846 (Cass) K2-56846 (CD)
ONLY THE LONELY (91) Music score (Maurice Jarre) Title
    song (Roy Orbison-Joe Melson) sung by Roy Orbison
    -S/T- *Varese (Pinn): VSC(VSD) 5324 (Cass/CD)*
OPERA (Terror At The Opera) (87) Music by Roger & Brian
    ENO-BILL WYMAN & extracts from various Operas -S/T-
    Cinevox Italy (Silva Screen): CIA 5074 (CD)
OPERETTE - *see* 'Noel Coward - The Great Shows'
ORCA - KILLER WHALE (77) Music score (Ennio Morricone)
    -S/T- *Legend Impt (Silva Screen): CD 10 (CD)*
ORDINARY PEOPLE (80) Theme 'Canon In D' (Pachelbel) *see*
    Coll 'IMAGINATIONS'/'SEASONS'
ORLANDO (92) Mus (David Motion-Sally Potter-Jimmy Somer
    ville) -S/T- *Varese (Pinn): VSD(VSC) 5413 (CD/Cass)*
ORPHEUS IN THE UNDERWORLD (MUSICAL OPERETTA) Music by
    Jacques Offembach / English text by S.Wilson and D.
    Pountney - *English National Opera* (Mark Elder) on
    TER: TER 1134 (LP) ZCTER 1134 (Cas) CDTER 1134 (CD)
OSCAR (91) Music score (Elmer Bernstein) -S/T- on *Vare*
    se (Pinn): VSD 5313 (CD) VSC 5313 (Cass)
OTHELLO (51-O.Welles) Music score (Francesco Lavagnino-
    Alberto Barberis)-S/T- *Varese (Pinn): VSD 5420 (CD)*
OUR MAN FLINT / IN LIKE FLINT (66/67) Music score(Jerry
    Goldsmith) -S/T- *Silva Screen: FILMC 046 (Cass)*
OUT FOR JUSTICE (91) Music score (David Michael Frank)
    with 'HARD TO KILL' (89) & 'ABOVE THE LAW' (88)
    GNP (Sil.Screen): GNPD 8028 (CD) GNP5-8028 (Cass)
    Var.artists *Varese (Pinn): VSD (VSC) 5317 (CD/Cass)*

OUT OF AFRICA (86) Music (John Barry) with Melissa Manc
hester-Al Jarreau -S/T- *MCA (BMG): MCLD(MCLC) 19092*
see also Coll 'MOVIEOLA'
OUT OF ORDER (Film) - see under 'Abwarts Out Of Order'
OUT OF THIS WORLD (ORIG BROADWAY CAST 1950) Songs (Cole
Porter) *feat:* Charlotte Greenwood-William Redfield-
William Eythe-Priscilla Gillette-Barbara Ashley-Dav
id Burns *Sony Broadway (Sony M): SK 48223 (CD)*
OUTLAND (81) Music score (Jerry Goldsmith) -S/T- (also
containing music from 'CAPRICORN ONE') on *GNP USA
(Silva Screen): GNPD 8035 (CD) GNP-5 8035 (Cass)*
OUTSIDERS The (83) Music score (Carmine Coppola) -S/T-
Silva Screen (BMG): FILM(CD) 051 (LP/CD)
"Stay Gold" (Stevie Wonder-Carmine Coppola)-sung by
Stevie Wonder / other versions Earl Klugh - *Capitol
(EMI) EJ 240228-1 (LP) -4 (Cass) CDP 746472-2 (CD)*
OVER HERE! (ORIG BROADWAY CAST 74) Songs (Richard M.and
RobertB.Sherman) *feat:* The ANDREWS SISTERS with Dou
glas Watson-April Shawan-Janie Sell-John Travolta-
Treat Williams-Bette Henritze-John Driver-McIntyre
Dixon-William Griffis *Sony Broadway: SK 32961 (CD)*

PACIFIC 1860 (ORIG LONDON CAST 46) Songs (Noel Coward)
with Mary Martin *TER (Con): (ZC)TER 1040 (Cass/LP)*
PACIFIC HEIGHTS (90) Music score (Hans Zimmer) -S/T- on
Varese (Pinn-S.Screen):VSD(VSC) 5286 (CD/Cass)
PACIFIC OVERTURES (ORIG BROADWAY CAST 76)Songs (Stephen
Sondheim) *RCA (S.Screen) RCD14407(CD) CBK14407(Cas)*
PACIFIC OVERTURES (MUSICAL SHOW) *English National Opera
Cast Prod. TER (Con): TER2 1151 (2LP) ZCTED (Cass)
CDTER 1151 (CD) / Complete Double CD: CDTER2 1152*
PADDINGTON BEAR'S MAGICAL MUSICAL (MUSICAL SHOW 89)
First Night (Pinn): TV 18 (LP) TVC 18 (Cass)
PAINT YOUR WAGON (FILM MUSICAL 69) Songs (Alan Jay Lern
er-Frederick Loewe) Feat: Lee Marvin-Clint Eastwood
-S/T- *MCA (BMG): MCLC 1667 (Cass) deleted*
PAINT YOUR WAGON (ORIG LONDON CAST 53) *feat:* Sally Ann
Howes-Bobby Howes-June Grant-Ken Cantrill & Company
TER (Conifer): TER 1061 (LP) ZCTER 1061 (Cass)
PAINT YOUR WAGON (ORIG BROADWAY CAST 51) *feat:* James Ba
rton-Robert Penn-Olga San Juan-Rufus Smith & Comp
RCA Victor (BMG): GD 60243 (CD) GK 60243 (Cass)
PAJAMA GAME The (FILM MUSICAL 57) Songs (Richard Adler-
Jerry Ross) Featuring Doris Day -S/T- songs on *Sony
467610-2 (CD)-4 (Cass)-1 (LP)* +'Calamity Jane' (53)
PAJAMA GAME The (ORIG BROADWAY CAST 54) with John Raitt
Columbia (S.Screen): CK 32606 (CD) JST 32606 (Cass)
PAL JOEY (ORIG BROADWAY CAST 40) Music (Richard Rodgers
Lyr (Lorenz Hart) *feat:* Harold Lang-Vivienne Segal
CBS USA (Silva Screen): CK 04364 (CD) JST 04364 (CS)
PAL JOEY (BROADWAY CAST OF 1952) Songs (Richard Rodgers
Lorenz Hart) *feat:* HAROLD LANG-VIVIENNE SEGAL-HELEN
GALLAGHER-LIONEL STANDER-PATRICIA NORTHROP-ELAINE
STRITCH *Angel (EMI): ZDM 764696-2 (CD)*

PAL JOEY (REVIVAL LONDON CAST 80) w:Sian Phillips-Denis
Lawson *TER (Con): CDTER 1005 (CD) ZCTER 1005 (Cass)*
PAL JOEY (REVIVAL USA CAST 50)with Harold Lang *Columbia
(Silva Screen): CK 04364 (CD) JST 04364 (Cass)*
PAPERHOUSE (88) Music score (Hans Zimmer-Stanley Myers)
-S/T- *Milan (S.Screen): CDCH 374 (CD) C.374 (Cass)*
see *COLLECT* 'HORROR AND SCIENCE FICTION FILM MUSIC'
PAPILLON (73) Music score (Jerry Goldsmith) -S/T- on
Silva Screen (Conif): FILMCD 029 (CD)
PARADE - *see* 'Under The Cherry Moon' (Film 86) Prince
PARADISE ALLEY (78) Music score (Bill Conti) -S/T- Impt
Import (Silva Screen): TCS 105-2 (CD)
PARADISE BEACH (93) -S/T- *East West (WEA): 4509 93447-2
(CD) 4509 93447-4 (Cass)*
PARENTHOOD (89) Music score (Randy Newman) -S/T- Import
Reprise (Silva Screen): 926001-2
PARIS S'EVEILLE (91) Music score (John Cale) -S/T- on
Crepuscule (APT): TWI 9522 (CD) deleted
PARIS TEXAS (84) Original Songs by Ry Cooder -S/T- Impt
W.Bros (S.Screen) 925 270-1 (LP) 925 270-4 (Cass)
PARK IS MINE The (91) Music score (Tangerine Dream)
-S/T- *Silva Screen (Conifer): FILMCD 080 (CD)*
PARTY WITH BETTY COMDEN AND ADOLPH GREEN, A (ORIG BROAD
WAY CAST 1959) on *EMI Angel (EMI): ZDM 764773-2 CD*
PASSAGE TO INDIA A (85) Music sco (Maurice Jarre) -S/T-
Capitol USA (Silva Screen): 92059-2 (CD) -4 (Cass)
PASSENGER 57 (92) Music score (Stanley Clarke) -S/T- on
USA Imprt: (through Movie Boulevard)
PASSION FISH (93) Music score (Mason Daring) -S/T- inc:
BALFA BROTHERS-DUKE LEVINE GROUP-JOHN DELAFOSE& THE
EUNICE PLAYBOYS-JAMES MACDONELL-ZYDECO EXPRESS-LE
TRIO CADIEN *Daring (Project-CMD-ADA):DRCD 3008 (CD)*
PASTIME (91) Music score (Lee Holdridge) -S/T- Import
Bay Cities (Silva Screen): BCD 3018 (CD)
PAT GARRETT & BILLY THE KID (73) Songs (Bob Dylan)-S/T-
reiss *Columbia (Sony) CD 32098 (CD) 40-32098 (Cass)*
PATCH OF BLUE A (65) Music score (Jerry Goldsmith) with
'David And Lisa' (62-Mark Lawrence) -S/T- Import on
Mainstream USA (Koch Int): MDCD 607 (CD)
PATIENCE (OPERETTA) (Gilbert & Sullivan)
PRO-ARTE ORCHEST (Malcolm Sargent) and GLYNDEBOURNE
FESTIVAL CHOIR Soloists: John Shaw-Trevor Anthony-
Alex Young-George Baker *EMI: CMS 764406-2 (2CDs)*
PATIENCE -*D'Oyly Carte. Opera Company* (Gilbert/Sullivan)
New Symphony Orchestra Of London (Isidore Godfrey)
London (Poly): 425 193-2 (CDx2)
PATRICK (81) / **ROADGAMES** (78) Music scores (Brian May)
-S/T- *Australian Imp (Silva Screen):1MICD 1014 (CD)*
PATRIOT GAMES (92) Music sco (James Horner) -S/T- *Milan
(Pinn): 101504 (Cass) 101502 (CD) also available on
RCA Imp (Silva Screen): 66051-2 (CD) 66051-4 (Cass)*
includes 'Harry's Game' theme by CLANNAD
PATTON LUST FOR GLORY (70)Music score (Jerry Goldsmith)
-S/T- *S.Screen (Con): FILM 047 (LP)*

PATTY HEARST (88) Music score (Scott Johnson) -S/T- on
   Geffen (WEA): 979186-1 (LP) -4 (Cass) -2 (CD)
PEE WEE'S BIG ADVENTURE (87) Music score (Danny Elfman)
   -S/T- *Varese: C704 380 (Cas) VCD 47281 (CD)*
PEG (ORIG LONDON CAST 84) Songs (David Heneker) *featur:*
   Sian Phillips & Co *TER (Koch) TER(ZC)1024 (LP/Cass)*
PEGGY SUE GOT MARRIED (86) Music score (John Barry)
   -S/T- *TER:(ZC)TER1126 (Cas/LP) Varese: VCD 47275 CD*
PELLE THE CONQUEROR (Den/Swe 88) Music (Stefan Nilsson)
   -S/T- *Milan (S.Screen): CDCH 364 (CD) C 264 (Cass)*
PEOPLE UNDER THE STAIRS The (91) Music score (Don Peak-
   Graeme Revell) DON PEAKE -S/T-*Milan (Pinn):87310 CD*
   GRAEME REVELL *B.Cities (SS):BCD(BCC) 3022 (CD/Cass)*
PERCY (71) Music (Ray Davies) Songs sung by The Kinks
   -S/T- *Castle Classics (Castle-BMG): CLACD 164 (CD)*
PERFORMANCE (70) Music score (Jack Nitzsche) Songs by
   RANDY NEWMAN-RY COODER-MERRY CLAYTON-BUFFY SAINTE
   MARIE-LAST POETS -S/T- *WB (WEA): 7599 26400-2 (CD)*
PERSONAL SERVICES (87) Music score (John Duprez) "Chris
   tine's Theme" *Juan Martin 1st Night: SCORE 8 (7"s)*
PET SEMATARY (89) Music score (Elliott Goldenthal)-S/T-
   Varese (Pinn-Silva Screen) VSC(VSD) 5227 (Cass/CD)
PETER PAN (Film) - *see* WALT DISNEY FILM INDEX
PETER PAN (ORIG USA TV PROD 54) Music (Moose Charlap)
   Lyr (Carolyn Leigh) add.music/songs (Leonard Bernst
   tein Jule Styne-Bette Comden-Adolph Green) *feat:*
   Mary Martin & Cyril Ritchard on *RCA (Silva Screen):*
   3762-2 (CD) 3762-4 (Cass)
PETER PAN (ORIG BROADWAY CAST 54) *with* Boris Karloff-
   Jean Arthur *CBS USA (S.Screen) CK(JST)04312 (CD/CS)*
PETER'S FRIENDS (92) The Album (various artists) *Epic*
   (Sony): MOODCD 27 (CD) MOODC 27 (Cass) MOOD 27 (LP)
PETE'S DRAGON - *see* WALT DISNEY FILM INDEX
PHAEDRA (61) Music score (Mikis Theodorakis) -S/T- on
   Sakkaris (Pinn): SR 50060 (CD) + *COLL* 'MIKIS THEO.'
PHANTASM (79) Music score (Fred Myrow-Malcolm Seagrave)
   -S/T- *Silva Screen (Conifer): FILMCD 071 (CD)* also
   contains Music by Fred Myrow from 'Phantasm II'
PHANTOM: The American Musical Sensation (ORIG CAST 93)
   Songs (Maury Yeston) *feat:* Glory Crampton-Richard
   White-Paul Schoeffler-Jack Dabdoub and Company
   RCA Victor (BMG): 09026 61660-2 (CD)
PHANTOM OF THE OPERA (1925 silent Lon Chaney) New score
   by Rick Wakeman on 'Phantom Power' *Ambient Records*
   (AMT): A10M2 (CD) A10MC2 (Cass)
PHANTOM OF THE OPERA (89 Robert Englund version) featur
   Symphonic music score (Mischa Segal) -S/T- *Silva Sc*
   reen (Conifer): FILMCD 069 (CD) FILM 069 (LP)
PHANTOM OF THE OPERA (1)(ORIG LONDON CAST 86) Mus (Andr
   ew Lloyd Webber) Lyr (Charles Hart-Richard Stilgoe)
   with: Michael Crawford-Sarah Brightman and Company
   Polydor: PODV(C) 9 (Dbl LP/Cas) 813 273-2 (CD) also
   HIGHLIGHTS *831563-2(CD) -5(DCC) POLH(C) 33(Cass/LP)*
   see also Coll 'MUSIC AND SONGS FROM 'THE PHANTOM..'

PHANTOM OF THE OPERA (1)(SHOWS COLLECT.93) Studio Vers.
feat PAUL JONES-STEPHANIE LAWRENCE-CARL WAYNE-FIONA
HENDLEY *Pickwick: PWKS 4164 (CD) PWKMC 4164 (Cass)*
also contains songs from 'ASPECTS OF LOVE'
PHANTOM OF THE OPERA (2)(ORIG STAGE MUSICAL 92) Lyr:KEN
HILL with Additional Music by ALASDAIR MacNEILL and
set to Music by VERDI-DONIZETTI-GOUNOD-MOZART-OFFEN
BACH and BIZET / *Directed by* KEN HILL *and featuring*
Christina Collier-Richard Tate-Michael McLean-Peter
Straker (Phantom)-Steven Pacey-Haluk Bilginer-Toni
Palmer-Reginald Marsh-Tracy Gillman-Jacquel.Barron
D.Sharp (Pinn): DSHCD 7005 (CD) DSHMC 7005 (Cass)
PHENOMENA aka CREEPERS (USA) (84) Music by IRON MAIDEN
SIMON BOSWELL TURNER-BILL WYMAN-GOBLIN-MOTORHEADetc
Cinevox Italy (Silva Screen): CDCIA 5062 (CD)
PHILADELPHIA EXPERIMENT The (84) Music score (Ken Wannb
erg) -S/T- *also contains score from 'Mother Lode'*
Prometheus (Silva Screen): PCD 121 (CD)
PHILADELPHIA STORY The (40) Music score (Franz Waxman)
see 'Sunset Boulevard' (coll) *RCA: RD 87017 (CD)*
PIANO The (93) Music score (Michael Nyman) -S/T- on
Venture-Virgin (Poly): CDVE 919 (CD)
PICNIC (56) Music score (George Duning) -S/T- *MCA USA*
Import (Silva Screen): MCAD 31357 (CD)
PICNIC AT HANGING ROCK (75) Theme by Gheorge Zamfir
Additional music score by Bruce Smeaton - theme on
'Music From Great Australian Films' *DRG: SBL 12582*
PINK PANTHER The (63) Music score (Henry Mancini) -S/T-
RCA: ND(NK) 80832 (CD/Cass) see also TV section
PINOCCHIO (Disney 39) Music and Songs (Leigh Harline-Pa
ul Smith-Ned Washington) -S/T- *reissue: Disney/Pick*
wick: DSMCD 461 (CD) DSCC 461 (Cass)
PIPEDREAM (ORIG BROADWAY CAST 55)Songs (Richard Rodgers
Oscar Hammerstein II) *feat:* Helen Traubel-William
Johnson-Judy Tyler-Mike Kellin-G.D.Wallace & Comp.
RCA Victor (BMG): 09026 61481-2 (CD)
PIRATE The (FILM MUSICAL 48) Songs (Cole Porter) featur
JUDY GARLAND-GENE KELLY -S/T- *USA Imp(Silva Screen)*
AK 48608 (CD) AT 48608 (Cass)
PIRATES (86) Music score (Philippe Sarde) Paris Orchest
-S/T- *Milan: CDFMC 233 (CD)*
PIRATES OF PENZANCE The (OPERETTA) (Gilbert & Sullivan)
PRO-ARTE ORCHEST (Malcolm Sargent) and GLYNDEBOURNE
FESTIVAL CHOIR Soloists:George Baker-James Milligan
John Cameron-Richard Lewis *EMI: CMS 764409-2 (2CDs)*
PIRATES OF PENZANCE (OPERETTA Gilbert & Sullivan) *1989*
digital rec. D'Oyly Carte O.C. & Marilyn Hill Smith
TER (Con): CDTER2 (ZCTED) (TER2) 1177 (2CD/Cas/2LP)
PIRATES OF PENZANCE *The D'Oyly Carte Opera Company* with
Royal Philharmonic Orchestra conducted by I.Godfrey
London (Poly): 425 196-2 (CDx2) 425 196-4 (Cass)
PIRATES OF PENZANCE The (1929 Recording) featur: GEORGE
BAKER-PETER DAWSON-DEREK OLDHAM and Light Opera Orc
(Sir M.Sargent) *Pro-Arte (Sil.Screen): CDD 597 (CD)*

PISTOL FOR RINGO A - *see under* 'DEATH RIDES A HORSE'
PLAIN AND FANCY (ORIG BROADFWAY CAST 55) Music (Albert
  Hague) Lyrics (Arnold B.Horwitt) *feat:* BARBARA COOK
  SHIRL CONWAY-RICHARD DERR-DAVID DANIELS *Angel (EMI)*
  ZDM 764762-2 (CD)
PLANET OF THE APES (68) Music score (Jerry Goldsmith)
  -S/T- *Intrada Imp (Koch): FMTCD 8006 (CD)*
PLATOON (87) Music score (Georges Delerue) Main theme
  'Adagio For Strings' (Samuel Barber) Vancouver S.O.
  -S/T- *Atlantic (WEA): 781 742-2 (CD) WX 95 (Cass)*
PLATOON LEADER (88) Music score (George S.Clinton)
  -S/T- *Crescendo (S.Screen): GNPS(PD) 8013 (LP/CD)*
PLAY MISTY FOR ME (71) Song "First Time Ever I Saw Your
  Face" (E.MacColl) Roberta Flack *Old Gold: OG 9524*
  and "Misty" (Errol Garner) *CBS 32260 (LP) 40-(Cass)*
PLAYER The (91) Music score (Thomas Newman) -S/T- Impt
  Varese USA (Pinn): VSD 5366 (CD) VSC 5366 (Cass)
POETIC JUSTICE (92) Music score (Stanley Clarke) -S/T-
  Var.Arts *Epic (Sony): 474072-2 (CD) 474072-4 (Cass)*
POINT BREAK (91) Music score (Mark Isham) +Jimi Hendrix
  PIL-Ratt-LA Guns-Westworld-Liquid Jesus-Wiretrain
  MCA Geffen (BMG): MCAD(MCAC)(MCA) 10202 (CD/Cas/LP)
POINT OF NO RETURN - see under 'ASSASSIN, The'
POINT The (70) Music and songs by NILSSON / re-release
  Edsel (Pinn): EDCD 340 (CD) ED 40 (LP)
POLTERGEIST (82) Music score (Jerry Goldsmith) -S/T- on
  Polydor Imp (Silva Screen): MG 5408 (LP) deleted
POLTERGEIST II (86) Music score (Jerry Goldsmith) -S/T-
  (limited edition-Silva Screen): VJF 5002D (CD)
POLTERGEIST III (88) Music score (Joe Renzetti) -S/T-
  Varese (S.Screen) (VCD)(C)704.620 (CD/Cass/LP)
POPPIE NON GENA (MUSICAL 83) S.African Musical Joe Boyd
  CAST *Hannibal (Rev/APT):HNCD 1351(CD) HNBL 6301 LP*
POPPY (ORIG ROYAL SHAKESPEARE CAST 82) Songs (Monty Nor
  man-Peter Nichols) *WEA: 250000-1(LP) -4(Cass)*
PORGY AND BESS (ORIG BROADWAY CAST 42)*feat:* Todd Duncan
  Anne Brown-Edward Matthews-Helen Dowdy and Company
  MCA (BMG): MCLD 19158 (CD) MCLC 19158 (Cass)
PORGY & BESS (GLYNDEBOURNE FESTIVAL OPERA 88) with Will
  ard White-Cynthia Haymon-Damon Evans-Bruce Hubbard-
  London Philharmonic Orchestra (Simon Rattle) on *EMI*
  Angel: CDS 749 568-2 (Complete Opera - 3CDs) or LDB
  491 131-2 (2CDs) or CDC 754 325-2 (CD Highlights)
PORGY AND BESS (MUSICAL) Songs (G.& I.Gershwin & DuBose
  Heyward) Houston Grand Opera: Donnie Ray Albert-Cla
  mma Dale-Andrew Smith-Wilma Shakesnider-Betty Lane
  Complete Rec: *RCA Red Seal (BMG): RD 82109 (3 CDs)*
  Highlights Only: *RCA Red Seal (BMG): RD 84680 (CD)*
POSSE The (92) Music score (tbc) -S/T- *A.& M. (Polygr):*
  540 081-2 (CD) 540 081-4 (Cass)
POWAQQATSI (88) Music score (Philip Glass) -S/T- on
  Elektra Nonesuch (WEA): 7559 79192-2 (CD) -4(Cass)
POWER OF ONE The (92) Music score (Hans Zimmer) -S/T-
  Elektra (WEA): 755961335-2 (CD) 755961335-4 (Cass)

POWER The (67) Music score (Miklos Rozsa) Suite with mu
sic from 'BEN HUR' & 'KING OF KINGS' (12 choral pie
ces) on *Prometheus (Silva Screen): PCD 122 (CD)*

PRAYER FOR THE DYING A (88) Orig score: John Scott
(replaced by Bill Conti score) - John Scott version
available on *JOS (58 Dean Street Records): JSCD 102
(CD)* inc John Scott's score for 'Winter People'(89)

PREDATOR - *see* COLL 'UNIVERSAL SOLDIER'

PRELUDE TO A KISS (92) Music score (Howard Shore) -S/T-
Milan (Pinn): 11125-2 (CD) 11125-4 (Cass)

PRESUMED INNOCENT (90) Music score (John Williams)
-S/T- *Varese (Pinn):* VSD 5280 (CD) VSC 5280 (Cass)

PRETTY IN PINK (86) Music score (Michael Gore) songs by
V/A -S/T- *A.& M.(Poly):* (C)(CD)MID 157 (Cass/CD)

PRETTY WOMAN (89) Music score (James Newton Howard)
-S/T- *EMI USA (EMI):* (CD)(TC)MTL 1052 (CD/Cass/LP)

PRETTYVILLE (ORIG USA STAGE CAST) *featuring* ANGELA LANS
BURY and Company *Varese (Pinn):* VSD 5439 (CD)

PRICK UP YOUR EARS (87) Music score (Stanley Myers)
-S/T- *Silva Screen:* FILM 014 (LP) FILMC 014 (CS)

PRIDE AND THE PASSION The (57) Music score (George Anth
eil) *with* 'AGONY & THE ECSTASY' (Alex North) 75mins
Cloud Nine (S.Screen-Conif): CNS 5001 (CD)

PRINCE AND THE PAUPER The (77) Music sc (Maurice Jarre)
-S/T- *Varese USA (Pinn):* VSD 5207 (CD)

PRINCE OF DARKNESS (88) Music sc (John Carpenter & Alan
Howarth) -S/T- *Varese (Pinn):* VCD 47310 (CD)

PRINCE OF THE CITY (81) Music score (Paul Chihara)-S/T-
TER (Conifer): TER 1012 (LP)

PRINCE OF TIDES (92) Music score (James Newton Howard)
featuring songs by BARBRA STREISAND -S/T- *Columbia
(Sony M):* 468 735-2 (CD) 468 735-4 (Cass) -1 (LP)

PRINCE VALIANT (54) Music score (Franz Waxman) *see* Coll
'Sunset Boulevard' *RCA (BMG):* RD 87017 (CD)

PRINCESS BRIDE The (87) Music score (Mark Knopfler)
-S/T- *Vertigo:* VERH 53C (Cass) 832864-2 (CD)
see also 'Screenplaying' Collection

PRIVATE LIVES OF ELIZABETH AND ESSEX The (39) Music sco
(Erich Wolfgang Korngold) *Premier recording of the
complete score* MUNICH SYMPHONY ORCHEST (CARL DAVIS)
Bay Cities (Silva Screen): BCD 3026 (CD)

PRIZZI'S HONOR (87) Music score (Alex North) theme on
'Film Classics' Coll *DG (Poly)* 419630-2(CD)(no-S/T)

PROFESSIONALS The (66) Music sco (Maurice Jarre) -S/T-
Silva Treasury (Conif): SSD 5002 (CD)

PROFUNDO ROSSO (Horror Film) Music score (Goblin) -S/T-
Cinevox (S.Screen) CIAK 75005 (Cass) CIA 5005 (LP)

PROOF (91) Music composed and performed by NOT DROWNING
WAVING -S/T- *Alhambra Imp (S.Screen):* A.8927 (CD)

PROSPERO'S BOOKS (91) Music (Michael Nyman) -S/T-
Philips (Polyg): 425224-2(CD) 425224-4(Cass)

PSYCHO (60) Music score (Bernard Herrmann) N.P.O. also
'Suite From Psycho'& 'North By Northwest' (Film 59)
Milan (S.Screen): ACH(CCH)(CDCH) 022 (LP/Cass/CD)

PSYCHO 2 (83) Music score (Jerry Goldsmith) -S/T- Imprt
   Varese (Pinn): VSD 5252 (CD) VSC 5252 (Cass)
PSYCHO 3 (86) Music score (Carter Burwell) -S/T- Import
   MCA: IMCA 6174 (LP) IMCAC 6174 (Cass) deleted
PSYCHODERELICT (Rock Opera 93) Songs (Pete Townshend)
   Atlantic/East West (WEA): 7567 82494-2(CD) -4(Cass)
PUBLIC EYE (92) Music score (Mark Isham) -S/T- *Varese*
   (Pinn): VSD 5374 (CD) VSC 5374 (Cass)
PUMP BOYS AND DINETTES (ORIG BROADWAY CAST 84) *featur:-*
   John Floey-Mark Hardwick-Cass Morgan-Debra Monk *CBS*
   USA (Silva Screen): MK 37790 (CD) FMT 37790 (Cass)
PUNISHER The - *see COLL* 'UNIVERSAL SOLDIER'
PURE COUNTRY (92) Music comp/performed by GEORGE STRAIT
   -S/T- *MCA (BMG): MCD 10651 (CD) MCC 10651 (Cass)*
PURE LUCK (91) Music score (Jonathan Sheffer) -S/T- on
   Varese (Pinn-S.Screen):VSD 5330 (CD) VSC 5330 (Cas)
PURLIE (ORIG BROADWAY CAST 70)with Cleavon Little-Melba
   Moore *Imp (S.Screen) 60229-2 (CD) 60229-4 (Cass)*
PURPLE HAZE (82) -S/T- *not issued (see TELE-TUNES 1991)*
PURPLE RAIN (84) Music by Prince & The Revolution -S/T-
   WBros (WEA): 759 925 110-2 (CD) -4 (Cass) -5 (DCC)
PURPLE ROSE OF CAIRO The (85) Music score (Dick Hyman)
   -S/T- *WEA France (S.Screen): 252 225-1(LP) -4(Cass)*

Q - THE WINGED SERPENT (83) Music score: Robert Ragland
   -S/T- *Cerebus USA (Silva Screen): C.206 (LP)*
QB VII (Film/TV 74) Music score (Jerry Goldsmith) -S/T-
   Warner Bros USA (Silva Screen): 254 890-1 (LP)
QUADROPHENIA (79) Songs (Pete Townshend) Feat: The WHO
   Polydor (Polyg): 813 074-2 (2CD's) also available
   -S/T- *Polydor (Poly): 519 999-2 (CD)*
QUARTET (81) Music score (Richard Robbins) see Collect:
   'Merchant-Ivory 25th Anniversary'
QUATERMASS EXPERIMENT The (55) Main theme "Mars" from
   'The Planets Suite' (Gustav Holst) many recordings
QUEST FOR FIRE (81) Music score (Philippe Sarde) -S/T-
   Import (Silva Screen): CDFMC 1 (CD)
QUICKSILVER (86) Music score (Tony Banks) +music 'Lorca
   & The Outlaws' *Charisma (Virgin): CASCD 1173 (CD)*
QUIEN SABE - see under 'BULLET FOR THE GENERAL'
QUIET EARTH The (85) Music score (John Charles) *see*
   COLLECT 'HORROR AND SCIENCE FICTION FILM MUSIC'
QUIGLEY DOWN UNDER (90) Music score (Basil Poledouris)
   -S/T- *Intrada (S.Screen): MAF 7006D (CD) 7006Cass*
QUILLER MEMORANDUM The (66) Music score (John Barry)
   -S/T- *Varese (Silva Screen): VSD 5218 (CD)*
QUO VADIS (51) Music score (Miklos Rozsa) *Decca (Poly)*
   421265-4 (Cas) / theme TER: (Con) (CD)(ZC)TER 1135

RACE FOR THE YANKEE ZEPHYR (81) / SURVIVOR (80) Music
   (Brian May) *Australian Imp (S.Screen):1MI 1008 (CD)*
RADIO DAYS (87) Woody Allen Film with Jazz -S/T- Featur
   Tommy Dorsey Orch-Artie Shaw Orch-Allan Jones-Frank
   Sinatra etc. *RCA: PD 83017 (CD) PK 83017 (Cass)*

RADIO FLYER (91) Music score (Hans Zimmer) -S/T- Import
  (Silva Screen): 24454-2 (CD) 24454-4 (Cass)
RADIO TIMES (ORIG LONDON CAST 92) Songs (Noel Gay etc.)
  feat Tony Slattery-Kathryn Evans-Jeff Shankley & Co
  Polydor: 517 474-2 (CD) -4(Cass)
RAGE IN HARLEM A (91) Music sco.(Elmer Bernstein) -S/T-
  Sire (WEA):759926617-2 (CD) 759926617-4 (Cass) also
  Varese USA (Pinn-S.Screen): VSD(VSC) 5325 (CD/Cass)
RAGGED CHILD The (ORIG LONDON CAST RECORDING)
  First Night (Pinn): CAST 12 (LP) CASTC 12 (Cass)
RAGGEDY MAN (81) Music score (Jerry Goldsmith) -S/T- on
  Varese Sarabande CD Club: VCL 9101.7 (CD)
RAGGEDY RAWNEY The (88) Music score (Michael Kamen) and
  Songs by John Tams (Albion Band)& Maggie Bell -S/T-
  Silva Screen (Conif): FILM(C)(CD) 033 (LP/Cass/CD)
RAGING BULL (80) Theme "Intermezzo" 'Cavalleria Rustica
  na' (Mascagni) *var.recordings available all formats*
RAIDERS OF THE LOST ARK (82) Music score: John Williams
  -S/T- Import *(Silva Screen): 821 583-4 (Cass)*
RAILWAY CHILDREN The (70) Music (Johnny Douglas) Theme
  by Johnny Douglas 'On Stage' *Dulcima (Taylors):*
  DLCD(DLCT)110 (CD/Cass) / 'Dancing Feet' Andy Ross
  Orch - *President: PCOM(PTLC)PTLS) 1107 (CD/Cass/LP)*
RAIN MAN (89) Mus score (Hans Zimmmer) plus:Belle Stars
  Delta R.Boys-Etta James-Iar Gillan-Roger Glover etc
  -S/T-*Capitol EMI: CZ456 (CD) TCATAK 180 (Cass)*
RAINBOW The (89) Music score (Carl Davis) Philharmonia
  & Graunke Orchestra of Munich (Carl Davis) -S/T-
  Silva Screen (Conif): FILM(C)(CD) 040 (LP/Cass/CD)
RAINTREE COUNTY (58) Music score (Johnny Green) -S/T-
  USA Import (Silva Screen): 2PRCD 1781 (CDx2)
RAISIN (ORIG BROADWAY CAST 73) Mus (Judd Woldin) Lyrics
  (Robert Brittan) feat: Virginia Capers-Joe Morton-
  Ernestine Jackson-Ralph Carter-Debbie Allen-Robert
  Jackson-Ted Ross *Sony Broadway (Sony):CD 32754 (CD)*
RAISING ARIZONA (87) Music score (Carter Burwell) -S/T-
  TER 1140 (LP) ZCTER 1140 (Cass) c/w 'Blood Simple'
RAISING CAIN (92) Music score (Pino Donaggio) -S/T- on
  Milan (Pinn): 101302 (CD) 101304 (Cass)
RAKE'S PROGRESS (48) Music sc (William Alwyn) 'Calypso'
  from film played by London Symphony Orch (Richard
  Hickox) on *Chandos: CHAN 9243 (CD) ABTD 1606 (Cass)*
RAMBLING ROSE (91) Music score (Elmer Bernstein) -S/T-
  Virgin Movie Music (Poly):CDVMM 5(CD) TCVMM 5(Cass)
RAMBO 'FIRST BLOOD PART 1' (82) Music (Jerry Goldsmith)
  Import (Silva Screen): FMT 8001D (CD)
RAMBO 'FIRST BLOOD PART 2' (85) Music (Jerry Goldsmith)
  -S/T- *Coloss.(Pinn):CST 348005(CD) CST 8005SMC(Cas)*
RAMBO III (88) Music score (Giorgio Moroder) -S/T- *Poly*
  834 929-2 (CD) POLD 5227 (LP) deleted / Full Orches
  tral Score: Impt *Intrada (Silva Sc): RVF 6006D (CD)*
RANSOM (aka The Terrorists) (75) Music score (Jerry Gol
  dsmith) -S/T- includes 'The Chairman' (69) reissued
  by *Silva Screen (Conif): FILMCD 081 (CD)*

RAPID FIRE (92) Music score (Christopher Young) -S/T-
Varese (Pinn): VSD 5388 (CD) VSC 5388 (Cass)

RATTLE AND HUM (88) Music by U2 -S/T- *Island (Polyg):*
U 27 (Dbl LP) UC 27 (Cass) CID U27 (CD)

RAW DEAL (86) Music score and songs (Tom Bahler and var
artists) -S/T- *Varese (Pinn): VSD 47286 (CD) note:*
2nd movement of 'Piano Concerto No.3 in C.minor' by
(Beethoven) *not on soundtrack recording*

RAZORBACK (84) Music score (Iva Davies) *see COLLECTION*
'HORROR AND SCIENCE FICTION FILM MUSIC' *(S.Screen)*

RAZOR'S EDGE The (84) Music score (Jack Nitzsche) -S/T-
Preamble-5th Continent (S.Screen): PRCD 1794 (CD)

REACH FOR THE SKY (56) Music score (John Addison) on
'BIG WAR THEMES' (coll) *MFP: HR 8140 (Cass only)*

RE-ANIMATOR / BRIDE OF THE RE-ANIMATOR (85/86) Music by
Richard Band -S/T- *S.Screen (Conif) FILMCD 082 (CD)*

REAL McCOY (93) Music score (Brad Fiedel) -S/T- issued
Varese (Pinn): VSD 5450 (CD)

REBECCA (40) Music score (Franz Waxman) see collection
'Sunset Boulevard' *RCA: RD 87017 (CD)*

REBEL WITHOUT A CAUSE (55) Music sco (Leonard Rosenman)
complete score +music from 'GIANT' & 'EAST OF EDEN'
Import (Silva Screen): CIN 2206-2 (CD) -4 (Cass)

RED DAWN (84) Music score (Basil Poledouris) -S/T- Impt
Intrada USA (Silva Screen): RVF 6001D (CD)

RED HEAT (88) Music score (James Horner) -S/T- *Virgin*
(Poly): CDV 2558 (CD)

RED HOT AND BLUE (MUSICAL 36) Songs (Cole Porter) feat
ETHEL MERMAN + songs from 'STARS IN YOUR EYES' on
AEI USA (Silva Screen): AEICD 001 (CD)

RED KING WHITE KNIGHT (89) Music sco (John Scott) -S/T-
Intrada (Koch/Silva Screen): MAF 7016D (CD)

RED SCORPION (89) Music score (Jay Chattaway) -S/T- Imp
Varese USA (S.Screen): VSD 5230 (CD) VSC 5230 (Cas)
see also COLLECTION 'UNIVERSAL SOLDIER'

RED SHOE DIARIES (92) Music score (George S.Clinton) &
Songs by JAMES BROWN-OLETA ADAMS-RICHIE SAMBORA etc
-S/T- *Imp (S.Screen): 515 584-2 (CD)*(WILD ORCHID 2)

RED SHOES The (48) Music score (Brian Easdale) see Coll
'CLASSIC BRITISH FILM MUSIC' *(Silva Screen)*

REGARDING HENRY (91) Music score (Hans Zimmer) -S/T- on
EMI USA:CDMTL 1064(CD) TCMTL 1064(Cass) all deleted

RE-JOYCE! (ORIG VAUDEVILLE SHOW 89) Maureen Lipman as
Joyce Grenfell - *Legacy (Castle Comm-BMG): LLCD 129*
(CD) LLP 129 (LP) LLK 129 (Cass) all deleted

RENT-A-COP (88) Music score (Jerry Goldsmith) -S/T- on
Silva Screen Imp: FILM 025 (LP)   MAF 7022D (CD)

REPO MAN (84) Mus by Iggy Pop-Circle Jerks-Plugz -S/T-
MCA Imp (Silva Screen): MCAD 39019 (CD)

REQUIEM (ROCK REQUIEM 85) Music (Andrew Lloyd Webber)
Placido Domingo-Sarah Brightman-Paul Miles Kingston
E.Chamber Orch *EMI: EL 270 242-2/-4/-1 (CD/Cass/LP)*

RESCUERS The - *see under* WALT DISNEY FILM INDEX

RESCUERS DOWN UNDER The - *see* **WALT DISNEY FILM INDEX**

RESERVOIR DOGS (92) Mus supervisor Karyn Rachtman -S/T-
+ V.Arts *MCA (BMG): MCD 10793 (CD) MCC 10793 (Cass)*
RETRIBUTION (88) Music score (Alan Howarth) -S/T- on
Silva Screen (BMG): FILMCD 068 (CD) + 'Lost Empire'
RETURN OF DRACULA (58) Music score (Gerald Fried) selec
see *Collection* 'VAMPIRE CIRCUS'
RETURN OF MARTIN GUERRE The (83) Music (Michel Portal)
-S/T- *DRG (Con): SL 9514 (LP) SLC 9514 (Cass)* c/w:
'Julia' (Film 77) with music by Georges Delerue
RETURN OF RINGO The - see under 'DEATH RIDES A HORSE'
RETURN OF THE JEDI The - see under 'Star Wars 3'
RETURN OF THE LIVING DEAD (85) Music sc (Matt Clifford)
-S/T- *Big Beat (Ace): WIK(C) 38 (LP/CS) CDWIK 38 CD*
RETURN OF THE LIVING DEAD 2 (88) Music score (J.Peter
Robinson) -S/T- *Island (Poly): ISTA(ICT)(CIDST) 17*
RETURN OF THE MUSKETEERS (89) Music score (Jean-Claude
Petit) -S/T- *Milan (S.Screen): (C)DCH 383 (Cass/CD)*
RETURN OF THE SEVEN The (Film) see 'Magnificent 7 The'
RETURN TO OZ (85) Music score (David Shire) -S/T- with
LSO (D.Shire) *Bay Cities (S.Screen): BCD 3001 (CD)*
RETURN TO THE FORBIDDEN PLANET (Musical89)Bob Carlton's
1950's Sci-Fi Musical *Orig London Cast recording* on
Virgin: CDV 2631 (CD) V 2631 (LP) TCV 2631 (Cass)
REVENGE (90) Music score (Jack Nitzsche) -S/T- on
Silva Screen (Conif): FILMC(CD) 065 (Cass/CD)
see Collection 'BEST OF KEVIN COSTNER'
REVENGE IN EL PASO (I QUATTRO DELL'AVE MARIA)(spaghetti
western) Music score (Carlo Rustichelli) -S/T- *Impt
Cinevox Italy (Silva Screen): CDCIA 5094 (CD)*
REVENGE OF THE PINK PANTHER The (78) Music score (Henry
Mancini) -S/T- *Impt (S.Screen):91113-2(CD) -4(Cass)*
REVERSAL OF FORTUNE (90) Music score (Mark Isham) -S/T-
Milan France (S.Screen): CDCD 528 (CD) C.528 (Cass)
REVOLVER (-) Music score (Ennio Morricone) -S/T- import
Alhambra (Pinn): A.8919 (CD)
RICH IN LOVE (92) Music score (Georges Delerue) -S/T-
Varese (Pinn): VSD 5370 (CD) VSC 5370 (Cass)
RICHARD III (55) Music sco (William Walton) Academy Of
St.Martin-In-The-Fields (Neville Marriner) with Sir
John Gielgud *Chandos: CHAN 8841(CD) ABTD 1460(Cass)*
RICOCHET (91) Music score (Alan Silvestri) -S/T- *Varese
(Pinn): VSD 5344 (CD) VSC 5344 (Cass)*
RIDER ON THE RAIN (70) Music score (Francis Lai) -S/T-
Alhambra (Pinn): A.8926 (CD)
RIGHT STUFF The (83) Music score (Bill Conti)+ mus from
'North & South' -S/T- *Varese (Pinn): VSD 47250 (CD)*
RINK The (ORIG LONDON CAST 87/88) Songs (John Kander &
Fred Ebb) with Diane Langton-Josephine Blake & Comp
TER (Con): CD(ZC)TER 1155 (CD/Cass) Ltd editions
RINK The (ORIG BROADWAY CAST 89) with Liza Minnelli &Co
TER (Con): ZCTER 1091 (Cass) CDTER 1091 (CD)
RIO BRAVO (59) Title theme (D.Tiomkin-P.F.Webster) sung
by Dean Martin - *MFP (EMI): CDMFP 6032 (CD) also*
contains 'That's Amore' *(see 'Moonstruck' Film)*

RIO CONCHOS (64) Music score (Jerry Goldsmith) -S/T- on
   Intrada (Silva Screen): RVF 6007D(CD) also includes
   prelude from 65 film 'The Agony & The Ecstasy'
RIO GRANDE (50) Music score (Victor Young) -S/T- *Varese
   (Pinn): `VSD 5378 (CD)*
RISKY BUSINESS (83) Music: Tangerine Dream-Bob Seger
   -S/T- *Virgin: CDV 2302 (CD) OVEDC 240 (Cass)*
RIVER OF DEATH (88) Music score (Sasha Matson) -S/T on
   Silva Screen (Conifer): FILMCD 053 (CD)
RIVER RUNS THROUGH IT, A (92) Music score (Mark Isham)
   -S/T- *Milan (Pinn): 12469-2 (CD) 12469-4 (Cass)*
RIVER The (85) Music score (John Williams) -S/T- reiss
   Varese (Pinn-S.Screen):VSD 5298 (CD) VSC5298 (Cass)
ROAD HOUSE (89) Music score (Michael Kamen) -S/T-
   Arista (BMG): 409948 (Cass) 259948 (CD) deleted
ROADGAMES (81) / **PATRICK** (78) Music scores (Brian May)
   -S/T- *Australian Imp (Silva Screen): 1MI 1014 (CD)*
ROAR OF THE GREASEPAINT The (ORIG BROADWAY CAST 65)
   Songs (Leslie Bricusse-Anthony Newley) *with* Anthony
   Newley-Cyril Ritchard-Sally Smith-Joyce Jillson-Gil
   bert Price - *RCA Vict (BMG): GD(GK) 60351 (CD/Cass)*
ROBBERY UNDER ARMS (85) Music sc (Garry McDonald-Laurie
   Stone) -S/T- *Australian Imp (S.Screen): 1MICD 1013*
ROBE The (53) Music score (Alfred Newman) -S/T- *Varese
   (Pinn): VSD 5295 (CD) VSC 5295 (Cass)*
ROBERT AND ELIZABETH (ORIG LONDON CAST 1965) Music (Ron
   Grainer) Lyrics (Ronald Miller) *feat:* KEITH MICHELL
   JUNE BRONHILL-ANGELA RICHARDS-JEREMY LLOYD-JOHN CLE
   MENTS-ROBERT VAHEY-ROD McLENNAN-STELLA MORAY Orch
   cond: ALEXANDER FARIS *EMI Angel (EMI):CDANGEL 2(CD)*
ROBERT AND ELIZABETH (ORIG CHICHESTER THEATRE CAST 87)
   Songs (Ron Grainer-Ronald Miller) *1st Night (Pinn):
   CAST 8 (LP) CASTC 8 (Cass)*
ROBIN HOOD (73 Cartoon) *see* WALT DISNEY FILM INDEX
ROBIN HOOD (91) (w: Patrick Bergin) Music sco (Geoffrey
   Burgon) -S/T- *Silva Screen (Conifer): FILMC(CD) 083*
ROBIN HOOD: MEN IN TIGHTS (93) Music sco (Hummie Mann)
   -S/T- *Milan (Pinn): 17639-2 (CD) 17639-4 (Cass)*
ROBIN HOOD: PRINCE OF THIEVES (91) (w: Kevin Costner)
   Music score (Michael Kamen) song "(Everything I Do)
   I Do It For You" (B.Adams-R.Lange-M.Kamen) sung by
   BRYAN ADAMS *(A.& M): AM(AMY)(AMC)(AMCD) 789*   -S/T-
   M.Creek-Poly: 511 050-2(CD) -4(Cass) -1(LP) -5(DCC)
   see also COLL 'BEST OF KEVIN COSTNER'
ROBINSON CRUSOE & MAN FRIDAY (TV mini-ser 87) Music
   (Maurice Jarre) -S/T- *Silva Screen Imp PST 501 (LP)*
ROBOCOP (87) Music score (Basil Poledouris) -S/T- *TER
   (Conifer): (CD)ZCTER 1146 (CD/Cass/*
ROBOCOP 2 (90) Music score (Leonard Rosenman) -S/T- Imp
   Varese USA (Pinn): VSD 5271 (CD) VSC 5271 (Cass)
ROBOCOP 3 (93) Music score (Basil Poledouris) -S/T- on
   Varese USA (Pinn): VSD 5416 (CD)
ROBOTJOX (89) Music score (Frederic Talgorn) PARIS PHIL
   ORCH (Talgorn) *Prometheus (S.Screen): PCD 125 (CD)*

ROCK-A-DOODLE (91 animated) Music score (Robert Folk) -S/T- *Varese (Pinn): VSC 5362 (CD) VSC 5362 (Cass)*

ROCKETEER The (91) Music score (James Horner) -S/T- on *Hollywood (Pinn-Sony): HWD(CD)(MC) 14 (CD/Cass)* and through *Silva Screen: 61117-2 (CD) 61117-4 (Cass)*

ROCKY 1 (76) Music sc (Bill Conti) Song "Gonna Fly Now" (B.Conti-C.Connors-A.Robbins) Frank Stallone -S/T- *Liberty (Silva Screen) 46081-2 (CD) 46081-4 (Cass)*

ROCKY 2 (79) Music score (Bill Conti) -S/T- *Liberty USA (Silva Screen): 46082-2 (CD) 46082-4 (Cass)*

ROCKY 3 (83) Music score (Bill Conti)"Eye Of The Tiger" by SURVIVOR -S/T- *(S.Screen): 46561-2(CD) -4 (Cass)*

ROCKY 4 (85) Music score (Vince Di Cola) Songs by V.Art -S/T- *Imp (S.Screen):75240-2(CD) -4(Cass)*

ROCKY 5 (91) Music sco (Bill Conti) Songs V.Arts -S/T- *Capitol: CDEST 2137 (CD) see also COLL.* ROCKY STORY

ROCKY HORROR PICTURE SHOW (FILM MUSICAL 75) Songs (Rich ard O'Brien) Feat: Tim Curry-Little Nell-Meatloaf-Susan Sarandon -S/T- *Castle Communic (BMG): ROCKY 1 (4 CDs* which also incl. Orig London Cast Recording)

ROCKY HORROR PICTURE SHOW The (REVIVAL LONDON CAST 90) Songs (Richard O'Brien) *feat:* Tim McInnery-Adrian Edmondson-Gina Bellman and Company / *reissued on Music For Pleaure (EMI): CD(TC)MFP 5977 (CD/Cass)*

ROCKY HORROR PICTURE SHOW The (ORIG LONDON CAST 1973) *with* Tim Curry-Richard O'Brien-Little Nell-Jonathan Adams *First Night (Pinn): SCENEC(CD) 17 (CD/Cass)*

ROMANCE ROMANCE (ORIG BROADWAY CAST 88) Songs (Keith He rrmann-Barry Harman) *TER (Koch): CD(MC)TER 1161*

ROMEO AND JULIET (68) Music score (Nino Rota) -S/T- on *Cloud Nine (S.Screen): CNS 5000 (CD) BCN 5000 (Cas)*

ROOM WITH A VIEW A (86) Music score (Richard Robbins) -S/T- *DRG USA (Pinn): CDSBL 12588 (CD)*

ROSARY MURDERS The (88) Mus (Bobby Laurel-Don Sebesky) Royal Phil Or -S/T- *Cinedisc (S.Screen) CDC 1004 CD*

ROSE The (79) Feat: Bette Midler -S/T- *Atlantic (WEA): K 50681 (LP) K4 50681 (Cass) K2 50681 (CD)*

ROSE GARDEN The (89) - *see under* 'CRY IN THE DARK, A'

ROSE MARIE (FILM MUSICAL 36) Songs (Rudolph Friml-Herbe rt Stothart) Jeanette MacDonald-Nelson Eddy -S/T- *MCA USA (S.Screen): MCA 25009 (LP) MCAC 25009 (CS)*

ROSELYNE AND THE LIONS (89) Music sc (Reinhardt Wagner) -S/T- *Virgin Fr (S.Screen): 30696 (CD) 50696 (Cass)*

ROSEMARY'S BABY (68) Music score (Krzysztof Komeda) see Collections 'Omen The: 50 Years Of Classic...'

ROSOLINO PATERNO SOLDATO / KAPO (Italian films 60s) Mus (Carlo Rusticelli) *Cinevox (S.Scr): CDCIA 5091 (CD)*

ROTHSCHILDS The (ORIG BROADWAY CAST 70) Songs (Jerry Bo ck-Sheldon Harnick) *with* Hal Linden-Paul Hect-Keene Curtis-Leila Martin-Jill Clayburgh-Chris Sarandon-Leo Leyden-Tim Jerome *Sony Broadway: SK 30337 (CD)*

ROUND MIDNIGHT (86) Music sco (Herbie Hancock) with Dex ter Gordon -S/T- *CBS: CD 70300(CD) also* -S/T-'Other Side Of Round Midnight' *Bluenote: CDP 746386-2 (CD)*

ROUSTABOUT (64) *featuring* ELVIS PRESLEY *reissued* -S/T-
with 'Viva Las Vegas' (64) *RCA (BMG):74321 13432-2
(CD) 74321 13432-4 (Cass)*
ROVER The (67) Music score (Ennio Morricone) -S/T- also
includes 'OCEANO' *Impt (Silva Screen): OST 120 (CD)*
ROXANNE (87) Music score (Bruce Smeaton) -S/T- on *Silva
Screen (Conifer): FILM(C) 023 (LP/Cas) CDC 1000(CD)*
RUBY (92) Music score (John Scott) -S/T- *Intrada USA
(Koch Int): MAFCD 7026 (CD)*
RUDDIGORE (OPERETTA) (Gilbert & Sullivan)
PRO-ARTE ORCHEST (Malcolm Sargent) and GLYNDEBOURNE
FESTIVAL CHOIR Soloists: George Baker-Richard Lewis
Owen Brannigan-Harold Blackburn *EMI:764412-2 (2CDs)*
RUDDIGORE (MUSICAL OPERETTA 86) (Gilbert & Sullivan)
*New Sadlers Wells Cast - TER: TER2 1128 (Dbl Album)
ZCTED 1128 (Dblplay Cass) CDTER2 1128 (Dbl Co.Disc)*
RUDY (93) Music score (Jerry Goldsmith) -S/T- issued on
Varese (Pinn): VSD 5446 (CD)
RUMBLE FISH (83) Music score (Stewart Copeland) -S/T-
A.& M. (Polyg): CAM 64985 (Cass)
RUNNING MAN The (88) Music score (Harold Faltermeyer)
-S/T- reissue - *Colosseum (Pinn): CST 348032 (CD)*
RUSH (92) Music score (Eric Clapton) songs "Tears In He
aven" and "Help Me Up" (Eric Clapton-Will Jennings)
-S/T- *Reprise-WB (WEA):759926794-2 (CD) -4 (Cass)*
RUSSIA HOUSE The (90) Music score (Jerry Goldsmith)
-S/T- *MCA USA (S.Screen): MCAD(MCAC) 10136 (CD/Cas)*
RYAN'S DAUGHTER (70) Music score (Maurice Jarre) -S/T-
also incl -S/T- music to 'THE TRAIN'/'GRAND PRIX
MGM USA (Silva Screen): AK 47989 (CD)

S'EN FOUT LA MORT (Film Fra) Music score (Abdullah Ibra
him) -S/T- *Tiptoe-Enja (Pinn): TIP 888815-2 (CD)*
SAHARA (83) Music score (Ennio Morricone) -S/T- reissue
Intrada (Koch): MAF 7047CD (CD)
SAIL AWAY (ORIG BROADWAY CAST 61) Songs (Noel Coward)
feat: ELAINE STRITCH *Angel (EMI): ZDM 764759-2 (CD)*
SAINT LOUIS WOMAN (ORIG BROADWAY CAST 46) Songs (Harold
Arlen-Johnny Mercer) *feat:* PEARL BAILEY-HAROLD & FA
YARD NICHOLAS-RUBY HILL *Angel (EMI):ZDM 764662-2 CD*
SALAAM BOMBAY! (88) Music score (L.Subramaniam) -S/T-
DRG (Conifer): (CD)SBL(C) 12595 (CD/LP/Cass)
SALAD DAYS (Musical Show 82) Songs:Julian Slade-Dorothy
Reynolds *Revival* London Cast with Elizabeth Seal-Sh
eila Steafel *TER: CDTER 1018 (CD) ZCTER 1018 (Cass)*
SALVADOR (88) Music score (Georges Delerue) -S/T- *TER
(Conif): TER 1154 (LP) ZCTER 1154 (Cass) CDTER 1154
(CD)* - c/w 'Wall Street' S/Track (Stewart Copeland)
SALVATION (88) Music score (Arthur Baker) and New Order
Cabaret Voltaire-Dominique Davalos-Jumpin'Jesus-The
Hood (theme) -S/T- *Les Disques Du Crepescule Import
(Pinn): TWI 774 (LP) TWIC 774 (Cass) TWICD 774 (CD)*
SAMANTHA (Film) Music score (Joel McNeely) -S/T- on
Intrada (Koch): MAF 7040CD (CD)

SAMMY AND ROSIE GET LAID (87) Music score Stanley Myers
    Selection 'My Beautiful Launderette'/'Wish You Were
    Here' *Milan (S.Screen): C.369 (Cass) CDCH 369 (CD)*
SAND PEBBLES The (66) Music score (Jerry Goldsmith)
    -S/T- *Silva Screen (Conifer): FILM(C) 048 (LP/Cass)*
SANTA SANGRE (90) Music sco (Simon Boswell)+Circus Orgo
    Silver Hombre-Concha Y Fenix *President PCOM 1104 CD*
SARAFINA (ORIG BROADWAY CAST 89) *RCA (BMG): RD 89307
    (CD) RL 89307 (LP) RK 89307 (Cass deleted)*
SARAFINA: THE SOUND OF FREEDOM (92) Mus score (Stanley
    Myers) -S/T- var.arts *W.Bros (WEA) 936245060-2 (CD)*
SATURDAY NIGHT FEVER (78) Music by The Bee Gees -S/T-
    RSO: SPDLP 5 (2LP) 3517 014 (Cass) 800 068-2 (CD)
SAVAGES (Film 72) Music score (Joe Raposo) - see colls
    'Merchant-Ivory 25th Anniversary' Film music collec
SAY AMEN SOMEBODY (83) Various blues artists -S/T- on
    DRG USA: SB2L 12584(2LP) SB2LC(Cas) CDXP 12584 (CD)
SCANNERS (80) - *see under* 'DEAD RINGERS'
SCENT OF A WOMAN (92) Music score (Thomas Newman) -S/T-
    MCA (BMG): MCD 10759 (CD) MCC 10759 (Cass)
SCHOOL TIES (92) Music score (Maurice Jarre) -S/T- Impt
    WB USA (S.Screen): 924476-2 (CD) 924476-4 (Cass)
SCROOGE (ORIG LONDON CAST) Songs (Leslie Bricusse) *feat*
    ALBERT FINNEY & Company *TER (Koch): CDTER 1194 (CD)*
SCROOGED (88) Music score (Danny Elfman)-S/T- recording
    A.& M.(Poly): AMA(CDA) 3921 (LP/CD)
SEA HAWK The (40) Music score (Erich Wolfgang Korngold)
    TER (Koch): (ZC)TER 1164 (Cass/LP) CDTER 1164 (CD)
SEA OF LOVE (89) Music score (Trevor Jones) -S/T- on
    Spectrum (Polygram): 550130-2 (CD) -4 (Cass)
SEARCHING FOR BOBBY FISHER (93) Music score (James Horn
    er) -S/T- *Impt (S.Screen): 924 532-2 (CD) -4 (Cass)*
SEASON IN HELL A (-) Music score (Maurice Jarre) -S/T-
    Alhambra (Pinn): A.8923 (CD)
SECOND TIME LUCKY (Australia) Music (Garry McDonald-Lau
    rie Stone) *OneMone (Silva Screen): IMICD 1016 (CD)*
SECRET GARDEN The (92) Music score (Zbigniew Preisner)
    "Winter Light" (Z.Preisner-L.Ronstadt-E.Kaz) sung
    by Linda Ronstadt -S/T- *Varese (Pinn):VSD 5443 (CD)*
SECRET OF MY SUCCESS The (87) Music score: David Foster
    -S/T- *MCA Import (Silva Screen): MCAD 6205 (CD)*
SECRET OF NIMH The (82) Mus sco (Jerry Goldsmith) Songs
    (Paul Williams) -S/T- *TER (Koch): TERCD 1026 (CD)*
SECRET OF THE ICE CAVE (89)- *see under* 'FIELD OF HONOR'
SEESAW (Musical 73) Songs (Cy Coleman-Dorothy Fields)
    Orig BROADWAY Cast *DRG USA (Conif): CDRG 6108 (CD)*
SELFISH GIANT The (ORIG CAST RECORDING 93) Songs (Micha
    el Jenkins-Nigel Williams) *TER (Koch):TERCD1206(CD)*
SERPICO (73) Music score (Mikis Theodorakis) -S/T- on
    Sakkaris (Pinn): SR 50061 (CD) + COLL 'MIKIS THEO.'
SEVEN BRIDES FOR SEVEN BROTHERS (FILM MUSICAL 54) Songs
    (Gene DePaul-Johnny Mercer) Howard Keel-Jane Powell
    -S/T- + 'Lillie' *EMI CD(TC)MGM 9 (CD/Cass) deleted*
SEVEN BRIDES FOR SEVEN BROTHERS (ORIG LONDON CAST 86)

with new songs by Al Kasha and Joel Hirschhorn *with*
Roni Page-Steve Devereaux-Geoff Steer-Peter Bishop-
Jackie Crawford *First Night (Pinn): OCRCD 8 (CD)*
SEVEN MAGNIFICENT GLADIATORS - *see* 'ALLAN QUATERMAIN'
SEVEN WAVES AWAY (56) Music score (Sir Arthur Bliss)
   see under 'CHRISTOPHER COLUMBUS'
SEVENTH SIGN The (88) Music score (Jack Nitzsche) -S/T-
   Cinedisc (S.Screen): EDL 2506-2 (CD) -1 (LP)
70 GIRLS 70 (ORIG LONDON CAST 91) Songs (John Kander-Fr
   ed Ebb) *with* Dora Bryan and Company
   TER (Conifer): CDTER 1186 (CD) ZCTER 1186 (Cass)
70 GIRLS 70 (ORIG BROADWAY CAST 71) Songs (John Kander-
   Fred Ebb) *feat* Mildred Natwick-Hans Conreid-Lillian
   Roth-Gil Lamb-Lillian Hayman-Lucie Lancaster-Goldye
   Shaw-Dorothea Freitag *Sony Broadway: SK 30589 (CD)*
1776 (ORIG BROADWAY CAST 69) Songs (Sherman Edwards)
   with William Daniels-Howard Da Silva-Ken Howard-BJ
   Slater-Betty Buckley *Sony Broadway: SK 48215 (CD)*
SEX LIES & VIDEOTAPE (89) Music score (Cliff Martinez)
   -S/T- *Virgin: CDV 2604 (CD)*
SHADOW OF THE WOLF (92) Music score (Maurice Jarre)
   -S/T- *Milan (Silva Screen): 35634-2 (CD) -4 (Cass)*
SHAFT (71) Music (Isaac Hayes) Theme: *Stax (Pinn):*
   STAX 810 (7") -S/T- (CD)SXD(C) 2021 (CD/Cass/2LP)
   also on Import (Silva Screen): 78.701 (Cass)
SHAKA ZULU *featuring* LADYSMITH BLACK MAMBEZO -S/T- on
   Warner Bros (WEA): 7599 25582-2 (CD) WX 94C (Cass)
SHAKESPEARE WALLAH (Film India 65) Music (Satyajit Ray)
   see Collections 'Merchant-Ivory 25th Anniversary'
SHANE (Film 53/TV 66) Song "Call Of The Faraway Hills"
   (Victor Young-Mac David) *Col* 'GREAT WESTERN THEMES'
SHATTERED (91) Music score (Alan Silvestri)song "Nights
   In White Satin" (J.Hayward) sung by The Moody Blues
   -S/T- *Milan (Pin-S.Screen): 262208(CD) 412208(Cass)*
   see COLL 'HORROR AND SCIENCE FICTION FILM MUSIC'
SHE (65) Music (James Bernard) - *see* Collections
   'Omen The: 50 Years of Classic Horror Film Music'
SHE LOVES ME (ORIG BROADWAY CAST 63) Songs (Jerry Bock-
   Sheldon Harnick) *feat:* Barbara Cook & Daniel Massey
   Imp (S.Scr):CD 831968-2(CD) Varese (Pinn): VSD 5464
SHE'S GOTTA HAVE IT (87) Music score (Bill Lee) with
   Ronnie Dyson-Cedar Walton-Harold Vick and others
   -S/T- *Antilles (Island): AN(C) 8713 (LP/Cass)*
SHELTERING SKY The (90) Music score (Ryuichi Sakamoto)
   -S/T- *Virgin (Poly): CDV (TCV) 2652 (CD/Cass)*
SHENANDOAH (ORIG BROADWAY CAST 75) Music (Gary Geld)
   Lyrics (Peter Udell) *with* John Cullum and Company
   RCA Victor (BMG): GD 83763 (CD) GK 83763 (Cass)
SHERLOCK HOLMES The Musical (ORIG LONDON CAST 92) Songs
   (Leslie Bricusse) *feat:* ROBERT POWELL-ROY BARRACLOU
   GH-LOUISE ENGLISH *TER (Koch): TERCD(TERZC) 1198*
SHERLOCK HOLMES (ORIG LONDON CAST 88) *RCA: BD(BK) 74145*
SHINING THROUGH (91) Music score (Michael Kamen) -S/T-
   Milan (Pinn): 262 742 (CD) 412 742 (Cass)

SHIP HUNTERS (-) Music score (Ennio Morricone) -S/T- *Im*
ort (Silva Screen): OST 109 (CD)
SHIRLEY VALENTINE (89)Music score (Willy Russell-George
Hatzinassios) "The Girl Who Used To Be Me" (Marvin
Hamlisch) sung by Patti Austin -S/T- *Silva Screen
(Conifer): FILM(C)(CD) 062 (LP/Cass/CD)*
SHOCK TO THE SYSTEM A (90) Music score (Gary Chang) and
TURTLE ISLAND STRING QUARTET on *Windham Hill Jazz
(New Note-Pinn): WD 0123 (CD)*
SHOCKER (89) Music **score** (William Goldstein) -S/T- Impt
Varese USA (Pin):VSD 5247 (LP) V(VC) 5247 (LP/Cass)
SHOGUN MAYEDA (91) Music score (John Scott) -S/T- Imprt
Intrada USA (Koch Int): MAFCD 7017 (CD)
SHOOT (92) Music score (Randy Edelman) -S/T- *Milan
(Pinn): 412371 (Cass) 262371 (CD)*
SHOOTING PARTY The (85) Music score (John Scott) Royal
Phil Orch (J.Scott) *J.Scott (Movie B) JSCD 113 (CD)*
SHOUT (91) Music score (Randy Edelman) -S/T- *USA Import
(Silva Screen): 262371 (CD) 412371 (Cass)*
SHOW OF FORCE A (89) Music score (Georges Delerue)-S/T-
Colosseum Impt (Pinn-S.Screen): XCD 1005 (CD)
SHOW BOAT (Film Musical 51) Songs (Jerome Kern-Oscar Ha
mmerstein) Howard Keel-Ava Gardner-Kathryn Grayson
-S/T- *MGM (EMI): CD(TC)MGM 10 (CD/Cass) all deleted*
SHOW BOAT (Shows Coll 93) *feat:* Gemma Craven-Denis Quil
ley-David Kernan-Tracey Miller *Pickwick: PWKS 4161
(CD) PWKMC 4161 (Cass)* see also under COLLECTIONS
SHOW BOAT (Studio Recording 93) National Symphony Orch
estra (John Owen Edwards) and Various Artists on
TER (Koch): CDTER 1199 (CD) ZCTER 1199 (Cass)
SHOW BOAT (Revival USA Cast 91) LINCOLN CENTER THEATRE
RCA (BMG): 09026 61182-23 (CD)
SHOW BOAT (Studio Recording 88)(1st complete) *featuring*
Frederica Von Stade-Jerry Hadley-Teresa Stratas-Bru
ce Hubbard-Karla Burns-David Garrison-Paige O'Hara-
Robert Nichols Nancy Kulp-Lillian Gish with the Amb
rosian Chorus and London Sinfonietta (John McGlinn)
*EMI HMV: RIVER 1 (3LP) TCRIVER 1 (3Cass) CDRIVER 1
(3CD)* HIGHLIGHTS:*CDC 749847-2 (CD) EL 749847-1/-4*
SHOW BOAT (Orig London Cast 71) *with* Cleo Laine-Thomas
Carey-Lorna Dallas-Miguel Godreau-Kenneth Nelson &
& Comp *TER (Koch): TER 1057 (LP) ZCTER 1057 (Cass)*
SHOW BOAT (Studio USA Cast 62) with John Raitt-Barbara
Cook *Col (S.Screen): CK 02220 (CD) JST 02220 (Cass)*
SHOW BOAT (Orig London Cast 59) *with* Shirley Bassey-Mar
lys Watters-Don McKay-IniaWiata-Dora Bryan-Geoffrey
Webb-Isobel Lucas & Michael Collins Orchestra & Com
reissue: *First Night (Pinn): OCR 1 (LP) OCRC 1 (CS)*
SHOW BOAT (Orig Broadway Revival Cast 46) *featur:* Jan
Clayton-Carol Bruce-Charles Fredericks-Kenneth Spen
cer-Colette Lyons *Sony Broadway: SK 53330 (CD)*
SHOWDOWN IN LITTLE TOKYO *see COLL* 'UNIVERSAL SOLDIER'
SHY PEOPLE (88) Music (Tangerine Dream) -S/T- Import on
Silva Screen (Con): FILM(C)(CD) 027 (LP/Cass/CD)

SICILIAN The (87) Music score (David Mansfield) -S/T-
     Virgin (Silva Screen): 90682-2 (CD)
SIDE BY SIDE BY SONDHEIM (ORIG LONDON CAST 84) *with* Mil
     licent Martin-David Kernan-Julia McKenzie and Comp
     RCA Victor (BMG): GD 81851 (CD) GK 81851 (Cass)
SIESTA (88) Music score (Marcus Miller and Miles Davis)
     -S/T- *W.Bros (WEA) K925655-4 (Cass) -2 (CD)*
SILENCE OF THE LAMBS The (91) Music sco. (Howard Shore)
     -S/T- *MCA (BMG): MCAD 10194 (CD)*
SILK STOCKINGS (FILM MUSICAL 57) Songs (Cole Porter)
     feat Fred Astaire-Cyd Charise + 'Les Girls' -S/T-
     EMI:CDMGM 16(CD) LPMGM 16(LP) TCMGM 16(Cas) deleted
SILK STOCKINGS (ORIG BROADWAY CAST 55) with Don Ameche
     Import (Silva Screen): 1102-2 (CD) 1102-4 (Cass)
SILVERADO (85) Music score (Bruce Broughton) -S/T- on
     Intrada (Koch): MAF 7035CD (CD)
SINCE YOU WENT AWAY (44) *see* 'STREETCAR NAMED DESIRE A'
SINGIN' IN THE RAIN (FILM MUSICAL 52) Songs (Nacio Herb
     Brown-Arthur Freed) Feat Gene Kelly-Debbie Reynolds
     -S/T- *MGM (EMI): CDMGM 4 (CD)*
SINGIN' IN THE RAIN (ORIG LONDON CAST 83) *with* Tommy St
     eele-Roy Castle-Sarah Payne-Danielle Carson & Comp.
     MD:Michael Reed *First Night (Pinn): OCRCD 6013 (CD)*
SINGLE WHITE FEMALE (92) Music (Howard Shore) *no -S/T-*
     "Spiritual High" by MOODSWINGS available on 'Moodfo
     od' *Arista (BMG): 74321 11170-29 (CD) -43 (Cass)*
SINGLES (92) -S/T- *Epic (Sony) 471 438-2(CD) -4(Cass)*
SINK THE BISMARCK! (60) Music (Clifton Parker) *see*
     'Big War Themes' (coll) *MFP: HR 8140 (Cass only)*
SISTER ACT (92) Music Score (Marc Shaiman) -S/T- *Holly
     wood (Sony Music): HWDCD 29 (CD) HWDMC 29 Cass)*
SISTERS (72) Music score (Bernard Herrmann) -S/T- Imprt
     Southern Cross (Silva Screen): SCCD 903 (CD)
SIX WEEKS (82) Music score (Dudley Moore) DUDLEY MOORE
     on *GRP (BMG): GRP 96612 (CD) GRP 96614 (Cass)*
633 SQUADRON (64) Music sco (Ron Goodwin) -S/T- *deleted*
     see COLL 'BIG WAR THEMES'/'SALUTE TO HEROES'
SKETCH ARTIST (92) Music score (Mark Isham) -S/T-*Varese*
     USA (Pinn): VSD 5376 (CD) VSC 5376 (Cass)*
SKIN The (LA PELLE/LA PEAU)(81) Mus sco (Lalo Schifrin)
     -S/T- *Cinevox Italy (Silva Screen): CDCIA 5095 (CD)*
SKY OVER BERLIN The (87) Music score (Jurgen Knieper)
     -S/T- *Milan (S.Screen): A316(LP) C316(CS) CD316(CD)*
SKY PIRATES (Austral) Music score (Brian May) -S/T- on
     OneMOne (Silva Screen): IMICD 1002 (CD)
SLAM DANCE (87) Music score (Mitchell Froom) -S/T- on
     Island: ISTA 15 (LP) ICT 15 (Cass) CIDST 15 (CD)
SLEEPING BEAUTY - *see under* WALT DISNEY FILM INDEX
SLEEPING WITH THE ENEMY (91) Music sc (Jerry Goldsmith)
     inc "Brown Eyed Girl" composed/sung by Van Morrison
     -S/T- *Columbia (SM) 468126-2 (CD) -4 (Cass) deleted*
SLEEPLESS IN SEATTLE (93) Music sc (Marc Shaiman) -S/T-
     feat:J.DURANTE-L.ARMSTRONG-N.KING COLE-DR.JOHN-GENE
     AUTRY etc.*Epic (Sony) 473 594-2(CD) -4(Cass) -1(LP)*

SLEEPWALKERS (92) Music score (Nicholas Pike) -S/T- Imp
  Milan (Pinn): 10132-4 (Cass) 10132-2 (CD)
SLICE OF SATURDAY NIGHT A (ORIG LONDON CAST 89 Arts The
  atre Club / Mus.Dir.(Keith Hayman) *with* Binky Baker
  David Easter-Claire Parker-Mitch Johnson-Roy Smiles
  Debi Thomson-James Powell-Lisa Hollander /recording
  on *First Night (Pinn): QUEUE(C)(CD) 2 (LP/Cass/CD)*
SLIPPER AND THE ROSE (76)Songs (Richard/Robert Sherman)
  -S/T- *MCA USA (S.Screen): MCA(MCAC) 1540 (LP/Cass)*
SLIVER (93) Music score (Howard Shore) var.artists inc:
  UB40 "Can't Help Falling In Love With You" & NENEH
  CHERRY-MASSIVE ATTACK-SHAGGY-ENIGMA etc. -S/T- on
  Virgin Movie Mus (EMI): CD(TC)VMMX 11 (CD/Cass)
SNAPPER The (93) - *see TELEVISION section*
SNEAKERS (92) Music sco (James Horner) *feat:* Branford
  Marsalis) -S/T- *Col (Sony): 472 427-2(CD) -4(Cass)*
SNOOPY THE MUSICAL (ORIG LONDON CAST 82) Songs (Larry
  Grossman-Hal Hackady) *with* Teddy Kempner-Zoe Bright
  TER (Koch): TERCD 1073(CD) see 'CHARLY BROWN' (TV)
SNOOPY THE MUSICAL (ORIG USA CAST RECORDING 81) on
  DRG USA (Pinn): CDRG 6103 (CD)
SNOW WHITE AND THE SEVEN DWARFS (37) Music Songs (Frank
  Churchill-Leigh Harline-Paul J.Smith) feat: ADRIANA
  CASELOTTI -S/T- *Reiss: Disney (Pick):DSTCD 456 (CD),
  DSTMC 456 (Cass) see* WALT DISNEY FILM INDEX
SNOWMAN The (Film Cart.C4 Xmas each year) Music score
  (Howard Blake) song "Walking In The Air" (H.Blake)
  sung by PETER AUTY with Sinfonia Of London -S/T- on
  Columbia (Sony Music): CD 71116 (CD) 40-71116 (Cas)
SNOWS OF KILIMANJARO The (52) Music score (Bernard Herr
  mann) 'Citizen Kane' *Decca 417852-2 (CD)-4 (Cass)*
SO I MARRIED AN AXE MURDERER (93) Music score (Bruce Br
  oughton)-S/T- featuring Various Artists on *Columbia
  (Sony Music): 474 273-2 (CD) 474 273-4 (Cass)*
SOAPDISH (91) Music score (Alan Silvestri) -S/T- *Varese
  (Pinn-S.Screen): VSC 5322 (Cass) VSD 5322 (CD)*
SOFT TOP HARD SHOULDER (92) Music score & songs (Chris
  Rea) title song sung by CHRIS REA - *East-West (WEA)
  YZ 710CD (CDsingle) YZ 710C (Cass) YZ 710 (7"s)*
SOME CAME RUNNING (58) Music sco (Elmer Bernstein) also
  incl -S/T- to KING'S GO FORTH (58-Elmer Bernstein)
  Cloud Nine/Silva Prod (Conif): CNS 5004 (CD)
SOME KIND OF WONDERFUL (87) Music prod.by Stephen Hague
  Various Artists include: STEPHEN DUFFY-JESUS AND
  MARY CHAIN-PETE SHELLEY-FURNITURE -S/T- *reissued on
  Beat Goes On (Pinn): BGOCD 178 (CD) also on import
  MCA USA (S.Screen): MCAD 6200 (CD) MCAC 6200 (Cass)*
SOME LIKE IT HOT (ORIG LONDON CAST 92)Music(Jule Styne)
  Lyrics (Bob Merrill) *with* Tommy Steele-Billy Boyce-
  Royce Mills-Mandy Perryment and Company *First Night
  (Pinn): CASTCD 28 (CD) CASTC 28 (Cass)* title number
  by TOMMY STEELE on *First Night: SCORECD 33 (CDs)*
SOME LIKE IT HOT (59) Music score (Adolph Deutsch) with
  Marilyn Monroe -S/T- *UA EMI: UAS 30226 (LP) deleted*

SOMETHING WILD (87) Music score (David Byrne) Featuring
Fine Young Cannibals-UB 40 others -S/T- *MCA (Silva
Screen): MCAD 6194 (CD) MCAC 6194 (Cass)*
SOMEWHERE IN TIME (80) Music score (John Barry) -S/T-
MCA Import (Silva Screen) MCAD 31164 (CD)
see *Coll* 'MOVIEOLA'
SOMMERSBY (93) Music score (Danny Elfman) -S/T- *Elektra
(WEA): 7559 61491-2 (CD) -4 (Cass)*
SON OF DARKNESS TO DIE FOR II (91) Music score (Mark Mc
Kenzie) -S/T- *Prometheus (S.Screen): PCD 110 (CD)*
SON OF THE PINK PANTHER (93) Music (Henry Mancini) with
theme performed by BOBBY McFERRIN -S/T- *USA Import
(Silva Screen): 66319-2 (CD) 66319-4 (Cass)*
SONDHEIM: A MUSICAL TRIBUTE ORIGINAL BROADWAY CAST *with*
Dorothy Collins-Chita Rivera-Angela Lansbury etc.
RCA Vict: RD 60515 (2CDs)
SONG AND DANCE (ORIG LONDON CAST 82) Songs (Don Black
Andrew Lloyd Webber) *feat* Marti Webb and Company
Polydor: 843 619-2 (CD) PODV 4 (2LP) PODVC 4 (2Cas)
SONG AND DANCE / TELL ME ON A SUNDAY (STUDIO RECORD 84)
featuring Sarah Brightman and Wayne Sleep *RCA (BMG)
BL 70480 (LP) BK 70480 (Cass)*
SONG OF NORWAY (STUDIO RECORDED MUSICAL) Songs (Robert
Wright-George Forrest adapted from music by Edvard
Grieg) *feat:* VALERIE MASTERSON-DONALD MAXWELL-DIANA
MONTAGUE-AMBROSIAN CHORUS-PHILH.ORCH (John Owen Edw
ards) *TER (Con): CDTER 21173 (2CD) ZCTED 1173 (Cas)*
SONG OF SINGAPORE (ORIGINAL USA CAST) *DRG USA (Conifer)
CDSBL 19003 (CD)*
SONG OF THE SOUTH - see WALT DISNET FILM INDEX
SOPHIE'S CHOICE (83) Orig music (Marvin Hamlisch) -S/T-
Southern Cross (S.Screen) SCCD 902(CD)
SOPHISTICATED LADIES (ORIG BROADWAY CAST) *feat* Duke Ell
ington songs *Impt (S.Screen):56208-2(CD) -4(Cass)*
SORCERER The - see *under* 'Wages Of Fear' (Film 78)
SOUND BARRIER The (52) Music score (Malcolm Arnold)
"Rhapsody" 'Film Music' London Symphony Orch (Rich
ard Hickox) *Chandos: CHAN 9100 (CD) ABTD 1600(Cass)*
also by Royal Philharmonic Orch (Kenneth Alwyn)
Cloud Nine (Conifer): CNS 5446 (CD single)
SOUND OF MUSIC The (FILM MUSICAL 65) Songs (Rodgers-Ham
merstein) Feat: Julie Andrews-Christopher Plummer-
-S/T- *RCA (BMG): ND 90368 (CD) NL/NK 90368 (LP/Cas)*
SOUND OF MUSIC The (ORIG BROADWAY CAST 59) with Mary Ma
rtin *Col (S.Screen): CK 32601 (CD) JST 32601 (Cass)*
SOUND OF MUSIC The (ORIG LONDON CAST 61)*with* Jean Bayle
ss-Constance Shacklock-Olive Gilbert-Sylvia Beamish
Lynn Kennington *1st Night (Pinn) OCR(C) 2 (LP/Cass)*
SOUND OF MUSIC The (REVIVAL LONDON CAST 81) *with* Petula
Clark-Honor Blackman-Dave Willetts and Company
CBS 40-32670 (Cass) CBS: CD 70212 (CD) deleted
SOUND OF MUSIC The (SHOWS COLLECT.STUDIO RECORD) *featur*
DENIS QUILLEY-LIZ ROBERTSON-LINDA HIBBERD-MASTER SI
GERS *Pickwick Shows:PWKS 4145(CD) PWKMC 4145 (Cass)*

SOUTH PACIFIC (FILM MUSICAL 58) Songs (Rodgers-Hammerst
    ein) Feat: Mitzi Gaynor-Rossano Brazzi (sung by Gio
    rgio Tozzi) John Kerr-Juanita Hall (sung by Muriel
    Smith) -S/T- *RCA (BMG): (ND)(NK)NL 83681 (CD/CS/LP)*
SOUTH PACIFIC (ORIG BROADWAY CAST 49) *feat:* Mary Martin
    Ezio Pinza-Juanita Hall-Barbara Luna-Michael DeLeon
    Myron McCormick-William Tabbert-Betta St.John
    Sony Broadway (Sony Music): SK 53327 (CD)
SOUTH PACIFIC (STUDIO RECORDING 86) *feat* Kiri Te Kanawa
    Jose Carreras-Sarah Vaughan-Mandy Patinkin-Ambrosia
    Singers-London Symphony Orc (Jonathan Tunick) - *CBS
    CD 42205 (CD) 40-42205 (Cass)* see also WEST SIDE S
SOUTH PACIFIC (REVIVAL LONDON CAST 88)*with* Gemma Craven
    Beatrice Reading and Company *First Night (Pinn):
    CAST 11 (LP) CAST C11 (Cass) CAST CD 11 (CD)*
SOUTH PACIFIC (SHOWS COLLECTION 1993) Various Artists
    Pickwick: PWKS 4162 (CD) PWKMC 4162 (Cass)
SPACEMAN AND KING ARTHUR The (79) Music score (Ron Good
    win)main theme on 'Drake 400' col *Chandos (Chandos)
    LBRD 001 (LP) LBTD 001 (Cass)*
SPARTACUS (USA-60/renovated 91) Music score: Alex North
    -S/T- reissue - *MCA USA (S.Screen): MCAD 10256 (CD)*
SPARTACUS (Jeff Wayne's Musical Version 92) *Columbia
    (Sony M): 472030-4 (2 Cass) 472030-2 (2CD)*
SPEEDWAY (68) - *see* 'Elvis Presley Film Index'
SPELLBOUND (45) Music (Miklos Rozsa) *Dunhill (S.Screen)
    DUN(CD) 116 (LP/CD)* / *see* Collec 'THIRD MAN'
SPINAL TAP - *see under* 'This Is Spinal Tap'
SPLIT SECOND (92) Music score (Stephen Parsons-Francis
    Haines) songs v.arts-S/T- *Milan (Pinn): 873117(CD)*
SPY WHO LOVED ME The - *see* JAMES BOND FILM INDEX
ST. - *see under* 'SAINT...'
STAGE DOOR CANTEEN (FILM MUSICAL 43) Music score (Fredd
    ie Rich) *feat* Benny Goodman-Guy Lombardo-Kay Kayser
    -S/T- *Sandy Hook USA (Derann-Pinn): CDSH 2093 (CD)*
STAGECOACH (66) Music score (Jerry Goldsmith) with 'The
    Trouble With Angels' (66-Jerry Goldsmith) -S/T- on
    Mainstream USA (Koch Int): MDCD 607 (CD)
STAIRWAY TO THE STARS (ORIG LONDON CAST) *First Night
    (Pinn): CAST(C)(CD) 21 (LP/Cass/CD)*
STAND BY ME (87) Music sco (Jack Nitzsche)+ Var.Artists
    Atlantic (WEA): 781 677-2 (CD) -4 (Cass
STANLEY AND IRIS (89) Music score (John Williams) -S/T-
    Varese (Pinn): VS(VSC)(VSD) 5255 (LP/Cas/CD)
STAR IS BORN A (54) Feat Judy Garland-James Mason -S/T-
    CBS USA (S.Screen): CK 44389 (CD) JST 44389 (Cass)
STAR IS BORN A (76) Featuring Barbra Streisand and Kris
    Kristofferson -S/T- *CBS 40-86021 (Cass)*
STAR SPANGLED RHYTHM (FILM MUSICAL 42) Songs (H.Arlan-
    J.Mercer) Feat: Bing Crosby-Betty Hutton -S/T- on
    Sandy Hook (USA) (Derann-Pinn): CDSH 2045 (CD)
STAR TREK 1 'The Motion Picture' (79) Music sco (Jerry
    Goldsmith) -S/T- *Columbia (S.Screen): CK 36334 (CD)
    PST 36334 (Cass)* with orig Alex.Courage theme

STAR TREK (2) 'The Wrath Of Khan' (82) Music sco (James
    Horner) -S/T- *GNP USA Import (S.Screen): GNPD 8022
    (CD) GNP-5 8022 (Cass)* with orig Alex.Courage theme
STAR TREK (3) 'Search For Spock'(84) Music score (James
    Horner) -S/T- *Silva Screen (Conif): FILMCD 070 (CD)
    GNP-5 8023 (Cass)*
STAR TREK (4) 'The Voyage Home' (87) Music sco (Leonard
    Rosenman) -S/T- *MCA (Silva Screen): MCAD 6195 (CD)*
STAR TREK (5) 'The Final Frontier' (89) Music sc (Jerry
    Goldsmith)-S/T- *Epic: 465925-2(CD) -4(Cass) deleted*
STAR TREK (6) 'The Undiscovered Country' (91) Music sco
    re (Cliff Eidelman) -S/T- *MCA USA: MCAD(MCAC) 10512*
STAR TREK - *see also* 'TELEVISION INDEX' section
STAR WARS (1) (77) Music score (John Williams) -S/T- on
    *RSO 2679 092 (LP) 800 096-2 (C.Disc) also available
    on RCA RCD 13650 (CD)* c/w 'Close Encounters..' (77)
STAR WARS (2) 'The Empire Strikes Back' (81)Music score
    (John Williams)-S/T-*Imp (S.Screen): 827580-4 (Cass)*
    National Philh Orch - *TER: TER 9002 (LP) CDTER (CD)*
STAR WARS (3) 'Return Of The Jedi' (83) Music score by
    (John Williams) - National Philharmonic Orchestra
    (Charles Gerhardt) *-RCA Victor (BMG): GD 60767 (CD)*
    -S/T- *RCA: RK 14748 (Cass) RCD 14748 (CD)*
STAR WARS TRILOGY - *see COLLECTIONS and next entry*
STAR WARS *(Trilogy)* Selected music from the 3 films and
    'Close Encounters Of T.Third Kind' UTAH SYMPH ORCH
    Varese (Pinn): VCVD 47201 (CD) CTV 704210 (Cass)
STARCRASH - *see 'UNTIL SEPTEMBER'*
STARLIGHT EXPRESS (Musical *Apollo Victoria*) New Re-vamp
    ed 1993 vers.ORIG CAST RECORDING *Polydor: 519 041-2
    (CD) 519 041-4 (Cass) 519 041-1 (LP) -5 (Mini-Disc)*
STARLIGHT EXPRESS (ORIG LONDON CAST 84) Songs (Andrew
    Lloyd Webber-Richard Stilgoe) *feat:* Stephanie Lawr
    ence-Ray Shell-Lon Satton and Company *Polydor:
    LNER 1 (2LP) LNCER 1 (2Cass) 821597-2 (2CD)*
STARMAN (85) Music score (Jack Nitzsche) -S/T- on *TER
    TER (Conif): CDTER 1097 (CD) ZCTER 1097 (Cass)*
STARS AND BARS (88) Music score (Stanley Myers) song
    "Englishman In New York" by STING - *A&M (Poly) AMCD
    580 (CDs) AM(Y) 580 (7"/12") AMMC 580 (Cas)* No-S/T-
STARTING HERE STARTING NOW (MUSICAL REVUE) Songs (David
    Shire-Richard Maltby Jr) *O.Cast (BMG): GD(GK) 82360*
STATE OF GRACE (90) Music score (Ennio Morricone) -S/T-
    MCA USA (S.Screen): MCAD(MCAC) 10119 (CD/Cass)
STATE OF SIEGE (Etat De Siege) (72) Music score (Mikis
    Theodorakis) -S/T- *Sakkaris (Pinn): SR 50063 (CD)*
    see also COLL 'MIKIS THEODORAKIS ON THE SCREEN'
STAY THE WAY YOU ARE (Italy) *see under* 'COSI COME SEI'
STAY TUNED (92) Music score (Bruce Broughton)+ Various
    Artists -S/T- *Polydor: 517472-2(CD) -4(Cass) -1(LP)*
STAYIN' ALIVE (83) Songs and music (Bee Gees) -S/T- on
    RSO (Polyg): 813 269-2 (CD)
STEALING HEAVEN (89) Music score (Nick Bicat) -S/T- on
    TER (Silva Screen-Conif): CDTER 1166 (CD)

STEEL MAGNOLIAS (89) Music score (Georges Delerue)-S/T-
  Polydor (Silva Screen) 841 582-2 / -4 (CD/Cass)
STEPPING OUT (91) Music score (Peter Matz) Title song
  "Stepping Out" (John Kander and Fred Ebb) -S/T- on
  Milan (S.Screen): 262062 (CD) 412062 (Cass)
STING The (73) Music sco (Marvin Hamlisch-Scott Joplin)
  -S/T- *MCA (BMG): MCLD(MCLC) 19027 (CD/Cass)*
STONE KILLER The (73) Music score (Roy Budd) -S/T- Impt
  (Silva Screen): LEGEND CD6 (CD)
STOP IN THE NAME OF LOVE (ORIG LONDON CAST 90) *with* The
  Fabulous Singlettes Live From The Piccadilly on
  First Night (Pinn): SCENE(C)(CD) 13 (LP/Cass/CD)
STOP MAKING SENSE (84) Music by TALKING HEADS -S/T- on
  EMI: EJ 240243-1/-4 (LP/Cass) CDP 746064-2 (CD)
STOP THE WORLD I WANT TO GET OFF (ORIG LONDON CAST 61)
  Songs by (Anthony Newley-Leslie Bricusse) *featur:*
  Anthony Newley-Anna Quayle-Susan & Jennifer Baker-
  Carole Keith-Marti Webb *Decca (Poly): 820958-2 (CD)*
STORMY MONDAY (88) Music score (Mike Figgis) also music
  by B.B.King -S/T- *Virgin: CDV 2537 (CD)*
STORMY WEATHER (43) Mus (Benny Carter) *feat:* LENA HORNE
  BILL ROBINSON-FATS WALLER-CAB CALLOWAY-ADA BROWN
  -S/T- *Fox USA (S.Screen): FOX 11007 (CD)*
STORY OF THREE LOVES The (53) 'Rhapsody On A Theme Of
  Paganini' (Rachmaninov) 'Classic Experience' *(EMI)*
STORYVILLE (92) Music score (Carter Burwell) -S/T- on
  Varese (Pinn): VSD 5347 (CD) VSC 5347 (Cass)
STRADIVARI (89) -S/T- Classical Mus: Telemann-H.Purcell
  Vivaldi-Pachelbel-Handel -S/T- *Philips: 422849-2 CD*
STRAIGHT TALK (92) Music score (Brad Fiedel) Songs by
  DOLLY PARTON & Other Artists -S/T- Import *(Silva Sc
  een): 61303-2 (CD) 61303-4 (Cass)*
STRAIGHT TO HELL (87) Feat: Pogues-Joe Strummer-Elvis
  Costello-Pray For Rain-Zander Schloss -S/T- on
  Repertoire (Pinn): REP 4224WY (CD)
STRANGERS ON A TRAIN (51) Music score (Dimitri Tiomkin)
  'Four Alfred Hitchcock Films' *TER: (ZC)TER 1109*
STREET OF NO RETURN (-) Music sco (Karl-Heinz Schafer)
  -S/T- *Alhambra (Pinn): A.8911 (CD)*
STREET SCENE (ORIG LONDON CAST 91) Music (Kurt Weill)
  Lyrics (Langston Hughes) with The English Nationa
  Opera Orch (Carl Davis) *TER: (Con) CD(ZC)TER2 1185*
STREETCAR NAMED DESIRE A (51) Music score (Alex North)
  also includes symphonic suites from 'The INFORMER'
  (35-Max Steiner) 'NOW VOYAGER' (42-Max Steiner) and
  'SINCE YOU WENT AWAY' (44-Max Steiner) *Film Music
  Archive Series Cloud Nine (S.Screen): CNS 5003 (CD)*
STREETS OF FIRE (84) Songs (Jim Steinman) -S/T- on
  MCA USA (Silva Screen) MCAD 5492 (CD)
STRICTLY BALLROOM (92) Music score (David Hirshfelder)
  -S/T- *Columbia (Sony): 472300-2(CD) -4(Cass) -1(LP)*
STRIKE UP THE BAND (ORIG USA CAST) Songs (G. & I.Gershw
  in) Brent Barrett-Rebecca Luker-Don Chastain-J.Mauc
  eri *Elektra-Nonesuch (WEA):7559 79273-2(CD)-4(Cass)*

STUDENT PRINCE The (FILM MUSICAL 54) Songs (Sigmund Rom
  berg) - MARIO LANZA on *RCA Red Seal (BMG): GD 60048
  (CD) GK 60048 (Cas)* also contains 'The Desert Song'
STUDENT PRINCE The (NEW STUDIO RECORD 90) *feat:* Norman
  Bailey-Marilyn Hill Smith-Diana Montague-David Rend
  all-Rosemary Ashe and The Ambrosian Chorus & Orches
  TER (Conif): CDTER2 1172 (2CDs) ZCTED 1172 (D.Cass)
STUDENT PRINCE The (MUSUCAL) Songs (Sigmund Romberg) fe
  aturing GORDON MacRAE - *see under* 'Desert Song The'
SUBTERRANEANS The (60) Music score (Andre Previn) with
  Red Mitchell-Art Farmer-Shelley Manne-Carmen McRae-
  -S/T- *Imp (S.Screen): AK 47486 (CD) AT 47486 (Cass)*
SUBWAY (85) (European version) Music score (Eric Serra)
  -S/T- *Virgin: OVED 223 (LP) / Import (Silva Screen)
  GMD 9702 (CD) GMK 9702 (Cass)* song "A Lucky Guy" Ri
  ckie Lee Jones on 'Pirates' *WB: K2(4)56816 (CD/Cas)*
SUBWAY (85) (USA version) Music score (Bill Conti)
  -S/T- *currently unavailable*
SUGAR BABIES (ORIG BROADWAY CAST 89) Songs (Dorothy Fie
  lds-Jimmy McHugh etc.*feat:* Mickey Rooney-Ann Miller
  Sid Stone-Jack Fletcher-Ann Jillian-Bob Williams on
  Varese Sarabande (Pinn): VSD 5453 (CD)
SULEYMAN THE MAGNIFICENT (88) Mus (Brian Keane-Omar Far
  uk Tekbilek)-S/T-*Celestial Harm (Con):CD(MC)CEL 023*
SUMMER HOLIDAY (FILM MUSICAL 63) Cliff Richard-Shadows
  -S/T- *MFP (EMI): (TC)MFP 5824 and CDMFP 6021 (CD)*
SUMMER MAGIC - *see* WALT DISNEY FILM INDEX
SUNDAY IN THE PARK WITH GEORGE (ORIG BROADWAY CAST 84)
  Songs (Stephen Sondheim) Mandy Patinkin-Bernadette
  Peters *RCA (Silva Screen): RCD1 5042 (CD) HBE1 5042
  (Cass)* also *RCA (BMG):RD 85042 (CD) RK 85042 (Cass)*
SUNDOWN (89) Music score (Richard Stone) selection
  see Collection 'VAMPIRE CIRCUS'
SUNDOWN: THE VAMPIRE IN RETREAT (90) Music sco (Richard
  Stone) -S/T- *S.Screen (Conifer): FILMCD 044 (CD)*
SUNRISE AT CAMPOBELLO (60) Music score (Franz Waxman)
  NPO (Fred Steiner) *Preamble (S.Screen) PRCD 1777 CD*
SUNSET (ORIG OFF-BROADWAY CAST 84) Music (Gary William
  Friedman) Words (Will Holt) *feat* Tammy Grimes-Ronee
  Blakley-Kim Milford-Walt Hunter and Company
  TER (Koch): CDTER 1180 (CD) ZCTER 1180 (Cass)
SUNSET BOULEVARD (ORIG LONDON CAST 93) Songs (Andrew Ll
  oyd Webber) *feat:* PATI LuPONE-KEVIN ANDERSON & Comp
  Really Useful (Poly) 519 767-2 (2CD) -4 (2Cass)
SUNSET BOULEVARD (50) Music score (Franz Waxman) on Col
  'Sunset Boulevard' *RCA (BMG): RD 87017 (CD only)*
SUPER MARIO BROS. (93) Music of Various Artists -S/T-
  Capitol (EMI): CDESTU 2201 (CD) TCESTU 2201 (Cass)
SUPERFLY (72) Music score (Curtis Mayfield) -S/T- on
  Ichiban (Backs-Cartel): (CD)CUR 2002 (CD/LP)
SUPERGIRL (84) Music score (Jerry Goldsmith) -S/T- on
  Silva Screen (Conifer): FILMCD 132 (CD)
SUPERMAN (78) Music score (John Williams) -S/T- Import
  WB USA (S.Screen): 3257-2 (CD) and K2.66084 (CD)

SURVIVOR (81) / RACE FOR THE YANKEE ZEPHYR (80) Music
     (Brian May) *Australian Imp (S.Screen):1MI 1008 (CD)*
SUSPECT (88) Music score (Michael Kamen) -S/T- *USA Impt*
     (Silva Screen): 704 390 (LP) C704 390 (Cass)
SUSPENDED STEP OF THE STORK (Film) Music (Eleni Karaind
     rou) -S/T- *ECM (Pinn): 511514-2 (CD) ECM 1456 (LP)*
SUSPICION (41) Music score (Franz Waxman) on 'Four Alfr
     ed Hitchcock Films' (coll) *TER 1109 (LP) ZC (Cass)*
SUSPIRIA (76) Music score (Dario Argento) Recorded by
     by Goblin -S/T- *Cinevox Italy (Silva Screen): CDCIA
     5005 (CD) CIAK 75005 (Cass)*
SWAN DOWN GLOVES The (ORIG LONDON CAST 82) Songs (Nigel
     Hess-Billie Brown and The Royal Shakespeare Company
     TER (Conifer): TER 1017 (LP) ZCTER 1017 (Cass)
SWEENEY TODD (ORIG BROADWAY CAST 79) Songs (Stephen So
     ndheim) Angela Lansbury-Len Cariou *RCA Imp (Silva
     Screen): 3379-2 (2CD) CBK2 3379 (2Cass)* HIGHLIGHTS
     on *RCD1 5033 (CD)*
SWEET CHARITY (FILM MUSICAL 69) Songs (Dorothy Fields-
     Cy Coleman) Featur Shirley MacLaine-Sammy Davis Jnr
     Chita Rivera -S/T- *EMI America: CDP 746562-2 (CD)*
SWEET CHARITY (ORIG BROADWAY CAST 66) feat Gwen Verdon
     CBS USA (S.Screen): CK 02900 (CD) JST 02900 (Cass)
SWELL PARTY (ORIG LONDON CAST 91) Music & Songs Of COLE
     PORTER *S.Screen (Conif): SONG(C)(CD) 905 (Cass/CD)*
SWING KIDS (93) Music score (James Horner) -S/T- *Milan
     (Pinn): 14210-2 (CD) 14210-4 (Cass)*
SWITCH (91) Music score (Henry Mancini) -S/T- score on
     Varese (Pinn-S.Screen): VSD(VSC) 5312 (CD/Cass)
SWORD IN THE STONE - *see* WALT DISNEY FILM INDEX

TAFFETAS The (ORIG OFF-BROADWAY CAST 88) *conceived arr
     anged & directed by* Rick Lewis) *with* Jody Abrahams
     Karen Curlee-Melanie Mitchell-Tia Speros & Company
     TER (Conifer): (CD)(ZC)TER 1167 (CD/Cass/LP)
TALES FROM THE CRYPT - see Television section
TALES FROM THE DARKSIDE-THE MOVIE (90) Music (Donald B
     Rubinstein-Pat Regan-Jim Manzie-Chaz Jankel) -S/T-
     GNP (S.Screen): GNPD 8021(CD) GNP-5 8021 (Cass)
TANGO ARGENTINA (ORIG LONDON CAST 91) *Atlantic (WEA):
     756791636-2 (CD) -4(Cass)* (ALDWYCH June/91)
TAP DANCE KID The (ORIG BROADWAY CAST 84) Songs (Henry
     Krieger-Robert Lorick *feat* Gail Melson-Jimmy Tape
     TER (Conifer): CDTER 1096 (CD) ZCTER 1096 (Cass)
TASTE THE BLOOD OF DRACULA *see COLL* 'HORROR OF DRACULA'
TATIE DANIELLE (France 90) - *see* 'AUNTIE DANIELLE'
TAXI DRIVER (76) Music score (Bernard Herrmann) -S/T-
     Alhambra Germany-New Note (Pinn): A.8912 (CD)
TEDEUM / MANNAJA (Italian Spaghetti Westerns) Mus score
     (G.& M.DeAngelis) *Import (S.Screen): OST 1212 (CD)*
TEEN WOLF (85) Music score (Miles Goodman) -S/T- Import
     Southern Cross (Silva Screen): SCRS 1010 (LP)
TEENAGE MUTANT NINJA TURTLES 3 (93) Mus (John Du Prez)
     -S/T- *SBK (EMI): SBK(CD)(TC)(LP) 20 (CD/Cass/LP)*

TELL ME ON A SUNDAY (STUDIO RECORDING 79) Songs (Don
     Black-Andrew Lloyd Webber) *with* Marti Webb & Comp
     Polydor: 833 447-2 (CD) see also 'Song and Dance'
TEMP (92) Music score (Frederic Talgorn) -S/T- on
     Varese (Pinn): VSD 5410 (CD) VSC 5410 (Cass)
TEN COMMANDMENTS The (56) Music score (Elmer Bernstein)
     -S/T- *MCA USA (Silva Screen): MCAD 42320 (CD)*
TEN TO MIDNIGHT (83) - *see under* 'DEATH WISH'
TENDERLOIN (ORIG BROADWAY CAST 60) Songs (Jerry Bock-
     Sheldon Harnick) *feat:* MAURICE EVANS and Company
     EMI Angel (EMI): ZDM 565 022-2 (CD)
TENEBRAE (82) Music score composed and performed by
     (Goblin) -S/T- on *TER (Conifer): TER 1064 (LP)* also
     CDCIA 5035 (CD) includes 'Zombie'
TERMINATOR The (84) Music score (Brad Fiedel) -S/T- *Sil
     va Screen (Conif): FILM(C)(CD) 101 (LP/Cass/CD)*
TERMINATOR 2 (91) Music sc (Brad Fiedel) -S/T- score on
     Varese (Pinn): VSD(VSC) 5335 (CD/Cass)
TERMS OF ENDEARMENT (83) Music sco (Michael Gore) -S/T-
     Capitol (Silva Screen): 46076-2(CD) -4(Cass)
TERRORISTS The - *see under* 'RANSOM'
THAT'S ENTERTAINMENT II (76) Various artists -S/T- on
     CBS (S.Screen): A2K 46872 (2CD) A2T 46872 (2Cass)
THAT'S THE WAY IT IS (70) Elvis Presley's 33rd movie
     for details see 'ELVIS PRESLEY FILM INDEX'
THELMA & LOUISE (91) Music score (Hans Zimmer) -S/T- on
     MCA (BMG): MCA(MCAD)(MCAC) 10239 (LP/CD/Cass)
THEY LIVE (88) Music score: John Carpenter-Alan Howarth
     -S/T- *Demon (Pinn): DSCD 1 (CD)*
THEY'RE PLAYING OUR SONG (ORIG LONDON CAST 80) Songs
     (Marvin Hamlisch-Carol Bayer Sager) *with* Gemma Crav
     en-Tom Conti *TER (Con): (CD)(ZC)TER 1035 (CD/Cass)*
THIEF - *see under* 'VIOLENT STREETS'
THIN BLUE LINE The (89) Music score (Philip Glass)
     -S/T- *Elektra Nonesuch (WEA): 7559 79209-2 (CD)*
THING CALLED LOVE The (93) Var.Country/Western Songs on
     Import USA (Silva Screen): (-) CD/CASS
THINGS TO COME (36) Music score (Sir Arthur Bliss) c/w
     'First Of The Few' (42) mus (William Walton) *see Co
     Collect* 'WARSAW CONCERTO'
THIRD MAN The (49) "The Harry Lime Theme" (Anton Karas)
     Anton Karas *see Coll* 'The THIRD MAN'
THIRST (Austral) Music score (Brian May) -S/T- *OneMone
     (S.Screen):IMICD 1003(CD) see also* 'VAMPIRE CIRCUS'
THIS EARTH IS MINE (59) Music score (Hugo Friedhofer)
     with 'THE YOUNG LIONS' *Varese (Pinn): VSD 5403 (CD)*
THIS IS ELVIS (81) - *see* 'ELVIS PRESLEY FLM INDEX'
THIS IS MY LIFE (92) Music score & songs (Carly Simon)
     -S/T- *Qwest (WEA): 759926901-2(CD) -4(Cass)*
THIS IS SPINAL TAP (84) Music composed & sung by Spinal
     Tap on *RAZOR (Castle-BMG): LUSLP(MC)2 (LP/Cass)*
THOMAS CROWN AFFAIR The (68) Music sco (Michel Legrand)
     Song "Windmills Of Your Mind" (Lyr: Alan & Marilyn
     Bergman) by Noel Harrison *Old Gold: OG 9090 (7"s)*

THOROUGHLY MODERN MILLIE Music score (Elmer Bernstein)
feat Julie Andrews -S/T- *MCA: MCL(MCLC)1723 deleted*

THREE COINS IN THE FOUNTAIN (54) title song (Sammy Cahn
Jule Styne) sung by FRANK SINATRA 'Screen Sinatra'
MFP (EMI): CDMFP 6052 (CD) TCMFP 5835 (Cass)

THREE COLOURS: BLUE (93) Music sco (Zbigniew Preisner)
Virgin France (EMI): CDVMM 12 (CD)

THREE GUYS NAKED FROM THE WAIST DOWN (ORIG OFF BROADWAY
CAST 85) Music/Lyrics (Michael Rupert-Jerry Colker)
TER (Koch): TER 1100CD (CD) TER 1100MC (Cass)

THREE MEN AND A BABY (87) Music sc (Marvin Hamlisch).*NA*
song "Goodnight Sweetheart Well It's Time To Go"
(Calvin Carter-James Hudson) by The SPANIELS on
'Play It Cool' *CHARLY R&B: CDCHARLY 222 (CD)* / "Bad
Boys"(L.Dermer-J.Galdo-R.Vigil) MIAMI SOUND MACHINE
with GLORIA ESTEFAN" on 'Primitive Love' *Columbia:
(Sony Music): 463400-2 (CD) 463400-4 (Cass)*

THREE MEN AND A LITTLE LADY (91) Music score (James New
ton Howard) Songs inc: "Waiting For A Star To Fall"
(George Merrill-Shannon Rubicam) by BOY MEETS GIRL
"Always Thinking Of You" by DONNA DeLORY + tracks
by David Baerwald-Najee-Selleck/Guttenberg/Danson
-S/T- on *Hollywood (Pinn): HWD(CD)(MC)(LP) 2*

THREE MUSKETEERS The (93) Music score (Michael Kamen)
Song "All For Love" (M.Kamen-B.Adams-R.Lange) sung
by BRYAN ADAMS ROD STEWART and STING. -S/T- on
A.& M. (Poly): 540 190-2 (CD) 540 190-4 (Cass)

THREE MUSKETEERS The (73) Music score (Michel Legrand)
-S/T- *Bay Cities (Pinn): CD 873 118 (CD)*

THREE SISTERS (70) Music score (Sir William Walton) New
Recording by Academy of St.Martin-in-the-Fields
(Neville Marriner)'William Walton Film Music Vol.2'
Chandos: CHAN 8870 (CD) ABTD 1485 (Cass)

THREE WISHES FOR JAMIE (87) Music (Paddy Moloney) SEE
Collections *'REEL MUSIC'*

THREE WISHES FOR JAMIE (ORIG BROADWAY CAST 52) *featur:*
JOHN RAITT-ANNE JEFFREYS-BERT WHEELER *EMI Angel
(EMI): ZDM 764888-2 (CD)*

THREEPENNY OPERA The (ORIG BROADWAY CAST 54) Songs Kurt
Weill-Marc Blitzstein featuring Lotte Lenya & Comp
TER (Conifer): (CD)(ZC)TER 1101 (CD/Cass/LP)

THUNDERBALL - *see* **JAMES BOND FILM INDEX**

THUNDERBIRDS ARE GO! (67) Music (Barry Gray) *reissue:*
Motion Picture Soundtrack and Thunderbirds Themes
EMI: CDGO 2041 (CD) TCGO 2041 (Cass) GO 2041 (LP)

THUNDERHEART (91) Music score (James Horner) -S/T- Imp
Intrada USA (Koch Int): MAFCD 7027 (CD)

TICKLE ME (65) - *see* 'Elvis Presley Film Index'

TIE ME UP TIE ME DOWN (Legami!) (90) Music score (Ennio
Morricone) -S/T- *RCA (S.Screen): 3095-2(CD)*

TIGER BAY (59) Music score (Laurie Johnson) Main Theme
see Collect 'ROSE AND THE GUN The' *FLY(CD)(MC) 103*

TIME AFTER TIME (80) Music score (Miklos Rozsa) -S/T-
Southern Cross (S.Screen): SCCD 1014 (CD)

TIME MACHINE The (60) Music (Russell Garcia) -S/T- on
   GNP (S.Screen) GNPD(GNPS)(GNP5) 8008 (CD/LP/CS)
TIMES OF HARVEY MILK The (84) Music score (Mark Isham)
   included on -S/T- to 'Mrs.Soffel'
TIN DRUM The (79) Music (Maurice Jarre) - *SEE 'Voyager'*
TO DIE FOR (89) Music score (Cliff Eidelman) / also
TO DIE FOR 2 (SON OF DARKNESS) (91) Mus (Mark McKenzie)
   see Collection 'VAMPIRE CIRCUS'
TO HAVE AND HAVE NOT (45) Music (Franz Waxman) see Coll
   'Classic Film Scores For Humphrey Bogart'
TO KILL A MOCKINGBIRD (62) Music sco (Elmer Bernstein)
   Mainstream USA (Koch Int): MDCD 602 (CD)
TO LIVE AND DIE IN L.A. (86) Music (Wang Chung) -S/T-
   reissued *Geffen (BMG): GFFLD (GFLC) 19055 (CD/Cass)*
TO THE ENDS OF THE EARTH (Film Document.84) Music score
   (John Scott)-S/T-*Prometheus (S.Screen) PCD 102(CD)*
TOM AND JERRY The Movie (92) Mus score (Henry Mancini)
   Songs (Henry Mancini-Leslie Bricusse) -S/T- on
   MCA (BMG): MCD 10721 (CD) MCC 10721 (Cass)
TOM FOOLERY (ORIG LONDON CAST 80) Songs (Tom Lehrer)
   TER (Conifer): (ZC)TER 1137 (Cass/LP)
TOMMY (ROCK OPERA) London Symph Orc with Pete Townshend
   Roger Daltrey-Maggie Bell-Rod Stewart-Sandy Denny-
   Ringo Starr-John Entwistle-Steve Winwood-Chambre Ch
   oir-Richie Havens / *Essential-Castle (BMG): ESSCD
   029 (CD) ESDMC 029 (D.Cass) ESDLP 029 (2LP's)*
TOMMY (FILM ROCK OPERA 75) Music (Pete Townshend) Feat:
   The Who-Elton John etc.-S/T- *Polydor 841 121-2 (CD)*
TOMMY (ORIG BROADWAY CAST 93) Songs (Pete Townshend)
   RCA Victor (BMG): 09026 6187402 (CD)
TONITE LET'S ALL MAKE LOVE IN LONDON (FILM MUSICAL 67)
   See For Miles (Pin) SEECD(SEEK) SEE 258 (CD/Cas/LP)
TOO HOT TO HANDLE *(USA:THE MARRYING MAN)* (91) Music sc
   (David Newman) songs (7) performed by Kim Basinger
   -S/T- *Hollywood (Pinn-Sony M): HWDCD(MC)(LP) 9*
TOOTSIE (82) Music score (Dave Grusin) -S/T- *Warner Brs
   USA (S.Screen): WB 23781 (LP)* see 'Cinemagic' Coll
TOP BANANA (ORIG BROADWAY CAST 1951) Songs (Johnny Merc
   er) featuring: Phil Silvers-Rose Marie and Company
   EMI Angel (EMI): ZDM 764772-2 (CD)
TOP GUN (86) Music sco (Harold Faltermeyer) "Take My Br
   eath Away" (Berlin) -S/T- *Columbia (Sony) CD 70296
   (CD) 40-70296 (Cass) MD 70296 (Mini Disc)*
TOP HAT with Yehudi Menuhin (violin) Stephane Grappelli
   (violin/piano) + N.Riddle *CFP (EMI):CDCFP 4509 (CD)*
TORN CURTAIN (66) Music score (John Addison) -S/T-reiss
   ue on *Varese (Pinn): VSD 5296 (CD) VSC 5296 (Cass)*
TOTAL RECALL (89) Music score (Jerry Goldsmith) -S/T-
   Varsese (Pinn): VSD 5267 (CD) VSC 5267 (Cass)
TOTO THE HERO (91) Music score (Pierre Van Dormael)song
   "Boum"(C.Trenet-Roma Campbell Hunter)singer Charles
   Trenet *Pathe Marconi (Conifer): 746567-2 (CD)* -S/T-
   Milan (Pinn): CDBM 001 (CD) CBM 001 (Cass)
TOUCH OF EVIL, A (58) Music score (Henry Mancini) -S/T-

TOUCH OF EVIL, A (58) Music score (Henry Mancini) -S/T-
   Varese (Pinn): VSD 5414 (CD) also on Fresh Sounds
   (Charly): MSCD 401 (CD)
TOUGH GUYS DON'T DANCE (87) - *see under* 'DEATH WISH'
TOUS LE MATINS DU MONDE (France 92) Music score (Jordi
   Savall) and music by Francois Couperin-Marin Marais
   Jean-Baptiste Lully-Sainte Colombe -S/T- on *Auvidis*
   Valoir (Koch): AUV 4640 (CD) AUV 54640 (Cass)
TOVARICH (ORIG BROADWAY CAST 63) Songs (Lee Pockriss-An
   ne Croswell) *feat:* VIVIEN LEIGH-JEAN PIERRE AUMONT
   EMI Angel (EMI): ZDM 764893-2 (CD)
TOWN FOX AND OTHER MUSICAL TALES The (SHOW Barbican 90)
   Stories and Lyrics (Carla Lane) Music (Carl Davis)
   featuring: Jean Boht-Kenneth Waller-Ronald Forfar
   1st Night (Pinn): SCENECD 19 (CD) SCENEC 19 (Cass)
TOY SOLDIERS (91) Music score (Robert Folk) -S/T- on
   Intrada USA (Silva Screen): MAF 7015D (CD)
TOYS (92) Music score (Hans Zimmer-Trevor Horn) -S/T-
   W.Bros/ZTT (WEA): 4509 91603-2 (CD) 91603-4 (Cass)
TRAIL OF THE PINK PANTHER (83) Music sc (Henry Mancini)
   -S/T- *Import (S.Screen): 90627-2 (CD) -4 (Cass)*
TRANSYLVANIA TWIST (91) Music sco (Chuck Cirino) select
   see Collection 'VAMPIRE CIRCUS'
TRANSYLVANIA 65000 (85) Music sco (Lee Holdridge) selec
   see Collection 'VAMPIRE CIRCUS'
TREASURE ISLAND (89) Music (Paddy Moloney) Chieftains
   SEE Collections *'REEL MUSIC'*
TREASURE OF THE SIERRA MADRE The (48) Music score (Max
   Steiner) *see* 'Classical Scores For Humphrey Bogart'
TREE GROWS IN BROOKLYN A (ORIG BROADWAY CAST 51) Songs
   (Arthur Schwartz-Dorothy Fields)*feat:* Shirley Booth
   Johnny Johnson-Marcia Van Dyke-Nathaniel Frey-Nomi
   Mitti-Harland Dixon- *Sony Broadway: SK 48014 (CD)*
TRELAWNY (ORIG LONDON CAST 72) Songs (Julian Slade)*with*
   Gemma Craven-Ian Richardson-Max Adrian and Company
   TER (Conif): TER 1081 (LP) ZCTER 1081 (Cass)
TRESPASS (93) Music score (Ry Cooder) (2 -S/T- Records)
   SCORE -S/T- *Sire (WEA): 759 926978-2 (CD) -4 (Cass)*
   SONGS -S/T- *WB (WEA): 936 245220-2 (CD) -4 (Cass)*
TRIAL BY JURY - *Pro-Arte Orch* - *see* 'HMS PINAFORE'
TRIAL BY JURY - *D'Oyly Carte Opera Company* (Gilbert and
   Sullivan)+'Yeomen Of The Guard' *London: 417 358-2CD*
TRIAL The (92) Music score (Carl Davis) -S/T- available
   on *Milan (Pinn): 873150 (CD)*
TRIBUTE TO THE BLUES BROTHERS A (ORIG LONDON CAST 91)
   feat Con O'Neill-Warwick Evans & Company
   First Night (Pinn): CASTCD 25 (CD) CASTC 25 (Cass)
TRIP The (67) Feat music by: Electric Flag & Mike Bloom
   field -S/T- *Demon Edsel (Pinn): ED 211 (LP) deleted*
TRIUMPH OF THE SPIRIT (89) Music score (Cliff Eidelman)
   -S/T- *Varese (Pinn): VS(VSC)(VSD) 5254 (LP/Cass/CD)*
TROIS PLACES POUR LE 26 (88) Music score Michel Legrand
   Lyrics (Jacques Demy) w.Yves Montand & Mathilda May
   -S/T- *Philips (Poly) 836733-2 (CD) -1 (LP) -4 (Cas)*

TROUBLE WITH ANGELS The (66) Music sc (Jerry Goldsmith) with 'Stagecoach' (66-Jerry Goldsmith) -S/T- Imp on *Mainstream USA (Koch Int): MDCD 608 (CD)*

TRUE GRIT (69) Music score (Elmer Bernstein) title song (Bernstein-Black) by GLEN CAMPBELL on 'Country Boy' *MFP (EMI): CDMFP 6034 (CD) TCMFP 5692 (Cass)*

TRUE ROMANCE (93) Music score (Hans Zimmer) -S/T- on *Morgan Creek-Polydor: 519 954-2 (CD) -4(Cass)* theme "You're So Cool" *Poly: PZCD 303(CDs) POCS 303(Cass)*

TRUE STORIES (86) Music sco (David Byrne) Talking Heads -S/T- *EMI: TC-EMC 3520 (Cass) CDP 746345-2 (CD)*

TRUMPET CALL The (Musical Rock Gospel Show) Feat songs by Valeri Barinov (USSR) *Myrrh: MYRC 1217 (Cass)*

TRUSTING BEATRICE (Film) Music sco (Stanley Myers) with Suite from 'COLD HEAVEN' (Myers) on *Intrada Imprt (Silva Screen): MAF 7048D (CD)*

TUNE IN TOMORROW (91) Music score by (Wynton Marsalis) -S/T- *Columbia (Sony): 467785-2(CD) -4(Cass) -1(LP)*

TURTLE BEACH (91) Music score (Chris Neal) -S/T- *Silva Screen (Conif): FILMCD 120 (CD)*

TWANG! (ORIG LONDON CAST 64) Songs (Lionel Bart) *featur* Barbara Windsor-James Booth-Ronnie Corbett and Comp *TER (Koch): TER 1055 (LP) ZCTER 1055 (Cass)*

TWELVE CHAIRS (70) Music score (John Morris) -S/T- on *TER (Conifer): TER 1033 (LP)*

TWILIGHT'S LAST GLEAMING (77) Mus sco.(Jerry Goldsmith) -S/T- *Silva Screen (Conifer): FILMCD 111 (CD)*

TWIN PEAKS: FIRE WALK WITH ME (92) Music score (Angelo Badalamenti) + Various Artists -S/T- *W.Bros (WEA): 9362 45019-2 (CD) -4 (Cass)* / SEE ALSO TV SECTION

TWO BY TWO (ORIG BROADWAY CAST 70) Songs (Richard Rodgers-Martin Charnin) *feat:* Danny Kaye-Joan Coppeland-Madeline Kahn *Sony Broadway (Sony M): CD 30338 (CD)*

TWO HEADED SPY The (58) Music score (Gerard Schurmann) Coll. 'Coastal Command' *(S.Screen: FILMCD 072)*

TWO WEEKS WITH LOVE (FILM MUSICAL 50) feat Jane Powell Debbie Reynolds-Donald O'Connor -S/T- *USA Imp(Silva Screen): AK(AT) 48609 (CD/Cass)* c/w 'I LOVE MELVIN'

200 MOTELS (71) Music and songs (Frank Zappa & Mothers Of Invention -S/T- *UA (Conif) 2CUAS 29218/9 (2LP's)*

2001-A SPACE ODYSSEY (68) Classical music featuring "Blue Danube" (J.Strauss) "Also Sprach Zarathustra" (R.Strauss) and other pieces -S/T- *MGM (EMI): CDMGM 6 (CD) TCMGM 6 (Cass) currently deleted*

2001-A SPACE ODYSSEY (REJECTED SCORE by ALEX NORTH) National Philharmonic Orchestra (Jerry Goldsmith) *Varese (Pinn): VSD 5400 (CD)*

TYCOON (92) Music sco (-) Var.arts: CYNDI LAUPER-MATT & LUKE GOSS-NINA HAGEN-CELINE DION-TOM JONES-KIM CARNES-KEVIN ROBINSON-RONNIE SPECTOR-PETER KINGSBERY -S/T- *Epic (Sony): 471923-2 (CD) -4 (Cass) -1 (LP)*

ULYSSES (54) Music score (Alessandro Cicognini) -S/T- *Legend Imp (Silva Screen): LEGEND CD 8 (CD)*

UMBRELLAS OF CHERBOURG The (FILM MUSICAL 64) Music (Mic
   hel Legrand) Song "I Will Wait For You" (Lyrics by
   Norman Gimbel) -S/T- *Imp (S.Screen): 834 139-2 (CD)*
   also 'Third Man' coll - *Decca 421264-2 (CD) -4 (CS)*
UNBEARABLE LIGHTNESS OF BEING The (88) Music score by
   (L.Janacek) also with 'Hey Jude' (Lennon-McCartney)
   -S/T- *Metronome (Poly): 835918-2 (CD)* deleted
UNDER SIEGE (92) Music score (Gary Chang) -S/T- *Varese*
   Sarabande USA (Pinn): VSD 5409 (CD) VSC 5409 (Cass)
UNDER THE CHERRY MOON (86) Music (Prince) -S/T- on
   Warner Bros (WEA): WX 39(C) (LP/Cas) 925 395-2 (CD)
UNDERNEATH THE ARCHES (ORIG LONDON CAST 82)The Songs of
   Flanagan & Allen *feat:* Roy Hudd-Christopher Timothy
   TER (Conifer): TER 1015 (LP) ZCTER 1015 (Cass)
UNFORGIVEN (92) Music score (Lennie Niehaus) -S/T- on
   Varese (Pinn): VSD 5380 (CD) VSC 5380 (Cass)
UNIVERSAL SOLDIER (92) Music score (Christopher Franke)
   -S/T- *Varese (Pinn): VSD(VSC) 5373 (CD/Cass)*
   see also Coll 'UNIVERSAL SOLDIER'
UNLAWFUL ENTRY (92) Music score (James Horner) -S/T-
   Intrada (Koch/S.Screen): MAFCD 7031 (CD)
UNS ET LES AUTRES Les *see under* 'INS AND THE OUTS The'
UNSINKABLE MOLLY BROWN The (ORIG BROADWAY CAST 60)Songs
   (Meredith Willson)*feat:* TAMMY GRIMES-HARVE PRESNELL
   CAMERON PRUD'HOLME *Angel (EMI): ZDM 764761-2 (CD)*
UNSINKABLE MOLLY BROWN The (ORIG BROADWAY CAST 61) with
   Tammy Grimes *Imp (S.Screen)92054-2 (CD) -4 (Cass)*
UNTAMED HEART (92) Music score (Cliff Eidelman) -S/T-
   Varese (Pinn): VSD 5404 (CD) VSC 5404 (Cass)
UNTIL SEPTEMBER (84) and STARCRASH (79-It) Music scores
   (John Barry) *Silva Screen (Conif): FILMCD 085 (CD)*
   see also John Barry Collections 'MOVIOLA' etc.
UNTIL THE END OF THE WORLD (91) Music by Var.Artists
   -S/T- *Warner Bros (WEA): 7599 267074-2(CD) -4(Cass)*
UNTOUCHABLES The (87) Music score (Ennio Morricone) and
   "Vesti La Giubba" from 'I Pagliacci' (Leoncavallo)
   -S/T- *A.& M.(Poly): 393909-2 (CD) -4 (Cass)*
   see Collection 'BEST OF KEVIN COSTNER'
URSUS/URSUS IN THE VALLEY OF LIONS/URSUS IN THE LAND OF
   FIRE/THE THREE INVICIBLES (Italian films 60s) Music
   scores: Roman Vlad-Riz Ortolani-Carlo Savina-Angelo
   Francesco Lavagnino *Cinevox (S.Scr):CDCIA 5090 (CD)*
USED PEOPLE (92) Music score (Rachel Portman) -S/T- on
   Big Screen (Movie Boulevard): 924 481-2 (CD)
UTU (84) Music score (John Charles) Symphonic -S/T- on
   Import (Silva Screen): LXCD 6 (CD)

VAGRANT (91) Music score (Christopher Young) -S/T- on
   Intrada (Koch/S.Screen): MAFCD 7028 (CD)
VALMOUTH (ORIG LONDON CAST 58) Songs (Sandy Wilson)*feat*
   Marcia Ashton-Cleo Laine-Fenella Fielding-Peter Gil
   more-Ian Burford-Barbara Couper-Doris Hare-Patsy Ro
   wlands-Betty Hardy-Denise Hurst-Geoffrey Dunn-Alan
   Edwards-Aubrey Woods *DRG (Conif): CDSBL 13109 (CD)*

VALMOUTH (ORIG CHICHESTER THEATRE PRODUCTION 82)
    TER (Conif): TER 1019 (LP) ZCTER 1019 (Cass)
VAMP (87) Music score (Jonathan Elias) selection
    see Collection 'VAMPIRE CIRCUS'
VAMPIRE CIRCUS (71) Music score (David Whittaker) selec
    see Collection 'VAMPIRE CIRCUS'
VAMPIRE LOVERS The (70) Music score Harry Robinson *see*
    Collections 'Omen The: 50 Years Of Classic...'
VANISHING The (93) Music score (Jerry Goldsmith) -S/T-
    Varese (Pinn): catalogue number to be confirmed
VERONIKA VOSS (82) Music score (Peer Raben) -S/T- *DRG*
    (Conif): SL9508 (LP) SLC9508 (Cass) c/w 'Lola' (82)
VERTIGO (58) Music (Bernard Herrmann) -S/T- on *Mercury*
    422 106-2 (CD)
VERY GOOD EDDIE (REVIVAL BROADWAY CAST 75) Songs(Jerome
    Kern-Schuyler Greene) *DRG (Pinn): CDRG 6100 (CD)*
VICTOR The (MUSICAL GOSPEL SHOW 84) Songs (Jimmie/Carol
    Owens)2nd Chapter Of Acts-Jamie Owens Collins-Efrem
    Zimbalist Jnr. - *Oak (Word): (TC)OAK 3001 (Cass/LP)*
VIEW TO A KILL A - see JAMES BOND FILM INCDEX
VIOLENT STREETS ('THIEF') (81) Music (Tangerine Dream)
    -S/T- *Virgin: OVEDC 72 (Cass) CDV 2198 (CD)*
VIRTUE IN DANGER (ORIG LONDON CAST 63) Songs (James Ber
    nard-Paul Dehn) *TER (Conif): (ZC)TER 1079 (Cass/LP)*
VISION QUEST (85) Music by var.artists inc: Madonna-For
    eigner-Sammy Hagar-Style Council etc. -S/T- reissue
    Geffen Impt (Silva Screen): GED 24063 (CD)
VISITOR The (Italy 80) Music score (Franco Micalizzi)
    -S/T- also inc 'ETOILE' (mus: Jurgen Knieper) on
    Import (Silva Screen): OST 108 (CD)
VIVA LAS VEGAS (64) *feat:* ELVIS PRESLEY *reissued* -S/T-
    with 'Roustabout' (64) *RCA (BMG):74321 13432-2 (CD)*
    74321 13432-4 (Cass)
VOYAGE OF TERROR: The Achille Lauro Affair (90) Music
    (Ennio Morricone) -S/T- *RCA (S.Screen): OST 101 CD*
VOYAGE OF THE DAMNED (76) Music score (Lalo Schifrin)
    Symphonic Suite on *USA Impt (S.Screen) LXCD 5 (CD)*
    see under 'EAGLE HAS LANDED'
VOYAGER (Homo Faber) (91) Music score (Stanley Myers)
    Song "Careless Love Blues" performed by Ute Lemper
    -S/T- with music from 'Tin Drum' (79-Maurice Jarre)
    Milan (Pinn): CDCH 804 (CD)

WAGES OF FEAR (78) 'The Sorcerer' Mus (Tangerine Dream)
    -S/T- *MCA Imp (Silva Screen): MCAD 10842 (CD)*
WALK DON'T RUN (66) Music score (Quincy Jones) -S/T- on
    Mainstrealm USA (Koch Int): MDCD 605 (CD)
WALK ON THE WILD SIDE (62) Music sco (Elmer Bernstein)
    -S/T- *Mainstream USA (Koch Int): MDCD 604 (CD)*
WALKABOUT (70) Music Sc (John Barry)*see Coll* 'MOVIEOLA'
WALL The (81) Music (Pink Floyd) -S/T- *Harvest (EMI):*
    CDS 746036-8 (2CD) SHDW 411(2LP) TC2 SHDW 411(2Cas)
WALL STREET (88) Music score (Stewart Copeland) -S/T-
    TER (Conif): CDTER 1154 (CD) c/w 'Salvador' -S/T-

WANDERERS The (79) Songs by various artists -S/T- on
    (Pickwick): PWK 058 (CD) SHM(HSC) 3069 (LP/Cass)
WAR REQUIEM (88) Music (Benjamin Britten) based on 'War
    Requiem Op.66' C.B.S.O.(Simon Rattle) *EMI: CDS 747
    034-8 (2CDs)* / London Symph.Orch (Benjamin Britten)
    Decca (Poly): 414 383-2DH2 (2CD) K27K22 (Cass's)
WARLOCK (88) Music score (Jerry Goldsmith) -S/T- *Silva
    Screen (Conifer): FILMCD 038 (CD)*
WARLOCK: THE ARMAGEDDON (93) Music sco (Mark McKenzie)
    -S/T- *Intrada (Silva Screen): MAF 7049D (CD)*
WARNING SIGN (85) Music score (Craig Safan) -S/T- Imprt
    Southern Cross (Silva Screen): SCCD 1012 (CD)
WAY WE WERE The (73) Music (Marvin Hamlisch) Lyrics (Al
    an/Marilyn Bergman) -S/T- feat Barbra Streisand on
    CBS (40)69057 (CS/LP) Elaine Paige on Coll 'Cinema'
WAYNE'S WORLD (92) Music score (J.Peter Robinson) -S/T-
    Reprise-Warner (WEA): 7599 26805-2 (CD) -4 (Cass)
WE OF THE NEVER NEVER (82) Music score (Peter Best) and
    DEVIL IN THE FLESH Music score (Philipe Sarde) on
    Australian Imp (S.Screen): 1MICD 1012 (CD)
WEB OF THE SPIDER *see under* 'IN THE GRIP OF THE SPIDER'
WEDDING BANQUET The (93) Music score (Mader) + 3rd m/m
    Piano Sonata in A.Major 'Turkish March' (Mozart) &
    songs by Var.Arts -S/T- *Import (S.Screen):(-) (CD)*
WEDLOCK - *see under* 'DEADLOCK'
WELCOME HOME ROXY CARMICHAEL (90) Music (Thomas Newman)
    -S/T- *Varese (Pinn-S.Screen): VSD(VSC)5300(CD/Cass)*
WENDY CRACKED A WALNUT Music score (Bruce Smeaton) on
    Austrailian Imp.(Silva Screen): 1MICD 1007 (CD)
WEST SIDE STORY (FILM 61) Songs (Leonard Bernstein-Step
    hen Sondheim) *with* NATALIE WOOD *(sung by Marnie Nix
    on)* RICHARD BEYMER *(sung by Jim Bryant)* RITA MORENO
    (sung by Betty Wand) CHITA RIVERA-GEORGE CHAKIRIS-
    RUSS TAMBLYN. This Recording also contains music fr
    om the original Soundtrack never before available
    Sony Broadway: SK 48211 (CD) ST 48211 (Cass)
WEST SIDE STORY (STUDIO RECORDING 93) Songs (Leonard Bé
    rnstein) Lyrics (Stephen Sondheim) *featur:* MICHAEL
    BALL-BARBARA BONNEY-LA VERNE WILLIAMS-CHRISTOPHER
    HOWERD-MARY CAREWE-JENNY O'GRADY-LEE GIBSON-MICHAEL
    PEARN-The Royal Philharmonic Orch: BARRY WORDSWORTH
    Pickwick-IMG (Pickwick): IMGCD(IMGMC)1801 (CD/Cass)
WEST SIDE STORY (LEICESTER HAYMARKET THEATRE PROD.93)
    Conducted by JOHN OWEN EDWARDS and recorded on
    TER (Koch): CDTER2 1197 (2CD) ZCTER2 1197 (2Cass)
WEST SIDE STORY (STUDIO RECORDING 84)(TV-BBC1 10/5/85)
    Kiri Te Kanawa-Jose Carreras-Tatiana Troyanos-Kurt
    Ollman-Marilyn Horn and Leonard Bernstein *DG (Poly)
    415253-2(2CD) -4(Cass) Highl: 431027-2 (CD) -4(Cas)*
WEST SIDE STORY (STUDIO RECORDING 89) *feat* Katia and Ma
    riebelle Labeque 'Symphonic Dances and Songs From
    West Side Sory' (Berstein) arranged for 2 pianos by
    Irwin Kostal - *CBSCD 45531 (CD) (40)45531 (Cass/LP)*
WEST SIDE STORY (ORIG BROADWAY CAST 57) *with* Carol Lawr

ence-Larry Kert-Chita Rivera *Columb (Silva Screen):*
CK 32603 (CD) JST 32603 (Cass)
WETHERBY (84) Music score (Nick Bicat) -S/T- recording
TER (Conifer): TER 12 010 (12" extended play)
WHALES OF AUGUST The (88) Music score (Alan Price)-S/T-
Varese (Silva Screen): STV(CTV) 81347 (LP/Cass)
WHAT A CRAZY WORLD (63) Songs (Alan Klein) Featuring:
Marty Wilde-Joe Brown-Susan Maughan-Alan Klein etc.
-S/T- on *President Evergreen: PLE 512 (LP)*
WHAT ABOUT LUV (Musical 90) Songs (Howard Marren-Susan
Birkenhead) *Premiere Cast* w: Judy Kaye-David Green-
Simon Green *TER (Conif): (CD)(ZCTER) 1171 (CD/Cass)*
WHAT'S UP, TIGER LILY (66) Music (John Sebastian) THE
LOVIN' SPOONFUL -S/T-with 'You're A Big Boy Now' on
Sequel-Knight: NEXTCD 176 (CD)
WHEN HARRY MET SALLY (89) Music adapted & arranged by
Marc Shaiman and performed by Harry Connick Jnr.on
-S/T- *CBS 465753-2 (CD) 465753-1 (LP) 465753-4 (CS)*
WHEN THE WHALES CAME (89) Music score (Christopher Gunn
ing) -S/T- *Silva Screen (Conifer): FILM(C)(CD) 049*
WHEN THE WIND BLOWS (Cartoon 87) Music score by (Roger
Waters) Title song sung by David Bowie / songs by
Genesis-Hugh Cornwell-Squeeze-Paul Hardcastle -S/T-
Virgin: CDV 2406 (CD)
WHERE'S CHARLEY ? (ORIG LONDON CAST 1958) Songs (Frank
Loesser) *feat:* NORMAN WISDOM-PIP HINTON-TERENCE COO
PER-PAMELA GALE-JILL MARTIN-JERRY DESMONDE-BARRY KE
NT-Cond MICHAEL COLLINS *EMI (EMI): CDANGEL 4 (CD)*
WHICH WITCH (OPERA MUSICAL) (Piccadilly 92) Songs by
Benedicte Adrian-Ingrid Bjornov recording on *First
Night (Pinn): SCOREC 38 (Cass ep) SCORECD 38 (CDep)*
WHILE I LIVE (47) Music score (Charles Williams) includ
ing *'The Dream Of Olwen'* see Coll 'WARSAW CONCERTO'
WHISPERS IN THE DARK (92) Music score (Thomas Newman)
-S/T- *Varese (Pinn): VSD 5387 (CD) VSC 5387 (Cass)*
WHISTLE BLOWER The (87) Music score (John Scott) -S/T-
feat Royal Philh Orch (John Scott) *TER 1139 (LP)*
WHISTLE DOWN THE WIND (61) Music score (Malcolm Arnold)
London Symphony Orchestra (Richard Hicox) on collec
'Film Music' *Chandos: CHAN 9011(CD) ABTD1600 (Cass)*
WHITE CHRISTMAS (FILM MUSICAL 54) Songs (Irving Berlin)
Featur Bing Crosby-Danny Kaye-Peggy Lee -S/T- *MCA
MCLD 19191 (CD) MCLC 19191 (Cass)*
WHITE MEN CAN'T JUMP (92) Music (Various Artists) -S/T-
*Manhattan Imp (Movie Boulevard): CDMTL 1067(CD)
(TC)MTL1067 (Cas/LP)* also available WHITE MEN CAN'T
RAP' *Manhattan (Movie Boulevard): CD(TC)MTL 1069*
WHITE MISCHIEF (88) Music score (George Fenton) title
song by Tim Finn/ "Alphabet Song" sung by Sarah Mil
es -S/T- T*ER (Koch): CDTER 1153 (CD)*
WHITE PALACE (90) Music score (George Fenton) -S/T- Imp
Varese (Pinn-S.Screen): VSD(VSC) 5289) (CD/Cass)
WHITE ROCK (76) Music scored and performed by Rick Wake
man available as CD box set *RW (President): RWCD 20*

WHITE SANDS (92) Music score (Patrick O'Hearn) -S/T- on
Morgan Creek/Poly: 573901-2(CD)-4(Cass) all deleted
WHO PLAYS WINS (ORIG LONDON CAST 85) Songs (Richard Sti
lgoe-Peter Skellern) *with* Richard Stilgoe-Peter Ske
llern *1st Night (Pinn) SCENE(C)1 (LP/Cass)*
WHO'S THAT GIRL (87) Music (Stephen Bray) -S/T- includ:
Madonna-Scritti Politti-Club Nouveau-Coati Mundi on
-S/T- *Sire (WEA): WX 102C (Cass) 925 611-2 (CD)*
WHO'S THE MAN (93) Music score (tbc) -S/T- *MCA (BMG):
MCD 10794 (CD) MCC 10794 (Cass)*
WILD AT HEART (90) Music score (Angelo Badalamenti)
-S/T- including 'Wicked Game' (Chris Isaak) -S/T-
London (Poly): 845 128-2 (CD) 845 128-4 (Cass)
WILD DUCK - *see under* 'FROG DREAMING'
WILD IS THE WIND (57) Music score (Dimitri Tiomkin)
see 'Film Music Of Dimitri Tiomkin' (collection)
WILD ORCHID (90) Music score (Geoff McCormack-Simon Gol
denberg) -S/T- *Sire (WEA): 759926127-2(CD) -4(Cass)*
WILD ORCHID: RED SHOE DIARIES - *see* 'RED SHOE DIARIES'
WILD PALMS (93) USA TV series Theme & incidental music
(Ryuichi Sakamoto) and songs by ZOMBIES-DON GARDNER
& DEE DEE FORD-MASON WILLIAMS-FRANKIE VALLI-LOU CHR
ISTIE TV -S/T- on *Capitol (EMI): CDEST 2204 (CD)*
WILD ROVERS (1) & **'THE FIRST GREAT TRAIN ROBBERY'** (78)
Music scores (Jerry Goldsmith) 2 -S/T- on *Memoir
(Castle-BMG): CDMOIR 601 (CD)*
WILD WEST (92) Music sc (Dominic Miller) -S/T- includes
songs by NANCI GRIFFITHS-STEVE EARLE-DWIGHT YOAKHAM
Cooking Vinyl (Pinn):COOKCD 056(CD) COOKC 056(Cass)
WILDCAT (ORIG USA CAST 60) Music (Cy Coleman) Lyr (Caro
lyn Leigh) *with* Lucille Ball-Keith Andes-Edith King
Paula Stewart-Clifford David-Don Tomkins-Howard Fis
cher-S.Swenson - *RCA (BMG): GD 60353 (CD)*
WILLOW (88) Music score (James Horner) -S/T- *Virgin
(Poly): CDV 2538 (CD)*
WIND AND THE LION The (75) Music score: Jerry Goldsmith
-S/T- *Intrada (Silva Screen): MAF 7005D (CD)*
WINGS OF DESIRE (88) Music score (Jurgen Knieper) -S/T-
*Mute: IONIC 2 (LP) CDIONIC 2 (CD) +Milan (S.Screen)
A.316 (LP) C.316 (Cass) CDCH 316 (CD)*
WINTER IN LISBON (92) Music sco (Dizzy Gillespie) -S/T-
Milan (Pinn): CDCH 704 (CD) C 704 (Cass)
WIRED (89) Music score (Basil Poledouris) with Joe Stru
mmer-Billy Preston-Blues Brothers -S/T- *Varese USA
(Silva Screen-Pinn): VS(VSC)(VSD) 5237 (LP/Cass/CD)*
WISH YOU WERE HERE (87) Music score (Stanley Myers)
Selection of -S/T- music + S.Myers scores from 'Sam
my & Rosie Get Laid' (87) & 'My Beautiful Launderet
te' (85) - *Milan (S.Screen): A.369 (LP) CD.369 (CD)*
WISH YOU WERE HERE (ORIG LONDON CAST 53) Songs (Harold
Rome) *feat* Shani Wallis-Dickie Henderson & Company
DRG USA Import (Silva Screen): DS 15015 (LP)
WITCHES OF EASTWICK The (87) Music score: John Williams
-S/T- *WB: 925607-4 (Cass) -2(CD)*

WITHNAIL AND I (87) Music score (David Dundas-Rick Went
worth) songs: Beatles-Jimi Hendrix-King Curtis
see under **'HOW TO GET AHEAD IN ADVERTISING'**
WITNESS (85) Music score (Maurice Jarre) -S/T- *Varese
(Pinn): VCD 47227 (CD) CST 8003SMC (Cass) also on
TER (S.Screen-Conif):CDTER 1098 (CD) ZCTER 1098 Cas*
WIZARD OF OZ The (39) Songs (Harold Arlen-Yip Harburg)
Judy Garland-Ray Bolger-Jack Haley-Bert Lahr-Frank
Morgan -S/T- *MGM EMI: CD(TC)(LP)MGM 7 all deleted*
WIZARD OF OZ The (MUSICAL SHOW) Music (Harold Arlen) Ly
rics (E.Y.Harburg) *Royal Shakespeare Company London
Cast (Barbican 1988) - TER (Con): (CD)(ZC)TER 1165*
WOLVES OF WILLOUGHBY CHASE The (89) Music (Colin Towns)
-S/T- *TER (Conif): CDTER(ZCTER) 1162 (CD/Cass)*
'Story Album' (Michael Hordern) *TER:ZCVIR 8311(Cas)*
WOMAN IN RED The (84) Songs (Stevie Wonder) featuring:
Stevie Wonder-Dionne Warwick -S/T- *Motown (Poly):
530 030-2 (CD) 530 030-4 (Cass)*
WOMAN NEXT DOOR The (La Femme D'a Cote)(Italy 81) Music
score (Georges Delerue) + 'Last Metro The' *Import
Prometheus (Silva Screen): PCD 113 (CD) /* also on
-S/T- *DRG USA (Con): SL(SLC) 9507 (LP/Cass) see
also COLL* 'TRUFFAUT AND DELERUE ON THE SCREEN'
WOMAN OF THE YEAR (ORIG BROADWAY CAST) Songs (John Kand
er-Fred Ebb) *with* Lauren Bacall and Company on
Bay Cities USA (Silva Screen): BCD 3008 (CD)
WONDERFUL TOWN (ORIG BROADWAY CAST 53) Songs (Leonard
Bernstein-Betty Comden-Adolph Green) *feat:* Rosalind
Russell-Sydney Chaplin *Sony Broadway: SK 48021 (CD)*
WONDERFUL TOWN (ORIG LONDON CAST 86)*feat* Maureen Lipman
John Cassady-Nicholas Colicos-Daniel Coll-Roy Durb
in-Ray Lonnen *First Night (Pinn): OCRCD 11 (CD)*
WONDERWALL (68) Music score (George Harrison) Re-issue:
EMI-Apple: CDSAPCOR 1 (CD) (TC)SAPCOR 1 (Cass/LP)
WOODSTOCK (70) 1969 Woodstock Music Festival: Joan Baez
Joe Cocker-Richie Havens-Country Joe & Fish-Crosby
Nash & Neil Young-Arlo Guthrie-Jimi Hendrix-Santana
ShaNaNa-John Sebastian-Sly & Family Stone-Ten Years
After-Who -S/T- *WEA: K60001 (3 LPs)*
WOODSTOCK II (70) Woodstock festival 69 feat v.artists
-S/T- re-issue: *Atlantic (WEA): 756781991-2 (CD)*
WORDS AND MUSIC (FILM MUSICAL 48) Songs (Lorenz Hart-
Richard Rodgers) and inc 'Three Little Words' -S/T-
MGM (Silva Screen): AK 47711 (CD) AT 47711 (Cass)
WORLD APART A (88) Music score (Hans Zimmer) -S/T- *Impt
Milan (S.Scre): A.302 (LP) C.302 (CS) CDCH 302 (CD)*
WUTHERING HEIGHTS (STUDIO RECORDING 91) Songs (Bernard
J.Taylor) *with* Dave Willetts-Lesley Garrett-Clive
Carter-Sharon Campbell-James Staddon & Philharmonia
Orchestra-Cantorum Choir (Nic Raine) *Silva Screen
(Conifer): SONGCD 904 (CD) SONGC 904 (Cass)*
WUTHERING HEIGHTS (Film) Music score (Ryuichi Sakamoto)
Virgin Classics: VC 759276-2 (CD)
X-RAY (80) - *see under* **'DEATH WISH'**

YAKSA (85) Feat music by Nancy Wilson-Toots Thielmans-
Masahiko Satoh -S/T- *Denon: C38-7556 (CD)*
YEAR OF LIVING DANGEROUSLY (81) Music (Maurice Jarre)
- *See* '**DEAD POETS SOCIETY**'/'**NO WAY OUT**' other music
'Opera Sauvage' (Vangelis) '4Last Songs' R.Strauss
YEAR OF THE COMET (91) Music score (Hummie Mann) -S/T-
Varese USA (Pinn): VSD 5365 (CD) VSC 5365 (Cass)
YEAR OF THE GUN (91) Music score (Bill Conti) -S/T-
Milan (S.Screen-Pinn): 873025 (CD)
YELLOW SUBMARINE (Cartoon 67) Songs (Lennon-McCartey)
-S/T- *Parlophone-EMI:CDP 746445-2 (CD) (TC)PCS 7070*
YEOMAN OF THE GUARD (OPERETTA) (Gilbert & Sullivan)
PRO-ARTE ORCHEST (Malcolm Sargent) and GLYNDEBOURNE
FESTIVAL CHOIR Soloists: Alex.Young-Denis Dowling-
Richard Lewis-John Cameron *EMI: CMS 764415-2 (2CDs)*
YEOMEN OF THE GUARD - *D'Oyly Carte Opera Comp.* (Gilbert
& Sullivan)+'Trial By Jury' *London: 417 358-2 (2CD)*
YEOMAN OF THE GUARD (1928 Recording)PETER DAWSON-GEORGE
BAKER-DEREK OLDHAM-WINIFRED DAWSON-Light Opera Orch
(Sir M.Sargent) *Pro-Arte (S.Screen): CDD 3417 (CD)*
YOL (82 Turkey/Switz) -S/T- *(S.Screen): CDFMC 405 (CD)*
YOR: Hunter From The Future (83) Music sco (John Scott)
version by Unione Musicisti Di Roma (Scott) on Impt
CBS USA (Silva Screen): LXCD 7 (CD)
YOU GOTTA WALK IT LIKE YOU TALK IT (71) Music score by
Walter Becker-Donald Fagen (from Steely Dan) -S/T-
on *See For Miles (Pinn): SEECD 357 (CD)*
YOU ONLY LIVE TWICE - see **JAMES BOND FILM INDEX**
YOUNG AMERICANS The (93) Music (David Arnold) Tracks by
DAVID ARNOLD-NINE INCH NAILS-SHEEP ON DRUGS-STEREO
MCs-DISPOSABLE HEROES OF HIPHOPRISY-KEITH LE BLANC
-S/T- *Island (Poly): CID 8019 (CD) ICT 8019 (Cass)*
YOUNG GIRLS OF ROCHEFORT The (68) Music score (Michel
Legrand) -S/T- *Imp (Silva Screen) 834140-2 (CD)*
YOUNG GUNS (88) Music sco (Anthony Marinelli) *no -S/T-*
YOUNG GUNS 2 (90) Music and songs (Jon Bon Jovi) inspir
ed by the film 'Young Guns 2' with "Blaze Of Glory"
Vertigo (Poly): 846 473-2/-4/ (CD/Cass)
YOUNG INDIANA JONES CHRONICLES The
see *TELEVISION* section
YOUNG LIONS The (58) Music sco (Hugo Friedhofer) -S/T-
with 'THIS EARTH IS MINE' *Varese (Pinn): VSD 5403CD*
YOUNG MAN OLDER WOMAN (ORIG CAST ALBUM) feat: Reynaldo
Rey on *Ichiban (Koch): ICHO 1159-2 (CD) -4 (Cass)*
YOUNG ONES The (Film 62) Cliff Richard & Shadows -S/T-
MFP (EMI): (TC)MFP 5823 (Cass/LP) CDMFP 6020 (CD)
YOUNG SOUL REBELS (91)Title song (Mica Paris)The Chimes
-S/T- *Big Life (Poly):BLRCD10 (CD) BLRMC10 (Cass)*
YOU'RE A BIG BOY NOW (67) Music (John Sebastian) THE
LOVIN' SPOONFUL -S/T-with 'What's Up,Tiger Lily' on
Sequel-Knight: NEXTCD 176 (CD)
YOURS ANNE (ORIG NEW YORK CAST 85) Songs (Michael Cohen
Enid Futterman)adapt.from 'The Diary Of Anne Frank'
TER (Conifer): TER 1118 (LP) ZCTER (Cass)

Z (69) Music score (Mikis Theodorakis) -S/T- reissue on
   Sakkaris (Pinn): SR 50062 (CD) see also Coll 'MIKIS
   THEODORAKIS ON THE SCREEEN'
ZABRISKIE POINT (69) Music: Pink Floyd-The Kaleidoscope
   Grateful Dead-Patti Page-Youngbloods-Jerry Garcia-
   Roscoe Holcomb-John Fahey -S/T- *MGM EMI CZ 285 (CD)*
ZACHARIAH (71) Rock'n'Roll film featuring: Country Joe
   & Fish-James Gang-Elvin Jones -S/T- titled 'A Head
   Of His Time' *See For Miles: SEE(SEEK) 91 (LP/Cass)*
ZEBRAHEAD (92) Music by TAJ MAHAL and Various Artists
   -S/T- *USA Import (Movie Boulevard) (CD)*
ZED AND TWO NOUGHTS A (85) Music score (Michael Nyman)
   -S/T- *Virgin (Poly): CDVE 54 (CD) (TC)VE 54 (CS/LP)*
ZERO DE CONDUITE (Film) Music sc (Maurice Jaubert) *also
   contains score from* L'ATALANTE (Maurice Jaubert) on
   Milan (Pinn): CDCH 0274 (CD)
ZIGGY STARDUST (THE MOTION PICTURE) (82) featur: DAVID
   BOWIE -S/T- *EMI: CDEMD 1037 (CD) TCEMD 1037 (Cass)*
ZOMBIES-DAWN OF THE DEAD (79) Elec.music (Goblin) -S/T-
   Cinevox (S.Screen): CDCIA 5035 (CD) CIAK 75035 Cass
ZORBA   (ORIG BROADWAY CAST 68) Songs (John Kander-Fred
   Ebb) *feat:* HERSCHEL BERNARDI-MARIA KARNILOVA-CARMEN
   ALVAREZ-JOHN CUNNINGHAM *Angel (EMI):ZDM 764665-2 CD*
ZORBA THE GREEK (64) Music composed and performed by
   MIKIS THEODORAKIS -*Intuition (Pinn): INT 31032 (CD)*
ZULU (64) Music score (John Barry)-S/T- + J.Bond themes
   Silva Screen (Con): FILMC 022(Cass) FILMCD 022 (CD)
ZULU DAWN (79) Music score (Elmer Bernstein) -S/T- Feat
   Royal Philharm Orch *Cerebus (Pinn): CSTCD 0201 (CD)*

---

*   T E L E - T U N E S   B A C K   I S S U E S   *

Some Of The Following BACK-ISSUES Are Available Direct
From: *MIKE PRESTON MUSIC,THE GLENGARRY,THORNTON GROVE,
MORECAMBE,LANCASHIRE LA4 5PU* Cheques Payable To 'MIKE
PRESTON MUSIC' (Prices Include Postage and Packing)

Tele-Tunes 1994 New Revised Ref Book Ed (344p)..£13.50
Tele-Tunes 1993 ....Out Of Print
Tele-Tunes 1992 New Revised Ref Book Ed (304p)..£12.50
Tele-Tunes 1991 New Revised Ref Book Ed (336p)..£12.50
Tele-Tunes 1990 New Revised Ref Book Ed (264p)..£10.50
Tele-Tunes 1988-89........................Out Of Print
Tele-Tunes 1987-88 Annual Book (208p)..(Ltd Ed).£10.50
Tele-Tunes 1986-87 Annual Book (192p)..(Ltd Ed).£10.50
Tele-Tunes 1985-86 Annual Book (160p)..(Ltd Ed).£10.50
Tele-Tunes 1981-84........................Out Of Print
Tele-Tunes 1978-80 Collectors Edition....(152p).£12.50
Tele-Tunes 1978-79 First Edition..........Out Of Print
Tele-Tunes Supplements (1984-93)..........Out Of Print
Tele-Tunes Supplements (1994 Subs.only)..see next page

S U B S C R I P T I O N S   T O   T E L E - T U N E S

TELE-TUNES Annual Reference Book Is Updated Quarterly
Cumulative Supplements Are Published During April, July
And October. In Addition To The Book And Supplements
MIKE PRESTON MUSIC Also Operates A Telephone Database
Information Service Monday To Friday 09.30am - 16.30pm.
Subscribers To The Full TELE-TUNES Service Have Access
To The Database. This Service Provides Extremely Fast
Answers To The Very Latest Queries On TV & Film Music.
PLEASE NOTE HOWEVER THAT THE TELEPHONE DATABASE INFORMA
TION LINE IS FOR SUBSCRIBERS TO THE FULL SERVICE ONLY.
If You Have A Music Query But Don't Subscribe You Can
Write To Us Enclosing A Stamped Addressed Envelope.
Subscription Service Details From:-
SUBSCRIPTION DEPT.,MIKE PRESTON MUSIC, THE GLENGARRY,
THORNTON GROVE, MORECAMBE, LANCASHIRE LA4 5PU
Telephone / Fax: (0 5 2 4)   4 2 1 1 7 2

S U P P L E M E N T S   1 9 9 4

JANUARY TO MARCH 1993   –   Published APRIL 1994
JANUARY TO JUNE 1993   –   Published   JULY 1994
JANUARY TO SEPT 1993   –   Published OCTOB 1994

4 AMERICA - Various Artists*   P.1992
  Silva Screen (Con):TVPMCD 801 (CD) TVPMC 801 (Cass)
  ROSEANNE-MY TWO DADS-THIRTYSOMETHING-THE COSBY SHOW
  CHEERS-L.A.LAW-ST.ELSEWHERE-NEWHART-HILL ST.BLUES-
  REMINGTON STEELE-LOU GRANT-NORTH & SOUTH-THE BRONX
  ZOO-WHITE SHADOW *Daniel Caine -prod: Michael Jones*
4 AMERICA TWO - Daniel Caine   P.1993
  Primetime (S.Screen-Con): TVPMCD(TVPMC) 803 CD/Cass
  WALTONS-NORTHERN EXPOSURE-I'LL FLY AWAY-LAND OF THE
  GIANTS-DREAM ON-MORK AND MINDY-THE MUNSTERS-BLOSSOM
  A DIFFERENT WORLD-HOGAN'S HEROES-EVENING SHADE-BARN
  EY MILLER-LITTLE HOUSE ON THE PRAIRIE-JOHNNY STACCA
  TO-FAMILY TIES-EERIE INDIANA
20 GREAT TV THEMES - Various Original Artists   P.1989
  Weekend (Total-BMG): WEEKCD2 (CD) WEEKMC2 (Cass)
  VANITY FAIR-THE ONE GAME-SQUARE DEAL-THE MATCH-EYE
  WITNESS-DOCTOR WHO-CAMPION-RUTH RENDELL MYSTERIES-
  AGATHA CHRISTIE'S POIROT-ME AND MY GIRL-WORLD CUP-
  WISH ME LUCK-INSPECTOR MORSE-FOREVER GREEN-7 FACES
  OF WOMAN-TALES OF THE UNEXPECTED-TO HAVE & TO HOLD-
  THE TWO OF US-THE PROFESSIONALS-UPSTAIRS DOWNSTAIRS
20 TOP TV THEMES - Various Original Artists   P.1990
  Weekend (Total-BMG): WEEKCD 3 (CD) WEEKMC 3 (Cass)
  THE RUTH RENDELL MYSTERIES-INSPECTOR MORSE-FOREVER
  GREEN-AGATHA CHRISTIE'S POIROT-TheNEW ADVENTURES OF
  BLACK BEAUTY-CHIMERA (Rosheen Du)-TESTAMENT-SUMMERS
  LEASE-HUNDRED ACRES-ITV WEATHER-CLOSE TO HOME-ON
  THE LINE-WORLD CUP 90(Tutti Al Mondo)-ITV ATHLETICS
  (Hot Foot)-CAPITAL CITY-THE MATCH (Goal Crazy)-THE
  PIGLET FILES-MOTORMOUTH-LONDON'S BURNING-ONE IN 4
A-Z OF TELEVISION THEMES FROM THE 60s & 70s *PLAY 004 CD*
  Play It Again from Screenthemes 22 Kensington Close
  Toton Beeston Notts. NG9 6GR / also: S.Screen-Conif
  AVENGERS-CAPTAIN SCARLET & MYSTERONS-CATWEAZLE-THE
  CHAMPIONS-CROSSROADS-DAD'S ARMY-DANGER MAN-DEPT.S
  DOCTOR IN THE HOUSE-DR.WHO-EMMERDALE FARM-FIREBALL
  XL5-FORSYTE SAGA-HADLEIGH-HANCOCK-MAIGRET-MAN ALIVE
  MAN IN A SUITCASE-NO HIDING PLACE-PLEASE SIR-POWER
  GAME-RETURN OF THE SAINT-THE SAINT-SPORTSNIGHT-STEP
  TOE AND SON-STINGRAY-THANK YOUR LUCKY STARS-THUNDER
  BIRDS-TOP SECRET-Z CARS *incl: 21 original versions*
AH SWEET MYSTERY OF LIFE Jeanette MacDonald-Nelson Eddy
  Flapper/Pavilion (Pinn): PASTCD 7026 (CD)   *p.1993*
  INDIAN LOVE CALL-WHO ARE WE TO SAY(OBEY YOUR HEART)
  ISN'T IT ROMANTIC-HILLS OF HOME-AUF WIEDERSEH'N-AH
  SWEET MYSTERY OF LIFE-ROSE MARIE-LOVER COME BACK TO
  ME-MOUNTIES-NEATH THE SOUTHERN MOON-BEYOND THE BLUE
  HORIZON-WHEN I GROW TOO OLD TO DREAM-ITALIAN STREET
  SONG-SONG OF LOVE-SYLVIA-SENORITA-I'M FALLING IN LO
  VE-FAREWELL TO DREAMS-GOODNIGHT-TREES-ONE KISS-WILL
  YOU REMEMBER
AMERICAN AND ITALIAN WESTERN SCREEN THEMES - Various Ar
  Milan (Pinn): 873 038 (CD)   P.1992
  BUTCH CASSIDY & SUNDANCE KID-STAGECOACH-RIVER OF NO

RETURN-SHE WORE A YELLOW RIBBON-HOW T. WEST WAS WON
HIGH NOON-PROUD ONES-RAWHIDE-SHANE-GUNFIGHT AT THE
OK CORRALL-ANOTHER DAY ANOTHER COUNTRY-ALAMO-ADIOS
GRINGO-MASSACRE TIME-HILLS RUN RED-ARIZONA COLT-ONE
SILVER DOLLAR-JOHNNY YUMA-MAGNIFICENT 7-RIO BRAVO

AMERICAN TELEVISION THEMES Volume 1 - Daniel Caine cond
Primetime (Conifer):TVPM(CD)(C)400 (CD/Cass) P.1991
TWIN PEAKS-LA LAW-STAR TREK: THE NEXT GENERATION-
MANCUSO FBI-HOOPERMAN-MURDER SHE WROTE-SPENSER FOR
HIRE-21 JUMP STREET-NEWHART-HUNTER-THE BRONX ZOO-
SONNY SPOON- NORTH AND SOUTH-MIDNIGHT CALLER

AMERICAN TELEVISION THEMES Volume 2 - Daniel Caine cond
Primetime (Conifer):TVPM(CD)(C)401 (CD/Cass) P.1991
THIRTYSOMETHING-DOOGIE HOWSER MD-HIGHWAY TO HEAVEN-
MACGYVER-THE SLAP MAXWELL STORY-HEAD OF THE CLASS-
ALF-WISEGUY-THE NUTT HOUSE-REMINGTON STEELE-FALCON
CREST-BRING 'EM BACK ALIVE-MEN-QUANTUM LEAP

AMERICAN TELEVISION THEMES Volume 3 - Daniel Caine cond
Primetime (Conifer):TVPM(CD)(C)404 (CD/Cass) P.1991
LAW AND ORDER-CAPITAL NEWS-SLEDGEHAMMER-CHINA BEACH
B.L.STRYKER-THE DAYS & NIGHTS OF MOLLY DODD-PARKER
LEWIS CAN'T LOSE-THE YOUNG RIDERS-NIGHT COURT-STING
RAY (USA series)-HOUSTON KNIGHTS-OVER MY DEAD BODY-
BUCK JAMES-TOP OF THE HILL *conductor: DANIEL CAINE*

ANDREW LLOYD WEBBER CLASSIC SONGS Royal Philharm.Orch*
Lesley Garrett-Christopher Howard-Meredith Braun-Ke
ith Burns-Sharon Campbell-Michele Hooper-Deborah St
eel-Andrew C.Wadsworth-Samuel Burkey /*Paul Bateman
Silver Screen (Con): SONG(C)(CD) 909 (Cass/CD) p.93
SUPERSTAR-UNEXPECTED SONG-STARLIGHT EXPRESS-ANGEL
OF MUSIC/THE POINT OF NO RETURN-TAKE THAT LOOK OFF
YOUR FACE-OH WHAT A CIRCUS-MACAVITY THE MYSTERY CAT
NEXT TIME YOU FALL IN LOVE-CLOSE EVERY DOOR-HIGH FL
YING ADORED-EVERYTHINGS ALRIGHT-SEEING IS BELIEVING
PIE JESU (Lesley Garrett-Samuel Burkey)

ANDREW LLOYD WEBBER COLLECTION The - Var.Artists P.1992
Pickwick Internat: PWKS 4065 (CD) PWKMC 4065 (Cass)
STARLIGHT EXPRESS(Carl Wayne) UNEXPECTED SONG *(Paul
Jones)* MEMORY *(Instrumental)* MACAVITY THE MYSTERY
CAT *(Stephanie Lawrence)* GUS THE THEATRE CAT *(Paul
Jones)* PUMPING IRON *(Jess Conrad)* TELL ME ON A SUND
AY *(Carl Wayne)* I DON'T KNOW HOW TO LOVE HIM *(Fiona
Hendley)* ANY DREAM WILL DO *(Jess Conrad)* LOVE CHANG
ES EVERYTHING *(Instrum)* ALL I ASK OF YOU *(Stephanie
Lawrence-Carl Wayne)* OH WHAT A CIRCUS *(Jess Conrad)*
WISHING YOU WERE SOMEHOW HERE AGAIN *(Stephanie Lawr
ence)* MEMORY *West End Concert Orc (Matthew Freeman)*

ANDREW LLOYD WEBBER LOVE SONGS Royal Philharmonic Orch
with Lesley Garrett-Chris Corcoran-Sharon Campbell-
and Dave Willetts / RPO conduct: Paul Bateman P.93
Silva Screen (Con):SONGCD 908 (CD) SONGC 908 (Cass)
ALL I ASK OF YOU-I DON'T KNOW HOW TO LOVE HIM-LOVE
CHANGES EVERYTHING-WISHING YOU WERE SOMEHOW HERE-
DON'T CRY FOR ME ARGENTINA-ONLY YOU-PHANTOM OF THE

OPERA-MUSIC OFTHE NIGHT-ANOTHER SUITCASE IN ANOTHER
HALL-MEMORY-TELL ME ON A SUNDAY-THINK OF ME
**ASSAULT ON PRECINCT 13: Music From The Movies Of John
Carpenter** *Silva Screen (Conif):* **FILM(C)(CD) 113**
DARK STAR-HALLOWEEN-THE FOG-ESCAPE FROM NEW YORK-
BIG TROUBLE IN LITTLE CHINA-CHRISTINE-STARMAN-THE
THING-PRINCE OF DARKNESS-THEY LIVE-ASSAULT ON PREC
INCT 13 - Music by John Carpenter-Ennio Morricone-
Jack Nitzsche-Alan Howarth   P.1992
AT THE MOVIES 1: DIRTY HARRY - Heroes & Tough Guys P.92
Silva Treasury (Con): **SILVAD(SILVAC) 3001** *(CD-Cass)*
DIRTY HARRY-RUNNING MAN-GODFATHER II-COOL HAND LUKE
ROBIN HOOD (Bergin)-RAIDERS OF THE LOST ARK-REVENGE
HUNT FIR RED OCTOBER-BULLITT-HIGH ROAD TO CHINA-THE
HITCHER-CROCODILE DUNDEE-BIG TROUBLE I.LITTLE CHINA
DOUBLE IMPACT-MISSING IN ACTION-LONG GOOD FRIDAY-
GREAT WALDO PEPPER-THE HEROES
AT THE MOVIES 2: STAR WARS/2001 A SPACE ODYSSEY   P.92
Silva Treasury (Con): **SILVAD(CILVAC) 3002** *(CD/Cass)*
STAR WARS-2001 A SPACE ODYSSEY-THE BIG COUNTRY-GONE
WITH THE WIND-LAWRENCE OF ARABIA-VERTIGO-TIME AFTER
TIME-BEST YEARS OF OUR LIVES-BRIT.FILM SCORES SUITE
ROYAL PHILH.ORCH-LONDON PHILH.ORCH-PHILHARMONIA ORC
AT THE MOVIES 3: PSYCHO - Horror & Fantasy   P.92
Silva Treasury (Con): **SILVAD(SILVAC) 3003** *(CD/Cass)*
PSYCHO-KRULL-SUPERMAN-IT'S ALIVE 2-RETURN OF T.JEDI
HALLOWEEN-BRIDE OF THE RE ANIMATOR-MOON 44-MASTERS
OF THE UNIVERSE-DARK STAR-SUNDOWN:THE VAMPIRE IN RE
TREAT-THEY LIVE-NEAR DARK-HELLRAISER-PHANTOM OF THE
OPERA-DRAGONSLAYER-DRACULA HAS RISEN FROM THE GRAVE
AUSTRALIAN TV'S GREATEST HITS - Var Orig Artists P.1986
Silva Screen (Conifer): **FILMC(CD) 028** *(Cass/CD)*
NEIGHBOURS-PAUL HOGAN SHOW-SULLIVANS-PRISONER CELL
BLOCK H-ANZACS-CARSONS LAW-SONS & DAUGHTERS-YOUNG
DOCTORS-A COUNTRY PRACTISE + *47 other tracks*
BACK TO BROADWAY - Barbra Streisand   P.1993
Columbia (Sony M): **473 880-2** *(CD)* **-4** *(Cass)* **-1** *(LP)*
SOME ENCHANTED EVENING *(South Pacific)* EVERYBODY SA
YS DON'T *(Anyone Can Whistle)* MUSIC OF THE NIGHT **du
et with Michael Crawford** *(Phantom Of The Opera)* SPE
AK LOW *(One Touch Of Venus)* AS IF WE NEVER SAID GOO
DBYE / WITH ONE LOOK *(Sunset Boulevard)* CHILDREN WI
LL LISTEN *(Into The Woods)* I HAVE A LOVE / ONE HAND
ONE HEART **duet with Johnny Mathis** *(West Side Story)*
I'VE NEVER BEEN IN LOVE BEFORE / LUCK BE A LADY TON
IGHT *(Guys & Dolls)* THE MAN I LOVE *(Lady Be Good)*
MOVE ON *(Sunday In The Park With George)*
BBC SPORTING THEMES - Var.Artists   P.1988   DELETED
BBC-Pickwick (Pickw): **PWKS 648** *(CD)* **HSC 648** *(Cass)*
GRANDSTAND 88-CRICKET-WORLD CUP GRANDSTAND-SNOOKER
SKI SUNDAY-RUGBY SPECIAL-WIMBLEDON 1-DARTS-QUESTION
OF SPORT-COMMONWEALTH GAMES-SPORTSNIGHT-WORLDCUP-RU
GBY-SPORT ON 2-ATHLETICS-BOWLS-WIMBLEDON ENDIND-MAT
CH OF THE DAY-GRANDSTAND 58

BE MY LOVE - Mario Lanza
    RCA Vic.(BMG): GD 60720 (CD) GK 60720 (Cass) p.1991
    BE MY LOVE-SERENADE-TEMPTATION-WANTING YOU-I'LL BE
    SEEING YOU-WITH A SONG IN MY HEART-WITHOUT A SONG-
    MY WILD IRISH ROSE-BECAUSE-ONLY A ROSE-FUNICULI FUN
    ICULA-COME BACK TO SORRENTO-AND THIS IS MY BELOVED-
    DANNY BOY-MARIA MARI-O SOLE MIO-NEAPOLITAN LOVESONG
    ARRIVEDERCI ROMA-AH SWEET MYSTERY OF LIFE-LOOK FOR
    THE SILVERLINING-MEMORIES-THE SONG IS YOU-AVE MARIA
    (Schubert)-YOU'LL NEVER WALK ALONE
BERNSTEIN: A MAN AND HIS MOVIES - Elmer Bernstein P.1992
    Mainstream (Koch): MDCD 601 (CD)
    RAT RACE-THREE TIMES BLUESER (Take 5)-RADIO HYSTERIA
    (Sudden Fear)-ANNA LUCASTA theme-HOP SKIP BUT JUMP-
    BIG TOP-SWEET SMELL OF SUCCESS-MAN WITH THE GOLDEN
    ARM-JUBILATION-WALK ON THE WILD SIDE-BIRDMAN OF ALCA
    TRAZ-TREE TREASURE (To Kill A Mockingbird)-BABY THE
    RAIN MUSIC FALL-TO KILL A MOCKINGBIRD (Main Theme)
BEST OF ARNOLD SCHWARZENEGGER - Various Artists   P.1992
    Silva Screen (Conifer): FILM(C)(CD) 100 (CD/Cass)
    CONAN T.BARBARIAN-TERMINATOR-CONAN T.DESTROYER-TOTA
    L RECALL-RUNNING MAN-RED HEAT-PREDATOR-RAW DEAL etc
BEST OF ARNOLD SCHWARZENEGGER Volume 2 - Various Arts
    Cinerama Imp (S.Screen): CIN 2205-2 (CD) -4 (Cass)
    CONAN THE BARBARIAN-CONAN THE DESTROYER-COMMANDO-
    RAW DEAL-KINDERGARTEN COP-RED SONJA-THE RUNNING MAN
    THE TERMINATOR-RED HEAT-TWINS-CHRISTMAS IN CONNECTI
    CUT-PREDATOR-TOTAL RECALL-TERMINATOR2:Judgement Day
BEST OF BBC TV THEMES Orig Arts. *PWKS 645 p.87* DELETED
    SINGING DETECTIVE-EASTENDERS-TENDER IS THE NIGHT-MI
    SS MARPLE-DRWHO-DALLAS-HOWARDS WAY-MASTERMIND-NEIGH
    BOURS-TOMORROWS WORLD-BERGERAC-STAR COPS-MY FAMILY
    & OTHER ANIMALS-SHOESTRING-KNOTS LANDING-WHICKER'S
    WORLD-LIFE & LOVES OF A SHE DEVIL-FLIGHT OF THE CON
    DOR-FAWLTY TOWERS-CONDOR-WHO PAYS THE FERRYMAN-LIFE
    & TIMES OF D.L.GEORGE-FORTUNES OF WAR-SKI SUNDAY
BEST OF BERNARD HERRMANN The - Royal Philharmonic Orch*
    Milan (Silva Screen): 14081-2 (CD) -4 (Cass)   p.93
    CITIZEN KANE-TAXI DRIVER-FAHRENHEIT 451-BRIDE WORE
    BLACK-WRONG MAN-MAN WHO KNEW TOO MUCH-PSYCHO-DEVIL
    & DANIEL WEBSTER-VERTIGO *conduct: Elmer Bernstein
BEST OF DEANNA DURBIN - Deanna Durbin   P.1992
    MCA (BMG): MCLD 19183 (CD) MCLC 19183 (Cass)
    IT'S RAINING SUNBEAMS-MY OWN-SPRING IN MY HEART-ONE
    FINE DAY-LOVE IS ALL-PERHAPS-LAST ROSE OF SUMMER-BL
    UE DANUBE-CAN'T HELP SINGING-CALIFORN.I.AY-BECAUSE-
    TURNTABLE SONG-SPRING WILL BE A LITTLE LATE THIS YE
    AR-HOME SWEET HOME-WALTZING IN THE CLOUDS-AVE MARIA
BEST OF ENNIO MORRICONE The - Ennio Morricone Or P.1987
    RCA (BMG): PD 70234 (CD)   FOR A FEW DOLLARS MORE-
    A FISTFUL OF DYNAMITE-GOD WITH US-MY NAME IS NOBODY
    A FISTFUL OF DOLLARS-SACCO & VANZETTI-ONCE UPON A T
    IME IN THE WEST-METELLO-MOSES THE LAWGIVER-1900-DEA
    TH RIDES A HORSE-LIFE'S TOUGH..-CIRIBIRIBIN-SCETATE

BEST OF JAMES BOND (30th Anniv.Coll) Orig Artists P.92
EMI: CDBOND 007 (CD) TCBOND 007 (Cas) BOND 007 (LP)
JAMES BOND THEME-GOLDFINGER-NOBODY DOES IT BETTER-A
VIEW TO A KILL-MR KISS KISS BANG BANG-FOR YOUR EYES
ONLY-WE HAVE ALL THE TIME IN THE WORLD-LIVE AND LET
DIE-ALL TIME HIGH-THE LIVING DAYLIGHTS-FROM RUSSIA
WITH LOVE-LICENCE TO KILL-THUNDERBALL-YOU ONLY LIVE
TWICE-MOONRAKER-ON HER MAJESTY'S SECRET SERVICE-MAN
WITH THE GOLDEN GUN-DIAMONDS ARE FOREVER-007

BEST OF JOHN BARRY The - Film & TV Themes - John Barry
Polydor: 849 095-2 (CD) 849 095-4 (Cass)   P.1991
GOLDFINGER-SAIL THE SUMMER WINDS (The Dove)-LOVE AM
ONG THE RUINS-LOLITA-A DOLL'S HOUSE-FOLLOW FOLLOW
(Follow Me)-DIAMONDS ARE FOREVER-BOOM-MIDNIGHT COWB
OY-THIS WAY MARY (Mary Queen Of Scots)-THE GLASS ME
NAGERIE-THUNDERBALL-007-PLAY IT AGAIN (The Tamarind
Seed)-ORSON WELLES GREAT MYSTERIES-WE HAVE ALL THE
TIME IN THE WORLD (On Her Majesty's Secret Service)
THE WHISPERERS-CURIOUSER AND CURIOUSER (Alice's Adv
entures In Wonderland)-BILLY-THE GOOD TIMES ARE COM
ING (Monte Walsh)-WALKABOUT-THE ADVENTURER

BEST OF KEVIN COSTNER - Various Artists   P.1993
Silva Screen (Conifer): FILM(C)(CD) 143 (CD/Cass)
Themes from KEVIN COSTNER films: ROBIN HOOD, PRINCE
OF THIEVES (91)-J.F.K.(92)-FANDANGO (85)-NO WAY OUT
(88)-REVENGE (90)-FIELD OF DREAMS (89)-THE UNTOUCHA
BLES (87)-SILVERADO (85)-DANCES WITH WOLVES (90)

BEST OF SCANDINAVIAN FILM MUSIC The - Various Artists
Milan France (Silva Screen): CDCH 760 (CD)   P.1991
PELLE THE CONQUEROR (88)-MY LIFE AS A DOG (85-music
Bjorn Isfalt)-BABETTE'S FEAST (87-mus: Per Norgard)

BEST OF SEAN CONNERY FILMS The - Various Artists
Silva Screen (Conif): FILMCD 142 (CD)   p.93
MEDICINE MAN-HIGHLANDER-GOLDFINGER-NAME OF THE ROSE
THE PRESIDIO-UNTOUCHABLES-RUSSIA HOUSE-FROM RUSSIA
WITH LOVE-NEVER SAY NEVER AGAIN-ROBIN AND MARIAN-
DIAMONDS ARE FOREVER-JAMES BOND THEME-THUNDERBALL-
YOU ONLY LIVE TWICE-TANGO TO THE DEATH-DR.NO-MARNIE

BEST OF STEPHEN KING The - Various Artists   p.93
Silva Prod (Conifer): CIN 22002 (CD) 22002-4 (Cass)
CHILDREN OF THE CORN and Suite from CHILDREN OF THE
CORN-THE SHINING Main title theme and Music For Per
cussion Strings and Celeste from THE SHINING-Suite
from MISERY-CREEPSHOW Main theme-GRAVEYARD SHIFT tr
ailer music-Suite from CHRISTINE-Mick's Broadcast
attack from THE RUNNING MAN

BIG SCREEN ADVENTURE - Roy Budd & London Symphony Orch
D.Sharp/Collins Cl.(Pinn): DSHCD(MC) 7004 (CD/Cass)
(1) RAIDERS OF THE LOST ARK / INDIANA JONES SUITE
(2) E.T.SUITE / (3) SUPERMAN SUITE: March Of The
Villains - Can You Read My Mind (Love Theme) - Main
Theme (4) STAR WARS TRILOGY:EMPIRE + RETURN OF:Main
Theme-Princess Leia's Theme-Imperial March-Yoda's
Theme-Han Solo & The Princess-Parade Of The Ewoks

BIG SCREEN CLASSICS - Royal Phiharmonic Orch *   p.1993
Quality TV (Pinn): BIGSCD 1 (CD) BIGSMC 1 (Cass)
TARA'S THEME *(Gone With The Wind)* MOON RIVER *(Break
fast At Tiffany's)* SPEAK SOFTLY LOVE *(Godfather)* AS
TIME GOES BY *(Casablanca)* LARA'S THEME *(Dr.Zhivago)*
WHERE DO I BEGIN*(Love Story)* UNCHAINED MELODY *Ghost*
CHARIOTS OF FIRE / TAKE MY BREATH AWAY *(Top Gun)* UP
WHERE WE BELONG *(An Officer & A Gentleman)* A SUMMER
PLACE / OVER THE RAINBOW *(Wizard Of Oz)* THE SOUNDS
OF SILENCE *(The Graduate)* CANON IN D Pachelbel *(Ord
inary People)* TIME OF MY LIFE *(Dirty Dancing)* HERO:
THE WIND BENEATH MY WINGS *(Beaches)* IT MUST HAVE BE
EN LOVE *(Pretty Woman)* CAVATINA *(Deer Hunter)* BEST
THAT YOU CAN DO *(Arthur)* EVERYTHING I DO (I DO IT
FOR YOU *(Robin Hood Prince Of Thieves)*I WILL ALWAYS
LOVE YOU *(The Bodyguard)* *conductor: **RICHARD HOLMES**
BIG WAR THEMES - Geoff Love Orch   P.1988
MFP Compacts FP (EMI): CC 211 (CD) / HR 8140 (Cass)
BRIDGE ON THE RIVER KWAI-LAWRENCE OF ARABIA-GUNS OF
NAVARONE-BATTLE OF BRITAIN-LONGEST DAY-WHERE EAGLES
DARE-DAM BUSTERS-633 SQUADRON-GREAT ESCAPE-GREEN BE
RETS-DEER HUNTER-COLDITZ-VICTORYAT SEA-SINK THEBISM
ARCK-WINDS OF WAR-REACH FOR THESKY-WE'LL MEET AGAIN
BOND AND BEYOND - Erich Kunzel & Cincinnati Pops Orches
Telarc USA (Conifer): CD-80251 (CD only)   P.1991
GOLDFINGER-JAMES BOND THEME-FROM RUSSIA WITH LOVE-
MAIN THEME/CRIME SPREE(D.Tracy)-MAINTHEME/AL CAPONE
IT'S A LONG ROAD-DRAGNET/PETER GUNN/PERRY MASON-FBI
HILL ST BLUES/MISSION IMPOSSIBLE/MAN F.UNCLE-LA LAW
MIAMI VICE/HAWAII 5:O-LIVE & LET DIE-FOR YOUR EYES
ONLY-AXEL F-LETHAL WEAPON-WOE THE DARKMAN-NOBODY DO
ES IT BETTER (Spy Who)-SHAFT-ALL TIME HIGH(Octopu.)
BOND COLLECTION (30th Anniversary) - Shirley Bassey
Icon (Pinn): ICOMCD 007 (CD) ICOMC 007 (Cass) P.93
A VIEW TO A KILL-NOBODY DOES IT BETTER-FROM RUSSIA
WITH LOVE-WE HAVE ALL THE TIME IN THE WORLD-YOU
ONLY LIVE TWICE-DIAMONDS ARE FOREVER-LIVE AND LET
DIE-MOONRAKER-FOR YOUR EYES ONLY-ALL TIME HIGH-
THUNDERBALL-GOLDFINGER
BOOM BOOM & Other Songs From TV Commercials - Var.Arts.
Movieplay (Tayl): MVP 5531 (CD) MPV 45331 (Cass)
BOOM BOOM:John Lee Hooker LITTLE RED ROOSTER:Howlin
Wolf ON THE ROAD AGAIN:Canned Heat CUPID:Sam Cooke
HAPPY TOGETHER:Turtles PIECE OF MY HEART:Erma Frank
lin HAVE YOU SEEN HER:Chi-lites FEVER:Peggy Lee OH
HAPPY DAY:Edwin Hawkins Singers THREE STEPS TO HEAV
EN:Eddie Cochran DREAM A LITTLE DREAM OF ME:Mama
Cass YOU MADE ME LOVE YOU:Harry James VENUS:Frankie
Avalon ONLY YOU:Platters SHAKE RATTLE AND ROLL:Bill
Haley &.SHOUT:Isley Bros VENUS IN BLUE JEANS: Jimmy
Clanton UNFORGETTABLE:Dinah Washington YOU'LL NEVER
WALK ALONE:Gerry &Pacemakers FEELINGS:Morris Albert
BLUE VELVET:Moonglows TO KNOW HIM IS TO LOVE: Shire
lles ISRAELITES:Desmond Dekker MOCKIN' BIRD HILL

BRIDESHEAD REVISITED: Televis.Scores Of Geoffrey Burgon
Silva Screen (Con): FILM(C)(CD) 117 (CD/Cass) p.92
THE CHRONICLES OF NARNIA-BLEAK HOUSE-TESTAMENT OF
YOUTH-BRIDESHEAD REVISITED (Suite)-NUNC DIMITTIS fr
om TINKER TAILOR SOLDIER SPY sung by *LESLEY GARRETT*
Philharmonia Orchestra conducted by Geoffrey Burgon
BUGS BUNNY ON BROADWAY - Warner Bros Symphony Orchestra
Warner USA (Silv.Screen): 926494-2(CD)-4(Cass) P.91
New music recordings from classic cartoons 'Merrie
Melodies' Music by **Carl Stalling** *and* **Milt Franklyn**
feat the voices of **MEL BLANC** *(Bugs Bunny-Daffy Duck*
Porky Pig-Elmer Fudd..) see also **'CARL STALLING..'**
CAGNEY & LACEY AND OTHER AMERICAN TV THEMES　Re-iss 90
Silva Screen (Con): FILMCD 704 (CD) FILMC 704 (Cas)
CAGNEY & LACEY-MIKE HAMMER-LOU GRANT-ST.ELSEWHERE-
MAGNUM, P.I.-TAXI-SIMON AND SIMON-HILL STREET BLUES
m.dir: **Derek Wadsworth** / *cond:* **Daniel Caine**　P.1985
CAPTAIN BLOOD - Classic Film Scores For Errol Flynn
RCA Victor (BMG): GD 80912 (CD) GK 80912 (Cass)
ADVENTURES OF DON JUAN:The King Main Title/Don Juan
The Brocade/Don Juan's Serenade/Parade Into London/
Don Juan and the Queen/Final Scene.THE SEA HAWK:The
Albatross/Throne Room Of Elizabeth I/Entrance Of T.
Sea Hawks/Orchid/Panama March/Duel/Strike For Shore
Of Dover.**CAPTAIN BLOOD:** Ship In The Night.**THEY DIED**
WITH THEIR BOOTS ON: Morning The Farewell Before The
Battle/Preparation& March/7th Cavalry/The Sioux/The
Battle Of Little Big Horn/Custer's Last Stand.**DODGE**
CITY: Warner Bros Fanfare/Main Title/Open Prairie/
Iron Horse/Surrett/Comrades/Covered Wagon/Grazioso/
Abbie & Children/Wade & Abbie/Blarney/Abbie's Theme
OBJECTIVE BURMA: Parachute Drop. **THE SUN ALSO RISES**
Prologue (Solenelle)/Lights Of Paris. ADVENTURES OF
ROBIN HOOD: Archery Tournament/Escape From T.Gallows
Robin and Lady Marian/Coronation Procession
NATIONAL PHILHARMONIC ORCHESTRA (CHARLES GERHARDT)
CAPTAIN FROM CASTILLE　Class.Film Scores: Alfred Newman
RCA Vic (BMG): GD 80184 (CD) GK 80184 (Cass) P.1990
HOW TO MARRY A MILLIONAIRE-CAPTAIN FROM CASTILLE-WU
THERING HEIGHTS-DOWN TO THE SEA IN SHIPS-THE SONG OF
BERNADETTE-THE BRAVADOS-ANASTASIA-THE BEST OF EVERY
THING-AIRPORT-THE ROBE *(selection)*-MAP OF JERUSALEM
National Philharmonic Orchestra (Charles Gerhardt)
CARL STALLING PROJECT - Warner Bros Cartoons 1936-1958
Warner USA (SILV.Screen): 926027-2(CD)-4(Cass) P.90
Music from the orig W.Bros 'Merrie Melodies' cartoo
ns inc: HILLBILLY HARE-DAFFY DOC-BEANSTALK BUNNY-SP
EEDY GONZALES.../*see also* 'BUGS BUNNY ON BROADWAY'
CASABLANCA - Classic Film Scores For Humphrey Bogart
RCA Victor (BMG): GD 80422 (CD) GK 80422 (Cas) P.90
CASABLANCA-PASSAGE TO MARSEILLE-TREASURE OF THE SIE
RRA MADRE-BIG SLEEP-CAINE MUTINY-TO HAVE & HAVE NOT
TWO MRS.CARROLLS-SABRINA-LEFT HAND OF GOD-SAHARA-VI
VIRGINIA CITY-KEY LARGO ***N.Phil.Or.Charles Gerhardt***

CHARLIE - Chaplin's Film Music: Munich Symphony Orch*
   Silva Screen (Con): FILMCD 711 (CD) FILMC 711(Cass)
   Suites from: LIMELIGHT-A KING IN NEW YORK-THE GREAT
   DICTATOR-CITY LIGHTS-MODERN TIMES-MONSIEUR VERDOUX
   A COUNTESS FROM HONG KONG conducted by *Francis Shaw*
CHILLER - Erich Kunzel & Cincinnati Pops Orchest.P.1989
   Telarc USA (Conifer): CD 80189 (CD)
   PHANTOM OF THE OPERA-NIGHT ON BALD MOUNTAIN-DANSE M
   ACABRE-MARCH TO THE SCAFFOLD-PANDEMONIUM DAMNATION
   OF FAUST-IN THE HALL OF THEMOUNTAIN KING-Theme From
   TWILIGHT ZONE-BRIDE OF FRANKENSTEIN-THE DEVIL & DAN
   IEL WEBSTER-PSYCHO-SLEUTH-POLTERGEIST-WITHOUTA CLUE
   FUNERAL MARCH OF A MARIONETTE:Alfred Hitchock Theme
CINEMA - Elaine Paige   P.1984
   Pickwick: PWKS 545 (CD) HSC 3285 (Cass)
   WINDMILLS OF YOUR MIND-OUT HERE ON MY OWN-PRISONER-
   SOMETIMES-MAHOGANY-UP WHERE Ee BELONG-UNCHAINED MEL
   ODY-BRIGHT EYES-ALFIE-MISSING-WAY WE WERE-THE ROSE
CINEMA DU MONDE - Various Artists   p.1993
   Music Club Int (TBD): MCCD 127 (CD) MCTC 127 (Cass)
   CARPE DIEM *(Dead Poets Society)*-GENERIQUE *(Fort Sag
   ne)*-UNCHAINED MELODY *(Ghost)*-GENERIQUE ET FIN *(Jean
   De Florette)*-ALMA EST PARTIE *(La Pirate)*-SERENADE
   FUR KLARA *(Klara)*-THEME DE CAMILLE *(Le Mepris)*- AU
   MOULIN *Apres La Guerre)*-UNCLE ARVIDSSON'S DREAM *(My
   Life As A Dog)*-L'AMOUR D'UGOLIN *(Manon Des Sources)*
   DREAM IN A BLUE NIGHT *(Concert For Alice)*-KWAN'S SA
   CRIFICE*(Year Of Living Dangerously)*-PELLE EROBREREN
   (Pelle The Conqueror)-L'ORAGE *(Jean De Florette)*-
   LOUIS ET MARTINE *(Le Grand Chemin)*-PASTORALE MODERA
   TP *(Babette's Feast)*-HABANERA*(Benvenuta)*-THEME FROM
   MY LIFE AS A DOG *(My Life As A Dog)*
CINEMAGIC - Dave Grusin - London Symphony Orch   P.1987
   GRP: (S.Screen): GRP(M) 91037 (LP/CS) GRPD 9547(CD)
   AN ACTOR'S LIFE/IT MIGHT BE YOU**(Tootsie)**-HEAVEN CAN
   WAIT-ON GOLDEN POND-3 DAYS OF THE CONDOR-HEART IS A
   LONELY HUNTER-GOONIES-CHAMP- *+ CD tracks:* PLO CAMP
   ENTRANCE-FALLING IN LOVE/LETTING GO **(Champ)**-LITTLE
   DRUMMER GIRL / *with* **Tom Scott & Lee Ritenour**
CITIZEN KANE - CLASSIC FILM SCORES OF BERNARD HERRMANN
   RCA Victor (BMG): GD 80707 (CD)   Re-issued 1991
   ON DANGEROUS GROUND: The Death Hunt-**CITIZEN KANE:**Pre
   lude-Xanadu-Snow Picture-Themes and Variations-Aria
   from Salammbo (with Kiri Te Kanawa)-Rosebud-Finale
   BENEATH THE 12-MILE REEF: The Sea-Lagoon-Descending-
   The Octopuss-Homecoming-**HANGOVER SQUARE:**Concerto Ma
   cabre for Piano & Orchestra-**WHITE WITCH DOCTOR:**Talk
   ing Drums-Prelude-The Riverboat-Petticoat Dance-The
   Safari-Tarantula-The Lion-Nocturne-Abduction Of The
   BakubaBoy-The Skulls-Lonni Bound By Ropes-Departure
CLASSIC BRITISH FILM MUSIC - Philharmonia Orch * P.1990
   *Silva Screen (Con): FILMCD 713 (CD) * Kenneth Alwyn*
   Coastal Command (42-R.V.Williams)-**Conquest Of The
   Air** (38-Arthur Bliss)-**Red Shoes** (48-Brian Easdale)

CLASSIC COMMERCIALS - Var.Artists (Decca Recordings)
Decca (Poly): 440 638-2 (CD) -4 (Cass)   *P.1993*
Old Spice: O FORTUNA Carmina Burana *(Orff)* / Hovis:
LARGO New World Symphony *(Dvorak)* / Royal Bank Of
Scotland: PLAYFUL PIZZICATO Simple Symph. *(Britten)*
British Airways: FLOWER DUET Lakme *(Delibes)* / L'Eg
oiste: DANCE OF THE KNIGHTS Romeo & Juliet *(Prokofi
ev)* / Hamlet: AIR ON A G.STRING Suite No.3 *(Bach)* /
Today Newspaper: DIES IRAE Requiem *(Verdi)* / Lloyds
Bank: SLEEPERS AWAKE Cantata 140 *(Bach)* / Jif Clean
er: DANCE OF THE HOURS La Gioconda *(Ponchielli)* /
Buxton Spring Water: CELLO CONCERTO 1st m/m *(Elgar)*
Lee Jeans: ANVIL CHORUS Il Trovatore *(Verdi)* / Peug
eot 605: DIE MOLDAU Ma Vlast *(Smetana)* /Batchelor's
Slimmer Soups: DANCE OF THE LITTLE SWANS Swan LAKE
(Tchaikovsky) / Twinings Tea: ONE FINE DAY Madame
Butterfly *(Puccini)* / Guardian: MAZURKA Coppelia
(Delibes) / Pedigree Chum: Symphony No.9 1st m/m
(Dvorak) / Fiat Strada: LARGO AL FACTOTUM Barber Of
Seville *(Rossini)* / Castrol GTX: Symp.No.7 2nd m/m
(Mahler) /Pretty Polly: MARIO MARIO Tosca *(Puccini)*
Dulux Weathershield: JUPITER Planets Suite *(Holst)*
CLASSIC FM: - see 'SOUND OF CLASSIC ROMANCE'
CLASSIC FANTASY FILM SCORES Conductor: Bernard Herrmann
Cloud Nine (Conifer): ACN 7014 (CD only)   *P.1989*
Symphonic Suites From 4 Films (All Music by Bernard
Herrmann): THREE WORLDS OF GULLIVER-MYSTERIOUS ISLA
ND-SEVENTH VOYAGE OF SINBAD-JASON AND THE ARGONAUTS
CLASSIC FILM SCORES FOR BETTE DAVIS - *N.P.O.   reiss 89
RCA Victor (BMG): GD 80183 (CD) GK 80183 (Cass)
NOW VOYAGER-DARK VICTORY-A STOLEN LIFE-THE PRIVATE
LIVES OF ELIZABETH AND ESSEX-MR.SKEFFINGTON-IN THIS
OUR LIFE-ALL ABOUT EVE-JEZEBEL-BEYOND THE FOREST-JU
UREZ-THE LETTER-ALL THIS & HEAVEN TOO / * *National
Philharmonic Orchestra conductor:* Charles Gerhardt
CLASSIC JOHN BARRY The - City Of Prague Symphony Orches
tra (Nicholas Raine) Digital Suites and Themes p.93
Silva Screen (Conifer): FILMCD 141 (CD)
ZULU-OUT OF AFRICA-BODY HEAT-MIDNIGHT COWBOY-THE
LAST VALLEY-BORN FREE-CHAPLIN-ELEANOR AND FRANKLIN-
DANCES WITH WOLVES-INDECENT PROPOSAL-THE PERSUADERS
ROBIN AND MARIAN-SOMEWHERE IN TIME-THE LION IN WINT
ER-HANOVER STREET-RAISE THE TITANIC
CLASSIC MIKLOS ROZSA FILM THEMES - Nuremberg Symph Orch
TER (Conifer): CDTER 1135 (CD) ZCTER 1135 (Cass)
EL CID-STORY OF 3LOVES-LOST WEEKEND-PRIVATE LIFE OF
SHERLOCK HOLMES-KING OFKINGS-DEAD MEN DON'T WEAR PL
AID-STRANGE LOVE OF MARTHA IVERS-PLYMOUTH ADVENTURE
QUO VADIS | *Orchestra conducted by* Elmer Bernstein
CLASSICS OF THE SILVER SCREEN - Erich Kunzel & *C.P.O.
Telarc USA (Conifer): CD 80221 (CD)   *P.1990*
Hot To Trot & Masterpiece Theme-Ordinary People-The
Witches Of Eastwick-Amadeus-Barry Lyndon-My Geisha-
Somewhere In Time-Moonstruck-Raging Bull-Who Framed

Roger Rabbit-Driving Miss Daisy-Elvira Madigan-Diva
Kramer Vs Kramer-Brief Encounter-A Room With A View
The Elephant Man & Platoon *Cincinnati Pops Orchest
CLIFF RICHARD DEFINITIVE FILMS AND MUSICALS ALBUM   p.93
EMI Impt (Arabesque Dist): 791961-4 (2Cass)
A MATTER OF MOMENTS-ON THE BEACH-DO YOU REMEMBER-
WHAT I'VE GOTTA DO-I COULD EASILY FALL IN LOVE WITH
YOU-FIDERS KEEPERS-TIME DRAGS BY-OH SENORITA-LA LA
SONG-IN THE COUNTRY-PEACE AND QUIET-TWO A PENNY-
I'LL LOVE YOU FOREVER TODAY-TAKE ME HIGH-THE WORD
IS LOVE-IT'S MONEY-LIVING DOLL-LOVE-A VOICE IN THE
WILDERNESS-THE SHRINE ON THE SECOND FLOOR-THE YOUNG
ONES-WHEN THE GIRL IN YOUR ARMS IS THE GIRL IN YOUR
HEART-WE SAY YEAH-LESSONS IN LOVE-GOT A FUNNY FEELI
NG-SUMMER HOLIDAY-THE NEXT TIME-DANCING SHOES-BACHE
LOR BOY-ALL AT ONCE-BIG NEWS-WONDERFUL LIFE
COASTAL COMMAND - *see under* Classic British Film Music
COMMERCIAL BREAKS - Various Original Artists   P.1991
Columbia (Sony M): 469048-2 (CD) -4 (Cass deleted)
ONLY YOU: Praise *(FIAT TEMPRA)*-LOVELY DAY: Bill Wit
hers(FORD ESCORT)-SUMMER BREEZE: Isley Bros *(WEIGHT
WATCHERS)*-LOVE TRAIN: O'JAYS *(BR.RAIL)*-HOW 'BOUT US
Champaign *(DATELINE)*-TURN TURN TURN: Byrds *(MIDLAND
BANK)*-IT'S OVER: Roy Orbison *(PANASONIC CAMCORDER)*-
MOVE OVER DARLING: Doris Day *(PRETTY POLLY)*-I CAN
SEE CLEARLY NOW:Johnny Nash *(NESCAFE)*-STAND BY YOUR
MAN: Tammy Wynette *(KIT-KAT)*-ALWAYS ON MY MIND:Will
ie Nelson(VAUXHALL ASTRA)-BLUE VELVET: Bobby Vinton
(NIVEA)-I CAN HELP: Billy Swann *(GENERAL ACCIDENT)*-
TAKE FIVE: Dave Brubeck *(FORD ORION)*-SUMMERTIME: Sa
rah Vaughan(PIMMS)-MANNISH BOY: Muddy Waters *(LEVI)*
SHOULD I STAY OR SHOULD I GO: The Clash *(LEVI'S)*
COPS AND PRIVATE EYES VOL.1 - conducted by DANIEL CAINE
Primetime (Conifer):TVPM(CD)(C)405 (CD/Cass) P.1991
LA LAW-SLEDGEHAMMER-HILL ST.BLUES-SPENSER FOR HIRE-
REMINGTON STEELE-LAW AND ORDER-MIKE HAMMER-RIPTIDE-
MIDNIGHT CALLER-HOOPERMAN-OVER MY DEAD BODY-HOUSTON
KNIGHTS-TWIN PEAKS-MAGNUM,P.I.
DIAL M FOR MURDER: A History Of Hitchcock (Film Music)
Czech Symphony Orchestra cond: Paul Bateman   p.1993
Silva Screen (Conifer): FILMCD 137 (CD)
New Digital Recordings Of Suites From A.H.Films
DIAL M FOR MURDER *(composed by DIMITRI TIOMKIN)*
UNDER CAPRICORN *(RICHARD ADDINSELL)* TOPAZ *(MAURICE
JARRE)* REBECCA and SUSPICION *(FRANZ WAXMAN)* SPELLB
OUND *(MIKLOS ROZSA)* VERTIGO-NORTH BY NORTHWEST-MAR
NIE-PSYCHO *(BERNARD HERRMANN)* FRENZY *(RON GOODWIN)*
DIRTY HARRY HEROES & TOUGH GUYS - *see* 'AT THE MOVIES 1'
DISNEY COLLECTION (Volume 1) - Var.Orig Artists   P.1992
Disney (Pickwick): DSTCD 453 (CD) DSTMC 453 (Cass)
I WANNA BE LIKE YOU *(JUNGLE BOOK)*-SUPERCALIFRAGILIS
TICEXPIALIDOCIOUS-A SPOONFUL OF SUGAR*(MARY POPPINS)*
WHISTLE WILE YOU WORK*(SNOW WHITE)*-ZIP A DEE DOO DAH
(SONG OF T.SOUTH)-BIBBIDI-BOBBIDI-BOO *(CINDERELLA)*

DISNEY COLLECTION (Volume 2) - Var.Orig Artists   P.1992
Disney (Pickwick): DSTCD 454 (CD) DSTMC 454 (Cass)
KISS THE GIRL *(LITTLE MERMAID)*-HE'S A TRAMP *(LADY &
THE TRAMP)*-BARE NECESSITIES *(JUNGLE BOOK)*-CHIM CHIM
CHEREE *(MARY POPPINS)*-WHEN I SEE AN ELEPHANT FLY
(DUMBO)-LITTLE APRIL SHOWER *(BAMBI)* + other tracks

DISNEY COLLECTION (Volume 3) - Var.Orig Artists   P.1992
Disney (Pickwick): DSTCD 455 (CD) DSTMC 455 (Cass)
WHEN YOU WISH UPON A STAR *(PINOCCHIO)*-ONCE UPON A
DREAM *(SLEEPING BEAUTY)*-SOMEDAY MY PRINCE WILL COME
(SNOW WHITE)-SECOND STAR TO THE RIGHT *(PETER PAN)*
SOMEONE'S WAITING FOR YOU*(THE RESCUERS)*-BELLE NOTTE
(LADY & THE TRAMP) / plus other unspecified tracks

DISNEY DREAMS - Original Recordings from DISNEY -S/T-
Disney (Pickw): DSMCD 465(CD) DSMMC 465 (Cass) p.93
A DREAM IS A WISH YOUR HEART MAKES:*Cinderella* -I'M
WISHING:*Snow White* -STAY AWAKE:*Mary Poppins* -LOVE:
Robin Hood -AVE MARIA: *Fantasia* -LA LA LU:*Lady And
The Tramp* -CANDLE ON THE WATER:*Pete's Dragon* -ONCE
UPON A DREAM:*Sleeping Beauty*-SOMEDAY MY PRINCE WILL
COME:*Snow White* -SECOND STAR TO THE RIGHT:*Peter Pan*
SOMEONE'S WAITING FOR YOU:*Rescuers* -LOVE IS A SONG
Bambi-ALL IN A GOLDEN AFTERNOON:*Alice In Wonderland*
PART OF YOUR WORLD:*Little Mermaid* -LOOKING FOR ROMA
NCE:*Bambi* -WHEN YOU WISH UPON A STAR:*Pinocchio*

DIVA! - A Soprano At The Movies: LESLEY GARRETT
Silva Screen (Conif): SONGC(CD)903 (Cass/CD) P.1991
La Boheme (MOONSTRUCK)-Gianni Schicchi (A ROOM WITH
A VIEW)-Rusalka(DRIVING MISS DAISY)-The Marriage Of
Figaro (THE MODERNS)-Carmen (CARMEN JONES)-La Wally
(DIVA)-Lakme Flower Duet (THE HUNGER) *PHILHARMONIA
ORCHESTA (Andrew Greenwood) LESLEY GARRETT Soprano*

DOLLAR'S TRILOGY The - Ennio Morricone   P.1991
RCA Italy (Silva Screen): ND 74021 (CD)
Over 65 mins. of music from the 3 Sergio Leone west
ern films starring Clint Eastwood. Great Ennio Morr
icone scores to A FISTFUL OF DOLLARS (64) FOR A FEW
DOLLARS MORE (65) THE GOOD THE BAD & THE UGLY (66)

DON BLACK SONGBOOK The - Various Artists   P.1993
Play It Again (S.Screen-Screenthemes):PLAY 005 (CD)
BORN FREE *(MATT MONRO)*- TO SIR WITH LOVE *(Lulu)* THE
GIRL WITH THE SUN IN HER HAIR *(Davy Clinton)* TRUE
GRIT *(Danny Street)* ON DAYS LIKE THESE *(Matt Monro)*
WISH NOW WAS THEN *(Matt Monro)* CURIOUSER AND CURIOU
SER *(Matt Monro)* THE ME I NEVER KNEW *(Matt Monro)*
BILLY *(Lena Martell)* THE LADY FROM L.A. *(Michael Cr
awford)*I MISSED THE LAST RAINBOW *(Michael Crawford)*
PLAY IT AGAIN *(Wilma Reading)* I'LL PUT YOU TOGETHER
AGAIN *(Hot Chocolate)* TELL ME ON A SUNDAY *(Marti We
bb)* THE LAST MAN IN MY LIFE *(Marti Webb)* ANYONE CAN
FALL IN LOVE *(Marti Webb)* ALWAYS THERE *(Marti Webb)*
THERE IS LOVE AND THERE IS LOVE *(Adam Faith)* IN ONE
OF MY WEAKER MOMENTS *(Anita Dobson)* ANYTHING BUT LO
NELY / LOVE CHANGES EVERYTHING *(both by Marti Webb)*

DORIS DAY GREATEST HITS - Doris Day   p.1993
Telstar (BMG): TCD(STAC)(STAR) 2659 (CD/Cass/LP)
MOVE OVER DARLING-EVERYBODY LOVES A LOVER-A VERY PR
ECIOUS LOVE-LOVER COME BACK-THE DEADWOOD STAGE-IF I
GIVE MY HEART TO YOU-ANYWAY THE WIND BLOWS-IT'S MAG
IC-THE BLACK HILLS OF DAKOTA-TEACHER'S PET-LOVE ME
OR LEAVE ME-PERHAPS PERHAPS PERHAPS-SECRET LOVE-QUE
SERA SERA (Whatever Will Be Will Be)-MY LOVE AND DE
VOTION-LET'S WALK THAT-A-WAY(duet with Johnnie Ray)
APRIL IN PARIS-READY WILLING AND ABLE-SUGARBUSH (du
et w.Frankie Laine)-WHEN I FALL IN LOVE-PILLOW TALK
THE SOUND OF MUSIC-LOVE HIM-I'LL NEVER STOP LOVING
YOU-BEWITCHED-SENTIMENTAL JOURNEY

DRACULA: Classic Scores from Hammer Horror Philharmonia
S.Screen (Con):FILMCD 714(CD) Orch Neil Richardson
DRACULA (58 James Bernard) DRACULA HAS RISEN FROM
THE GRAVE (68 James Bernard)TASTE THE BLOOD OF DRAC
ULA (70 James Bernard) VAMPIRE CIRCUS (71 David Whi
taker) HANDS OF THE RIPPER (71 Christopher Gunning)

DRAKE 400 Concert Suite & Film Music - Ron Goodwin P.80
Chandos: CHAN 8811 (CD) LBTD 001 (Cass)
DRAKE 400 Orchestral Suite-Love Theme From BEAUTY &
THE BEAST-Festival Time-CANDLESHOE-Amazing Grace-
FORCE 10 FROM NAVARONE-Minuet In Blue-SPACEMAN AND
KING ARTHUR-Girl With The Misty Eyes-Auld Lang Syne
The Bournemouth Symphony Orchestra **Ron Goodwin**

DREAM MUSIC - Movie Music Of TANGERINE DREAM   p.1993
Silva Screen (Con): FILMCD 125 (CD) Selections from
THE PARK IS MINE - DEADLY CARE - DEAD SOLID PERFECT

ELAINE PAIGE - The Collection   P.1990
Pickwick: PWKS 4021 (CD) PWKMCS 4021 (Cass)
SOMETIMES (Champions Theme)-THE ROSE-MacARTHUR PARK
WINDMILLS OF YOUR MIND-WITHOUT YOU-SECRETS-WALKING
IN THE AIR-THE LAST ONE TO LEAVE-MEMORY (Cats)-AVE
MARIA-A WINTERS TALE-ANOTHER SUITCASE IN ANOTHER HA
LL-SO SAD TO WATCH GOOD LOVE GO BAD-IF YOU DON'T WA
NT MY LOVE-HOT AS SUN-THE WAY WE WERE

**ELIZABETH AND ESSEX - CLASSIC FILM SCORES OF ERICH WOLF
GANG KORNGOLD - *RCA (BMG): GD 80185 (CD) Reiss: 91***
PRIVATE LIVES OF ELIZABETH 7 ESSEX:Overture- PRINCE
& THE PAUPER:Main Title-Boys Got To Play-Epilogue-
ANTHONY ADVERSE:In The Forest-THE SEA WOLF: Main Ti
tle-Escape In The Fog-Love Scene-Finale-DECEPTION:-
Cello Concer.In C.Op37 (Francisco Garbarro) ANOTHER
DAWN:-Night Scene-OF HUMAN BONDAGE: Main Title-Chri
stmas-Sally-Lullaby-Finale.
NATIONAL PHILHARMONIC ORCHESTRA (Charles Gerhardt)

ELMER BERNSTEIN BY ELMER BERNSTEIN - Royal Philh. Pops*
Denon (Conifer): CD 75288 (CD)   p.1993
THE MAGNIFICENT 7-TO KILL A MOCKINGBIRD-MAN WITH
THE GOLDEN GUN-THE GRIFTERS-WALK ON THE WILD SIDE-
HAWAII-THE GREAT ESCAPE-GHOSTBUSTERS-HOLLYWOOD AND
THE STARS-RAMBLING ROSE-HEAVY METAL-MY LEFT FOOT-
THE TEN COMMANDMENTS / R.P.O. cond: Elmer Bernstein

EMBER YEARS 1: John Barry / Elizabeth Taylor In London
  Play It Again (Silva Screen): PLAY 002 (CD)   P.1992
  JOHN BARRY: -S/T- to 'Four In The Morning' (65) and
  ELIZABETH TAYLOR IN LONDON (63) Music by JOHN BARRY
EMBER YEARS 2: John Barry / Annie Ross
  Play It Again (Silva Screen): PLAY 003 (CD)   P.1992
  JOHN BARRY: FROM RUSSIA WITH LOVE-HIGH GRASS-KINKY-
  ZULU STAMP-LONELINESS OF AUTUMN-NGENZENI-BIG SHIELD
  ALIKI-TETHA LEYANTO-TROUBADOR-MONKEY FEATHERS-007
  ANNIE ROSS:RHYTHM OF THE WORLD-A LOT OF LIVIN'TO DO
  LET ME LOVE YOU-ALL THE THINGS YOU ARE-I'M GONNA GO
  FISHIN-LIKE SOMEONE IN LOVE-LIMEHOUSE BLUES-HANDFUL
  OF SONGS-ALL OF YOU-NATURE BOY-WHAT'S NEW & others
EMPIRE-MOVIE MUSIC COLLECTION (Virgin -S/T- Sampler)
  Virgin (Poly): (CD)(TC)VMM 1 (CD/Cass/LP)   P.1990
  THE LAST EMPEROR-THE MISSION-MERRY XMAS MR.LAWRENCE
  BLACK RAIN-SEX LIES & VIDEOTAPE-HOMEBOY-BETTY BLUE-
  DANGEROUS LIASIONS-KILLING FIELDS-GLORY-THE MODERNS
ENNIO MORRICONE FILM HITS - E.Morricone Orch Reiss. 90
  RCA (BMG): ND 70091 (CD) NK 70091 (Cass)
  ONCE UPON A TIME IN THE WEST-FOR A FEW DOLLARS MORE
  MOSES THEME-BYE BYE COLONEL-A FISTFUL OF DOLLARS-A
  GUN FOR RINGO-BALLAD OF SACCO & VENZETTI-HERE'S TO
  YOU-VICE OF KILLING-PAYINGOFF SCORES-THE ADVENTURER
  WHAT HAVE YOU DONE TO SOLANGE-VIOLENT CITY-METELLO
EPIC The - (Cinema Gala Series) - London Festival Orch
  Decca Classics: 417 845-2 (CD)   P.1987
  EXODUS-LAWRENCE OF ARABIA-MAGNIFICENT 7-CLEOPATRA-
  ALAMO-DR.ZHIVAGO-STAGECOACH-FOF WHOM THE BELL TOLLS
  SEA HAWK-PATTON *London Festival Orch* **Stanley Black**
EROTIC CINEMA - Mouvie Sounds Orchestra and L.A.Voices
  Laserlight (Taylors): 12167 (CD) 72167 (Cass) p.93
  UP WHERE WE BELONG:*An Officer And A Gentleman* -I DO
  WHAT I DO:*9½ Weeks* -TIME OF MY LIFE:*Dirty Dancing* -
  SKIN DEEP:*Senza Buccia* -PARADISE-BLACK EMMANUELLE-
  BASIC INSTINCT-YOU CAN LEAVE YOUR HAT ON:*9½ Weeks* -
  BILITIS-WICKED GAME:*Wild At Heart* -HISTOIRE D'O:*His
  tory Of O* -IT MUST HAVE BEEN LOVE:*Pretty Woman*-LAST
  TANGO IN PARIS-LADY CHATTERLEY'S LOVER-EMMANUELLE-
  BOLERO:*10*
ESCAPE FROM TELEVISION - Jan Hammer   P.1987
  MCA (BMG): MCLD 19133 (CD) MCLC 19133
  CROCKETT'S THEME-THERESA-COLOMBIA-RM CAY-THE TRIAL
  AND THE SEARCH-TUBBS AND VALERIE-FOREVER TONI-LAST
  FLIGHT-RICO'S BLUES-BEFORE THE STORM-NIGHT TALK-
  MIAMI VICE MAIN THEME-FOREVER TONIGHT Extended Mix
ESSENTIAL JAMES BOND The - City Of Prague Symphony Orch
  estra (Nicholas Raine)   p.1993
  Silva Screen (Con):FILMCD 007 (CD) FILMC 007 (Cass)
  DR.NO-FROM RUSSIA WITH LOVE-007-GOLDFINGER-THUNDERB
  ALL-YOU ONLY LIVE TWICE-ON HER MAJESTY'S SECRET SER
  VICE-DIAMONDS ARE FOREVER-MAN WITH T.GOLDEN GUN-SPY
  WHO LOVED ME-MOONRAKER-FOR YOUR EYES ONLY-OCTOPUSSY
  THE LIVING DAYLIGHTS-VIEW TO A KILL-LICENCE TO KILL

EUROPE GOES TO HOLLYWOOD - Royal Philharmonic Pops Orch
cond by John Scott / *Denon (Conif): CO 75470 (CD)*
ADVENTURES OF ROBIN HOOD *(Korngold)* ALAMO *(Tiomkin)*
GODFATHER *(Rota)* BEN HUR *(Rozsa)* GONE WITH THE WIND
(Steiner) REBECCA *(Waxman)* CITIZEN KANE *(Herrmann)*
EVIL TRACKS - Claudio Simonetti   P.1991
Italian Import (Silva Screen): OST 104 (CD)
Claudio Simonetti was the force behind the Italian
rock group GOBLIN. Both the group and Simonetti as
a solo composer have written many scores for Horror
films. This CD contains previously unavailable scor
es for: DEMONS-PRIMAL RAGE-NIGHTMARE BEACH & THREAT
F.A.B. -THUNDERBIRDS Music from world of Gerry Anderson
Silva Screen (Con):FILMCD 124 (CD) FILMC 124 (Cass)
ROYAL PHILHARMONIC ORCHESTRA New Digital Recordings
Themes and Suites from STINGRAY-SPACE 1999-JOE 90-
U.F.O.-CAPTAIN SCARLET + 30 min.suite THUNDERBIRDS
MUSIC COMPOSED BY BARRY GRAY and DEREK WADSWORTH
FAMOUS THEMES (1)-Remember These? - Var.Artists   P.1986
Grasmere (Tay): GRCD 10 (CD) GRALP (GRTC)10
PUFFIN' BILLY (Childrens Fav)-MUSIC EVERYWHERE (Red
iffusion)-CORONATION SCOT (Paul Temple)-ON A SPRING
NOTE (Pathe Gazette)-RHYTHM ON RAILS Morning Mus-BY
THE SLEEPY LAGOON(Desert Island Discs) HORSE GUARDS
WHITEHALL (Down Your Way)-DEVIL'S GALLOP (Dick Bart
on)-DESTRUCTION BY FIRE (Pathe News)-ALL SPORTS MAR
CH (Pathe News)-SPORTSMASTER (Peter Styvestant)-ALP
INE PASTURES (My Word)-CAVALCADE OF YOUTH (Barlowes
Of Beddington)-DRUM MAJORETTE (Or Match Of The Day)
ELIZABETHAN SERENADE (Music in Miniature)-MELDOY ON
THE MOVE/YOUNG BALLERINA (The Potter's Wheel)-GIRLS
IN GREY (BBC TV News)-WILLO THE WISP/PORTRAIT OF A
FLIRT/JUMPING BEAN (In Town Tonight)-HORSE FEATHERS
Meet The Huggetts)-JOURNEY INTO MELODY/SAPPHIRES &
SABLES/INVITATION WALTZ (Ring Around The Moon)
FAMOUS THEMES (2) - More Famous Themes - V.Artists P.87
Grasmere (Taylors): GRALP 20 (LP) GRTC 20 (Cass)
VOICE OF LONDON-Sig Tune *Queens Hall Light Orch*-MUS
IC WHILE YOU WORK-CURRENT RELEASE (Movietime)-HELLO
MUM-MISS WORLD-SEEING SPORT-WESTMINSTER WALTZ-ASTAR
IS BORN-HOLIDAY SPIRIT-HIGH ADVENTURE- QUIET STROLL
KALEIDOSCOPE-APPLEHARDS-HORSEMAN RIDING BY-MOOMIN'-
MUSIC GOES ROUND-JENNINGS AT SCHOOL-MELODY FAIR-WIM
BLEDON *Orig Recordings From Chappell Music Library*
FAMOUS THEMES (3) - London Calling - V.Artists   P.88
Grasmere (Taylors): GRALP 30 (LP) GRTC 30 (Cass)
LONDON CALLING (BBC Radio O/S Service)-ON THE SEA
SHORE (Players Cigarettes)-SHADOW WALTZ (Teckman Bi
ography)-PICTURE PARADE-SWIFTLY (APlace In The Sun)
RIPPLING WATERS (BBC TV Angel Fish Interlude)-ROYAL
REVIEW (BBCTV News)-SHOPPING CENTRE (Picture Page)-
SEASCAPE (Windjammers)-JAMBOREE (Out Of The Blue)-
OPENINGS & ENDINGS (early Panorama)-TRAPEZE WALTZ-
(Guy de Maupassant)-JOCKEY ON THE CAROUSEL-(Mainly

FAMOUS THEMES (3) - *Continued from p.261*
Continued from p.261
    For Women) (Mainly For Women)-DALILIA/DESPERADOS
    (Desperate People)-AUTUMN LOVE (Spring & Autumn) BR
    ING ON THE GIRLS (Time For Titch)-PROSCENIUM (Armch
    air Theatre)-PASTORAL MONTAGE (BBC TV Windmill Int)
    JOLLY JUGGLER (Sunday Afternoon)-SENTIMENTAL (R.Att
    enborough Presents)-MET.MARCH-Calling All Sportsmen
    all original tracks from the CHAPPELL MUSIC LIBRARY
FAN CLUB The - DEANNA DURBIN   **P.1992**
    Flapper-Pavilion (Pinn): PASTCD 9781 (CD)
    AMAPOLA-BECAUSE-WHEN APRIL SINGS-WALTZING IN THE CL
    OUDS-MY OWN-BRINDISI-BENEATH THE LIGHTS OF HOME-SPR
    ING IN MY HEART-IT'S RAINING SUNBEAMS-MUSETTA'S WAL
    TZ SONG-LOVE IS ALL-PERHAPS-ONE FINE DAY-HOME SWEET
    HOME-LAST ROSE OF SUMMER-IL BACIO-AVE MARIA-LOCH LO
    MONS-ALLELULIA-AVE MARIA   *DEANNA DURBIN Film Songs*
FANTASTIC JOURNEY - **Erich Kunzel & Cincinnati Pops Orch**
    Telarc USA (Conifer): CD 80231 (CD)   **P.1990**
    BATMAN SUITE-DAY THE EARTH STOOD STILL-WAR OF THE W
    ORLDS-THE BLACK HOLE-TWILIGHTZONE-BOY WHO COULD FLY
    THE BEASTMASTER-EXPLORERS-DRAGONSLAYER-MOONWALKER-
    POLTERGEIST-STAR TREK V THE FINAL FRONTIER-INDIANA
    JONES & THE LAST CRUSADE-STAR WARS-LAST STARFIGHTER
FANTASTIC TELEVISION THEMES - **Daniel Caine**   **P.1991**
    Primetime-S.Screen (Conif): TVPMC(CD) 402 (Cass/CD)
    QUANTUM LEAP-V-FREDDY'S NIGHTMARES-STARTREK: THE NE
    XT GENERATION-KNIGHT RIDER-HIGHWAY TO HEAVEN-STREET
    HAWK-BATTLESTAR GALACTIC-AIRWOLF-BUCK ROGERS IN THE
    25TH CENTURY-NORTH STAR: THE TV MOVIE-BRING'EM BACK
    ALIVE-RETURN O.THE MAN FROM UNCLE-TALES OF THE GOLD
    MONKEY / Producer: Michael Jones
FAVOURITE MOVIE CLASSICS - **Various Artists**   **P.1992**
    EMI: CDCFP 4606 (CD) TCCFP 4606 (Cass)
    APOCALPYSE NOW/EXCALIBER *(Wagner: RIDE OF THE VALKY
    RES)*-PLATOON/THE ELEPHANT MAN *(Barber: ADAGIO FOR
    STRINGS)*-MY LEFT FOOT *(Mozart: COSI FAN TUTTE)*-2001
    A SPACE ODYSSEY *(Strauss: BLUE DANUBE)*-DRIVING MISS
    DAISY *(Dvorak: SONG TO THE MOON from RUSALKA)*-FANTA
    SIA *(Ponchielli: DANCE OF THE HOURS)*-OUT OF AFRICA
    (Mozart: ADAGIO from CLARINET CONCERTO IN A)-CLOCKW
    ORK ORANGE *(Rossini: THIEVING MAGPIE OVERTURE)*-ROOM
    WITH A VIEW *(Puccini: O MIO BABBINO CARO)*-DEATH IN
    VENICE *(Mahler: ADAGIETTO from SYMPH.NO.5)*-THE LADY
    KILLERS *(Boccherini: MINUET (STRING QUARTET IN E)*
    DANGEROUS MOONLIGHT *(Addinsell: WARSAW CONCERTO)*
FAVOURITE SPORTING THEMES - **Power Pack Orchestra P.1988**
    MFP (EMI): TCMFP 5818 (Cass)
    Offside (Match Of the Day)-Drag Racer (BBC Snooker)
    Aztec Gold (Big Match)-Sportsnight-Chase Side Shoot
    Up (BBC Golf)-Pop Looks Bach (Ski Sunday / Winter
    Olympics)-Question Of Sport-Out Of The Blue (Radio
    Sports Report)-Gonna Fly Now 'Rocky' (ITV Boxing)
    Soul Limbo (BBC Cricket)-Light & Tuneful (BBC Wimbl
    edon)-Saint & Greavsie-BBC Grandstand-Holy Mackerel

(BBC Rugby Special)-ITV World Of Sport-Riptide BBC
87 World Champ'ship Athletics)

FAVOURITE TV CLASSICS (Volume 1) - Various Artists P.92
Classics FP (EMI): CDCFP 4613 (CD) TCCFP 4613(Cass)
Old Spice: O FORTUNA Carmina Burana *(Orff)* /Citroen
BX: WINTER 4th m/m Four Seasons *(Vivaldi)* / IBM Com
puters/Ryvita Sesame Seeds/Uncle Ben's Classic Reci
pes: FUR ELISE *(Beethoven)* / Heineken/Sybaris Perfu
me: ADAGIO in G.Min.for Organ & Strings *(Albinoni)*
ALLA HORNPIPE Water Music *(Handel)* / Vauxhall Carlt
on: RONDO 3rd m/m Concerto Horn & Orch No.4 in D.
K495 *(Mozart)* / British Airways/Jif: FLOWER DUET fr
om LAKME *(Delibes)* / Pomagne: PIZZICATI Sylvia *(Del
ibes)* / Black & Decker Paintstipper: FLIGHT OF THE
BUMBLEBEE *(Rimsky-Korsakov)* / AEG/Alton Towers/Nat.
Savings 1st Option Bonds/Nescafe: MORNING MOOD Peer
Gynt Suite *(Grieg)* / Aerial Liquid/Fiat La Strada:
LARGO AL FACTOTEUM Barber Of Seville *(Rossini)* /
Fiesta Kitchen Towel/Lea & Perrins Worcester Sauce/
Royal Bank Of Scotland/Tetley Tea: THE SORCERER'S
APPRENTICE *(Dukas)* / Hovis: LARGO 2nd m/m Symphony
9 in E (New World)*(Dvorak)* / Brirish Airways/Petite
Toys: VA PENSIERO (Chorus Of The Hebrew Slaves) Nab
ucco *(Verdi)* / Strepsils: GYMNOPEDIES NO.3 *(Satie)*
Hamlet Cigars: AIR ON THE G.STRING Suite No.3 in D.
BWV 1068 *(Bach)* / Peugeot 605: VITAVA (MOLDAU) Ma V
last *(Smetana)* / Baci Chocolates/British Airways/Pi
relli: NESSUN DORMA Turandot *(Puccini)*

FAVOURITE TV CLASSICS (Volume 2) - Various Artists P.93
Classics FP (EMI): CDCFP 4626 (CD) TCCFP 4626(Cass)
Citroen ZX: OVERTURE Marriage Of Figaro *(Mozart)* /
Lloyds Bank: SLEEPERS AWAKE Cantata No.140 *(Bach)* /
Dulux Weathershield: JUPITER Planets Suite *(Holst)*
Thresher Wines/Br.Gas/Wool: Kanon In D *(Pachelbel)*
LA CAMPANELLA *(Listz)* / Lux Beauty Soap: PAVANE *(Fa
URE)* This Week (TV): INTERMEZZO Karelia Suite Op.11
(Silbelius) / Cadbury's Fruit and Nut: DANCE OF THE
MIRLITONS Nutcracker Suite *(Tchaikovsky)* / Bailey's
Irish Cream: BARCAROLLE Tales Of Hoffmann *Offenbach*
Baci Chocolates/Kleenex Tiss: INTERMEZZO Cavalleria
Rusticana *(Mascagni)*/ Galaxy Choc: RHAPSODY IN BLUE
(Gershwin) / Boursin Cheese: CLAIR DE LUNE Suite Be
rgamasque No.3 *(Debussy)* / Royal Doulton: NIMROD En
igma Variations Op.36 *(Elgar)* / Walls Cornetto/Bodd
ingtons Beer: O SOLE MIO Neapolitan song *(Di Capua)*

FAVOURITE TV THEMES - Various Artists   P.1992
Music Club Int (TBD): MCCD 069 (CD) MCTC 069 (Cass)
INSPECTOR MORSE-RUTH RENDELL MYSTERIES-SEVEN FACES
OF WOMAN-UPSTAIRS DOWNSTAIRS-AGATHA CHRISTIE'S POIR
OT-A WOMAN OF SUBSTANCE-TALES OF THE UNEXPECTED-THE
PROFESSIONALS-THE MATCH-THE AVENGERS-FOREVER GREEN-
NEW ADVENTURES OF BLACK BEAUTY-CHIMERA-LONDON'S BUR
NING-DR.WHO-THE ONE GAME-WORLD CUP 90-ON THE LINE-
A HUNDRED ACRES-WISH ME LUCK-SUMMER'S LEASE-ITV ATH

LETICS-THE GOOD GUYS-CLASSIC ADVENTURE
FELLINI / ROTA Collection of Music by Nino Rota for the
Films of Federico Fellini - Carlo Savina Orch P.87
Silva Screen (Conif): FILMC(CD) 004 (Cass/CD)
GODFATHER-TAMING OF THE SHREW-LA DOLCE VITA-ROCCO &
BROTHERS-ROMEO &JULIET-NAPOLI MILIONERA-WAR & PEACE
NUITS DE CABIRIA-AMARCORD-THE LEOPARD-JULIET OF THE
SPIRITS-I VITELLONI-LA STRADA
FILM & TV MUSIC OF BRUCE ROWLAND - Bruce Rowland P.1990
Bay Cities USA (Silva Screen): BCD 3009 (CD)
THE MAN FROM SNOWY RIVER-RETURN TO SNOWY RIVER-ALL
THE RIVERS RUN-PHARLAP HERO OF A NATION and others
FILM AND TV THEMES VOL.3 - Various Artists   P.1992
PMF (Kingdom): 90 681-2 (CD)
EVERYTHING I DO I DO IT FOR YOU (*ROBIN HOOD PRINCE*
OF THIEVES)-THANK YOU FOR BEING A FRIEND (*GOLDEN GI*
RLS)-GOING HOME (*LOCAL HERO*)-RICO'S BLUES (*MIAMI VI*
CE)-LOVE AND MARRIAGE (*MARRIED WITH CHILDREN*)-SUPER
MAN MAIN THEME-MISSING MAIN THEME-BEN-LAST TANGO IN
PARIS-DO YOU KNOW WHERE YOU'RE GOING TO (*MAHOGANY*)-
ZORBA'S DANCE(*ZORBA THE GREEK*)-THE BOXER-BONNIE AND
CLYDE-PICNIC AT HANGING ROCK MAIN THEME
FILM AND TV THEMES VOL.4 - Various Artists   P.1992
PMF (Kingdom): 90 685-2 (CD)
TWIN PEAKS MAIN THEME-WHERE EVERYBODY KNOWS YOUR NA
ME (*CHEERS*)-TAKE A LOOK AT ME NOW(*AGAINST ALL ODDS*)
MIAMI VICE MAIN THEME-WITHOUT US (*FAMILY TIES*)-WHO
PAYS THE FERRYMAN-RAIDERS OF THE LOST ARK-TO THE UN
KNOWN MAN-A SUMMER PLACE THEME-COSBY SHOW THEME-ON
GOLDEN POND THEME-NEVER ON SUNDAY-SUICIDE IS PAINLE
SS (*MASH*)-ALSO SPRACH ZARATHRUSTA (*2001: A SPACE..*)
FILM CLASSICS - Various Orchestras and Artists   P.1987
DG (Polygram): 419 630-2 (CD)
APOCALYPSE NOW-DEER HUNTER (Cavatina)-2001 A SPACE
ODYSSEY-HANNAH AND HER SISTERS-10-PRIZZI'S HONOUR-
OUT OF AFRICA-THE ELEPHANT MAN and PLATOON
FILM MUSIC OF DIMITRI TIOMKIN - R.C.M.O.*   P.1986
USA Imp (Silva Screen):CK 44370(CD) JST 44370(Cass)
ROMAN EMPIRE-PAX ROMANA-GUNS OF NAVARONE-RHAPSODY
OF STEEL-WILD IS THE WIND-PRESIDENT'S COUNTRY Suite
THE ALAMO-RAWHIDE-HIGH NOON / 26 Theme Collection
FILM MUSIC OF ENNIO MORRICONE The - Ennio Morricone
Virgin VIP (EMI): CDVIP 123 (CD) TCVIP 123 (Cass)
THE GOOD THE BAD AND THE UGLY-THE SICILIAN CLAN-CHI
MAI (Life And Times Of David Lloyd George)-THE MAN
WITH THE HARMONICA (Once Upon A Time In The West)-
LA CALIFFA (Lady Caliph)-GABRIEL'S OBOE (Mission)-
A FISTFUL OF DYNAMITE-ONCE UPON A TIME IN THE WEST-
COCKEYE'S THEME (Once Upon A Time In America)-THE
MISSION (remix from The Mission)-COME MADDELENA (Ma
delena)-MOSES THEME (Moses The Lawgiver)-THE FALLS
(The Mission)-MY NAME IS NOBODY-LE VENT LE CRI (The
Professional)-DEBORAH'S THEME (Once Upon A Time In
America)

FILM MUSIC OF FRANZ WAXMAN - Digital Recordings   P.1990
RCA USA (Silva Screen): RCA 2283-2 (CD)
THE SPIRIT OF ST.LOUIS-PEYTON PLACE-MY GEISHA-SAYON
ARA-HEMINGWAYS ADVENTURES OF A YOUNG MAN *(F.Waxman)*
All Remastered From Orig Motion Picture Soundtracks

FILM MUSIC OF HANS ZIMMER - Hans Zimmer   p.1991
Milan (S.Screen): CDCH 530 (CD) Suites from BURNING
SECRET (89) FRUIT MACHINE (88) DIAMOND SKULLS (89)

FILM MUSIC OF JERRY FIELDING - (Limited Edition P.1990)
Bay Cities (Silva Screen): BCD 4001-2 (2CD's)
Music from Original Soundtracks of:- LAWMAN-THE BIG
SLEEP-STRAW DOGS-MECHANIC-CHATO'S LAND-NIGHTCOMERS

FILM MUSIC OF JERRY FIELDING VOL 2 - (Ltd Edition) p.92
Bay Cities (Silva Screen): BCD LE 4003 (CD)
SCORPIO-JOHNNY GOT HIS GUN-A WAR OF CHILDREN+others

FILM MUSIC OF LEE HOLDRIDGE The   P.1992
Varese Sarabande (Pinn-S.Screen): VCD 47244 (CD)
WIZARDS AND WARRIORS (Overture)-SPLASH (Love Theme)
GREAT WHALES (Introduction & Theme)-HEMINGWAY PLAY
(Parisian Sketch)-GOING HOME(The Journey)-THE BEAST
MASTER (Suite) JONATHAN LIVINGSTON SEAGULL (Music
For Strings)-EAST OF EDEN (Suite)

FILM MUSIC OF MALCOLM ARNOLD - London Symphony Orchest*
Chandos (Chandos): CHAN 9100 (CD) ABTD 1600 (Cass)
THE BRIDGE ON THE RIVER KWAI (Suite For Large Orch
feat 'Colonel Bogey' (Kenneth Alford)-WHISTLE DOWN
THE WIND (Small Suite For Small Orchest)-THE SOUND
BARRIER (A Rhapsody For Orchestra Op.38)-HOBSON'S
CHOICE (Orchestral Suite)-THE INN OF THE SIXTH HAPP
INESS (Orchestral Suite) *Conductor: *RICHARD HICKOX*

FILM MUSIC OF NICOLA PIOVANI The   P.1991
Milan Import (Silva Screen): CDCH 541 (CD)
HORS LA VIE-PALOMBELLA ROSSA-IL MALE OSCURO

FILM MUSIC OF PINO DONAGGIO - Various   P.1992
Silva Screen (Conifer): FILMCD 093 (CD) Symphonic
Suites: DEJA VU-GOING BANANAS-ORDEAL OF INNOCENCE

FLIGHT OF THE CONDOR - Magical Sound Of The Pan Pipes
Telstar (BMG): TCD 2576 (CD) STAC 2576 (Cass)
WIND OF CHANGE-CARIBBEAN BLUE-FALLING *(Twin Peaks)*-
SADNESS-CACHARPAYA-CONCIERTO DE ARANJUEZ-TAKE MY
BREATH AWAY-FLIGHT OF THE CONDOR-ORINOCO FLOW-GYMNO
PEDIE NO.1-FOOL ON THE HILL-YOUR SONG-LILY WAS HERE
(Theme)-BILITIS*(Theme)*-IF YOU LEAVE ME NOW-SONGBIRD
NOTHING COMPARES 2 U / *PROJECT D (R.HOOK-NORTON and*
NICK GLENNIE SMITH-PAUL RIORDEN   P.1992

FREDDIE'S FAVOURITES - Best Of Nightmare On Elm Street
Varese (Pinn): VSD 5427 (CD)
Selections of music from all six movies. Music by:-
CHARLES BERNSTEIN-CHRISTOPHER YOUNG-ANGELO BADALAME
NTI-CRAIG SAFAN-JAY FERGUSON and BRIAN MAY

GALWAY AT THE MOVIES - James Galway   P.1993
RCA Victor (BMG): 09026 61326-2 (CD) -4 (Cass)
IN MY LIFE *(FOR THE BOYS)* THE ROSE - ON GOLDEN POND
SELECTION-LOSS OF LOVE *(SUNFLOWER)* WHISTLING AWAY

THE DARK *(DARLING LILI)* MOON RIVER *(BREAKFAST AT TI
FFANY'S)* SOMEWHERE OUT THERE *(AN AMERICAN TAIL)* THE
WAY WE WERE-NEVER ON SUNDAY-ZORBA THE GREEK-I WILL
WAIT FOR YOU *(UMBRELLAS OF CHERBOURG)* BEAUTY & THE
BEAST-OVER THE RAINBOW/WE'RE OFF TO SEE THE WIZARD
(WIZARD OF OZ) GABRIEL'S OBOE *(THE MISSION)* GODFATH
ER SUITE-SOMEWHERE HERE IN MY MEMORY *(HOME ALONE 2)*
LOVE STORY-MORE *(MONDO CANE)* CAVATINA *(DEER HUNTER)*

GEORGES DELERUE - THE LONDON SESSIONS (1)   P.1990
Varese USA (Pinn): VSD 5241 (CD) VSC 5241 (Cass)
*Music (Suites and Themes) by Georges Delerue from
his scores for* PLATOON-RICH AND FAMOUS-HER ALIBI-
BEACHES-EXPOSED-BILOXI BLUES-CRIMES OF THE HEART

GEORGES DELERUE - THE LONDON SESSIONS (2)   P.1990
Varese USA (Pinn): VSD 5245 (CD) VSC 5245 (Cass)
*Music (Suites and Themes) by Georges Delerue from
his scores for* STEEL MAGNOLIAS-INTERLUDE-THE ESCAPE
ARTIST-SALVADOR and 'HOMMAGE TO FRANCOIS TRUFFAUT'

GEORGES DELERUE - THE LONDON SESSIONS (3)   P.1992
Varese USA (Pinn): VSD 5256 (CD) VSC 5256 (Cass)
SOMETHING WICKED THIS WAY COMES-THE HOUSE ON CAROLL
STREET-A LITTLE SEX-MAID TO ORDER-MAN WOMAN AND CHI
LD-MEMORIES OF ME-AGNES OF GOD-TRUE CONFESSIONS

GILBERT & SULLIVAN The Best Of - Various Artists P.1989
MFP-Laser (EMI): CDCFP 4238 (CD) LZ 762532-4 (Cass)
Songs And Choruses from: The Mikado-The Gondoliers-
Iolanthe-Pirates Of Penzance-HMS Pinafore-Yeoman Of
The Guard: *Glyndebourne Fest.Chorus & Pro-Arte Orch*

GLENN MILLER   - The Ultimate Glenn Miller   P.1993
RCA Victor (BMG): 74321 13137-2 (CD) / -4 (Cass)
IN THE MOOD-LITTLE BROWN JUG-SLIPHORN JIVE-MYPRAYER
TUXEDO JUNCTION-FOOLS RUSHIN-PENNSYLVANIA 6-5000-BL
UEBERRY HILL-SONG OF THE VOLGA BOATMEN-PERFIDIA-CHA
TTANOOGA CHOO CHOO-I KNOW WHY (AND SO DO YOU)-ADIOS
A STRING OF PEARLS-SKYLARK-DON'T SIT UNDERTHE APPLE
TREE-AMERICAN PATROL-SERENADE IN BLUE- (I'VE GOT A
GAL IN) KALAMAZOO-ST.LOUIS BLUES MARCH-AT LAST-MOON
LIGHT SERENADE

GODFATHER SUITE The - The Milan Philharmonic Orchestra
Silva Screen (Conifer): FILM(C)(CD) 077   P.1991
CARMINE COPPOLA conducts the Milan Philharmonic Orc
hestra in selections of music featured in all three
of THE GODFATHER Films (Music: NINI ROTA-C.COPPOLA)

GOLD - 18 Epic Sporting Themes - Various Artists P.92
Telstar (BMG): TCD 2563 (CD) STAC 2563 (Cass)
NESSUN DORMA *(WORLD CUP)*-POP GOES BACH *(SKI SUNDAY-
WINTER OLYMPICS)*-GOLD-BARCELONA *(OLYMPIC GAMES 92)*-
WORLD IN UNION *(WORLD CUP RUGBY91)*-CHARIOTS OF FIRE
(ATHLETICS)-GONNA FLY NOW *(BOXING)*-BEETHOVEN'S 9TH
(OLYMPICS 92)-VA PENSIERO *(WINTER GAMES92)*-GRANDSTA
ND-TOUR DE FRANCE *CYCLING (1)*-SOUL LIMBO *(CRICKET)*-
THE CHAIN *(MOTOR RACING)*-TUTTI AL MONDO-WORLD IN MO
TION *(FOOTBALL)*-BOLERO *(ICE SKATING)*-QUESTION OF SP
ORT-CHASE SIDE SHOOT UP(GOLF)-ATHLETICS-SPORTSNIGHT

GRANADA STUDIO TOURS SOUVENIR ALBUM - Various Artists
  Granada/Telstar (Granada TV Studios Only)(CD/LP/CS)
  CORONATION ST-NEAREST & DEAREST-FAMILY AT WAR-SHERL
  OCK HOLMES-TRAVELLING MAN-CONNECTIONS-KINDOF LOVING
  RETURN OF THE ANTELOPE-ALBION MARKET-BROTHER'S McGR
  EGOR-BRIDESHEAD REVISITED-LOST EMPIRES-JEWEL IN THE
  CROWN-COUNTRY MATTERS-FALLEN HERO-THE LOVERS-CRIBB-
  BUSMAN'S HOLIDAY-FIRST AMONG EQUALS-WORLD IN ACTION
GREAT BRITISH LIGHT ORCHESTRAS - Charles Williams
  HMV (EMI): CDHMV 6 (CD) TCHMV 6 (Cass)
  DEVIL'S GALLOP (Dick Barton Theme)-SPELLBOUND CONCE
  RTO-VANESSA-VOICE OF LONDON-REVEILLE FOR A TOY SOLD
  IER-THE RUNAWAY ROCKING HORSE-JEALOUS LOVER-RHYTHM
  ON THE RAILS-SKYSCRAPER FANTASY-SHOPPING CENTRE-THE
  NOOSE-WILL O'THE WISP-A QUIET STROLL-SPACE SHIP-MAR
  CH OF THE BOWMEN (Robin Hood Suite)-SLEEPY MARIONET
  TE-RING ROUND THE MOON (Invitation Waltz)-SIDE WALK
  CANYON CANTER-ROMANTIC INTERLUDE-THE OLD CLOCKMAKER
  GALAVANT-HEART O LONDON-PUFFIN'BILLY-DREAM OF OLWEN
GREAT BRITISH LIGHT ORCHESTRAS - Eric Coates   **p.1992**
  HMV (EMI): CDHMV 1 (CD) TCHMV 1 (Cass)
  LONDON SUITE inc: Covent Garden/Westminster/Knights
  bridge-I SING TO YOU (Souvenir)-LONDON BRIDGE March
  BY THE SLEEPY LAGOON (Desert Island Discs)-SUMMER
  DAYS SUITE: In A Country Lane/At The Edge Of The La
  ke/At The Dance-TELEVISION MARCH-THREE BEARS SUITE-
  LONDON AGAIN SUITE: Oxford Street March/Elegy Langh
  am Place/Mayfair-SPRINGTIME SUITE: Fresh Morning/No
  onday Song-THREE MEN SUITE NO.2: The Man About Town
  RHAPSODY-CALLING ALL WORKERS (Music While You Work)
GREAT BRITISH LIGHT ORCHESTRAS - George Melachrino
  HMV (EMI): CDHMV 5 (CD) TCHMV 5 (Cass)
  STARLIGHT ROOF WALTZ-BUTANTAN-COPPER CONCERTO-MASQU
  ERADE-NO ORCHIDS FOR MISS BLANDISH: Introduction/Da
  nse D'Extase/Song Of The Orchid-PINK LADY WALTZ-WIN
  TER SUNSHINE-FESTIVAL-PARIS PROMENADE-PARIS METRO-
  MY SONG OF SPRING (London Melody)-LADY OF SPAIN-LES
  JEUX (Playing)-PARK AVENUE WALTZ-LEGEND-BUSYBODIES-
  VIOLINS IN THE NIGHT-BEYOND THE BLUE HORIZON-SCRUB
  BROTHER SCRUB-LEGEND OF THE GLASS MOUNTAIN
GREAT BRITISH LIGHT ORCHESTRAS - Sidney Torch   **p.1992**
  HMV (EMI): CDHMV 2 (CD) TCHMV 2 (Cass)
  JUST ONE OF THOSE THINGS-GOING FOR A RIDE-HORSE GUA
  RDS WHITEHALL-CARIBBEAN CAPRICE-OBSESSION-BARWICK
  GREEN (The Archers)-JUMPING BEAN-HIGH HEELS-BIG GUI
  TAR (Stranger Than Fiction)-ON A SPRING NOTE-LONDON
  FANTASIA Pts.1/2-CORONATION SCOTT (Top Of The Form)
  REACH FOR THE SKY-FANDANGO-FRONT PAGE STORY (Theme)
  ALL STRINGS AND FANCY FREE-DAM BUSTERS MARCH-COMIC
  CUTS-NOLA-SHOTTING STAR-CHANGING MOODS2(PC49 theme)
  BEACHCOMBER-SHORTCAKE WALK-A CANADIAN IN MAYFAIR
GREAT LOVE THEMES - Francis Lai:
  Prestige (Complete): CDPC(ZPREC) 5002 (CD/Cass)
  BILITIS-LOVE STORY-THE BLUE ROSE-EMOTION-HAPPY NEW

YEAR-LOVE IN THE RAIN-SEDUCTION-IMTIMATE MOMENTS-
PAR LE SANG DES AUTRES-A MAN AND A WOMAN-LIVE FOR
LIFE-AFRICAN SUMMER-SUR NOTRE ETOILE-LA RONDE-LES
UNES ET LES AUTRES-SMIC SMAC-SOLITUDE-WHITECHAPEL
GREAT TV THEMES - 4 CD Set Of 80 Classic TV Themes p.91
Tring Int (Taylors): TFP 029(4CDs) MCTPF 029(4Cass)
VOL 1 MIAMI VICE-CHEERS-HAPPY DAYS-QUINCY-CHARLIE'S
ANGELS-CROSSROADS-LITTLE HOUSE ON T.PRAIRIE-OWEN MD
NIGHT COURT-MUPPET SHOW-BONANZA-UPSTAIRS DOWNSTAIRS
MASH-FAME-DUKES OF HAZZARD-MINDER-KIDNAPPED-HUNTER-
STAR TREK / *VOL 2* DALLAS-MOONLIGHTING-CHIPS-HAWAII
5.0-AGAINST THE WIND-HARRY'S GAME-THIS IS YOUR LIFE
HIGH CHAPARRAL-SESAME ST.-RICH MAN POOR MAN-THORNBI
RDS-DOCTOR AT LARGE-BARETTA-THOSE WERE THE DAYS-SUP
ERMAN-MIAMI VICE-SIMON & SIMON-VEGAS-SOAP-VIRGINIAN
VOL 3 L.A.LAW-DYNASTY-ALL CREATURES GREAT AND SMALL
EASTENDERS-EMMERDALE FARM-STARSKY AND HUTCH-VAN DER
VALK-ROCKFORD FILES-COVER UP-HOWARD'S WAY-MAGNUM-IN
CREDIBLE HULK-MAN FROM THE MOUNTAINS-KUNG FU-WHO PA
YS THE FERRYMAN-KOJAK-MARTIN EDEN-KNIGHT RIDER-9TO5
ALIAS SMITH AND JONES / *VOL 4* HILL ST.BLUES-A.TEAM
MATCH OF THE DAY-NO HONESTLY-ODD COUPLE-PAUL TEMPLE
MAN FROM UNCLE-PERSUADERS-REILLY ACE OF SPIES-THE
WOMBLES-SAILING-RAGAMUFFIN-SMURFS-TAXI-THIRTYSOMETH
ING-WHEELS-PETER GUNN-DAD'S ARMY-PEYTON PLACE
GREAT WESTERN THEMES   - Geoff Love Orchestra
MFP (EMI): CC 204 (CD) 41 8109-4 (Cass)   P.1988
BIG COUNTRY (Another Day Another Sunset)-FISTFUL OF
DOLLARS-SHANE (Call Of The Far-Away Hills)-HOW THE
WEST WAS WON-ALAMO (Green Leaves Of Summer)-MAGNIFI
CENT7-FOR A FEW DOLLARS MORE-WILD BUNCH Song-BALLAD
OF CAT BALLOU-MAVERICK-TheVIRGINIAN-LEGEND OF JESSE
JAMES-HIGH NOON (Do Not Forsake Me)-GOOD THE BAD &
THE UGLY-GUNFIGHT AT OK CORRAL-TRUE GRIT-ONCE UPON
A TIME IN THE WEST-MAN WHO SHOT LIBERTY VALANCE-LAR
AMIE-HOMBRE-BIG VALLEY-RAWHIDE-GUN LAW-WAGON TRAIN
GREATEST MUSIC OF JOHN WILLIAMS - Various Arts   P.1992
Milan (Pinn): 873 044 (CD)
STAR WARS-BORN ON THE FOURTH OF JULY-STANLEY & IRIS
EMPIRE OF THE SUN-RAIDERS OF THE LOST ARK MARCH-IND
IANA JONES SHORT ROUNDS THEME-CLOSE ENCOUNTERS-SUPE
RMAN-JAWS-MIDWAY MARCH-ET and ET AND ME-RETURN OF
THE JEDI-JAWS 2-EARTHQUAKE THEME-POSEIDON THEME
GREATEST SCI-FI HITS Vol.1 - Neil Norman Orchest P.1981
GNP USA (S.Screen): GNPD 2128 (CD) GNP-5 2128(Cass)
STAR WARS-EMPIRE STRIKES BACK-SINBAD AND THE EYE OF
THE TIGER-VOYAGE TO BOTTOM OF THE SEA-TIME TUNNEL-
ALIEN-TWILIGHT ZONE-BUCK ROGERS IN 25th CENTURY-GOD
ZILLA-WAR OF SATELLITES-Dr WHO-DAY THE EARTH STOOD
STILL-DARK STAR-MOONRAKER-STAR TREK-BATTLESTAR GALA
CTICA-OUTER LIMITS-BLACK HOLE-CLOSE ENCOUNTERS OF
THE THIRD KIND-SUPERMAN-SPACE 1999
GREATEST SCI-FI HITS Vol.2 - Neil Norman Orchestra P.84
GNP USA (S.Screen): GNPD 2133 (CD) GNP-5 2133(Cass)

LAND OF GIANTS-SPACE 1999-THING FROM ANOTHER WORLD-
ANGRY RED PLANET-BLADERUNNER-LOST IN SPACE-INVADERS
WAR OF THE WORLDS-CAPRICORN ONE-PRISONER-RAIDERS OF
LOST ARK-ET-FLASH GORDON-RETRUN OF THE JEDI-UFO *etc*

GREATEST SCI-FI HITS VOL.3 - Neil Norman Orchestra P.85
GNP USA (S.Screen): GNPD 2163 (CD) GNP-5 2163(Cass)
BLADE RUNNER-E.T.-FLASH GORDON-LOST IN SPACE-THE TH
ING-RAIDERS OF THE LOST ARK-UFO-WAR OF THE WORLDS +

GREEN AND PLEASANT LAND - UK Symphony Orch featuring
Christopher Warren Green (conductor/violin)
Music Club Int (VCI-TBD): MCCD(MCTC) 084 (CD/Cass)
Music from TV Commercials and Film Themes
GREENSLEEVES *(arr.Vaughan Williams)* PASTORAL *(Beeth
oven)* WINTER (4 SEASONS) *(Vivaldi)* NIMROD (ENIGMA
VARIATIONS *(Elgar)* AIR ON A G.STRING *(Bach)* MINUET
(Boccherini) MORNING (PEER GYNT) *(Grieg)* MELDOY OF
ENGLISH AIRS *(Trad)* PIANO CONCERTO NO.21 *(Mozart)*
LARGO (NEW WORLD) *(Dvorak)* ELIZABETHAN SERENADE
(Binge) CANON IN D *(Pachelbel)* JERUSALEM *(Parry)*

HALLOWEEN: The Best of JOHN CARPENTER (Film Music)
Silva Screen (Conifer): FILMCD 113 (CD)   *p.1993*
HALLOWEEN-ASSAULT ON PRECINCT13-THE FOG-STARMAN-THE
THING-BIG TROUBLE IN LIT.CHINA-DARK STAR-CHRISTINE-
ESCAPE FROM NEW YORK-PRINCE OF DARKNESS-THEY LIVE

HEARTBEAT - Hank Marvin   *p.1993*
Polydor (Polyg): 521 232-2 (CD) 521 232-4 (Cass)
HEARTBEAT-OXYGENE PT.IV-MRS.ROBINSON-SPACE ODDITY-
ACHY BREAKY HEART-I WILL ALWAYS LOVE YOU-THE CRYING
GAME-CABLE BEACH-WONDERFUL LAND-HOT ROX-ROCKET MAN-
TAKE FIVE-WICHITA LINEMAN-LIVE AND LET DIE-CRYING+1

HENRY MANCINI: THE GODFATHER London Symphony Orchestra
RCA Victor (BMG): 09026 61478-2 (CD)   *p.1993*
ROMEO & JULIET LOVE THEME-DRINK MORE MILK from BOCC
ACCIO 70-AMACORD LOVE THEME-GODFATHER LOVE THEME
(Nino Rota) WHITE DAWN SYMPHONIC SUITE *(Henry Manci
ni)* THEMES FROM EARTHQUAKE-JAWS-SONG FROM TOWERING
INFERNO *(John Williams)* THE FRENCH CONNECTION *(Don
Ellis)* WINDMILLS OF YOUR MIND from Thomas Crown Aff
air *(M.Legrand)*A MAN AND A WOMAN-LOVE STORY-*(F.Lai)*
SUMMER OF 42 *(Legrand)* GREAT WALDO PEPPER *(Mancini)*
DREAM OFA LIFETIME-STRINGS ON FIRE-CAMEO FOR VIOLIN
DRUMMER'S DELIGHT-BALLERINA'S DREAM-SPEEDY GONZALES
BEAVER VALLEY SUITE-RIVER-BLACK SNOW-SONS OF ITALY

HERE'S A HOWDY DO! - The King's Singers - A Gilbert and
Sullivan Festival *RCA (BMG): 09026 61885-2 (CD)* *-4*
A BRITISH TAR*(HMS Pinafore)* SUN WHOSE RAYS *(Mikado)*
TAKE A PAIR OF SPARKLING EYES *(Gondoliers)* GHOST'S
HIGH NOON *(Ruddigore)* AH LEAVE ME NOT *(Pirates Of
Penzance)* A WAND'RING MINSTREL *(Mikado)* PIRATE KING
(Pirates Of Penzance) TIT WILLOW *(Mikado)* WITH CAT
LIKE TREAD *(Pirates Of Penzance)* BRIGHTLY DAWNS OUR
WEDDING DAY / A MORE HUMANE MIKADO *(Mikado)* RISING
EARLY IN THE MORNING *(Gondoliers)* PATTER MATTER (Me
dley) HERE'S A HOWDY DO *(Mikado)*

HEROES OF THE AIR - Central Band Of The Royal Air Force
EMI Premier: CDPR 500 (CD) TCPR 500 (Cass)   *P.1992*
BATTLE OF BRITAIN SUITE (William Walton)-SPITFIRE
PRELUDE AND FUGUE (William Walmton)-CONQUEST OF THE
AIR (Arthur Bliss)-BATTLE OF BRITAIN SUITE (Wilfred
Josephs)-COASTAL COMMAND (Vaughan Williams)

HIT AND MISS - John Barry (Early Recordings)   P.1988
C5-See For Miles (Pinn): CD 516 (CD) C5-516 (LP)
HIT & MISS-BIG GUITAR-RODEO-BIG FELLA-WALK DON'TRUN
BEE'S KNEES-EVERY WHICH WAY-BEAT GIRL Title theme-
HUMAN JUNGLE Theme-I'M MOVIN' ON-ZAPATA-LIKE WALTZ-
BLACK STOCKINGS-JAMES BOND Theme-LOST PATROL-MAGNIF
ICENT 7-HIDEAWAY-THE MENACE-NEVER LET GO-THE SHARKS
(Note: Original Columbia (EMI) Recordings From 60s)

HIT THEMES 1: BEST OF BRITISH TV MUSIC   Various Artists
EMI Soundtrack: CDSTM 3 (CD) TCSTM 3 (Cass)   *P.1992*
LONDON'S BURNING-FOREVER GREEN-THE PROFESSIONALS-AG
ATH CHRISTIE'S POIROT-TO HAVE AND TO HOLD-UPSTAIRS
DOWNSTAIRS-THOMAS & SARAH-THE GOOD GUYS-THE GENTLE
TOUCH-BOUQUET OF BARBED WIRE-PARTNERS IN CRIME-WISH
ME LUCK-BUDGIE-LOVE FOR LYDIA-LILLIE-ADVENTURES OF
BLACK BEAUTY-DEMPSEY AND MAKEPEACE

HITCHCOCK: MASTER OF MAYHEM - Lalo Schifrin   P.1991
Pro-Arte USA (Silva Screen): CDS 524 (CD)
San Diego Symphony Orch. conducted by LALO SCHIFRIN
NORTH BY NORTHWEST-PSYCHO-VERTIGO-MARNIE-REBECCA &
REAR WINDOW-ALFRED HITCHCOCK PRESENT-MANNIX-MISSION
IMPOSSIBLE-BULLITT-DIRTY HARRY-MAGNUM FO.-DEAD POOL

HOLLYWOOD BACKLOT VOL.3 - Big Movie Hits - Var.Artists
Varese (Pinn): VSD 5361 (CD) VSC 5371 (Cass) P.1992
TERMINATOR 2-MEDICINE MAN-CITY SLICKERS-FATHER OF
THE BRIDE-NAKED GUN 2.5-LITTLE MAN TATE-THE LAST BU
TTERFLY-THE GREAT MOUSE DETECTIVE-YEAR OF THE COMET
HUDSON HAWK-FINAL ANALYSIS-ARTICLE 99-DEAD AGAIN-BA
SIC INSTINCT-THE PLAYER-DOC HOLLYWOOD-MY COUSIN VIN
NY-SOAPDISH-A RAGE IN HARLEM-BLACK ROBE

HOLLYWOOD GREAT SONGS FROM MOVIES - Nana Mouskouri
Philips (Polyg): 518 350-2 (CD) -4 (Cass)   *p.1993*
A DAY IN THE LIFE OF A FOOL-THE WIND BENEATH MY WIN
GS-AUTUMN LEAVES-OVER THE RAINBOW-HOW DO YOU KEEP
THE MUSIC PLAYING-THE SUMMER KNOWS-MY OWN TRUE LOVE
FALLING IN LOVE AGAIN-THE WAY WE WERE-SMILE-AS TIME
GOES BY-LAURA-BEAUTY AND THE BEAST-THE WINDMILLS OF
YOUR MIND-HIGH NOON (Duet with Harry Belafonte)

HOLLYWOOD MARCHES (Those Fabulous) San Diego Symph Orch
Pro-Arte USA (S.Screen):CDD 504 (CD) PCD 504 (Cass)
SUPERMAN-RAIDERS OF THE LOST ARK-BRIDGE OVER THE RI
VER KWAI-CAPTAIN FROM CASTILLE-THE GREAT ESCAPE-PAT
TON-RETURN OF THE JEDI-THE MUSIC MAN-WHAT DID YOU
DO IN THE WAR DADDY-THE STATUE OF LIBERTY MARCH-APO
CALYPSE NOW-THE HUNT FOR RED OCTOBER-THE DIRTY DOZ.
THE GREAT WALDO PEPPER-THE JOHN PHILLIP SOUSA STORY
(Liberty Belle/Washington Post/El Capitan/Stars and
Stripes Forever) *SAN DIEGO S.O. LALO SCHIFRIN* p.91

HOOKED ON THEMES - Var.Orchestras and Soloists   P.1993
Ariola Express (BMG): 74321 15559-2 (CD) -4 (Cass)
STAR WARS-ALL TIME HIGH (Octopussy)-FAME-FLASHDANCE
CHAMPIONS MAIN THEME-TERMS OF ENDEARMENT-GREATEST
LOVE OF ALL-LOVE STORY-CHARIOTS OF FIRE-FLYING (ET)
ARTHUR'S THEME-FOR YOUR EYES ONLY-IT MIGHT BE YOU
(Tootsie)-SPY SHIP-BRIGHT EYES (Watership Down)-
AMERICA (The Jazz Singer) *feat LONDON SYMPHONY ORCH*
ROYAL PHILHARMONIC ORCH-PIERRE BELMONDE-MASTERWORKS

HORROR AND SCIENCE FICTION FILM MUSIC - Various scores
Milan (Silva Screen): 889707 (CD)   P.1992
RAZORBACK-HARDWARE-THE QUIET EARTH-PAPERHOUSE-SHATT
ERED-FRIDAY THE 13TH-BODY DOUBLE-THE HUNGER-THE STR
OBE-CLOSE ENCOUNTERS OF THE THIRD KIND-BACKDRAFT-
THE LIFT and others

HORROR OF DRACULA The - Music from Hammer Movies
Silva Screen (Conifer): FILMCD 708 (CD)   P.1992
THE HORROR OF DRACULA (58)-DRACULA: PRINCE OF DARKN
ESS (66)-TASTE THE BLOOD OF DRACULA (70) All Music
scored by James Bernard. Narrator: Christopher Lee
Recording includes sound effects & symphonic score

HORRORS OF THE BLACK MUSEUM - Gerard Schurmann
Cloud Nine import (Conifer): CNS 5005 (CD)   P.1993
TITLE FILM MUSIC (59)-THE BEDFORD INCIDENT (65) KON
GA (61)-THE LONG ARM (56)-ATTACK ON THE IRON COAST
(67)-THE LOST CONTINENT (68)-CONE OF SILENCE (60)

HORRORVISIONS - Various Artists   P.1991
Edel Ger (S.Screen): EDL 2572-2(CD) -4(Cass) -1(LP)
HALLOWEEN-IT'S ALIVE 2-RETRIBUTION-HELLRAISER-PHANT
ASM-FRANKENHOOKER-NEAR DARK-THE FOG-DRACULA-HAUNTED
SUMMER-SUNDOWN-BASKETCASE-THE SEVENTH SIGN-PHANTOM
OF THE OPERA-THE THING

IF I LOVED YOU- Thomas Allen and Valerie Masterson p.93
TER VIP (Koch): VIRCD 8317 (CD) VIRMC 8317 (Cass)
with THE PHILHARMONIA ORCHESTRA (John Owen Edwards)
ALL I ASK OF YOU *Phantom Of The Opera* THE HEATHER
ON THE HILL *Brigadoon* THEY SAY IT'S WONDERFUL *Annie*
Get Your Gun TILL THERE WAS YOU *Music Man* MY TIME
OF DAY/I'VE NEVER BEEN IN LOVE BEFORE *Guys & Dolls*
PEOPLE WILL SAY WE'RE IN LOVE *Oklahoma* TONIGHT *West*
Side Story I HAVE DREAMED *The King & I* MAKE BELIEVE
Show Boat INDIAN LOVE CALL *RoseMarie* IF I LOVED YOU
Carousel HELLO YOUNG LOVERS /SOME ENCHANTED EVENING

IMAGES - Guitar Corporation   P.1992
Quality Television (Pinn): QTVC(CD) 002 (Cass/CD)
ROBIN HOOD PRINCE OF THIEVES (Everything I Do I Do)
WILD AT HEART(Wicked Game)-DANCES WITH WOLVES-MIAMI
VICE (Crockett's Theme)-TWIN PEAKS-SYLVIA-WONDERFUL
LAND-TIME AFTER TIME-NIGHTS IN WHITE SATIN-EDGE OF
DARKNESS-LADY IN RED-DEER HUNTER (Cavatina)-GHOST
(Unchained Melody)-ALBATROSS-SCARLET O'HARA-WONDERF
UL TONIGHT-BUSTER (Groovy Kind Of Love)-LOCAL HERO

IMAGES - Jean Michel Jarre   P.1991
Polydor-Dreyfus: 511 306-2 (CD) -4 (Cass) -1 (LP)

OXYGENE 4-EQUINOXE 5-MAGNETIC FIELDS 2-OXYGENE 2-CO
MPUTER WEEKEND-EQUINOX 4-BAND INTHE RAIN-RENDEZVOUS
2-LONDON KID-ETHNICOLOR 1-ORIENT EXPRESS-CALYPSO 1&
3-RENDEZVOUS 4-MOON MACHINE-ELDORADO-GLOBE TROTTER
IMAGINATIONS - 'Further Reflections' - Various Artists
    CBS (Sony Music): 40-10044 (Cass)   P.1983
AMERICAN ,GIGOLO-TO THE UNKNOWN MAN-HARRYS GAME-PICN
IC AT HANGINGROCK-LOCAL HERO-ORDINARY PEOPLE-FACADE
SONG FOR GUY-STRANGER-ONCE UPON A TIME IN THE WEST-
OFFICER & A GENTLEMAN-MERRY XMAS MR.LAWRENCE-KARI
BALLAD OF ADELINE-REILLY-ACE OF SPIES-FLIGHT OF THE
CONDOR-FOCUS 1-BELLADONNA - see also 'REFLECTIONS'
INQUIRER: THE FILM MUSIC OF BERNARD HERRMANN   P.1992
    Preamble 5th Continent (S.Screen): PRCD 1789 (CD)
CITIZEN KANE-THE MAGNIFICENT AMBERSONS-THE DAY THE
EARTH STOOD STILL-SISTERS-NIGHT DIGGER-BATTLE OF NE
RETVA-THE KENTUCKIAN-WILLIAMSBURG ORCH: AUSTRALIAN
PHILHARMONIC-ROYAL PHILHARMONIC-NATION.PHILHARMONIC
ITV AMERICA : Murder She Wrote - Various Arts*   P.1992
    Primetime-S.Screen (Conif): TVPMC(CD) 802 (Cass/CD)
MURDER SHE WROTE-BEVERLY HILLS 90210-BAYWATCH-HIGHW
AY TO HEAVEN-ATEAM-MAGNUM-YOUNG RIDERS-SLEDGEHAMMER
BRING'EM BACK ALIVE-STREETHAWK-SIMON & SIMON-MEN-BL
BL STRYKER-HOOPERMAN-HARDCASTLE & McCORMICK-AIRWOLF
    *Daniel Caine - Produced by Michael Jones
ITV CHILDREN'S THEMES - Silver Screen Orchestra P.1989
    Pickwick: PWK 108 (CD) w.Sheila Gott & Steve Butler
SUPERGRAN-KNIGHT RIDER-JOE 90-CAPTAIN SCARLET-FALL
GUY-SOOTY SHOW-DANGERMOUSE-FRAGGLEROCK-GHOSTBUSTERS
STINGRAY-A.TEAM-BATMAN-BLACK BEAUTY-DOGTANIAN-BLOCK
BUSTERS-THUNDERBIRDS-A HANDFUL OF SONGS-FOLLYFOOT
ITV THEMES - London Symphony Orchestra (Stanley Black)
    Pickwick: PWKM 4007 (CD) HSC 3247 (Cass)   p.1988
THUNDERBIRDS-PROFESSIONALS-NEW AVENGERS-UPSTAIRS DO
WNSTAIRS-DUCHESS OF DUKE STREET-BLACK BEAUTY-MINDER
TWO OF US-HAPPY DAYS-TALES OF THE UNEXPECTED-CORONA
TION STREET-THE SWEENEY-THE BILL-HANNAY-WORLD OF SP
ORT-AZTEC GOLD-CARMEN TO THE RING (Wrestling)-SAINT
& GREAVSIE-HILL ST.BLUES-L.A.LAW-HOOPER MAN-A.TEAM
THIS IS YOUR LIFE-HIGHWAY-BLOCKBUSTERS
JAMES LAST PLAYS ANDREW LLOYD WEBBER   p.1993
    Polydor: 519 910-2 (CD) 519 910-4 (Cass)
WITH ONE LOOK-JESUS CHRIST SUPERSTAR-MEMORY-I DON'T
KNOW HOW TO LOVE HIM-MUSIC OF THE NIGHT-ANY DREAM
WILL DO-LOVE CHANGES EVERYTHING-DON'T CRY FOR ME AR
GENTINA-TELL ME ON A SUNDAY-TAKE THAT LOOK OFF YOUR
FACE-THE PHANTOM OF THE OPERA-THE POINT O.NO RETURN
JOHN BARRY - THE BEST OF THE EMI YEARS Vol.1 1957-60
    EMI (EMI): CDEMS 1497 (CD)   P.1993
    John Barry 7-John Barry & His Orch-John Barry 7 + 4
LET'S HAVE A WONDERFUL TIME-ROCK A BILLY BOOGIE-ZIP
ZIP-THREE LITTLE FISHES-EVERY WHICH WAY-BIG GUITAR-
YOU'VE GOTTA AWAY-RODEO-FARRAGO-BEES KNEES-WHEN THE
SAINT FO MARCHING IN-PANCHO-LONG JOHN-LITTLE JOHN-

SNAP'n'WHISTLE-FOR PETE'S SAKE-REBEL ROUSER-MAB MAB
TWELFTH STREET RAG-CHRISTELLA-ROCKIN'ALREADY-WALK
DON'T RUN-SATURDAY'S CHILD-PANCHO-HIDEAWAY-BEES KNE
ES-GOOD ROCKIN'TONIGHT-HIT & MISS-I'M MOVIN'ON-BEAT
GIRL THEME-BEAT FOR BEATNIKS-BIG FELLA-NEVER LET GO
BLUEBERRY HILL-BLACK STOCKINGS-GET LOST JACK FROST

JOHN BARRY - THE BEST OF THE EMI YEARS Vol.2 - 1961
EMI (EMI): CDEMS 1501 (CD) also 789586-2   p.1993
MAGNIFICENT SEVEN-SKID ROW-DARK RIDER-IRON HORSE-A
MATTER OF WHO-THE MENACE-ROCCO'S THEME-SPINERREE-
IT DOESN'T MATTER ANY MORE-SWEET TALK-MOODY RIVER-
THERE'S LIFE IN THE OLD BOY YET-A HANDFUL OF SONGS-
LIKE WALTZ-RODEO-DONNA'S THEME-STARFIRE-BAUBLES BAN
GLES AND BEADS-ZAPATA-RUM DEE DUM DEE DAH-MAN FROM
MADRID-SPANISH HARLEM-THE CHALLENGE-WATCH YOUR STEP
TWIST IT-WATCH YOUR STEP2-SATIN SMOOTH-THE AGRESSOR

JOPLIN'S GREATEST HITS - Dick Hyman / James Levine p.93
RCA Victor (BMG): GD 60842 (CD) GK 60842 (Cass)
MAPLE LEAF RAG-ORIGINAL RAGS-SWIPESY-PEACHERINE RAG
THE EASY WINNERS-SUNFLOWER SLOWDRAG-THE ENTERTAINER
ELITE SYNCOPATIONS-THE STRENUOUS LIFE-A BREEZE FROM
ALABAMA-PALMLEAF RAG-SOMETHING DOING-WEEPING WILLOW
THE CHRYSANTHEMUM-THE CASCADES-THE SYCAMORE-PARAGON
RAG-SUGAR CANE - **all composed by SCOTT JOPLIN**

JOSE CARRERAS SINGS ANDREW LLOYD WEBBER - Jose Carreras
WEA: 256 924-2 (CD) WX 325C (Cass)   P.1989
MEMORY-PHANTOM OF THE OPERA-THE MUSIC OF THE NIGHT-
WISHING YOU WERE SOMEWHERE HERE AGAIN-ALL I ASK OF
YOU (with Barbara Dickson) - PIE JESU-TELL ME ON A
SUNDAY-HALF A MOMENT -THERE'S ME- STARLIGHT EXPRESS
UNEXPECTED SONG - LOVE CHANGES EVERYTHING
JOSE CARRERAS with The ROYAL PHILHARMONIC ORCHESTRA

JOSEPH AND THE AMAZING TECHNICOLOUR DREAMCOAT (SHOWS CO
LLECTION) (Andrew Lloyd Webber-Tim Rice)
Pickwick Shows Coll: PWKS 4163(CD) PWKMC 4163(Cass)
featuring: **Robin Cousins-Jacqui Scott-Nick Curtis-**
Steve Butler-Bobby Crush & Co. *Songs:-* JACOB & SONS
JOSEPH'S DREAMS-ANY DREAM WILL DO-ONE MORE ANGEL IN
HEAVEN-POTIPHAR-CLOSE EVERY DOOR-GO GO GO JOSEPH-
PHAROAH'S STORY-POOR POOR PHAROAH-THOSE CANNAN DAYS
BENJAMIN'S CALYPSO-ANY DREAM WILL DO

KERN GOES TO HOLLYWOOD - Various Artists   P.1985
First Night (Pinn): OCRCD 6014 (CD)
featuring: **Elaine Delmar-Liz Robertson-David Kernan**
Elisabeth Welch. Music director: Clive Chaplin
THE SONG IS YOU-I'VE TOLD EVERY LITTLE STAR-I'LL BE
HARD TO HANDLE-SMOKE GETS IN YOUR EYES-YESTERDAYS-
I WON'T DANCE-I'M OLD FASHIONED-DEATLY BELOVED-PICK
YOURSELF UP-SHE DID'NT SAY YES-THE FOLKS WHO LIVE
ON THE HILL-LONG AGO AND FAR AWAY-LOVELY TO LOOK AT
JUST LET ME LOOK AT YOU-REMIND ME-THE LAST TIME I
SAW PARIS-OL' MAN RIVER-WHY WAS I BORN-BILL-CAN'T
HELP LOVIN' DAT MAN OF MINE-ALL THE THINGS YOU ARE-
THEY DIDN'T BELIEVE ME

LAUREL & HARDY - Best Of Songs and Dialogue   P.1992
Another Fine Mess (Pinn): MESS(CD)(MC) 123(CD/Cass)
CUCKOO SONG-AT THE BALL-TRAIL OF THE LONESOME PINE-
THERE'S GONNA BE A FIGHT-SCHOOL ROOM-LAZY MOON-HIGH
ER ENDEAVOURS-WAY DOWN SOUTH IN DIXIE-LONG DISTANCE
ANNUAL CONVENTION-HONOLULU BABY-LET ME CALL YOU SWE
ETHEART-BOX 204J-FURNITURE PAYMENT-SHINE ON HARVEST
MOON-BED SPRINGS-HIGH MULTITUDE-VICTIMS OF THE DEPR
ESSION-COURT ROOM with James Finlayson and others
LAUREL & HARDY - EMI Comedy Classics (Dialogue & Songs)
EMI Comedy Classics: ECC 13 (2 Cass)   P.1991
THE CUCKOO SONG-FRESH FISH-VICTIMS O.THE DEPRESSION
FURNITURE PAYMENT-LET ME CALL YOU SWEETHEART-HIGHER
ENDEAVOURS-WHAT FLAVOURS HAVE YOU-MISTAKEN IDENTITY
TRAIL OF THE LONESOME PINE-LONG DISTANCE-OH GASTON-
STAGECOACH MANNERS-AT THE BALL THAT'S ALL-NEW RECRU
ITS-THEERE'S A DOLLAR-HARD BOILED EGGS/IN THE GOOD
OLD SUMMERTIME-WHER WERE YOU BORN-UNITED WE STAND-
ANNUAL CONVENTION-WE'RE GOING NOW-WAY DOWN SOUTH/I
WANT TO BE IN DIXIE-TURN ON THE RADIO-EVEN AS YOU &
A-A CLEAN SWEEP-THE FUTURE MRS.HARDY-EVERYCLOUD HAS
A SILVER LINING-LAZYMOON-WHEN THE CAT'S AWAY-DANGER
BY CLOCKWORK-FOOD FOR THOUGHT-COURT AGAIN-DUAL DECE
IT includ: HONOLULU BABY/SONS OF THE DESERT-GOODBYE
LAUREL & HARDY'S MUSIC BOX - Ronnie Hazlehurst Orchest
Silva Screen: LH 1001-2(CD) FILM(C)012(LP/Cass) P83
New Recordings Of The Original Scores From Laurel &
Hardy's Films Arr. & Conducted By Ronnie Hazlehurst
LAUREL & HARDY'S MUSIC BOX Vol.2 Ronnie Hazlehurst Orch
Silva Screen: LH 1002.2 (CD)   P.1990
Our Relations Suite-MGM Fanfare-Ku Ku-We're Just A
Happy Family-Little Dancing Girl-If Only It Were Tr
ue-In My Canoe-Cops-Meow-Golfer's Blues-Colonial Ga
yeties-Antics-Candy Candy-We're Going To Arrowhead-
Change My Clothes-Up In A Room-Our Relations-Ku Ku-
Way Out West-Stepping Along With A Song *and others*
LEAN BY JARRE - Tribute To David Lean by Maurice Jarre*
Milan (Pinn): 10131-2 (CD) 10131-4 9Cass)   P.1992
*ROYAL PHILHARMONIC ORCH (Maurice Jarre) live record
ing at The Barbican 1992* - REMEMBRANCE-OFFERING-and
Suites from David Lean's: RYAN'S DAUGHTER-A PASSAGE
TO INDIA-DOCTOR ZHIVAGO-LAWRENCE OF ARABIA
LEGENDS OF HOLLYWOOD: Franz Waxman   P.1990
Varese (Pinn) VSD 5242 (CD) VSC 5242 (Cass)
New recordings of Franz Waxman's film scores:- TASK
FORCE-OBJECTIVE BIRMA-PEYTON PLACE-SORRY WRONG NUMB
ER-THE PARADINE CASE-DEMETRIUS AND THE GLADIATORS
LEGENDS OF HOLLYWOOD: Franz Waxman - Volume 2   P.1991
Varese (Pinn) VSD 5257 (CD) VSC 5257 (Cass)
BRIDE OF FRANKENSTEIN-MR.ROBERTS-POSSESSED-CAPTAINS
COURAGEOUS-THE NUN'S STORY-HUCKLEBERRY FINN etc.
LONDON CALLING - see 'FAMOUS THEMES 3'
LONDON PRIDE: NOEL COWARD and GERTRUDE LAWRENCE p.1993
Happy Days (Conifer): CDHD 216 (CD) MCHD 216 (Cass)

WE WERE DANCING-PARISIAN PIERRO-POOR LITTLE RICH GI
RL-AROOM WITH A VIEW-DANCE LITTLE LADY-SOMEDAY I'LL
FIND YOU-ANY LITTLEFISH-IF YOU COULD ONLY COME WITH
ME-I'LL SEEYOU AGAIN-THE DREAM IS OVER-ZIGEUNER-WOR
LD WEARY-LET'S SAY GOODBYE-LONDON PRIDE-LAST TIME I
SAW PARIS-COULD YOU PLEASE OBLIGE US WITHA BREN GUN
IMAGINE THE DUCHESSES'FEELINGS-PRIVATE LIVES(Scenes
from Acts 1/2-SHADOW PLAY(THEN PLAY ORCHESTRA PLAY)
AS YOU WERE THERE-RED PEPPERS feat: AS ANYONE SEEN
OUR SHIP & MAN ABOUT TOWN-FAMILY ALBUM featuring
HERE'S A TOAST and HEARTS AND FLOWERS

LOST HORIZON - **Classic Film Scores Of Dimitri Tiomkin**
*RCA Victor (BMG): GD(GK) 81669 (CD/Cass) *NPO   P.90*
LOST HORIZON SUITE-THE GUNS OF NAVARONE-THE BIG SKY
THE FOURPOSTER-FRIENDLY PERSUASION-SEARCH FOR PARAD
ISE   *National Philharmonic Orch (Charles Gerhardt)*

LOVE AT THE MOVIES - **Various Orig Artists**   P.1991
Telstar: TCD 2545 (CD) STAC(STAR) 2545 (Cass/LP)
I'VE HAD THE TIME OF MY LIFE:Dirty Dancing (Bill Me
dley-Jennifer Warnes)-IT MUST HAVE BEEN LOVE:Pretty
Woman (Roxette)-WICKED GAME:Wild At Heart (Chris Is
aak)-UNCHAINED MELODY:Ghost (Righteous Bros)-IT HAD
TO BE YOU:When Harry Met Sally (Harry Connick Jnr)-
TELL IT LIKE IT IS:The BiG Easy(Aaron Neville)-BLUE
VELVET (Bobby Vinton)-MONA LISA (Nat King Cole)-THE
BEST THAT YOU CAN DO:Arthur (Christopher Cross)-THE
GLORY OF LOVE:Karate Kid II (Peter Cetera)-LILY WAS
HERE (David A.Stewart/Candy Dulfer)-UP WHERE WE BEL
ONG:Ann Officer & A Gentleman (Joe Cocker-Jennifer
Warnes)-COMING ROUND AGAIN:Heartburn (Carly Simon)-
HOW DEEP IS YOURLOVE:Saturday N.Fever(Bee Gees)-SEA
OF LOVE (Marty Wilde)-KOKOMO:Cocktail (Beach Boys)

LOVEJOY AND OTHER ORIGINAL TV THEMES by DENIS KING
Westmoor Music (IMD): CDWM 104 (CD)   P.1992
LOVEJOY-WE'LL MEET AGAIN-DICK TURPIN-ALL AT NUMBER
20-WITHIN THESE WALLS-TAKING THE FLOOR-WISH ME LUCK
BLACK BEAUTY-ABOUT FACE-A DAY TO REMEMBER-MOON AND
SON-HANNAY-RUNNING WILD-BETWEEN THE WARS - *COMPOSED*
ARRANGED CONDUCTED AND PRODUCED BY DENIS KING

MAC'S BACK - **Ken Mackintosh and His Orchestra**   P.1992
President: PLCD 532 (CD) TC-PLE 532 (Cass)
TAKE THE A TRAIN-MOONLIGHT SERENADE-JEALOUS HEART-
SWINGING SHEPHERD BLUES-BIG NOISE FR.WINNETKA-UHOH
JUMPING AT THE WOODSIDE-BIRTHDAY CAKEWALK-SKYLINER-
TUXEDO JUNCT.-SEPTEMBER SONG-INTERMISSION RIFF-MAD
ABOUT THE BOY-THE KNACK-VARIATIONS ON PAGE NINE-DAT
DERE-STRANGE MUSIC-CREEP-NAKED CITY THEME-HARLEM
NOCTURNE-IF DREAMS COME TRUE

MAGIC FROM THE MUSICALS - **Various Artists**
Music Club Int (TBD): MCCD 012 (CD) MCTC 012 (Cass)
ONLY YOU (Starlight Express) *Brian Blessed* / GOOD
MORNING STARSHINE (Hair) *Petula Clark* / IF IF WERE
A RICH MAN (Fiddler On The Roof) *Topol* / LULCK BE A
LADY (Guys'n'Dolls) *Paul Jones* / MEMORY (Cats) *Petu*

la Clark / SEND IN THE CLOWNS(A little Night Music)
Marti Webb / IMPOSSIBLE DREAM (Man Of La Mancha) *Br
ian Blessed* / BLESS YOUR BEAUTIFUL HIDE (7 Brides.)
Howard Keel / THANK HEAVEN FOR LITTLE GIRLS (Gigi)
Topol / LULLABY OF BROADWAY(42nd Street) *Paul Jones*
IF HE WALKED INTO MY LIFE (Mame) *Marti Webb* / ANNIE
GET YOUR GUN MEDLEY *Howard Keel* / I DON;YT KNOW HOW
TO LOVE HIM (Jesus Christ S) *Marti Webb* /I'VE GROWN
ACCUSTOMED TO HER FACE (My Fair Lady) *Paul Jones)*
MAGIC OF THE MUSICALS The - Marti Webb & Mark Rattray
   Quality TV (Pinn): QTVCD(QTVC) 013 (CD/CASS) P.1992
   IT AIN'T NESESSARILY SO-PLENTY OF NOTHIN'-THERE'S A
   BOAT-PORGY I'S YOUR WOMAN NOW-LULLABY OF BROADWAY-
   I GOT RHYTHM-I GET A KICK OUT OF YOU-SUMMERTIME-LOS
   ING MY MIND-BLOW GABRIEL BLOW-NOT WHILE I'M AROUND-
   SEND IN THE CLOWNS-DO YOU HEAR THE PEOPLE SING-I DR
   AMED A DREAM-EMPTY CHAIR AT EMPTY TABLES-LAST NIGHT
   OF THE WORLD-BUI.DOI-DON'T CRY FOR ME ARGENTINA-JES
   US CHRIST SUPERSTAR-MAMA-TAKE THAT LOOK OFF YOUR FA
   CE-IN ONE OF MY WEAKER MOMENTS-ANTHEM-TELL ME IT'S
   NOT TRUE-YOU AND I-ONLY HE-LOVE CHANGES EVERYTHING-
   THE MUSIC OF THE NIGHT-MEMORY
MAGNUM,P.I. THE AMERICAN TV HITS ALBUM   Re-issued 1990
   Silva Screen (Con): FILMCD 703 (CD) FILMC 703 (Cas)
   MAGNUM,P.I-AIRWOLF-COSBY SHOW-MIKE HAMMER-LOU GRANT
   CHEERS-HILL STREET BLUES-HOLLYWOOD WIVES-CAGNEY and
   LACEY-ST.ELSEWHERE-A TOUCH OF SCANDLE-TAXI-SIMON &
   SIMON-ROCKFORD FILES *conducted by Daniel Caine 1986*
MAIGRET & OTHER TV THEMES BY NIGEL HESS - Nigel Hess
   Fly (Total-BMG): FLYCD 104(CD) FLYMC 104(Cass) P.92
   MAIGRET-CLASSIC ADVENTURES-PERFECT SCOUNDRELS-A HUN
   DRED ACRES-CHIMERA (Rosheen Du)-MAIGRET (Paris)-GRO
   WING PAINS-ARDEN OF FAVERSHAM-FOR TONIGHT(Atlantis)
   US GIRLS-TITMUSS REGAINED-HENRY VIII (Stage)
MAN FROM U.N.C.L.E. - MUSIC FROM THE CULT TV CLASSICS
   Silva Screen (Con): FILM(C)(CD) 712 (CD/Cass) P.92
   THE AVENGERS-MANNIX-DANGER MAN-BATMAN-ALFRED HITCHC
   OCK PRESENTS-ADVENTURES OF ROBINSON CRUSOE-TOMORROW
   PEOPLE-JOE 90-MAN FROM U.N.C.L.E-THE SAINT & others
MANCINI'S GREATEST HITS - Erich Kunzel & *C.P.O.   P.90
   Telarc USA (Conifer): CD 80183 (CD)
   PINK PANTHER-MOON RIVER-DAYS OF WINE & ROSES-IT HAD
   BETTER BE TONIGHT (Pink Panther)-THE WHITE DAWN-MR.
   LUCKY-HATARI-THORN BIRDS-CHARADE-MOMENT TO MOMENT-
   GREAT WALDO PEPPER-TWO FOR THE ROAD-THE MOLLY MAGUI
   RES-DEAR HEART-BREAKFAST AT TIFFANY'S-SPEEDY GONZAL
   ES (Mr.Lucky)-PUNCH & JUDY (Charade)-MARCH WITH MAN
   CINI-BABY ELEPHANT WALK(Mr.Lucky)-PETER GUNN-VICTOR
   VICTORIA-STRINGS ON FIRE-SYMPHONIC SOUL-DRUMMER DEL
   IGHT /   * *Cincinnati Pops Orchestra (Erich Kunzel)*
MANCINI IN SURROUND - Mostly Monsters Murder & Mystery
   RCA (BMG): RD(RK) 60471 (CD/Cass) Mancini Pops Orch
   SURROUND FANTASIQUE-ARCTIC WHALE HUNT (White Dawn)-
   MOMMIE DEAREST-FRENZY REJECTED (Main Theme)-MONSTER

MOVIE CLASS SUITE: Creature From The Black Lagoon-
It Came From Outer Space-Tarantula-Fear-The Man Who
Loved Women-Suite From The PrisonerOf Zenda-Without
A Clue-Sunset : *Henry Mancini & Pops Orchest.P.1990*
MANTOVANI AT THE MOVIES - Mantovani Orchestra   p.1993
Memoir Castle (BMG): CDMOIR 506(CD) CMOIR 506(Cass)
TRUE LOVE *(from HIGH SOCIETY)* YOU KEEP ME COMING BA
CK LIKE A SONG*(BLUE SKIES)* NEARNESS OF YOU *(ROMANCE
IN THE DARK)* AN AFFAIR TO REMEMBER-MY FOOLISH HEART
THREE COINS IN THE FOUNTAIN-LAURA-SEPTEMBER SONG-
TAMMY-HIGH AND THE MIGHTY-AS TIME GOES BY *(CASABLAN
CA)* I WONDER WHO'S KISSING HER NOW *(MOONLIGHT IN HA
VANA)* A SUMMER PLACE-STARDUST *(EDDIE DUCHIN STORY)*
GREEN LEAVES OF SUMMER *(THE ALAMO)* MONA LISA *(AFTER
MIDNIGHT)* SIBONEY *(GET HEP TO LOVE)* WHEN I FALL IN
LOVE *(ONE MINUTE TO ZERO / ISTANBUL)* ADIOS
MARILYN HILL SMITH SINGS IVOR NOVELLO - Chandos Concert
Orchestra conducted by Stuart Barry   P.1993
Chandos (Chandos): CHAN 9142 (CD)
SOMEDAY MY HEART WILL AWAKE *(KINGS RHAPSODY)*-PRIMRO
SE *(DANCING YEARS)*-LOVE IS MY REASON *(PERCHANCE TO
DREAM)*-DARK MUSIC *(ARC DE TRIOMPHE)*-THE LITTLE DAMO
ZEL-WHEN THE GYPSY PLAYED *(GLAMOROUS NIGHT)*-ON SUCH
A NIGHT AS THIS *(GAY'S THE WORD)*-FLY HOME LITTLE HE
ART *(KINGS RHAPSODY)*-KEEP THE HOME FIRES BURNING-
MUSIC IN MAY *(CARELESS RAPTURE)*-A VIOLIN BEGAN TO
PLAY *(KINGS RHAPSODY)*-SPRING OF THE YEAR-MY DEAREST
DEAR *(DANCING YEARS)*-FINDER PLEASE RETURN*(GAY'S THE
WORD)*-LOOK IN MY HEART *(VALLEY OF SONG)*-WHEN I CURT
SIED TO THE KING *(PERCHANCE TO DREAM)*-WE'LL GATHER
LILACS *PERCHANCE TO DREAM)*-FAIRY LAUGHTER-GLAMOROUS
NIGHT-WHY IS THERE EVER GOODBYE *(CARELESS RAPTURE)*
MATT MONRO SINGS DON BLACK - Matt Monro   P.1990
EMI (EMI): CZ 272 (CD) (TC)EMS 1355 (Cass/LP)
ON DAYS LIKE THESE-ALL THE WISHING IN THE WORLD-IF
I NEVER SING ANOTHER SONG-BEYOND THE HILL-FOR MAMA-
ONE DAY SOON-BORN FREE-IF THERE EVER IS A NEXT TIME
WISH NOW WAS THEN-ALL OF A SUDDEN-PRETTY POLLY-TWO
PEOPLE-WHEN YOU BECAME A MAN-WALK AWAY
MAURICE JARRE AT ABBEY ROAD - Royal Philharmonic Orch
Milan (Pinn): 262 321 (CD) 412 321 (Cass)   P.1992
THE KEEPERS-THERESE-HORROR CHAMBER OF DR.FAUSTUS-JU
DEX-BEHOLDA PALE HORSE-GHOST-WITNESS-JACOB'S LADDER
PRANCER-GORILLA'S IN THE MIST-FATAL ATTRACTION-MOON
OVER PARADOR-DEAD POET'S SOCIETY-PASSAGE TO INDIA
MERCHANT-IVORY 25th Anniversary (62-87) Various Artists
RCA (BMG): BD 87773 (CD) BK 87773 (Cass)
SAVAGES (Joe Raposo 72)-QUARTET (Richard Robbins81)
EUROPEANS (Richard Robbins 79)-THE BOSTONIANS (Rich
ard Robbins 84)-A ROOM WITH A VIEW (R.Robbins-Pucch
ini 86)-MAURICE (R.Robbins 87)-THE HOUSEHOLDER (62)
SHAKESPEARE WALLAH (Satyajit Ray 65)-COURTESANS OF
BOMBAY (Zubaida Khanam)-MAHATMA & MAD BOY (Vivaldi)
GURU (Ustad Vilay.Khan 69)-HEAT & DUST (Robbins 82)

MICHAEL CRAWFORD PERFORMS ANDREW LLOYD WEBBER   P.1991
Telstar: TCD 2544 (CD) STAC(STAR) 2544 (Cass/LP)
TELL ME ON A SUNDAY-ALL I ASK OFYOU:Phantom-WISHING
YOU WERE SOMEHOW HERE AGAIN:Phantom-ANY DREAM WILL
DO:Joseph & A.T.D.-AND THE MONEY KEEPS ROLLING IN:
Evita-NOTHING LIKE YOU'VE EVER KNOWN:Song & Dance-
PHANTOM OF THE OPERA-MUSIC OF THE NIGHT:Phantom
MEMORY:Cats-ONLY YOU:Starlight Express-GETHSEMANE:
Jesus C.Superstar-OTHER PLEASURES/FIRST MAN YOU
REMEMBER/LOVE CHANGES EVERYTHING:Aspects Of Love

MIDNIGHT MOODS The Lighter Side Of Jazz - Various Arts
Verve (Polygram): 515 816-2 (CD) -4 (Cass)   p.1993
UNFORGETTABLE: Nat King Cole *(ROVER 400)* / FEVER:
Peggy Lee *(IMPULSE FREE SPIRIT)* / MAD ABOUT THE BOY
Dinah Washington *(LEVI 501)* / GIRL FROM IPANEMA: As
trud Gilberto / SMOOTH OPERATOR: Sade / LILY WAS HE
RE: David A.Stewart & Candy Dulfer *(Film Theme)* /
IT HAD TO BE YOU: Harry Coonnick Jnr. *(SAMSUNG)* /
TAKE 5: Dave Brubeck *(FORD ORION/CADBURY'S TWIRL)* /
A FINE ROMANCE: Billie Holiday *(Swing Time Film)* /
EVERY TIME WE SAY GOODBYE: Ella Fitzgerald / MISTY:
Errol Garner *(Play Misty For Me Film)* / CRY ME A RI
VER: Mari Wilson *(Girl Can't Help It Film)* / GOING
OUT OF MY HEAD: Wes Montgomery / TAKE THE 'A' TRAIN
Anita O'Day / WALK ON THE WILD SIDE: Jimmy Smith
(COLMAN'S MELLO & MILD/TECHNICS CD'S) / THE SHADOW
OF YOUR SMILE: Oscar Peterson / SUMMERTIME: Sarah
Vaughan *(PIMMS)* / RELAX: Leon Redbone *(B.RAIL INTER
CITY)* / PASSING STRANGERS: Sarah Vaughan-Billy Ecks
tine / WHAT A WONDERFUL WORLD: Louis Armstrong

MIKIS THEODORAKIS ON THE SCREEN - Mikis Theodorakis
DRG (Pinn): 32901-4 (2Cass)   p.1993
Instrument.Suites: PHAEDRA-SERPICO-STATE OF SIEGE-Z

MIKLOS ROZSA: HOLLYWOOD SPECTACULAR- R.P.O. (R.Padberg)
Bay Cities (Silva Screen): BCD 3028 (CD)   p.93
KING OF KINGS-THE STORY OF THREE LOVES-SODOM AND GO
MORRAH-JULIUS CAESAR-EL CID-BEN HUR plus 16 minute
FANTASY ON THEMES FROM 'YOUNG BESS'

MILITARY BANDS PLAY FAVOURITE THEMES - Various Bands
Conifer: CFRC 503 (LP) MCFRC 503 (Cass)   P.1986
HORSE OF THE YEAR SHOW-CHI MAI-CHARIOTS OF FIRE-MR.
BENN-ACES HIGH-SQUADRON-NOBILMENTE (Elgar)-IMPERIAL
ECHOES-HORSE GUARDS-MACK& MABEL-TRUMPTON-THE FLUMPS
POSTMAN PAT-THUNDERBIRDS-KNIGHTSBRIDGE MARCH

MISS MARPLE FILMS - Ron Goodwin & Odense Symphony Orch.
Legend Impt (Silva Screen): LXE 706 (CD)   p.1993
New Digital Recordings Of Suites from The Miss Marp
le Films and other scores composed by **Ron Goodwin**
MURDER SHE SAID-MURDER AT THE GALLOP-MURDER MOST FO
UL-MURDER AHOY-FORCE TEN FROM NAVARONE-LANCELOT AND
GUINEVERE. *Ron Goodwin and The ODENSE Symphony Orch*

MOODS - Various Artists   P.1991
Virgin (Poly): VTCD 5 (CD) VTMC 5 (Cas) VTLP 5 (LP)
SADNESS(Enigna)-ORINOCO FLOW(Enya)-ONLY YOU(Praise)

CROCKETT'S THEME(Jan Hammer)-LIILY WAS HERE(David A
Stewart)-SONG FOR GUY(Elton John)-INSPECTOR MORSE
(Barrington Pheloung)-TWIN PEAKS(Julee Cruise)-CHAR
IOTS OF FIRE(Vangelis)-MERRY CHRISTMAS MR.LAWRENCE
(Ryuichi Sakamoto)-SONGBIRD(Kenny G)-SPANISH STEPS
(Van Morrison)-C'EST LE VENT:BETTY BLUE(Gabriel Yar
ed)-CHI MAI(Ennio Morricone)-ARRIVAL(Mike Oldfield)
AH SWEET DANCER(Michael O'Suilleabhain)

MOODS 2 - Various Artists P.1992
Virgin: VTCD 12 (CD) VTMC 12 (Cass) VTLP 12 (LP)
CARIBBEAN BLUE (Enya)-ALBATROSS (Fleetwood Mac)-TUB
ULAR BELLS (Mike Oldfield)-AFTER THE ORDEAL Genesis
ROWENA'S THEME (The Edge)-OXYGEN PT 4 (Jean Michel
Jarre)-SUN RISING (Beloved)-MORSE HE'S A MYSTERY TO
ME (Codex)-THEME FROM POIROT (Chistopher Gunning)-
THROUGH THE BLUE(Eno)-JESSICA (Allman Bros)-SO WHAT
(Ronny Jordan)-TAKE FIVE (Dave Brubeck)-I WISH I KN
EW HOW TO FEEL FREE (FILM 92 THEME)(Billy Taylor)-
TIME AFTER TIME(Miles Davis)-INARTICULATE SPEECH OF
THE HEART 1 (Van Morrison)-THE MISSION REMIX (Ennio
Morricone)-MOMENTS OF LOVE(Art Of Noise)-THEME FROM
THIRTYSOMETHING (Daniel Caine)-TARA (Roxy Music)

MORE FAMOUS THEMES - see 'FAMOUS THEMES 2'

MOVIE BRASS - Various Bands P.1992
Pickwick Int (Pickw): PWKM 4112P (CD) PWKMC (Cass)
GUNS OF NAVARONE-THE LONGEST DAY-HEIGH HO/WHISTLE
WHILE YOU WORK-THE VICTORS-COLONEL BOGIE(RIVER KWAI
MARCH)-HOW THE WEST WAS WON-76 TROMBONES-MARCH OF
THE SIAMESE CHILDREN-EXODUS-BUTCH CASSIDY & THE SUN
DANCE KID-ZORBA THE GREEK-OLIVER SELECTN-LIMELIGHT-
MAGNIFICENT SEVEN-BAD DAY AT BLACK ROCK-DAM BUSTERS

MOVIE HITS - Various Artists P.1992
Telstar (BMG): TCD 2615 (CD) STAC 2615 (Cass) + LP
WE DON'T NEED ANOTHER HERO *(Tina Turner)* NEUTRON DA
NCE *(Pointer Sisters)* MUSTANG SALLY *(Commitments)*
IT HAD TO BE YOU *Harry Connick Jnr* OH PRETTY WOMAN
Roy Orbison UP WHERE WE BELONG *(Joe Cocker-Jennifer
Warnes)* SISTERS ARE DOING IT *(Eurythmics & Aretha)*
LIVING IN AMERICA *(James Brown)* UNCHAINED MELODY
(Righteous Brothers) ARTHUR'S THEME *(Christopher Cr
oss)* CALLING YOU *(Jevetta Steele)* IT'S PROBABLY ME
(Sting & Eric Clapton) BOOK OF DAYS *(Enya)* DO IT AG
AIN *(Steely Dan)* PEOPLE ARE STRANGE *Echo & Bunnymen*
BROWN EYED GIRL *(Van Morrison)*

MOVIE SOUNDS - MORRICONE 93 - Ennio Morricone Orchestra
Epic (Sony M): 473802-2 (CD) -4 (Cass) P.1993
FISTFUL OF DOLLARS-MISSION-SHIP HUNTERS-TO FORGET
PALERMO-CITY OF JOY-ONCE UPON A TIME IN AMERICA-MY
NAME IS NOBODY-CASUALTIES OF WAR-GOTT MIN UNS-MADDE
LENA + 4 prev.unreleased tracks: Baroque Intermezzo
-Pan's Sons-New Madness-C'era Una Volta Il Trenino

MOVIOLA - John Barry P.1992
Epic (Sony Music): 472490-2 (CD) -4 (Cass) -1 (LP)
OUT OF AFRICA-MIDNIGHT COWBOY-BODY HEAT-SOMEWHERE

IN TIME-MARY QUEEN OF SCOTS-BORN FREE-DANCES WITH
WOLVES-CHAPLIN-COTTON CLUB-WALKABOUT-FRANCES-ON HER
MAJESTY'S S.SERVICE (WE HAVE ALL THE TIME)-MOVIOLA
MURDER SHE WROTE - see 'ITV AMERICA'
**MUSIC AND SONGS FROM 'THE PHANTOM O.THE OPERA'/'ASPECTS
OF LOVE'** Various Artists (Studio Recording) P.1993
Pickwick Shows: PWKS 4164 (CD) PWKMC 4164 (Cass)
Phantom: THE PHANTOM OF THE OPERA *(Paul Jones-Fiona
Hendley)* ALL I ASK OF YOU *(Stephanie Lawrence-Carl
Wayne)* WISHING YOU WERE SOMEHOW HERE AGAIN/THINK OF
ME *(S.Lawrence)* THE MUSIC OF THE NIGHT *(Paul Jones)*
Aspects: LOVE CHANGES EVERYTHING *(Or)* THERE IS MORE
TO LOVE *(Stephanie Lawrence)*THE FIRST MAN YOU REMEM
BER *(Stephanie Lawrence-Dave Willetts)* CHANSON D'EN
FANCE *(Stephanie Lawrence-Jack Emblow)* ANYTHING BUT
LONELY *(S.Lawrence)* SEEING IS BELIEVING *(Paul Jones
Fiona Hendley)* JOURNEY OF A LFETIME *(Dave Willetts)*
MUSIC FOR A DARKENED THEATRE Music Of Danny Elfman P.90
MCA USA (Silva Screen): MCAD(MCAC) 10065 (CD/Cass)
DICK TRACY-BATMAN-NIGHTBREED-BEETLEJUICE-MIDNIGHT
RUN-DARK MAN-SCROOGED-THE SIMPSONS (TV)-PEE WEE'S
BIG ADVENTURE-BACK TO SCHOOL-WISDOM-TALES FROM THE
CRYPT-ALFRED HITCHCOCK PRESENTS THE JAR-HOT TO TROT
FORBIDDEN ZONE-BIG TOP PEE WEE-BEETLEJUICE CARTOON
MUSIC FROM GREAT AUSTRALIAN FILMS - Var Artists P.1982
DRG (Conifer) SBLC) 12582 (Cass) CDSBL 12582(CD)
NEWSFRONT-GALLIPOLI-MY BRILLIANT CAREER-TALLTIMBERS
CATHY'S CHILD-ELIZA FRASER-BREAKER MORANT-CHANT OF
JIMMIE BLACKSMITH-THE PICTURE SHOW MAN-PICNIC AT HA
NGING ROCK-DIMBOOLA-CADDIE-THE MANGO TREE
MUSIC FROM HAMMER FILMS - Philharmonia Orchest* P.1990
Silva Screen (Conifer): FILMC(CD) 066 (Cass/CD)
DRACULA-DRACULA: PRINCE OF DARKNESS-TASTE THE BLOOD
OF DRACULA (all composed by James Bernard)-VAMPIRE
CIRCUS (David Whittaker)-HANDS OF THE RIPPER (Chris
topher Gunning) *Philharmonia Or. (Neil Richardson)*
MUSIC FROM THE FILMS OF CHARLIE CHAPLIN - M.Villard Orc
*GNP USA (Silva Screen): GNPS 2064 (LP)Also on Vogue
(Discovery): 670057 (CD) 771057 (Cass)*
MODERN TIMES-CITY LIGHTS-A DOG'S LIFE-GOLD RUSH-THE
KING IN NEW YORK-THE GREAT DICTATOR-LIMELIGHT *etc.*
MUSIC FROM THE FILMS OF CLINT EASTWOOD - City Of Prague
Symphony Orchestra (Derek Wadsworth)   p.1993
Silva Screen (Con): FILMCD 138 (CD) FILMC 138(Cass)
THE UNFORGIVEN-THE GOOD THE BAD AND THE UGLY-A FIST
FUL OF DOLLARS-FOR A FEW DOLLARS MORE-HANG 'EM HIGH
WHERE EAGLES DARE-PLAY MISTY FOR ME-OUTLAW JOSEY WA
LES-RAWHIDE-DIRTY HARRY-SUDDEN IMPACT-MAGNUM FORCE-
TWO MULES FOR SISTER SARA-IN THE LINE OF FIRE
MUSIC FROM THE FILMS OF PETER GREENAWAY - Michael Nyman
Essential Michael Nyman Band   P.1992
Argo/Decca (Polyg): 436 820-2 (CD) 436 820-4 (Cass)
CHASING SHEEP IS BEST LEFᵀ TO SHEPHERDS/AN EYE FOR
OPTICAL THEORY/THE GARDEN IS BECOMING A ROBE ROOM

(all: The Draughtsman's Contract) PRAWN WATCHING/TI
ME LAPSE (A Zed & Two Noughts) FISH BEACH/WHEELBARR
OW WALK/KNOWING THE ROPES (Drowning By Numbers)
MISERERE PARAPHRASE/MEMORIAL(The Cook The Thief His
Wife And Her Lover) STROKING/SYNCHRONISING (Water
Dances) MIRANDA   (Prospero's Books)

**MUSIC FROM THE FILMS OF RAINER WERNER FASSBINDER - Peer
Raben (Music scores)**
Alhambra/New Note (Pinn): A.38938 (CDx3)   P.1992
KATZELMACHER-GOD OF THE PLAGUE-PIONEERS IN INGOLSTA
DT-WHITTY-BEWARE OF THE HOLY WHORE-NICLEHAUSEN JOUR
NEY-I ONLY WANT YOU TO LOVE ME-FOX AND HIS FRIENDS
MOTHER KUSTER'S TRIP TO HEAVEN-SATAN'S BREW-CHINESE
ROULETTE-SCHATTEN DER ENGEL-FEAR OF FEAR-THE ST
ATION MASTER'S WIFE-DESPAIR-WOMEN IN NEW YORK-THIRD
GENERATION-MARRIAGE OF MARIA BRAUN-BERLIN ALEXANDER
PLATZ-LILI MARLEEN-LOLA-VERONIKA VOSS-QUERELLE

MUSIC FROM THE FILMS OF SYLVESTER STALLONE - Var.Arts
Silva Screen (Con): FILM(C)(CD) 139 (Cass/CD)   p.93
Music from: ROCKY (76-Bill Conti)-ROCKY 2 (79-Bill
Conti)-ROCKY 3 (82-Bill Conti)-ROCKY 4 (85-Bill Con
ti)-FIRST BLOOD (82-Jerry Goldsmith) RAMBO FIRST BL
OOD 2 (85-J.Goldsmith)-RAMBO 3 (88-Giorgio Moroder)
COBRA (86-Sylvester Levay)-LOCK UP (89-Bill Conti)-
NIGHTHAWKS (81-Keith Emerson)-PARADISE ALLEY (78-Bi
ll Conti)-OVER THE TOP (87-Giorgio Moroder)-F.I.S.T
(78-Bill Conti)-CLIFFHANGER (93-Trevor Jones)

MUSIC FROM THE FILMS OF YVES MONTAND - Various Artists
Polydor Impt (Silva Screen): 873 027 (CD)   P.1992
FILMS Include: CESAR AND ROSALIE-VINCENT FRANCOIS
PAUL AND THE OTHERS-POLICE PYTHON 357-GARCON-NETCHA
IEV HAS RETURNED-JEAN DE FLORETTE-MANON DES SOURCES

MUSIC OF ERICH WOLFGANG KORNGOLD - Lionel Newman (cond)
Dunhill USA (S.Screen): STZ 117 (CD) P.61 re-iss 91
New on CD a rare 1961 recording conducted by Lionel
Newman of scores digitally re-mastered from Warner
Bros movies of music by Erich Wolfgang Korngold.
Suites from THE SEA HAWK-ANTHONY ADVERSE-KING'S ROW
and THE ADVENTURES OF ROBIN HOOD

MUSIC OF MICHEL LEGRAND - Michel Legrand & His Orch
MFPleasure (EMI): CDMFP(TCMFP) 5925 (CD/Cass) P.92
WINDMILLS OF YOUR MIND-SUMMER OF 42-I STILL SEE YOU
(THE GO-BETWEEN)-SEA AND SKY *sung by DUSTY SPRINGFI
ELD*-CONCERTO FOR CABS-THE STREET WHERE THEY LIVED
WHERE LOVE BEGINS-IN LOVE IN NORMANDY-A PLACE IN PA
RIS *sung by MATT MONRO*-OLD LOVERS NEVER DIE-ON THE
ROAD (LADY IN THE CAR)-DO YOU COME HERE OFTEN-THEY
SIMPLY FADE AWAY-WHERE LOVE ENDS-PAVANNE FOR PEOPLE
PARIS WAS MADE FOR LOVERS-THE BURNING SHORE THEME
featuring JULIE COOPER (piano)

MUSICAL ALBUM The - Julia McKenzie   **p.1992**
First Night (Pinn): CASTCD 32 (CD) CASTC 32 (Cass)
I DREAMED A DREAM (Les Miserables) UNEXPECTED SONG
(Song and Dance) WHAT I DID FOR LOVE (Chorus Line)

SEND IN THE CLOWNS *(Little Night Mus)*-I DON'T KNOW
HOW TO LOVE HIM *(Jesus Christ S)* TIME HEALS EVERYT
HING *(Mack & Mabel)* TELL ME ITS NOT TRUE *(Blood Br
others)* BOY FROM..*(The Mad Show)* ON MY OWN *(Les Mi
erables)* MEMORY *(Cats)* LOSING MY MIND *(Follies)*
SOMEWHERE and TONIGHT *(West Side Story)*

MY KIND OF MUSIC – Ron Goodwin & Bournemouth Symph Orch
Chandos: CHAN 8797 (CD) LBTD 025 (Cass)   *P.1989*
THE TRAP (London Marathon Theme)-HERE WHERE YOU ARE
KOJAK-HILL STREET BLUES-STAR TREK-DYNASTY-DALLAS-HE
RE'S THAT RAINY DAY-A Tribute To *Miklos Rosza:* Love
Theme From BEN HUR/The RED HOUSE/The FOUR FEATHERS/
PARADE OF THE CHARIOTEERS| TROLLEY SONG-*Disneytime:*
Zip A Dee Doo Dah/Someday My Prince Will Come/I Wan
na Be Like You-Little April Shower-When You Wish Up
on A Star| CARAVAN-THE GIRL FROM CORSICA-*Stephen Fo
ster Tribute:* OH SUSANNA/SWANNEE RIVER/BEAUTIFUL DR
EAMER/CAMPTOWN RACES| INTRO: DRAKE 400 SUITE-BATTLE

MY RIFLE MY PONY AND ME: Film Western Songs – V.Artists
Bear Family (Rollercoast/Swift):BCD 15625 (CD) P.93
MY RIFLE MY PONY AND ME:Dean Martin-Ricky Nelson fr
om *RIO BRAVO (59)* / LEGEND OF SHENANDOAH: James Ste
wart *SHENANDOAH (65)* / MONTANA *MONTANA (50)* THE SEA
RCHERS *THE SEARCHERS (56)* WAGON'S WEST/SONG OF THE
WAGONMASTER *WAGONMASTER(50)* All sung by Sons Of The
PIONEERS / NEVADA SMITH: Merle Kilgore *NEVADA SMITH
(56)* / BALLAD OF THE ALAMO: Marty Robbins *THE ALAMO
(60)* / THE HANGING TREE: Marty Robbins *THE HANGING
TREE (59)* / BALLAD OF PALADIN: Johnny Western *HAVE
GUN WILL TRAVEL (TV 57)* / THE SONS OF KATIE ELDER:
Johnny Cash *THE SONS OF KATIE ELDER (65)/* THE REBEL
JOHNNY YUMA: Johnny Cash / RAWHIDE: Frankie Laine
RAWHIDE (TV 58) / GUNFIGHT AT OK CORRALL: Frankie
Laine *GUNFIGHT AT OK CORRALL (57)* / BALLAD OF DAVY
CROCKETT: Fess Parker *DAVY CROCKETT (55)* /RIO BRAVO
Dean Martin *RIO BRAVO (59)* / I'M A RUNAWAY: Tab Hun
ter / BONANZA: Lorne Greene *BONANZA (TV 59)* / NORTH
TO ALASKA: Johnny Horton *NORTH TO ALASKA (59)* /HIGH
NOON: Tex Ritter *HIGH NOON (52)* / AND THE MOON GREW
Kirk Douglas *MAN WITHOUT A STAR (55)* / PECOS BILL:
Roy Rogers & Sons Of The Pioneers / YELLOW ROSE OF
TEXAS/ROLL ON TEXAS MOON: Roy Rogers / DON'T FENCE
ME IN: Roy Rogers *HOLLYWOOD CANTEEN (44)* / COWBOY:
Dickson Hall

NO STRINGS ATTACHED – Barry Gray Orchestra   **P.1981**
Castle Classics (BMG): CLACD 204 (CD)   *Re-Iss.1990*
The original themes from the ATV 1960's TV series
THUNDERBIRDS-CAPTAIN SCARLETT-STINGRAY-AQUA MARINA
WELL DONE PARKER-JOE 90-MYSTERONS Theme
See Also Under Entries (TV Section) THUNDERBIRDS-
THUNDERBIRDS ARE GO!-STINGRAY-CAPTAIN SCARLETT etc.

NOEL – Noel Coward Classic Recordings 1928-1938   P.1990
Happy Days (Conifer): CHCD(MHCD)CHD 168 (CD/Cas/LP)
POOR LITTLE RICH GIRL-ZIGEUNER-DEAR LITTLE CAFE-TOK

AY-CALL OF LIFE-WORLD WEARY-CABALLERO-I'LL SEE YOU
AGAIN-GREEN CARNATIONS-STATELY HOMES OF ENGLAND-LOV
ER OF MY DREAMS-MAD DOGS & ENGLISHMEN-WE WERE SO YO
UNG-GYPSY MELODY-MRS.WORTHINGTON-DANCE LITTLE LADY-
JUST LET ME LOOK AT YOU-SOMETHING TO DO WITH SPRING
DEAREST LOVE-FARE THEE WELL-A ROOM WITH A VIEW-HALF
CASTE WOMAN-WHERE ARE THE SONGS-PLAY ORCHESTRA PLAY

NOEL COWARD : The Masters Voice - HMV RECORDINGS 1928-
1953 (Complete) on *EMI COWARD 1 (4 CD SET)*   *P.1992*

NOW VOYAGER - Classic Film Scores Of Max Steiner*   P.90
RCA Victor (BMG): GD 80136 (CD) GK 80136 (Cass)
NOW VOYAGER-KING KONG-SARATOGA TRUNK-CHARGE OF THE
LIGHT BRIGADE-FOUR WIVES-THE BIG SLEEP-JOHNNY BELIN
DA-SINCE YOUWENT AWAY-THE INFORMER-THE FOUNTAINHEAD
*National Philharmonic Orchestra (Charles Gerhardt)

NYMAN-GREENAWAY SOUNDTRACKS - Michael Nyman   P.1989
Virgin: DVEBN 55 (CD Box Set) VEBN 55 (LP Box Set)
Michael Nyman's S/Tracks To Peter Greenaways Films:
THE DRAUGHTSMAN'S CONTRACT / A ZED AND TWO NOUGHTS
DROWNING BY NUMBERS / THE COOK THE THIEF HIS WIFE..

OMEN The: 50 Years Of Classic Horror Film Music   P.1988
The National Philharmonic Orchestra (Stanley Black)
Silva Screen (Conif): FILM(C)(CD) 017 (LP/Cass/CD)
THE OMEN-ROSEMARY'S BABY-THE EXCORCIST II-KING KONG
DR.JEKYLL & MR.HYDE-THE VAMPIRE LOVERS-FEAR IN THE
NIGHT-DR.JEKYLL AND SISTER HYDE-SHE

ON AND OFF STAGE - Dave Willetts & The *P.O.   P.1990
Silva Screen (Conif): SONG(C)(CD) 902 (LP/Cass/CD)
Songs from: PHANTOM OF THe OPERA-LES MISERABLES-LA
CAGE AUX FOLLES-NINE-GUYS & DOLLS-PENNY MILLIONAIRE
plus the following songs: TI AMO-NIGHTS ARE FOREVER
THE ROSE-HELLO AGAIN *etc.* / ***Philharmonia Orchestra**

ONCE UPON A TIME IN CHINA - Best Of Chinese Film Music
Volume 1 / *Varese (Pinn): VSD 5455 (CD)*   *p.93*
THE NEW CHINA WOMAN-SUPERCOP: POLICE STORY 3-PEACH
BLOSSOM-THE EAST IS RED-THE WICKED CITY-ONCE UPON A
TIME IN CHINA etc.

OPERA GOES TO THE MOVIES Boston Pops (Arthur Fieldler)
RCA Victor (BMG): GD 60841 (CD) GK 60841 (Cass)
FATAL ATTRACTION: *(Puccini: "Un Bel Di" MADAMA BUTTE*
RFLY, Act.2) **WITCHES OF EASTWICK:** *(Puccini: "Nessun*
Dorma" TURANDOT,Act 3) **MOONSTRUCK:** *(Puccini: "Quando*
M'en Vo" LA BOHEME, Act 2) (Puccini: "Don de Lieta
Usci" LA BOHEME,Act 3) **DARK EYES:** *(Rossini:"Una Voce*
Poco Fa" BARBER OF SEVILLE, Act 1) **APOCALYPSE NOW:**
(Wagner: "Ride Of The Valkyries" DIE WALKURE,Act 2)
JEAN DE FLORETTE: *(Verdi: "Overture" LA FORZA DEL*
DESTINO) **PRIZZI'S HONOR:** *(Rossini:"Overture" BARBER*
OF SEVILLE) **A ROOM WITH A VIEW:** *(Puccini: "Firenze*
E Coome Un Albero Fiorito" and "O Mio Babino Caro"
GIANNI SCHICCHI) and "Chi Il Bel Sogno Di Doretta"
LA RONDINE) **GODFATHER III:** *(Mascagni:"Intermezzo"*
CAVALLERIA RUSTICANA) **UNTOUCHABLES:** *(Leoncavallo:*
"Vesti La Giubba" PAGLIACCI, Act 1)

ORCHESTRAL GOLD - Music Of Famous Film Themes * P.1992
Stardust (TBD-Conifer): STACD(STAMC) 033 (CD/Cass)
WARSAW CONCERTO-THE DREAM OF OLWEN-A TALE OF TWO CI
TIES-SLAUGHTER ON TENTH AVENUE-THE NIGHT HAS EYES-
THE LEGEND OF THE GLASS MOUNTAIN-JEALOUS LOVER-CORN
ISH RHAPSODY-SPELLBOUND * *Hamburg Radio Dance Orche
stra conducted by Gilbert Vintner*

ORIGINALS - The Levi Jeans Ad Collection - Var.Artists
Columbia (Sony Music): MOOD(C)(CD) 29   P.1993
WONDERFUL WORLD: Sam Cooke-I HEARD IT THROUGH THE
GRAPEVINE: Marvin Gaye-STAND BY ME: Ben E.King-WHEN
A MAN LOVES A WOMAN: Percy Sledge-C'MON EVERYBODY:
Eddie Cochran-MANNISH BOY:Muddy Waters-AIN'T NOBODY
HOME: B.B.King-CAN'T GET ENOUGH.: Bad Company-THE JO
KER: Steve Miller Band-SHOULD I STAY OR SHOULD I GO
The Clash-20TH CENTURY BOY: T.Rex-MAD ABOUT THE BOY
Dinah Washington-PIECE OF MY HEART: (Erma Franklin)
HEART ATTACK AND VINE: Screamin' Jay Hawkins
original music tracks used in the LEVI 501 TV Ads

PERFORMANCE - Marti Webb & Philharmonia Orchest P.1989
Telstar (BMG): TCD(STAR)(STAC) 2391 (CD/LP/Cass)
Intro: I DREAMED A DREAM (Les Miserables)-ALMOST LI
KE BEING IN LOVE (Brigadoon)-MUSIC OF THE NIGHT (Ph
antom)-LOSING MY MIND (Follies)-ANYTHING BUT LONELY
(Aspects Of Love)-ONLY HE(Starlight Express)-MEMORY
(Cats)-LOVE CHANGES EVERYTHING (Aspects)-ONCE YOU
LOSE YOUR HEART (Me & My Girl)-LAST MAN IN MY LIFE
(Tell Me On A Sunday)-BLOW GABRIEL (Anything Goes)

POWER THEMES 90 - F.A.B. - Top TV Classic REMIXES P.90
Ronco (BMG): CDSR 022 (CD) TCSR 022 (Cass) reiss 93
THUNDERBIRDS AREGO-JOE 90-UFO-CAPTAIN SCARLET-SPACE
1999-THE STINGRAY Megamix-THE PRISONER Free Man Mix
THE SAINT-THE AVENGERS-DANGERMAN-DERPARTMENTS-JASON
KING-THE PERSUADERS *(original composers: Barry Gray
Edwin Astley-Laurie Johnson-Ron Grainer-John Barry)*
           - *see also* 'NO STRINGS ATTACHED'

PREMIERE COLLECTION The -Best Of Andrew Lloyd Webber 88
Polydor:ALWTC 1 (Cass) and 837282-2 (CD) -5 (DCC)
PHANTOM OF THE OPERA *(Steve Harley-Sarah Brightman)*
TAKE THAT LOOK OF YOUR FACE *(Marti Webb)*-ALL I ASK
OF YOU *(C.Richard-Sarah Brightman)*-DON'T CRY FOR ME
ARGENTINA *(Julie Covington)*-MAGICAL MR.MISTOFFELEES
(Paul Nicholas)-VARIATIONS *(Julian Lloyd Webber)*-SU
PERSTAR *(Murray Head)*-MEMORY *(E.Paige)*-STARLIGHT EX
PRESS *(Ray Shell)*-TELL ME ON A SUNDAY *(Marti Webb)*
MUSIC OF THE NIGHT *(Michael Crawford)*-ANOTHER SUITC
ASE IN ANOTHER HALL *(Barbara Dickson)*-I DON'T KNOW
HOW TO LOVE HIM *(Y.Elliman)*-PIE JESU *(S.Brightman)*
and Miles Kingston & Winchester Cathedral Choir)

PREMIERE COLLECTION The - Andrew Lloyd Webber ENCORE
Polydor: ALWTV(TC) 1 (LP/Cass) 837282-2 (CD) P.1988
MEMORY *(Barbra Streisand)* LOVE CHANGES EVERYTHING
(Michael Ball) AMIGOS PARA SIEMPRE *(Jose Carreras-
Sarah Brightman)* ANY DREAM WILL DO *(Jason Donovan)*

CLOSE EVERY DOOR *Phillip Schofield)* OH WHAT A CIRC
US *(David Essex)* POINT OF NO RETURN *(Sarah Brightm
an-Michael Crawford) plus following tracks* I AM THE
STARLIGHT-WISHING YOU WERE SOMEHOW HERE AGAIN-ARGEN
TINE MELODY-SEEING IS BELIEVING-THE JELLICLE BALL-
EVERYTHING'S ALRIGHT-THE FIRST MAN YOU REMEMBER-ANY
THING BUT LONELY-HOSANNA

PSYCHO HORROR AND FANTASY - *see* 'AT THE MOVIES 3'

REEL MUSIC-Filmscore Music by Paddy Moloney   P.1991
   RCA Victor (BMG): RD 60412 (CD) RK 60412 (Cass)
   TREASURE ISLAND (89): Opening Theme/Loyals March/Is
   land Theme/Setting Sail/French Leave/Blind Pew/Trea
   sure Cave/The Hispaniola (Silver & Loyals March)
   BARRY LYNDON (75): Love Theme From Barry Lyndon
   THREE WISHES FOR JAMIE (87): Love Theme/The Matchma
   king/Mountain Fall (Main Theme)
   LOVESPELL (79):Tristan & Isolde Love Theme/March Of
   King O.Cornwall/The Falcon/Escape & Chase/Departure
   THE GREY FOX (82): Main Theme from The Grey Fox
   THE YEAR OF THE FRENCH (BBC/RTE 82): The French Mar
   ch/Cooper's Tune (The Bolero)/Closing Theme & March

REFLECTIONS - **Original Instrumental Hits / Var Artists**
   CBS: CBSCD 10034 (CD) (40)10034 (Cass)   *CD.P.1990*
   BRIDESHEAD REVISITED-CHARIOTS OF FIRE-3 GYMNOPEDIES
   SHEPHERD'S SONG-FLAME TREESOF THIKA-COSMOS-LIGHT OF
   EXPERIENCE-CAVATINA-ALBATROSS-CHI MAI-BILITIS-MIDNI
   GHT EXPRESS-ANNIE'S SONG-DON'T CRY FOR ME ARGENTINA
   HANDS AND CLOUDS-ARIA-SAMBA PATI-ARRIVAL

REMEMBER THESE FAMOUS THEMES - *see* 'FAMOUS THEMES'

ROADMUSIC - **Wim Wenders and Jurgen Knieper**   P.1991
   Milan/RTM (Pinn): 873 089 (CD)
   THE AMERICAN FRIEND-THE GOALIES FEAR OF THE PENALTY
   KICK-WRONG MOVEMENT-THE SCARLET LETTER-THE STATE OF
   THINGS-WINGS OF DESIRE

ROCKY STORY The - **Various Artists (From Soundtracks)**
   Polydor: 848 242-2 (CD) -4 (Cass) -1 (LP)   *P.1991*
   EYE OF THE TIGER (Survivor)-BURNING HEART(Survivor)
   LIVING IN AMERICA (James Brown)-NO EASY WAY OUT (Ro
   bert Tepper)-HEARTS OF FIRE (John Cafferty)-WAR (Vi
   nce DiCola)-GONNA FLY NOW 'ROCKY'THEME (Bill Conti)
   TRAINING MONTAGE (Vince DiCola) GONNA FLY NOW Instr

RODGERS & HAMMERSTEIN SONGBOOK The - **Various Artists**
   Sony Broadway (Sony Music): SK 53331 (CD)   *p.1993*
   OH WHAT A BEAUTIFUL MORNING-THE SURREY WITH THE FRI
   NGE ON TOP-PEOPLE WILL SAY WE'RE IN LOVE-OUT OF MY
   DREAMS **(Oklahoma)** *feat: NELSON EDDY-PORTIA NELSON-
   VIRGINIA HASKINS.* CAROUSEL WALTZ **(Carousel)***NEW YORK
   PHILHARMON.* SOME ENCHANTED EVENING-THERE IS NOTHIN'
   LIKE A DAME-A WONDERFUL GUY-YOUNGER THAN SPRINGTIME
   (South Pacific)*feat: EZIO PINZA-MARY MARTIN-WILLIAM
   TABERT.* I WHISTLE A HAPPY TUNE-GETTING TO KNOW YOU-
   SHALL WE DANCE **(The King & I)** *feat: BARBARA COOK-TH
   EODORE BIKEL.* IN MY OWN LITTLE CORNER-DO I LOVE YOU
   BECAUSE YOU'RE BEAUTIFUL **(Cinderella)** *featur: JULIE*

ANDREWS-JON CYPHER. I ENJOY BEING A GIRL-SUNDAY (Fl
ower Drum Song) feat:PAT SUZUKI-LARRY BLYDEN. DO-RE
ME-CLIM EVERY MOUNTAIN-EDELWEISS (Sound Of Music)
feat: MARY MARTIN-PATRICIA NEWEY-LAURIE PETERS
ROMANCE AND THE STAGE - Elaine Paige   P.1993
RCA (BMG): 74321 13615-2 (CD) -4 (Cass) -5 (DCC)
THEY SAY IT'S WONDERFUL / I GOT LOST IN HIS ARMS-AS
TIME GOES BY-FEELING GOOD-MORE THAN YOU KNOW-MAD
ABOUT THE BOY-WITH EVERY BREATH I TAKE-I GAZE IN YO
UR EYES-KISMET SUITE: STRANGER IN PARADISE /HE'S IN
LOVE /THIS IS MY BELOVED-LONG BEFORE I KNEW YOU-HOW
LONG HAS THIS BEEN GOING ON-SMOKE GETS IN YOUR EYES
SEPTEMBER SONG-SONG OF A SUMMER NIGHT
ROMANCING THE SCREEN - Various Artists   P.1992
Epic (Sony Music): 471901-2 (CD) -4 (Cass) -1 (LP)
TRY A LITTLE TENDERNESS (Commitments) BROWN EYED GI
RL (Van Morrison) SHOW ME HEAVEN (Maria McKee) STOR
MS IN AFRICA (Enya) FALLING (Julee Cruise) CITY OF
JOY (Ennio Morricone) OUT OF AFRICA (John Barry) TA
KE MY BREATH AWAY (Berlin) LADY IN RED (Chris De Bu
rgh) ACT OF FAITH (Ennio Morricone) PROMISE ME YOU'
LL REMEMBER (Harry Connick Jnr) HOW ABOUT YOU (Nils
son) BLUE VELVET (Bobby Vinton) ONLY THE LONELY(Roy
Orbison) UNCHAINED MELODY (Righteous Brothers) OH
PRETTY WOMAN (Roy Orbison) MY GIRL (Temptations)
ROSE AND THE GUN - The Music Of Laurie Johnson * P.1992
Fly-U.Kanchana (H.Mundi):FLY(CD)(MC) 103 (CD/Cass)
LADY AND THE HIGHWAYMAN (TVM 89)-A HAZARD OF HEARTS
(TVM 87)-A DUEL OF HEARTS (TVM 88)-A GHOST IN MONTE
CARLO (TVM 90)-THE AVENGERS (Theme/Tag)-THE NEW AVE
NGERS-TIGER BAY THEME-WHEN THE KISSING HAD TO STOP
CAESAR SMITH/THERE IS ANOTHER SONG/THIS TIME (from:
Hot Millions)-SHIRLEY'S THEME/RICKSHAW RIDE (from:
Shirley's World)-I AIM AT THE STARS Theme-THIS IS
YOUR LIFE (Gala Performance)-JASON KING theme-ROMAN
CE (The First Men In The Moon)-THE PROFESSIONALS
*LONDON STUDIO SYMPHONY ORCHESTRA (Laurie Johnson)
ROUND MIDNIGHT 20 More Cool Cuts On The Lighter Side Of
Jazz - V.Arts Verve (Poly): 516 471-2(CD) -4(Cass)
LET THERE BE LOVE-NAT KING COLE MANHATTAN-ELLA FITZ
GERALD MY BABY JUST CARES FOR ME-NINA SIMONE / YOUR
LOVE IS KING-SADE DESAFINADO-STAN GETZ / AIR ON A G
STRING-JACQUES LOUSSIER VERY THOUGHT OF YOU-TONY BE
NNETT CALL ME IRRESPONSIBLE-DINAH WASHINGTON IMAGIN
ATION-BILLY ECKSTINE I GET A KICK OUT OF YOU-BILLIE
HOLIDAY UNSQUARE DANCE-DAVE BRUBECK SHINY STOCKINGS
COUNT BASIE MAKIN'WHOOPPEE-LOUIS ARMSTRONG & OSCAR
PETERSON LOVER MAN-SARAH VAUGHAN WHEN IFALL IN LOVE
BEN WEBSTER ROUND MIDNIGHT-MEL TORME MEDITATION-AST
RUD GILBERTO LULLABY OF BIRDLAND-GEORGE SHEARING
THE CAT-JIMMY SMITH WHAT'S NEW-GEORGE BENSON
ROYAL PHILHARMONIC ORCH. PLAY SUITES FROM Miss Saigon
and Les Miserables   P.1991
Pickwick: PWKS 4079 (CD) PWKMC 4079 (Cass)   P.1991

LES MISERABLES: PROLOGUE-AT THE END OF THE DAY-I DR
EAMED A DREAM-LOVELY LADIES-FANTINE'S DEATH-MASTER
OF THE HOUSE-STARS-DO YOU HEAR THE PEOPLE SING-A HE
ART FULL OF LOVE-ON MY OWN-DRINK WITH ME-BRING HIM
HOME-THE FINAL BATTLE-EPILOGUE: VALJEAN'S DEATH-DO
YOU HEAR THE PEOPLE SING (REPRISE)
MISS SAIGON: OVERTURE-THE HEAT IS ON IN SAIGON-THE
MOVIE IN MY MIND-WHY GOD WHY-SUN AND MOON-THE CERE
MONY-THE LAST NIGHT OF THE WORLD-FALL OF SAIGON-I
STILL BELIEVE-IF YOU WANT TO DIE IN BED-TRUTH INSI
DE YOUR HEAD-LITTLE GOD OF MY HEART.*Tony Britten*
**ROYAL PHILHARMONIC ORCH. PLAY SUITES FROM - Aspects Of
Love / Joseph And The Amazing T.Dreamcoat / Cats**
Pickwick Int: PWKS 4115 (CD) PWKMC 4115 (Cass) P.92
ASPECTS OF LOVE: LOVE CHANGES EVERYTHING-SEEING IS
BELIEVING-A MEMORY OF A HAPPY MOMENT-CHANSON D'ENFA
NCE-EVERYBODY LOVES A HERO-SH'ED BE BETTER OFF WITH
YOU-STOP WAIT PLEASE-OTHER PLEASURES-THERE IS MORE
TO LOVE-THE FIRST MAN YOU REMEMBER-HAND ME THE WINE
&THE DICE-ANYTHING BUT LOVE-LOVE CHANGES EVERYTHING
JOSEPH & THE AMAZING TECHNICOLOR DREAMCOAT: JACOB &
SONS-JOSEPH'S COAT-JOSEPH'S DREAMS-POOR POOR JOSEPH
ONE MORE ANGEL IN HEAVEN-POTIPHAR-CLOSE EVERY DOOR-
PHARAOH STORY-THOSE CANNON DAYS-JACOB IN EGYPT-ANY
DREAM WILL DO-GIVE ME MY COLOURED COAT
CATS: OVERTURE-OLD GUMBIE CAT-RUM TUM TUGGER-GRIZAB
ELLA-GLAMOUR CAT-BUSTOPHER JONES-OLD DEUTERONOMY-JE
LLICAL BALL-GUS THE THEATRE CAT-SKIMBLESHANKS THE
RAILWAY CAT-MACAVITY MYSTERY CAT-MR.MISTOFFELEES-ME
MORY-THE JOURNEY TO THE HEVISIDE LAYER
SALUTE TO HEROES - Central Band Of The R.A.F.   P.1990
MFP (EMI): CDRAF 1 (CD) TCRAF 1 (Cass)*
ROYAL AIR FORCE MARCH-PATHFINDERS MARCH-DAMBUSTERS
THOSE MAGNIFICENT MEN.-REACH FOR THE SKY-OUT OF THE
BLUE-CROWN IMPERIAL-633 SQUADRON-COLDITZ MARCH-CAVA
LRY OF THE CLOUDS-SECRET ARMY-ACES HIGH-SPITFIRE PR
ELUDE-BATTLE OF BRITAIN-WE'LL MEET AGAIN *extra tra
cks on CD:* THE VALIANT YEARS-WHITE CLIFFS OF DOVER-
RUN RABBIT RUN. *Central Band Of The Royal Air Force*
SCREEN SINATRA - Frank Sinatra with Var Orchestras P.88
MFP (EMI): CDMFP 6052 (CD) TCMFP 5835 (Cass)
FROM HERE TO ETERNITY-YOUNG AT ♥EART-SOMEONE TO WAT
CH OVER ME-TENDER TRAP-ALL THE WAY-MONIQUE-TO LOVE
AND BE LOVED-ALL MY TOMORROWS-C'EST MAGNIFIQUE-JUST
ONE OF THOSE THINGS-THREE COINS IN THE FOUNTAIN-NOT
AS A STRANGER-JOHNNY CONCHO THEME-CHICAGO-THEY CAME
TO CORDURA-HIGH HOPES-IT'S ALL RIGHT WITH ME-DREAM
SCREEN THEMES - Royal Philharmonic Orch (John Scott)
Varese (Pinn): VSD 5208 (CD) VSC 5208 (Cass) P.1991
BEETLEJUICE: MAIN THEME-*BIG:* GOODBYE-*SHOOT TO KILL:*
END TITLE-*CROSSING DELANCEY:* PORTRAIT OF IZZY -*COC
OON THE RETURN:* BASKETBALL SWING-*COMING TO AMERICA:*
KING'S MOTORCADE-*MADAME SOUZATSKA:* THE RIVER-*CRIMIN
AL LAW:* GARDEN PAVILLION-*NIGHTMARE ON ELM ST.4:* COR

PUS KRUEGER-*BETRAYED:* THE WAY-*MASQUERADE:* END TITLE
DA: MAIN THEME-*DIE HARD:* TERRORISTS-*MILAGRO BEANFIE
LD WAR:* END TITLE-*WHO FRAMED ROGER RABBIT:* TITLE

SCREENPLAYING - Mark Knopfler   p.1993
Vertigo (Poly): 518 327-2 *(CD)* 518 327-4 *(Cass)*
Local Hero: WILD THEME-BOOMTOWN (Louis's Favourite)
THE MIST COVERED MOUNTAINS-SMOOCHING-GOING HOME
Cal: THE IRISH BOY-IRISH LOVE-FATHER AND SON-POTATO
PICKING-THE LOND ROAD
Princess Bride: ONCE UPON A TIME....STORYBOOK LOVE
(Love theme)-MORNING RIDE-THE FRIEND'S SONG-GUIDE
MY SWORD-A HAPPY ENDING
Last Exit To Brooklyn:VICTIMS-A LOVE IDEA-LAST EXIT
TO BROOKLYN FINALE

SCREENS & STAGES - The Music Of Nigel Hess *LFO P.1990
Fly (Total-BMG): FLY*(CD)(LP)(MC)* 101 *(CD/LP/Cass)*
CYRANO DE BERGERAC *(RSC)*-The ONE GAME 'Saylon Dola'
(Central)(sung by Chameleon)-ANNA OF THE FIVE TOWNS
(BBC)-A WOMAN OF SUBSTANCE *(C4)*-SECRET OF SHERLOCK
HOLMES *(West End)*-ALL PASSION SPENT *(BBC)*-TESTAMENT
(C4)-CAMPION *(BBC)*-THE LONDON EMBASSY *(Thames)*-AN
AFFAIR IN MIND *(BBC)*-TO US A CHILD *(Thames)*VIDAL IN
VENICE *(C4)*-SUMMER'S LEASE *(BBC)(sung by Chameleon)*
ATLANTIS *(BBC)*-VANITY FAIR *(BBC) *London Film Orch.*

**SEA HAWK The - National Philharmonic Orchestra ***   p.91
RCA Victor (BMG): GD 60863 *(CD)* deleted 93
*THE SEA HAWK:*MAIN TITLE-REUNION-FINALE *OF HUMAN
BONDAGE:*NORA'S THEME *ADVENTURES OF ROBIN HOOD:*
MARCH OF THE MERRY MEN-BATTLE *JUAREZ:*LOVE THEME
*KINGS ROW:*MAIN TITLE *THE CONSTANT NYMPH:*TOMORROW
*CAPTAIN BLOOD:*OVERTURE *ANTHONY ADVERSE:* NO FATHER
NO MOTHER NO NAME *BETWEEN TWO WORLDS:*MAIN TITLE-
MOTHER AND SON *DECEPTION:*MAIN TITLE *DEVOTION:*THE
DEATH OF EMILY BRONTE *ESCAPE ME NEVER:*MAIN TITLE-
VENICE-MARCH-LOVE SCENE-FINALE *Charles Gerhardt*

SHOWBOAT (SHOWS COLLECT)(Jerome Kern-Oscar Hammerstein)
Pickwick Shows Coll: PWKS 4161*(CD)* PWKMC 4161*(Cass)*
featuring: **Gemma Craven-Denis Quilley-David Kernan-**
Tracey Miller and Co. *Songs:*- OL'MAN RIVER-WHERE'S
THE MATE FOR ME-MAKE BELIEVE-CAN'T HELP LOVIN' DAT
MAN-I MIGHT FALL BACK ON YOU-LIFE UPON THE WICKED
STAGE-YOU ARE LOVE-WHY DO I LOVE YOU-BILL-GOODBYE
MY LADY LOVE-AFTER THE BALL-OL' MAN RIVER (reprise)

SILENTS The - Carl Davis with London Philh Orch p.1988
Virgin Classics (Poly): VC790785-2 *(CD)* -4 *(Cass)*
*The Musical Scores For 10 Classic Silent Films Comp
osed/Conducted by* **Carl Davis** *with* **Philharmonic Orch**
Commissioned by Channel 4 (1988) NAPOLEON-THE CROWD
FLESH 7THE DEVIL-SHOW PEOPLE-BROKEN BLOSSOMS-THE WI
ND-THIEF OF BAGHDAD-BIG PARADE-GREED-OLD HEIDELBERG

SLEEPY SHORES The Instrumental Classics - V.Arts p.1988
Old Gold: OG 3703 *(CD)* OG 2703 *(Cass)*
IL SILENZIO (Nino Rosso)-CAST YOUR FATE TO THE WIND
(Sounds Orchestr)-ARIA (Acker Bilk)-TRUDIE (Joe Hen

derson)-CAVATINA (John Williams)-EYE LEVEL *(Van Der*
alk/ Simon Park)-FLORAL DANCE (Brighouse & Rastrick
Brass Band)-PETITE FLEUR (Chris Barber-Monty Sunshi
ne)-MIDNIGHT IN MOSCOW (Kenny Ball) Z-CARS (Johnny
Keating Z Men)-SLEEPY SHORES *('Owen MD'/* J.Pearson)
ZORBA'S DANCE (Marcello Minerbi) *orig recordings*

SONDHEIM: A Celebration at Carnegie Hall - Various Arts
RCA Victor (BMG): 09026 61484-2 (2CDs) Complete
RCA Victor (BMG): 09026 61516-2 (CD) - Highlights
Songs from SWEENEY TODD-FOLLIES-COMPANY-FUNNY THING
HAPPENED ON THE WAY TO THE FORUM-DICK TRACY-MERRILY
WE ROLL ALONG-INTO THE WOODS-SINGING OUT LOUD-PACIF
IC OVERTURES-ASSASSINS-SEVEN PER CENT SOLUTION-ANYO
NE CAN WHISTLE-A LITTLE NIGHT MUSIC-SUNDAY IN THE
PARK WITH GEORGE

SONGS FROM THE SHOWS - Shirley Bassey   p.1991
EMI Compacts For Pleasure: CC 272 (CD)
MOON RIVER-PEOPLE-TONIGHT-IF LOVE WERE ALL-DAYS OF
WINE AND ROSES-I BELIEVE IN YOU-I'VE NEVER BEEN IN
LOVE BEFORE-FAR AWAY-THE LADY IS A TRAMP-SOMEWHERE
IT MIGHT AS WELL BE SPRING-DON'T RAIN ON MY PARADE
I GET A KICK OUT OF YOU-JUST ONE OFTHOSE THINGS-AS
LONG AS HE NEEDS ME-WHERE OR WHEN-S'WONDERFUL-SOME
THING WONDERFUL-EVERYTHING'S COMING UP ROSES-IF EV
ER I WOULD LEAVE YOU-YOU'LL NEVER WALK ALONE

SONGS FROM THE STAGE AND SCREEN - Michael Crawford with
London Symphony Orchestra / *Telstar Records p.1987*
(BMG): STAR 2308 (LP) STAC 2308 (CS) TCD 2308 (CD)
WEST SIDE STORY-WHAT'LL I DO-UNEXPECTED SONG-IF I
LOVED YOU-BEFORE THE PARADE PASSES BY-WHEN YOU WISH
UPON A STAR-IN THE STILL OF THE NIGHT-MEMORY-NOT A
DAY GOES BY-BRING HIM HOME-YOU'LL NEVER WALK ALONE

SOUND OF CLASSIC ROMANCE / CLASSIC FM - Collect Various
EMI Classics: CDC 555003-2 (CD) EL 555003-4 (Cass)
Including Music from TV Commercials and Films
PIANO CONCERTO NO.2 1st m/m *(Rachmaninov)* / PAVANE
(Faure) / BAILERO Songs Of The Auvergne*(Cánteloube)*
INTERMEZZO Cavalleria Rusticana *(Mascagni)* / CHE GE
LIDA MANINA La Boheme *(Puccini)* / MOONLIGHT SONATA
1st m/m *(Beethoven)* / THE SWAN Carnival Of The Anim
als *(Saint-Saens)* / GYMNOPEDIE NO.1 *(Satie)* /ADAGIO
(Barber) / SONG TO THE MOON Rusalka *(Dvorak)* / GUIT
AR CONCERTO Slow m/m *(Rodrigo)* / SWAN LAKE Final Sc
ene *(Tchaikovsky)* - *Artists Include: JACQUELINE DU*
PRE-RICCARDO MUTI-ANDRE PREVIN-JULIAN BREAM-LUCIA
POPP-VICTORIA DE LOS ANGELES-SIMON RATTLE

SOUNDS VISUAL - Various Original Artists   p.1983
Radio Six Prod.Glasgow: YRS 603 (Cass.only) deleted
TELEVISION MARCH-ITN NEWS-MAINLY FOR WOMEN-POTTER'S
WHEEL-SATURDAY NIGHT OUT-PICTURE PARADE-FARMING-BIG
NIGHT OUT-ITV SOCCER-COMPACT-ANIMAL MAGIC-OWEN MD
MASTERMIND-NEWS AT TEN-THIS IS YOUR LIFE *(orig Rec)*

SOUTH PACIFIC (Shows Collect.)(R.Rodgers-O.Hammerstein)
Pickwick Shows Coll: PWKS 4162(CD) PWKMC 4162(Cass)

Gemma Craven-David Kernan-Linda Hibberd-Master Sing
ers-Nic Curtis & Co. *Songs:-* BALI HA'I-TWIN SOLILOQ
UYS-SOME ENCHANTED EVENING-BLOODY MARY-A COCK-EYED
OPTIMIST-THERE'S NOTHIN'LIKE A DAME-I'M GONNA WASH
THAT MAN RIGHT OUTA MY HAIR-YOUNGER THAN SPRINGTIME
HAPPY TALK-HONEY BUN-CAREFULLY TAUGHT-THIS NEARLY
WAS MINE-DITES MOI-I'M IN LOVE WITH A WONDERFUL GUY

SPECTACULAR WORLD OF CLASSIC FILM SCORES - *N.P.O
RCA Victor (BMG): GD 82792 (CD)   *p.1992*
Fanfares For Motion Pictures UNIVERSAL (McHugh)-MGM
(Franz Waxman)-SELZNICK INT (Alfred Newman)-WARNER
BROS (Max Steiner)-20TH CENTURY FOX (Alfred Newman)
SELECTIONS FROM STAR WARS-CAPTAIN BLOOD-NOW VOYAGER
GONE WITH THE WIND-ELIZABETH AND ESSEX-CAINE MUTINY
CITIZEN KANE-KNIGHT OF THE ROUND TABLE-OBJECTIVE BU
RMA-GUNS OF NAVARONE-JULIUS CAESAR-PEYTON PLACE-THE
THING FROM ANOTHER WORLD-KING OF THE KHYBER RIFLES-
SALOME *Nat.Philharmonic Orchest (Charles Gerhardt)*

SPELLBOUND - Classic Films Scores Of Miklos Rosza P.90
RCA Victor (BMG): GD(GK) 80911 (CD/Cass) *N.P.O.
THE RED HOUSE-THE THIEF OF BAGHDAD-THE LOST WEEKEND
THE FOUR FEATHERS-DOUBLE INDEMNITY-KNIGHTS OF THE
ROUND TABLE-THE JUNGLE BOOK-SPELLBOUND-IVANHOE

SPIELBERG / WILLIAMS COLLABORATION - Boston Pops Orch*
Sony Music: SK 45997 (CD)   *P.1991*
RAIDERS OF THE LOST ARK:Raider's March-ALWAYS:Theme
ET:Adventures On Earth-SUGARLAND EXPRESS:Theme-JAWS
Theme:Out To Sea:Shark Cage Fugue-EMPIRE OF THE SUN
Exsultate Justi-INDIANA JONES TEMPLE OF DOOM:Parade
Of The Slave Children-ET:Over The Moon-1941:March-
EMPIRE OF THE SUN:Cadillac Of The Skies-INDIANA JON
ES LAST CRUSADE:Scherzo For Motorcycle & Orchestra
CLOSE ENCOUNTERS OF THE THIRD KIND:Excerpts
BOSTON POPS ORCHESTRA conducted by JOHN WILLIAMS

STAGE HEROES - Colm Wilkinson   P.1989
RCA (BMG) BD 74105 (CD) BK 74105 (Cass)
MAN OF LA MANCHA-IMPOSSIBLE DREAM-PITY THE CHILD-AN
THEM-MARIA-SOMEWHERE-PHANTOM OF THE OPERA-MUSIC OF
THENIGHT-BRING HIM HOME-EMPTY CHAIRS-SOME ENCHANTED
EVENING-THIS NEARLY WAS MINE-HOW TO HANDLE A WOMAN-
IF EVER I WOULD LEAVE YOU-SUMMERTIME-IT AIN'T NECES

STAGES - Elaine Paige   P.1983
WEA (WEA): 240 228-2 (CD) -4 (Cass) : MEMORY-BE ON
YOUR OWN-ANOTHER SUITCASE-SEND IN THE CLOWNS-RUNNIN
BACK FOR MORE-GOOD MORNING STARSHINE-DON'T CRY FOR
ME ARGENTINA-WHAT I DID FOR LOVE-I DON'T KNOW HOW
TO LOVE HIM-ONE NIGHT ONLY-LOSING MY MIND-TOMORROW

STAGES OF LOVE - Dave Willetts   P.1992
Pickwick Int: PWKS 4130P (CD) PWKMC 41340P (Cass)
STAGES OF LOVE-ALMOST LIKE BEING IN LOVE-IMPOSSIBLE
DREAM-YOU'D BE SO NICE TO COME HOME TO-BABY MINE-I
LOVE YOU SAMANTHA-LOVE IS HERE TO STAY-COME RAIN OR
COME SHINE-MY FUNNY VALENTINE-SOMEWHERE OUT THERE-
IF I LOVED YOU-SOLILOQUY-OUR SONG-SHOW'S AT AN END

STAR WARS TRILOGY - The Utah Symphony Orchestra *
TER (Koch Int): CDTER 1067   reissued: 1985
Suites & Themes from STAR WARS / THE EMPIRE STRIKES
BACK / THE RETURN OF THE JEDI *Conducted by* Varujan
Kojian / all music composed by JOHN WILLIAMS
STRESS BUSTERS: Music for a Stress-Less World - Various
RCA Victor (BMG): 09026 60071-2 (CD) -4 (Cass) P.93
CANON IN D *(Pachelbel)* AIR ON A G.STRING *(J.S.Bach)*
ANDANTE: SYMPHONY 40 *(Mozart)* SERSE-LARGO *(Handel)*
MESSIAH-PASTORAL SYMPH *(Handel)* ADAGIO *(Albinoni)*
2ND mm SYMPHONY 6 Op.68 *(Beethoven)* ADAGIO CONCERTO
for GUITAR in G*(Vivaldi)* JESU JOY OF MAN'S DESIRING
(J.S.Bach) ANDANTE PIANO CONCERTO No.21 *(Mozart)*
SUNSET BOULEVARD - Classic Film Scores Of Franz Waxman
RCA Victor (BMG): GD 80708 (CD)   Re-iss: 91
PRINCE VALIANT:Prelude/King Aguar's Escape/The Fens
First Chase/The Tournament/Sir Brack's Death/Finale
A PLACE IN THE SUN:Suite. THE BRIDE OF FRANKENSTEIN
Creation Of The Female Monster. SUNSET BOULEVARD:
Main Title/Norma Desmond/The Studio Stroll/The Come
back (Norma as Salome). OLD AQUAINTANCE: Elegy For
Strings and Harp. REBECCA: Prelude/After The Ball/
Mrs.Danvers/Confession Scene/Manderley In Flames.
THE PHILADELPHIA STORY: MGM Fanfare/Main Title/The
True Love. TARAS BULBA: The Ride To Dubno.
NATIONAL PHILHARMONIC ORCHESTRA (CHARLES GERHARDT)
SYMPHONIC FELLINI / ROTA - Czech Symphony Orchestra *
Silva Screen (Con): FILMCD 129(CD) FILMC 129(Cass)
Music Of NINO ROTA For The FEDERICO FELLINI Films
LA DOLCE VITA-LA STRADA-IL BIDONE-THE WHITE SHEIKH
ROMA-SATYRICON-CASANOVA-ORCHESTRA REHEARSAL-NIGHTS
OF CABIRIA-THE CLOWNS-I VITELLONI-AMARCORD-BOCCACC
IO 70-JULIET OF THE SPIRITS * Derek Wadsworth cond
SYNTHESIZER ALBUM The - 18 Contemporary Masterpieces
Music Club International (TBD): MCCD 061 (CD) P.92
CHARIOTS OF FIRE-OXYGENE-LOVE THEME FROM MIDNIGHT
EXPRESS-MIAMI VICE THEME-AUTOBAHN-AXEL F-MAGIC FLY-
POPCORN-METROPOLIS-MAMMAGAMMA-AURORA-I HEAR YOU NOW
EQUINOXE-FORBIDDEN COLOURS-LUCIFER-DAS MADCHEN AUF
DER TREPPE-CHI MAI-SONG FOR GUY
SYNTHESIZER 2: 14 Contemporary Themes: Project D. P.90
Telstar (BMG): TCD(STAC)(STAR) 2428 (CD/Cass/LP)
Toccata (Bach)-Theme From Antarctica (Vangelis)-Syl
via (Van Leer)-Lily Was Here (D.A.Stewart)-Friends
Of Mr.Cairo (Vangelis/Anderson)-Italian Song (Ander
son/Vangelis)-Bolero (Ravel)-Axel F (H.Faltermeyer)
Calypso 3 (Jarre)-Tutti Al Mondo (Argent/Van Hooke)
Etude (Tarrega)-Tubular Bells (Oldfield)-The Race
(Blank/Meyer)The Chain (FM)-Winter Games (D.Foster)
Eve Of The War (Wayne)-Oxygene (Jarre)-Telstar (Joe
Meek)-Autobahn(Hutter/Schneider)-Pulstar (Vangelis)
TELEVISION MUSIC OF MIKE POST - Daniel Caine   P.1991
Primetime-S.Screen (Conif): TVPMC(CD) 403 (Cass/CD)
DOOGIE HOWSER-LA LAW-ATEAM-QUANTUM LEAP-HUNTER-HILL

STREET BLUES-RIPTIDE-HOOPERMAN-WISEGUY-THE ROCKFORD
FILES-TALES OF THE GOLD MONKEY-STUDIO 5B-HARDCASTLE
AND McCORMICK-SONNY SPOON-THE WHITE SHADOW

TELEVISION'S GREATEST HITS (1) - Orig Television Themes
Silva Screen (Con): FILMC(CD) 024 (Cass/CD) P.1987
CAPTAIN KANGAROO-LITTLE RASCALS-FLINSTONES-WOODY WO
ODPECKER SHOW-BUGS BUNNY-CASPAR THE FRIENDLY GHOST-
FELIX THE CAT-POPEYE-YOGI BEAR-MAGILLA GORILLA-TOP
CAT-JETSONS-FIREBALL XL5-HOWDY DOODY-BEVERLY HILLBI
LLIES-PETTICOAT JUNCTION-GREEN ACRES-MR.ED-MUNSTERS
ADDAMS FAMILY-MY THREE SONS-DONNA REEDSHOW-LEAVE IT
TO BEAVER-DENNIS THE MENACE-DOBIE GILLIS-PATTY DUKE
SHOW-DICK VAN DYKE SHOW-GILLIGAN'S ISLAND-McHALE'S
NAVY-I DREAM OF JEANNIE-I LOVE LUCY-ANDY GRIFFITH
SHOW-STAR TREK-LOST IN SPACE-TWILIGHT ZONE-SUPERMAN
ALFRED HITCHCOCK PRESENTS-BATMAN-FLIPPER-RIFLEMAN-
COMBAT-BONANZA-BRANDED-F.TROOP-RIN TIN TIN-WILDWILD
WEST-DANIEL BOONE-LONE RANGER-HAPPY TRAILS-MISSION
IMPOSSIBLE-MAN FROM UNCLE-GET SMART-SECRET AGENTMAN
DRAGNET-PERRY MASON-ADAM 12-FBI-HAWAII 50-77 SUNSET
STRIP-SURFSIDE 6-IRONSIDE-MANNIX-MOD SQUAD-TONIGHT

TELEVISION'S GREATEST HITS (2) - Orig Television Themes
Silva Screen (Con): FILMC(CD) 034 (Cass/CD) P.1988
3 STOOGES-MERRIE MELODIES-ROCKY & BULLWINKLE-HUCKLE
BERRY HOUND-MIGHTY MOUSE-COURAGEOUS CAT & MINUTE MO
USE-PINK PANTHER-ROAD RUNNER-GEORGE OF THE JUNGLE-
JONNY QUEST-SPIDERMAN-UNDERDOG-LOONEY TUNES-PEANUTS
THEME-MISTER ROGER'S NEIGHBOURHOOD-ODD COUPLE-COURT
SHIP OF EDDIE'S FATHER-MARY TYLER MOORE-GIDGET-THAT
GIRL-BEWITCHED-LOVE AMERICAN STYLE-HONEYMOONERS-THE
MONKEES-I MARRIED JOAN-BRADY BUNCH-PARTRIDGE FAMILY
MY MOTHER THE CAR-CAR 54 WHERE ARE YOU-IT'S ABOUT
TIME-MY FAVOURITE MARTIAN-JEOPARDY-HOGAN'S HEROES-
GOMER PYLE-RAT PATROL-TWELVE O'CLOCK HIGH-TIME TUNN
EL-VOYAGE TO THE BOTTOM OF THE SEA-SEA HUNT-DAKTARI
TARZAN-ADVENTURES OF ROBIN HOOD-RAWHIDE-BAT MASTERS
ON-MAVERICK-WAGON TRAIN-HAVE GUN WILL TRAVEL-REBEL-
THE VIRGINIAN-PETER GUNN-ROUTE 66-ISPY-THE AVENGERS
THE SAINT-HAWAIIAN EYE-GREEN HORNET-OUTER LIMITS-
DARK SHADOWS-BEN CASEY-MEDICAL CENTER-MYSTERY MOVIE
ABC'S WIDE WORLD OF SPORTS-JACKIE GLEASON-SMOTHERS
BROTHERS COMEDY HOUR-MONTY PYTHON'S FLYING CIRCUS

TELEVISION'S GREATEST HITS (3) - Orig Television Themes
Silva Screen (Con): FILMC(CD) 035 (Cass/CD) P.1988
SESAME STREET-MUPPET SHOW-ALVIN SHOW-SPEED RACER-MR
MAGOO-INSPECTOR GADGET-THE SMURFS-DASTARDLY& MUTLEY
SCOOBY DOO-FAT ALBERT & CROSBY KIDS-ARCHIES-JOSIE &
PUSSYCATS-DUDLEY DORIGHT-FRACTURED FAIRY TALES-BOB
NEWHART SHOW-CHEERS-GREATEST AMERICAN HERO-WELCOME
BACK KOTTER-ROOM 222-WKRP IN CINCINNATI-TAXI-BARNEY
MILLER-THREE'S COMPANY-HAPPY DAYS-LAVERNE & SHIRLEY
FACTS OF LIFE-GOOD TIMES-ONE DAY AT A TIME-GIMME A
BREAK-MAUDE-JEFFERSONS-ALL INTHE FAMILY-SANFORD AND
SON-DALLAS-DYNASTY-KNOTS LANDING-L.A.LAW-MARCUS WEL

BY MD-ST.ELSEWHERE-MASH-WALTONS-LITTLE HOUSE ON THE
PRAIRIE-HART TO HART-CHARLIE'S ANGELS-WONDER WOMAN-
LOVE BOAT-AMERICAN BANDSTAND-SOLID GOLD-ENTERTAINME
NT TONIGHT-MIAMI VICE-SWAT-BARETTA-STREETS OF SAN
FRANCISCO-BARBABY JONES-STARSKY & HUTCH-ROOKIES-KOJ
AK-A.TEAM-NAME O.T.GAME-QUINCY-HILL ST.BLUES-SIMON
& SIMON-MAGNUM-ROCKFORD FILES-SATURDAY NIGHT LIVE

THEMES & DREAMS - The SHADOWS   **P.1991**
Polydor-Rollover: 511 374-2 (CD) -4 (Cass) -1)(LP)
CROCKETT'S THEME:Miami Vice-TAKE MY BREATH AWAY:Top
Gun-UP WHERE WE BELONG:An Officer & A Gentleman-CAV
ATINA:The Deerhunter-WALKING IN THE AIR:The Snowman
IF YOU LEAVE ME NOW-ONE DAY I'LL FLY AWAY-EVERY BRE
ATH YOU TAKE-AFRICA-MEMORY:Cats-CANDLE IN THE WIND-
NIGHTS IN WHITE SATIN-YOU WIN AGAIN-SAILING-JUSTTHE
WAY YOU ARE-MOONLIGHT SHADOW

THEMES AND DREAMS - Johnny Pearson Orchestra   **P.1989**
President: PRCD 132 (CD) TCPRCV 132 (Cass)
THE GODFATHER-ALL CREATURES GREAT AND SMALL-CHI MAI
TRIANGLE Theme/Intro-SEDUCTION from AMERICAN GIGOLO
LOVE DREAMER-FILM 72 Theme-HOUSE OF CARADUS Theme-
LOVE DREAM-FIRST LOVE-CHARIOTS OF FIRE-YOU ARE THE
ONE-CAVATINA from THE DEER HUNTER-LOVE STORY Theme

THEMES FROM CHILDREN'S BBC - Various Org Artists P.1988
BBC-Pickwick (Pickwick): HSC 650 (Cassette)
POSTMAN PAT-FIREMAN SAM-DOCTOR WHO (80)-MUPPET BABI
ES-BLUE PETER (Barnacle Bill)-JIM'LL FIX IT-GRANGE
HILL-MOP'N SMIFF-TRUMPTON-HEADS & TAILS-FAMILY NESS
PADDINGTON BEAR-WILLY FOG-CAMBERWICK GREEN-MAGIC RO
UNDABOUT-HOKEY COKEY-BERTHA-HENRY'S CAT-WILLO THE
WISP-PLAYSCHOOL-DOGTANIAN AND THE THREE MUSKEHOUNDS

THEMES FROM CLASSIC SCIENCE FICTION FILMS - Var.Artists
Varese (Pinn): VSD 5407 (CD)   **P.1993**
THE MOLE PEOPLE-THE CREATURE FROM THE BLACK LAGOON-
THIS ISLAND EARTH-THE INCREDIBLE SHRINKING MAN-IT
CAME FROM OUTER SPACE-THE CREATURE WALKS AMONG US-
HOUSE OF FRANKENSTEIN-HORROR OF DRACULA-TARANTULA-
SON OF DRACULA-REVENGE OF THECREATURE-DEADLY MANTIS

THEMES OF STAGE AND SCREEN - (Orig PRT recordings)
Castle Comm.(BMG): MATCD 254 (CD) V.artists P.1993
EYE LEVEL (Van Der Valk)-ELIZABETH TUDOR (Forstye
Saga)-PINK PANTHER-AQUA MARINA-MASH-SAILING-ONEDIN
LINE-MAIGRET-BOUQUET OR BARBED WIRE-I WISH I KNEW
(Film 93)-Z.CARS-MARCH FROM A LITTLE SUITE (Doctor
Finlay's Casebook)-THE SAINT-THUNDERBIRDS-SOAP-THE
WORLD AT WAR-SPORTSNIGHT-EMMERDALE FARM-SUCU SUCU-
PERRY MASON-NO HIDING PLACE-SLEEPY SHORES-CHAI MAI-
THE ODD COUPLE-DEATH IN VENICE-CROSSROADS THEME

THIRD MAN The - Various Artists & Orchestras   **P.1988**
Decca (Cinema Gala) (Poly): 421 264-2 (CD)
THIRD MAN-CHARADE-MONDO CANE-GOOD BAD &THE UGLY-THE
SANDPIPER-NEVER ON SUNDAY-BIG COUNTRY-BORN FREE-BRE
AKFAST AT TIFFANYS-THE UMBRELLAS OF CHERBOURG-ALFIE
A SUMMER PLACE-SPELLBOUND-ZORBA THE GREEK

TOP HAT WHITE TIE AND TAILS - Fred Astaire Soundtracks
Saville (Conif): **CDSVL 184 (CD) CSVL 184 (Cas)** *P.87*
Night & Day-After You Who-Flying Down To Rio-Music
Makes Me-Cheek toCheek-No Strings-Top Hat White Tie
&Tails-Isn't This A Lovely Day-Piccolino-Let's Face
The Music-I'm Putting All My Eggs In One Basket-We
Saw The Sea-Let Yourself Go-I'd Rather Lead A Band
Building Up To An Awful Let Down-Way You Look Tonig
ht-Fine Romance-Pick Yourself Up-Never Gonna Dance

TOUCH OF MUSIC IN THE NIGHT, A - Michael Carwford   p.93
Telstar (BMG): **TCD(STAC)(STAR) 2676 (CD/Cass/LP)**
THE POWER OF LOVE-WITH YOUR HAND ON MY HEART (Duet
with Patti Labelle)-IF YOU COULD SEE ME NOW-STORMY
WEATHER-IT GOES LIKE IT GOES-SHE USED TO BE MINE-
THE MUSIC OF THE NIGHT (Barbra Streisand duet)-SERE
NADE IN BLUE-SPEAK LOW-SINCE YOU STAYED HERE-ONE OF
MY BEST FRIENDS-PAPA CAN YOU HEAR ME/A PIECE OF SKY

TRUE LOVE - Various Artists   p.1993
Telstar (BMG): **TCD(STAC)(STAR) 2692 (CD/Cass/LP)**
FALLING IN LOVE *from Blue Angel* **Marlene Dietrich** /
SECRET LOVE *Calamity Jane* **Doris Day** / MOON RIVER *Br
eakfast At Tiffany's* **Andy Williams**/ AS TIME GOES BY
Casablanca **Peggy Lee** /CRY ME A RIVER *The Girl Can't
Help It* **Julie London** /OVER THE RAINBOW *Wizard Of Oz*
Judy Garland / TRUE LOVE *High Society* **Bing Crosby** /
OH WHAT A BEAUTIFUL MORNING *Oklahoma* **Howard Keel** /
SOMEWHERE *West Side Story* **Matt Monro** /WHEN YOU WISH
UPON A STAR *Pinocchio* **Michael Crawford** / SHADOW OF
YOUR SMILE *The Sandpiper* **Tony Bennett** / WITH A SONG
IN MY HEART **Jane Froman** /I COULD HAVE DANCED ALL NI
GHT *My Fair Lady* **Julie Andrews** / THAT'S AMORE *The
Caddie* **Dean Martin** / THEY CAN'T TAKE THAT AWAY FROM
ME *Shall We Dance* **Fred Astaire** / AN AFFAIR TO REMEM
BER **Vic Damone** / LOVE IS A MANY SPLENDORED THING **Fo
or Aces** /WHEN I FALL IN LOVE *One Minute To Zero* **Nat
King Cole** / I'VE GROWN ACCUSTOMED TO HER FACE *My
Fair Lady* **Rex Harrison** /MONA LISA *Captain Carey USA*
Nat King Cole

TRUFFAUT AND DELERUE ON THE SCREEN - Georges Delerue
DRG (Pinn): **32902 (CD)**   *p.1993*
Francois Truffaut Films With Georges Delerue's Mus
Suites: CONFIDENTIALLY YOURS-A BEAUTIFUL GIRL LIKE
ME-DAY FOR NIGHT-THE LAST METRO-THE WOMAN NEXT DOOR

TV CLASSICS (Volumes 1-4) - Various Artists   p.1993
Castle Communications (BMG): **MBSCD 412 (4CDBox Set)**
(CD1): FIREBALL XL5 *(FLEE REKKERS)* CAPTAIN SCARLET-
JOE 90-PARKER WELL DONE *(BARRY GRAY ORCH)* STINGRAY
(GARRY MILLER vocal) MYSTERONS THEME *(BARRY GRAY O)*
THUNDERBIRDS MAIN THEME *(BARRY GRAY ORCH)* AVENGERS
(LAURIE JOHNSON) ROBIN HOOD *(GARY MILLER)* THE SAINT
(LES REED BRASS) RETURN OF THE SAINT *(SAINT ORCH)*
(CD2): MAIGRET 62 *(EAGLES)* A MAN IN A SUITCASE *(RON
GRAINER ORCH)* AQUA MARINA *(GARRY MILLER vocal)* HIJA
CKED *(BARRY GRAY ORCH)* THE CHAMPIONS *(TONY HATCH O)*

Z CARS *(JOHNNY KEATING & Z.MEN)* THE FUGITIVE *(JOHN
SCHROEDER ORCH)* HANCOCK'S THEME *(DEREK SCOTT MUSIC)*
POWER GAME THEME *(CYRIL STAPLETON ORCH)* THE FORSYTE
SAGA THEME-DEPARTMENT S. *(CYRIL STAPLETON ORCH)* DR.
WHO *(ERIC WINSTONE ORCH)***(CD3):** MR.ROSE INVESTIGATES
(ROY BUDD & TONY HATCH ORCH) WHO DO YOU THINK YOU
ARE KIDDING MR.HITLER *(BUD FLANAGAN)* OLD NED (STEPT
OE AND SON THEME)-HAPPY JOE *(RON GRAINER ORCHESTRA
HADLEIGH-MAN ALIVE *(TONY HATCH SOUND)* LUNAR WALK
(JOHNNY HAWKESWORTH ORCH) THANK YOUR LUCKY STARS
(PETER KNIGHT & KNIGHTRIDERS) HIGH WIRE (DANGER MAN
THEME)*(BOB LEAPER ORCH)* RED ALERT (GENERAL HOSPITAL
THEME) *(JOHNNY PEARSON ORCH)* GIRL IN THE WHITE COAT
(DEREK SCOTT ORCH) SIR FRANCIS DRAKE-OUR HOUSE *(PIC
CADILLY STRINGS)* **(CD4):** CROSSROADS-EMMERDALE FARM-
SPORTSNIGHT *(TONY HATCH OR)* ROLL ALONG WAGON TRAIN
(ROBERT HORTON) THE SHAKE-WEST END (WHICKER'S WORLD
THEME)-NO HIDING PLACE-SUCU SUCU (TOP SECRET THEME)
LATIN QUARTER-ECHO FOUR TWO *(LAURIE JOHNSON ORCHES)*
MR.& MRS.*(JACKIE TRENT & TONY HATCH)* original sound
recordings made by PRT (UK) / Castle Communications
TV CLASSICS - Arthur Fiedler-Eug.Ormandy-Canadian Brass
    RCA Victor (BMG): **09026 60935-2 (CD) -4 (Cass)**
    THE LONE RANGER:- 'WILLIAM TELL OVERTURE' (Rossini)
    MASTERPIECE THEATRE:- 'RONDEAU' (Mouret) - *M*A*S*H**
    'CLARINET QUINTET' (Mozart) - *MONTY PYTHON'S FLYING
    CIRCUS:-* 'LIBERTY BELL'(J.Sousa) - *ALFRED HITCHCOCK
    PRESENTS:-* 'FUNERAL MARCH OF A MARIONETTE' (Gounod)
    note: *this track also on collection* **'Chiller'**
UNCHAINED MELODY - THE FILM THEMES OF ALEX NORTH
    Bay Cities (S.Screen): **BCD 3010 (CD)**   *P.1991*
    UNCHAINED (55) and GHOST (90)-VIVA ZAPATA-THE BAD
    SEED-A STREETCAR NAMED DESIRE-THE ROSE TATTOO-DES
    IREE-THE BACHELOR PARTY-THE 13TH LETTER-I'LL CRY TO
    MORROW-LES MISERABLES-THE RACERS-STAGE STRUCK
UNIVERSAL SOLDIERS - Lundgren-Van Damme-Schwarzenegger
    Film Music - Various Artists   P.1993
    Silva Screen Imp: **SIL 5107-2 (CD) SIL 5107-4 (Cass)**
    UNIVERSAL SOLDIER (92-Christopher Franke)-RED SCORP
    ION (89-Jay Chattaway)-PREDATOR (87-Alan Silvestri)
    COMMANDO (85-James Horner)-THE PUNISHER (89-Dennis
    Dreith)-SHOWDOWN IN LITTLE TOKYO
VAMPIRE CIRCUS - Original Horror Movie -S/T- selections
    Silva Screen (Conifer): **FILMCD 127 (CD)**   *P.1993*
    RETURN OF DRACULA (1958 mus: Gerald Fried)- VAMPIRE
    CIRCUS (71-David Whittaker)- FRIGHT NIGHT (85-Brad
    Fiedel)- TRANSYLVANIA TWIST (91-Chuck Cirino)- VAMP
    (86-Jonathan Elias)- CHILDREN OF THE NIGHT (92-Dani
    el Licht)- THIRST (79-Brian May)-TRANSYLVANIA 65000
    (85-Lee Holdridge)- FOREVER KNIGHT (TV 92-Fred Moll
    in)- TO DIE FOR (89-Cliff Eidelman)-SON OF DARKNESS
    (TO DIE FOR 2) (91-Mark Mackenzie)- THE HUNGER ('Fl
    ower Duet' from LAKME sung by LESLEY GARRETT)- DRAC
    ULA (73-Robert Cobert)- SUNDOWN (89-Richard Stone)

VANGELIS - THEMES - Vangelis   P.1989
  Polydor:839518-2 (CD) VGTVC 1 (Cass) 839518-5 (DCC)
  End Titles From BLADERUNNER-Main Theme From MISSING
  L'ENFANT-HYMN-CHUNG KUO-THE TAO OF LOVE-Theme From
  ANTARCTICA-Love Theme From BLADERUNNER-Opening and
  Closing Titles From MUTINY ON THE BOUNTY-MEMORIES
  OF GREEN-LA PETITE FILLE DE LA MER-CHARIOTS OF FIRE
VERY BEST OF ENNIO MORRICONE - Ennio Morricone   P.1992
  Music Club Int (TBD): MCCD 056 (CD) MCTC 056 (Cass)
  HERE'S TO YOU-BALLAD OF SACCO &VANZETTI-FAREWELL TO
  CHEYENNE-MAN WITH T.HARMONICA-THE MAN-DEATH RATTLE-
  FINALE ONCE UPON A TIME IN THE WEST-GOOD THE BAD &
  THE UGLY-A FISTFUL OF DOLLARS-BATTLE OF ALGIERS-PAY
  ING OFF SCORES-VICE OF KILLING-FISTFUL OF DOLLARS 2
  ADVENTURER-FOR A FEW DOLLARS MORE-GUN FOR RINGO-MET
  ELLO-TITOLI-BYE BYE COLONEL
VERY BEST OF DISNEY The - Various Original Artists p.93
  Disney (Pickwick-Pinn): DISCD(MC) 471 (CD/Cass)
  I WANNA BE LIKE YOU *(Jungle Book)* GIVE A LITTLE WHI
  STLE *(Pinocchio)* LITTLE APRIL SHOWER *(Bambi)* EVERYB
  ODY WANT TO BE A CAT *(Aristocats)* HEIGH-HO *(Snow Wh
  ite)* CRUELLA DE VILLE *(101 Dalmations)* A WHOLE NEW
  WORLD *(Aladdin)* A SPOONFUL OF SUGAR *(Mary Poppins)*
  PART OF YOUR WORLD *(Little Mermaid)* HE'S A TRAMP
  (Lady And The Tramp) ONCE UPON A DREAM *(Sleeping Be
  auty)* ZIP-A-DEE-DOO-DAH *(Song Of The South)* BEAUTY
  AND THE BEAST *(Beauty And The Beast)* FOLLOWING THE
  LEADER *(Peter Pan)* THE BARE NECESSITIES *Jungle Book*
  I'VE GOT NO STRINGS *(Pinocchio)* WHISTLE WHILE YOU
  WORK*(Snow White)* SUPERCALIFRAGILISTICEXPEALIDOCIOUS
  (Mary Poppins) SECOND STAR TO THE RIGHT *(Peter Pan)*
  LOVE IS A SONG *(Bambi)* UNDER THE SEA *Little Mermaid*
  A FRIEND LIKE ME *(Aladdin)* WHEN I SEE AN ELEPHANT
  FLY *(Dumbo)* YOU CAN FLY YOU CAN FLY YOU CAN FLY *(Pe
  ter Pan)* BIBBIDY-BOBBIDY-BOO *(Cinderella)* BELLA NOT
  TE *(Lady And The Tramp)* BE OUR GUEST *Beauty And The
  Beast)* WHEN YOU WISH UPON A STAR *(Pinocchio)*
VICTORY AT SEA -Eric Kunzel & Cincinnati Pops Orchestra
  Telarc USA (Conifer): CD 80175 (CD only)   P.1989
  VICTORY AT SEA (5 selections from 1950's TV Series)
  THE WINDS OF WAR/WAR & REMEMBRANCE-CASABLANCA Suite
  COLONEL BOGEY March-WARSAW CONCERTO-VALIANT YEARS-
  Main Title from BATTLE OF BRITAIN-OVER THERE-March
  THE LONGEST DAY-GENERAL'S MARCH-ARMED FORCES Medley
VOICE SONGS AND FILMS OF MARILYN MONROE The   P.1992
  RCA (BMG): ND 893425 (CD deleted)
  20thCENT.FOX FANFARE-YOU'D BE SURPRISED-A FINE ROM
  ANCE-BYE BYE BABY-I'M GONNA FILE MY CLAIM-MY HEART
  BELONGS TO DADDY-HEAT WAVE-STREET SCENE-RIVER OF
  NO RETURN-SHE ACTS LIKE A WOMAN SHOULD KISS-AFTER
  YOU GET WHAT YOU WANT-DIAMONDS ARE A GIRLS BEST
  FRIEND-LAZY *with Bob Fogu and his Ensemble*
WARSAW CONCERTO & OTHER FILM THEMES Bournemouth S.O.*
  CFP (EMI) CFP 41 4493-1/-4 (LP/CS) CD-CFP 9020 (CD)

WARSAW CONCERTO from 'Dangerous Moonlight'(Film 41)
(Richard Addinsell)- THE DREAM OF OLWEN from 'While
I Live' (Film 47) (Charles Williams)-SPELLBOUND CON
CERTO from 'Spellbound' (Film 45)(Miklos Rozsa)-THE
CORNISH RHAPSODY from 'Love Story' (Film 44)(Hubert
Bath) -RHAPSODY IN BLUE (Film 45) (George Gershwin)
*(K.Alwyn) feat Daniel Adni (Piano) P.80 reiss 1988
WILD BUNCH The: Best Of The West - Various Themes with
Czech Symphony Orchestra conduct by William Motzing
Silva Screen (Conifer): FILMCD 136 (CD)   P.1993
DANCES WITH WOLVES-THE ALAMO-THE MAGNIFICENT SEVEN-
THE SONS OF KATIE ELDER-THE BIG VALLEY-RAWHIDE-THE
BIG COUNTRY-RETURN OF A MAN CALLED HORSE-RIO LOBO-
BALLAD OF CABLE HOGUE-BLUE AND THE GREY-SILVERADO-
GUNFIGHT AT THE O.K.CORRAL-ONCE UPON A TIME IN THE
WEST-A FISTFUL OF DYNAMITE-YOUNG GUNS 2-WILD BUNCH
WITH A SONG IN MY HEART - Deanna Durbin   P.1993
President (Rio-Target): PLCD 534
WALTZING IN THE CLOUDS-MY OWN-BRINDISI-IT'S RAINING
SUNBEAMS-BENEATH THE LIGHTS OF HOME-LOVE IS ALL-LES
FILLES DE CADIZ-PERHAPS-ONE FINE DAY-AMAPOLA-SPRING
IN MY HEART-ESTRELLITA (MY LITTLE STAR)-WHEN APRIL
SINGS-MUSETTA'S WALTZ SONG-BECAUSE-POOR BUTTERFLY-
BLUE DANUBE DREAM-THE LAST ROSE OF SUMMER-IT'S FOOL
ISH BUT IT'S FUN-HOME SWEET HOME
WITH LOVE - Michael Crawford with *L.S.O.   P.1989
Telstar (BMG): TCD(STAC)(STAR) 2340 (CD/Cass/LP)
I DREAMED A DREAM-WHAT ARE YOU DOING THE REST OF YO
UR LIFE-WITH YOU I'M BORN AGAIN-BEINGALIVE-STORY OF
MY LIFE-EVERY TIME WE SAY GOODBYE-WHEN I FALL IN LO
VE-MUSIC OFTHE NIGHT-ON MY OWN-WHY DID I CHOOSE YOU
COME RAIN OR COME SHINE /*London Symphony Orchestra
WORLD OF BBC TV THEMES - Various Orig Artists   P.1989
BBC (Pinn): BBCCD 705(CD) ZCF 705(Cass) DELETED 92
SHADOW OF THE NOOSE-BREAD-EAGLES EYE VIEW-THE GREAT
RIFT-SUPERSENSE-ROCKCLIFFE'S BABIES-BLIND JUSTICE-
FRANCHISE AFFAIR-TOP OF THE POPS-VICTORIAN KITCHEN
GARDEN-ATLANTIC REALM-PULASKI-CHRISTABEL-CAMPION-DR
WHO-CHELWORTH-SOUTH OF THE BORDER-THUNDER DRAGONS-
ROCKCLIFFE'S FOLLY-FIRST BORN-TheCELTS-ANIMAL SQUAD
SOME ENCHANTED EVENING - Phil Kelsall (Yahama FX 20)
Grasmere (Taylors): GRCD 54 (CD)   p.92
PHANTOM OF THE OPERA-SOME ENCHANTED EVENING-THOROUG
HLY MODERN MILLIE-BOY FRIEND-NO NO NANETTE-HEYTHERE
CAN'T HELP LOVIN'DAT MAN-AND THIS IS MY BELOVED-IVE
GOT THE SUN IN THE MORNING-I WHISTLE A HAPPY TUNE-
BEST OF TIMES-I DON'T KNOW HOW TO LOVE HIM-MARCH OF
THE SIAMESE CHILDREN-OUT OF MY DREAMS-THE GIRL THAT
I MARRY-WALTZ AT MAXIMS-IF I LOVED YOU-WOULDN'T IT
BE LUVERLY-SPRING SPRING SPRING-MAME-ANY DREAM WILL
DO-LEAP YEAR WALTZ-HIGHWAYMAN LOVE-FOLD YOUR WINGS-
ONE FLOWER GROWS ALONE..-ONE ALONE-INDIAN LOVE CALL
A WONDERFUL DAY LIKE TODAY-THERE IS NOTHING LIKE A
DAME-DO RE MI-I COULD HAVE DANCED ALL...-OKLKAHOMA

A CHRONOLOGICAL FILM INDEX OF THE JAMES BOND MOVIES

(1) **DOCTOR NO** (62) / *Sean Connery / Ursula Andress Bernard Lee-Lois Maxwell-Jack Lord-Joseph Wiseman* Title theme 'The James Bond Theme' (Monty Norman) -S/T- *Liberty EMI: CDP 796210-2 (CD) E4 96210(Cass)*

(2) **FROM RUSSIA WITH LOVE** (63) / *Sean Connery / Daniela Bianchi-Robert Shaw-Pedro Armendariz-Lottie Lenya* "From Russia With Love" (Lionel Bart) MATT MONRO -S/T- *Liberty EMI: CDP 795344-2 (CD) E4 95344(Cass)*

(3) **GOLDFINGER** (64) / *Sean Connery /Honor Blackman-Gert Frobe-Shirley Eaton-Harold Sakata-B.Lee-L.Maxwell* Title song "Goldfinger" (John Barry-Leslie Bricusse Anthony Newley) sung by SHIRLEY BASSEY -S/T- *Liberty EMI: CDP 795345-2 (CD) E4 95345(Cass)*

(4) **THUNDERBALL** (1965) / *Sean Connery / Claudine Auger Adolfo Celi-Luciana Paluzzi-Rick Van Nutter-Martine Beswick* "Thunderball" (J.Barry-Don Black) TOM JONES -S/T- *Liberty EMI: CDP 790628-2 (CD) E4 90628(Cass)*

(5) **YOU ONLY LIVE TWICE** (1967) / *Sean Connery / Tetsuro Tamba-Akiko Wakabayashi-Mie Hama-Karin Dor-Bern.Lee* Title song (J.Barry-Leslie Bricusse) NANCY SINATRA -S/T- *Liberty EMI: CDP 790626-2 (CD) E4 90626(Cass)*

(6) **ON HER MAJESTY'S SECRET SERVICE** (69) *George Lazenby Diana Rigg-Telly Savalas-Ilse Steppat-Gabr.Ferzetti* Title song "We Have All The Time In The World"(Hal David-John Barry) sung by LOUIS ARMSTRONG -S/T- *Liberty EMI: CDP 790618-2 (CD) E4 90618(Cass)*

(7) **DIAMONDS ARE FOREVER** (71) / *Sean Connery / Jill St. John-Charles Gray-Lana Wood-Jimmy Dean-Bruce Cabot* Title song (John Barry-Don Black) by SHIRLEY BASSEY -S/T- *Liberty EMI: CDP 796209-2 (CD) E4 96209(Cass)*

(8) **LIVE AND LET DIE** (73) / *Roger Moore / Jane Seymour-Yaphet Kotto-Clifton James-David Hedison-BernardLee* Title song (Paul & Linda McCartney) PAUL McCARTNEY -S/T- *Liberty EMI: CDP 790629-2 (CD) E4 90629(Cass)*

(9) **THE MAN WITH THE GOLDEN GUN** (74) *Roger Moore /Britt Ekland-Christopher Lee-Maud Adams-Herve Villechaize* Title song (Don Black-John Barry) sung by LULU -S/T- *Liberty EMI: CDP 790619-2 (CD) E4 90619(Cass)*

(10) **THE SPY WHO LOVED ME** (77) / *Roger Moore / Barbara Bach-Curt Jurgens-Richard Kiel-Caroline Munro* "Nobody Does It Better" (Carol Bayer Sager-Marvin Hamlisch) sung by CARLY SIMON -S/T- -S/T- *Liberty EMI: CDP 796211-2 (CD) E4 96211(Cass)*

(11) **MOONRAKER** (79) / *Roger Moore / Lois Chiles-Michael Lonsdale-Richard Kiel-Geoffrey Keen-Bernard Lee* "Moonraker" (John Barry-Hal David) SHIRLEY BASSEY -S/T- *Liberty EMI: CDP 790620-2 (CD) E4 90620(Cass)*

(12) **FOR YOUR EYES ONLY** (81) *Roger Moore-Carole Bouquet Topol-Lynn HollyJohnson-Julian Glover-Jill Bennett* Title song "For Your Eyes Only" (Michael Leeson-Bill Conti) by SHEENA EASTON -S/T- *to be confirmed*

(13) OCTOPUSSY (83) / *Roger Moore /Maud Adams-Louis Jor
dan-Kristina Wayborn-Kabir Bedi-Desmond Llewellwyn*
Title "All Time High" (John Barry-Tim Rice) - RITA
COOLIDGE -S/T- *A & M: AMLX(CAM) 64967 -   DELETED*

(14) NEVER SAY NEVER AGAIN (83) / *Sean Connery /Barbera
Carrera-Kim Basinger-Klaus M.Branduaer-Max V.Sydow*
Title song "Never Say Never Again" (Michel Legrand
Alan and Marilyn Bergman) and sung by LANI HALL
-S/T- *Import only (Silva Screen): SSD 1017 (CD)*

(15) A VIEW TO A KILL (85) / *Roger Moore /Tanya Roberts
Christopher Walken-Grace Jones-Patrick Macnee*
Title song "A View To A Kill" (That Fatal Kiss) by
DURAN DURAN -S/T- *EMI: CDP 746159-2 (CD)   DELETED*

(16) THE LIVING DAYLIGHTS (87) *Timothy Dalton / Maryam
D'Abo-Jeroen Krabbe-Joe Don Baker-John Rhys Davies*
Title song "The Living Daylights"(John Barry-A.HA)
-S/T- *W.Bros: WX 111C (Cass) 925616-2 (CD) DELETED*

(17) LICENCE TO KILL (89) *Timothy Dalton / Carey Lowell
Robert Davi-Talisa Soto-Anthony Zerbe*
Title Song "Licence To Kill" (Walden-Cohen-Afansie
ff) GLADYS KNIGHT / Mus score (Michael Kamen)-S/T-
MCA: MCGC 6051 (Cass)

(18) ?   (94) ?

B O N D   C O L L E C T I O N S

BEST OF JAMES BOND (30th Anniv.Coll) Orig Artists   1992
EMI: CDBOND 007 (CD) TCBOND 007 (Cass)
                    track details page 252

BEST OF SEAN CONNERY   1993
Silva Screen (Conifer): FILMCD 142 (CD)
                    track details page 252

BOND AND BEYOND - Erich Kunzel & Cincinnati Pops Orches
Telarc USA (Conifer): CD-80251 (CD only)   1991
                    track details page 253

BOND COLLECTION The - Shirley Bassey   1991
Icon (Pinn): ICOMCD 007 (CD) ICOMC 007 (Cass)
                    track details page 253

ESSENTIAL JAMES BOND The   1993
Silva Screen (Con): FILMCD 007(CD) FILMC 007 (Cass)
                    track details page 260

John Barry-James Bond: *write to* S C R E E N T H E M E S
22 Kensington Close, Toton, Beeston, Nottingham NG9 6GR
For List Of Available Film & TV Soundtracks

```
(1)   LOVE ME TENDER------------------------------(1956)
(2)   LOVING YOU----------------------------------(1957)
(3)   JAILHOUSE ROCK------------------------------(1957)
(4)   KING CREOLE---------------------------------(1958)
(5)   G.I.BLUES-----------------------------------(1960)
(6)   FLAMING STAR--------------------------------(1961)
(7)   WILD IN THE COUNTRY-------------------------(1961)
(8)   BLUE HAWAII---------------------------------(1961)
(9)   FOLLOW THAT DREAM---------------------------(1962)
(10)  KID GALAHAD---------------------------------(1962)
(11)  GIRLS GIRLS GIRLS---------------------------(1962)
(12)  IT HAPPENED AT THE WORLD'S FAIR-------------(1963)
(13)  FUN IN ACAPULCO-----------------------------(1963)
(14)  KISSIN' COUSINS-----------------------------(1964)
(15)  VIVA LAS VEGAS (Love In Las Vegas)----------(1964)
(16)  ROUSTABOUT----------------------------------(1964)
(17)  TICKLE ME-----------------------------------(1965)
(18)  GIRL HAPPY----------------------------------(1965)
(19)  HARUM SCARUM (UK title - Harum Holiday)-----(1965)
(20)  PARADISE HAWAIIAN STYLE---------------------(1965)
(21)  FRANKIE AND JOHNNY--------------------------(1966)
(22)  SPINOUT (UK title - California Holiday)-----(1966)
(23)  EASY COME EASY GO---------------------------(1966)
(24)  DOUBLE TROUBLE------------------------------(1967)
(25)  CLAMBAKE------------------------------------(1967)
(26)  STAY AWAY JOE-------------------------------(1968)
(27)  SPEEDWAY------------------------------------(1968)
(28)  LIVE A LITTLE LOVE A LITTLE-----------------(1968)
(29)  CHARRO!-------------------------------------(1969)
(30)  CHANGE OF HABIT-----------------------------(1969)
(31)  THE TROUBLE WITH GIRLS----------------------(1969)
(32)  ELVIS - NBC TV SPECIAL (Television Only)----(1968)
(33)  ELVIS - THAT'S THE WAY IT IS----------------(1970)
(34)  ELVIS - ON TOUR-----------------------------(1972)
(35)  THIS IS ELVIS (Compilation)-----------------(1981)
```

RCA (BMG) SOUNDTRACKS AVAILABLE

```
BLUE HAWAII                              ND 83683 (CD)
ELVIS-NBC TV SPECIAL 1968        ND(NK) 83894 (CD/Cass)
FUN IN ACAPULCO      + No.12   74321 113431-2(CD) -4(Cass
G.I.BLUES                        ND(NK) 83735 (CD/Cass)
GIRL HAPPY           + No.19   74321 13433-2(CD) -4(Cass)
GIRLS GIRLS GIRLS    + No.10   74321 13430-2(CD) -4(Cass)
HARUM SCARUM         + No.18   74321 13433-2(CD) -4(Cass)
IT HAPPENED AT T.WORLD'S FAIR     - see Fun In Acapulco
JAILHOUSE ROCK              6 songs on 'Essential Elvis'
KID GALAHAD          + No.11   74321 13430-2(CD) -4(Cass)
KING CREOLE                      ND(NK) 83733 (CD/Cass)
LOVE ME TENDER             4 songs on 'Essential Elvis'
LOVING YOU                       ND(NK) 81515 (CD/Cass)
ROUSTABOUT           + No.15   74321 13432-2(CD) -4(Cass)
VIVA LAS VEGAS       + No.16   74321 13432-2(CD) -4(Cass)
```

ELVIS PRESLEY FILM COLLECTIONS

ELVIS PRESLEY DEFINITIVE FILMS ALBUM   p.93
RCA Impt (Arabesque Dist): ND(NK) 90418 (CD/Cass)
RETURN TO SENDER-GIRLS GIRLS GIRLS-CAN'T HELP FALLI
NG IN LOVE-BLUE HAWAII-ROCK A HULA BABY-KISMET-I SL
IPPED I STUBLED I FELL-WILD IN THE COUNTRY-WOODEN
HEART-G.I.BLUES-TONITE IS SO RIGHT FOR LOVE-I GOT
LUCKY-STAY AWAY JOE-ALMOST IN LOVE-FRANKIE & JOHNNY
FUN IN ACAPULCO-MEXICO-BOSSA NOVA BABY-YOU CAN'T
SAY NO IN ACAPULCO-FOLLOW THAT DREAM-GIRL HAPPY-ROU
STABOUT-DOUBLE TROUBLE-KING CREOLE-LOVING YOU-FLAMI
NG STAR-KISSIN'COUSINS-RUBBERNECKIN'-VIVA LAS VEGAS
WHAT'D I SAY
ESSENTIAL ELVIS (Film Soundtracks) *RCA: PD 89980 (CD)*
LOVE ME TENDER (2)-LET ME-POOR BOY-WE'RE GONNA MOVE
LOVING YOU (3)-PARTY-HOT DOG-TEDDY BEAR-MEAN WOMAN
BLUES-GOT A LOT O'LIVIN; TO DO (2)-LONESOME COWBOY
JAILHOUSE ROCK (2)-TREAT ME NICE-YOUNG & BEAUTIFUL
DON'T LEAVE ME NOW-I WANT TO BE FREE-BABY I DON'T
CARE-MEAN WOMAN BLUES-LOVING YOU-TREAT ME NICE
32 FILM HITS - VOLUME 1 - *RCA: PD 89388 (2CD)*
FUN IN ACAPULCO-MEXICO-MARGUERITA-BOSSA NOVA BABY-
BLUE HAWAII-CAN'T HELP FALLING IN LOVE-ROCK-A-HULA
BABY-KUUIPO-KING CREOLE-HARD HEADED WOMAN-TROUBLE-
DIXIELAND ROCK-FRANKIE AND JOHNNY-PLEASE DON'T STOP
LOVING ME-EASY COME EASY GO-SING YOU CHILDREN-TONIT
E'S ALL RIGHT FOR LOVE-FRANKFURT SPECIAL-WOODEN HEA
RT-GI BLUES-BLUE SUEDE SHOES-DOIN' THE BEST I CAN-A
DOGS LIFE-CHARRO-ROUSTABOUT-LITTLE EGYPT-POISON IVY
GIRLS GIRLS GIRLS-WHERE DO YOU COME FROM-RETURN TO
SENDER-FOLLOW THAT DREAM-ANGEL
32 FILM HITS - VOLUME 2 - *RCA: PD 89550 (2CD)*
JAILHOUSE ROCK-YOUNG & BEAUTIFUL-BABY I DON'T CARE-
THEY REMIND ME TOO MUCH OF YOU-BEYOND THE BEND-ONE
BROKEN HEART FOR SALE-RELAX-I'M FALLING IN LOVE TON
IGHT-NO MORE-ISLAND OF LOVE-MOONLIGHT SWIM-HAWAIIAN
SUNSET-BEACH BOY BLUES-HAWAIIAN WEDDING SONG-HARD K
NOCKS-ONE TRACK HEART-WHEELS ON MY HEELS-SHOPPIN'AR
OUND-WHAT'S SHE REALLY LIKE-POCKETFUL OF RAINBOWS-
LOVE MACHINE-I'LL TAKE LOVE-RUBBERNECKIN'-CHANGE OF
HABIT-LET US PRAY-EL TORO-VINO DINERO Y AMOR-LOVER
DOLL-CRAWFISH-NEW ORLEANS
COLLECTOR'S GOLD - *RCA (BMG): PD(PK) 90574 (3CD/3Cass)*
Consisting of 3 'Themed' Collections:
(1) The Hollywood Album:
GI BLUES-POCKETFUL OF RAINBOWS-BIG BOOTS-BLACK STAR
SUMER KISSES WINTER TEARS-I SLIPPED I STUMBLED I FE
LL-LONELY MAN-WHAT A WONDERFUL LIFE-AWHISTLING TUNE
BEYOND THE BEND-ONE BROKEN HEART FORSALE-YOU'RE THE
BOSS-ROUSTABOUT-GIRL HAPPY-SO CLOSE YET SO FAR-STOP
LOOK AND LISTEN-AM I READY-HOW CAN YOU LOSE WHATYOU
NEVER HAD **(2) The Nashville Album** (15 Tracks) and
(3) Live In Las Vegas 1969 (20 Tracks)

S O U N D T R A C K S   A N D   V I D E O S

Some Disney Videos Are Available Only
For A Limited Period
Check With Your Local Video Stockist
For Latest Details

A WALT DISNEY CHRISTMAS -S/T- *not available*
                        VHS Video: Buena Vista: D.200922
ALADDIN (1993) Music and songs (Alan Menken-Howard Ashm
an-Tim Rice) -S/T- *Disney-Pickwick: DISCD 470 (CD)*
DISMC 470 (Cass) & PDC 310 (Cass) / Video not avail
ALICE IN WONDERLAND (1951) Music (Oliver Wallace)
-S/T- *deleted   / VHS Video: Buena Vista: D.200362*
ARISTOCATS The (1970) Songs (Richard & Robert Sherman)
-S/T- *deleted   / VHS Video: not available*
BAMBI (1943) Songs (F.Churchill-E.Plumb-Larry Morey)
-S/T- *deleted   / VHS Video: not available*
Children's Collection Spoken Word & Songs available
on Pickwick (Pinn): PDC 304 (Cass)
BASIL THE GREAT MOUSE DETECTIVE (1991) Music (Henry
Mancini) *-S/T- (-) VHS Video: Buena Vista: D.213602*
BEAUTY AND THE BEAST (92) Music sco (Alan Menken) Songs
(Alan Menken-Howard Ashman) -S/T- *Disney (Pickwick)*
DSTCD 458(CD) DSTMC 458(Cass) ALSO ON Pickwick Disn
ey Coll: PDC 309(CD) / VHS Video: B.Vista: D.213252
BEDKNOBS AND BROOMSTICKS (1971) Songs (R. & R.Sherman)
-S/T- *deleted   / VHS Video: Buena Vista: D.200162*
BLACK HOLE The (1979) Music Score (John Barry)
-S/T- *deleted   / VHS Video: Buena Vista: D.200112*
BLACKBEARD'S GHOST (1967) Music score (Robert Brunner)
-S/T- *deleted   / VHS Video: Buena Vista: D.200622*
CINDERELLA (50) Music and songs (Oliver Wallace-Paul J.
Smith-Mac David-Al Hoffmann-Jerry Livingston)
-S/T- *deleted / VHS Video: Buena Vista: D.204102*
Children's Collection Spoken Word & Songs available
on Pickwick (Pinn): PDC 300 (Cass)
DISNEY COLLECTION The (Volumes 1-3) Var.Orig Artists
Track Listing for these albums on page 257-258
DUCKTAILS THE MOVIE (91) Music score (David Newman)
-S/T- *N/A   /   VHS Video: Buena Vista: D.210822*
DUMBO (1941) Music (F.Churchill-O.Wallace-N.Washington)
-S/T- *deleted   / VHS Video: Buena Vista: D.202472*
FANTASIA (Film 1940) (Various Classical Music)
-S/T- *Pickwick: DSTCD 452D (2CD) DSTMC 452MC (2Cas)*
VHS Video: Buena Vista: D.211322 (deleted)
FOX AND THE HOUND The (1981) Songs (R.& R.Sherman)
-S/T- *deleted   / VHS Video: not available*
HONEY I SHRUNK THE KIDS / VHS Video - B.Vista: D.209092
-S/T *N/A*

JUNGLE BOOK (67) Songs (Richard & Robert Sherman) sung
by LOUIS PRIMA-PHIL HARRIS-STERLING HOLLOWAY etc.
-S/T- *Disney (Pickwick): DSMCD(DSMMC) 457 (CD/Cass)*
/ VHS Video - B.Vista: D.211222
Children's Collection Spoken Word & Songs available
on Pickwick (Pinn): PDC 305 (Cass)

LADY AND THE TRAMP The (1956) Songs (Peggy Lee-J.Burke)
Music (Oliver Wallace) sung by Peggy Lee
-S/T- *deleted   VHS Video:Buena Vista D.205822 (ltd)*
Spoken Word & Songs Coll on Pickwick:PDC 301 (Cass)

LEGEND OF SLEEPY HOLLOW The */ VHS Vid: Disney: D.210342*

LITTLE MERMAID The (1990) Songs (Alan Menken-Howard Ash
man) -S/T- *Pickwick: DSTCD 451 (CD) DSTMC 451 (Cas)*
ALSO ON Pickwick Disney Collection: PDC 307 (CD)
VHS Video: Buena Vista: D.209132

MARY POPPINS (64) Songs (Richard & Robert Sherman) sung
by JULIE ANDREWS-DICK VAN DYKE-DAVID TOMLINSON etc
-S/T- *Disney (Pickwick): DSMCD(DSMMC) 459 (CD/Cass)*
VHS Video: Buena Vista: D.200232

MICKEY AND THE BEANSTALK   */ VHS Video: Disney: 206912*

MICKEY'S CHRISTMAS CAROL (1983) -S/T- *Pickwick Disney*
PDC 312 (Cass)   / VHS Video: Buena Vista: D.201882

OLIVER AND COMPANY (1989) Music score (J.A.C.Redford)
-S/T- *Disneyland-Pickwick: PCD(PWK) 450 (CD/Cass)*
VHS Video: not available

101 DALMATIONS (1961) Songs (Mel Levin) m: Bruns/Dunham
-S/T- *deleted   / VHS Video: not available*

PETER AND THE WOLF   */ VHS Video - Disney: D.211872*

PETER PAN (1953) Songs (Oliver Wallace-Paul J.Smith)
-S/T- *Disneyland-Pickwick: DSMCD(DSMMC) 466 (CD/Cass)*
VHS Video: Buena Vista: D.202452
Children's Collection Spoken Word & Songs available
on Pickwick (Pinn): PDC 306 (Cass)

PETE'S DRAGON (77) Music director (Irwin Kostal)
-S/T- *deleted   / VHS Video: Buena Vista: D.200102*

PINOCCHIO (1939) Music (L.Harline-P.Smith-N.Washington)
-S/T- *deleted   / VHS Vid: Buena Vista: D.202392 ltd*
Spoken Word & Songs Coll on Pickwick: PDC 302 (Cas)

PRINCE AND THE PAUPER   */ VHS Video: Disney: D.211852*

RELUCTANT DRAGON The   */ VHS Video: Disney: D.205332*

RESCUERS The (1976) 'Story Of The Rescuers' -S/T- *delet*
VHS Video: Buena Vista: D.240642 (ltd)

RESCUERS DOWN UNDER The (90) Music score (Bruce Brought
on) -S/T- *Imp (Silva Screen): 60613-2 (CD) -4(Cass)*
ALSO ON Pickwick Disney Collection: PDC 308 (CD)
VHS Video: Buena Vista: D.211422

ROBIN HOOD (1973) Songs (George Bruns-Floyd Huddleston)
with Roger Miller-Phil Harris-TerryThomas-P.Ustinov
-S/T- *deleted / VHS Vid: Buena Vista: D.202282*

SHIPWRECKED   */ VHS Video - Disney: D.211682*

SINGALONG SONGS (Bare Necessities) *Various Artists*
/ VHS Video: Buena Vista: D.205812

SINGALONG SONGS (Be Our Guest)   *Var.Disney -S/T- Songs*
/ VHS Video: Buena Vista: D.213112

SINGALONG SONGS (Disneyland Fun) *Var.Disney -S/T- Songs
      / VHS Video: Buena Vista: D.209352 (deleted)*
SINGALONG SONGS (Heigh Ho)   *Various Disney -S/T- Songs
      / VHS Video: Buena Vista: D.205312*
SINGALONG SONGS (I Love To Laugh) *Var.Disney-S/T- Songs
      / VHS Video: Buena Vista: D.210292 (deleted)*
SINGALONG SONGS (Under The Sea)   *Var.Disney -S/T- Songs
      / VHS Video: Buena Vista: D.209082*
SINGALONG SONGS (You Can Fly) *Various Disney-S/T- Songs
      / VHS Video: Buena Vista: D.206622*
SLEEPING BEAUTY (1959) Music (George Bruns) -S/T- *delet
      / VHS Video: Buena Vista: D.204782*
SNOW WHITE & THE SEVEN DWARFS (37) Songs (Frank Churchi
   ll-Leigh Harline-Paul Smith)feat: ADRIANA CASELOTTI
   -S/T- *Disney (Pickwick): DSTCD(DSTMC) 456 (CD/Cass)
      / VHS Video: not available
Children's Collection Spoken Word & Songs available
      on Pickwick (Pinn): PDC 303 (Cass)*
SONG OF THE SOUTH (1946) Music (Daniel Amfitheatrof-Cha
   rles Wolcott-Paul J.Smith-Allie Wrubel-Ray Gilbert)
   -S/T- *not available / VHS Vid: Buena Vista:D.201022*
SUMMER MAGIC (1963) Songs (Richard and Robert Sherman)
   featuring BURL IVES-HAYLEY MILLS etc. -S/T- *deleted
      / VHS Vid:Buena Vista: D.*
SWORD IN THE STONE (1963) Songs: Richard/Robert Sherman
   -S/T- *not available / VHS Vid:Buena Vista: D.202292*
THREE CABALLEROS The (1945) Music (Charles Wolcott-Paul
   J.Smith-Edward Plumb) -S/T- *not available / VHS
      Video - Disney: D.200912*
VERY BEST OF WALT DISNEY (CD/cass) see COLLECTIONS sect
WHITE FANG (91) Music score (Basil Poledouris) -S/T-
   -S/T- *not available / VHS Vid:Buena Vista: D.211512*
WILLIE THE OPERATIC WHALE   */ VHS Vid: Disney: D.211862*
WIND IN THE WILLOWS The   */ VHS Video - Disney: D.204272*
WINNIE THE POOH AND A DAY FOR EEYORE (-) Music & Songs
   (Richard & Robert Sherman) feat: Sterling Holloway
   -S/T- *not avail. / VHS Video: Buena Vista: D.205322*
WINNIE THE POOH AND CHRISTMAS TOO / -S/T- *not available
      / VHS Video: Buena Vista: D.241232*
WINNIE THE POOH AND THE BLUSTERY DAY (1968) Songs (Rich
   ard and Robert Sherman) with Sterling Holloway
   -S/T- *deleted   / VHS Video: Buena Vista: D.200632*
WINNIE THE POOH AND THE HONEY TREE (1966)   Songs (Rich
   hard and Robert Sherman) with Sterling Holloway
   -S/T- *deleted   / VHS Video: Buena Vista: D.200492*
WINNIE THE POOH AND TIGGER TOO (64) Songs (Richard and
   Robert Sherman) with Sterling Holloway-Paul Winchel
   -S/T- *not avail. / VHS Video: Buena Vista: D.200642*
WINNIE THE POOH: BUBBLES AND TROUBLES */D.210442 deleted*
WINNIE THE POOH: GOODBYE MR.POOH (NEW ADVENTURES OF)
      / VHS Video: Buena Vista: D.240532
WINNIE THE POOH:POOH BEARS BIG SURPRISE *D210332 deleted*
WINNIE THE POOH: THE GREAT RIVER RESCUE (New Adventures
      Of) / VHS Video: Buena Vista: D.241032*

LONDON THEATRE MUSICALS 1990 to 1994

(*) in bold type: CURRENTLY RUNNING IN THE WEST END

ANNIE GET YOUR GUN - *Prince Of Wales 25/11/92-10/1/93*
    KIM CRISWELL-JOHN DIEDRICH-NORMAN ROSSINGTON etc
ANYTHING GOES - *Prince Edward* (4 Jul 89 - Oct 90)
    ELAINE PAIGE-BERNARD CRIBBINS-HOWARD McGILLIN
ASSASSINS - *Donmar Warehouse from Oct 92 - Feb 1993*
    HENRY GOODMAN-CIARAN HINDS-ANTONY BARCLAY & Comp
ASPECTS OF LOVE *Prince of Wales 17/4/89-20/6/92 also*
    20/12/93 - 15/1/94 MICHAEL BALL-SARAH BRIGHTMAN-
    MICHAEL PRAED-BARRIE INGHAM and Company
BAKERS WIFE The - *Phoenix* (27 Nov 89 - Jan 90)
    SHARON LEE HILL as The Bakers Wife
BERNADETTE - *Dominion* (21 Jun 90 - 14 Jul 90)
    NATALIE WRIGHT & COMPANY
BLITZ - *Playhouse* (10 Sep 90 - 22 Sep 90)
    NYT - JESSICA STEVENSON-ELIZABETH MILLS-LIZ KING
*BLOOD BROTHERS - *Phoenix (Orig Albery) from 28/7/88*
    STEPHANIE LAWRENCE-CARL WAYNE-RUSSELL BOULTER & Com
BLUE ANGEL The *Globe 20/5/92-27/6/92* Royal Shakespeare
    Prod.of PAM GEMS musical play with KELLY HUNTER
*BUDDY - *Victoria Palace Theatre from 19/10/89*
    CHIP ESTEN-GARETH MARKS-ENZO SQUILLINO & Company
CARMEN - *Royal Opera House Theatre (May 91)*
    MARIA EWING-LUIS LIMA-GINAO QUILICO-JUAN ORTEGA
CARMEN JONES - *Old Vic Theatre from 27/3/91-16/1/93*
    Music (Bizet) Production Director Simon Callow
*CAROUSEL -*Shaftesbury Theatre from 10 Sep 93 to Feb 94*
    MICHAEL HAYDN or HAL FOWLER-JOANNA RIDING-JANIE DEE
*CATS - *New London Theatre from 11/5/81*
    NEW LONDON THEATRE CAST
CHILDREN OF EDEN - *Prince Edward* (16 Jan 91 - 6 Apr 91)
    Stephen Schwartz Musical
CITY OF ANGELS - *Prince Of Wales 30 Mar 93- 13 Nov 93*
    HENRY GOODMAN-HAYDN GWYNNE & Company
COTTON CLUB The - *Aldwych from 24/1/92 - 27/6/92*
    DEBBIE BISHOP and Company
*CRAZY FOR YOU -*Prince Edward Theatre from 3 March 1993*
    RUTHIE HENSHALL-KIRBY WARD & Co. Dir: MIKE OCKRENT
*FIVE GUYS NAMED MOE *Lyric Shaftesbury Ave.fr: 14/12/90*
    CLARKE PETERS-CHARLES AUGIN and Company
*EUROVISION *Vaudeville London from 10 Nov 93*
    ANITA DOBSON and Company / Songs by JASON CARR
*FOREVER PLAID *Apollo Shaftesbury Ave from 16 Sep 1993*
    AMERICAN HIT MUSICAL WITH SONGS FROM 50's & 60's
    STAN CHANDLER-DAVID ENGEL-LARRY RABEN-GUY STROMAN
42ND STREET - *Dominion* (Mar 91 - 20 Apr 91)
    Dominion Theatre Production Company
FROM A JACK TO A KING *Ambassadors from 20/7/92-16/1/93*
    BOB CARLTON'S Rock'n'Roll version of Macbeth
GOOD GOLLY MISS MOLLY - *Arts Theatre from 4/9/91- 3/92*
    BOB EATON'S Rock'n'Roll Musical

GOOD ROCKIN' TONITE *Playhouse from 30/1/92 (TRANSFERED*
   TO THE PRINCE OF WALES THEATRE from 21 July 92)
   Prince Of Wales 21/7/92-14/11/92 JACK GOOD MUSICAL
   PHILIP BIRD-TIM WHITNALL-GAVIN STANLEY and Company
GRAND HOTEL - *Dominion from 6/7/92 - 28/11/92*
   The Smash Hit American Musical / Dir: Tommy Tune
*GREASE *Dominion Theatre from 15/7/93 Prd PAUL NICHOLAS*
   CRAIG McLACHLAN-DEBBIE GIBSON-VOID EVANS and Comp
HAIR - *Old Vic Theatre from 14 Sept 93 - 20 Nov 1993*
   PAUL HIPP-JOHN BARROWMAN-PEPSI DEMACQUE-ANDREE BERN
   ARD-FELICE ARENA-PAUL J.MEDFORD and Company
*HOT STUFF *Cambridge Theatre from 18 Aug 1993*
   THE 70'S MUSICAL
HUNTING OF THE SNARK *Prince Edward (24/10/91-14/12/91)*
   KENNY EVERETT-VERONICA HART-JOHN PARTRIDGE & Co.
INTO THE WOODS - *Phoenix (25 Sep 90 - Feb 91)*
   JULIA McKENZIE-IMELDA STAUNTON-PATSY ROWLANDS
INVISIBLE MAN The - *Comedy Theatre 7/6/93 to 11/9/93*
   MICHAEL HARBOUR & Company / Directed by Ken Hill
*IRON MAN The - *Young Vic from 18 NOV 93 - 12 FEB 1994*
   PETE TOWNSHEND'S ROCK OPERA
JOSEPH & AMAZING T.DREAMCOAT *London Palladium 12/6/91-*
   15/1/94 JASON DONOVAN alternating PHILLIP SCHOFIELD
KING - *Piccadilly (11 Apr 90 - 2 Jun 90)*
   SIMON ESTES-CYNTHIA HAYMON AND COMPANY
KING & I The - *Sadlers Wells (4 Jun 91 - 13 Jul 91)*
   SUSAN HAMPSHIRE-DAVID YIP & COMPANY
LEONARDO *Strand Theatre from 21 May 1993 - 10 July 1993*
   A NEW MUSICAL directed by Rob Bettinson
*LES MISERABLES - *Palace Theatre from 4/12/85*
   DANIEL J.TRAVANTI & Palace Theatre Cast
LITTLE NIGHT MUSIC A *Piccadilly (10 Oct 89 - 90)*
   SUSAN HAMPSHIRE-DOROTHY TUTIN-PETER McENERY
*LOOKING THROUGH A GLASS ONION *Criterion from 18 Oct 93*
   JOHN LENNON IN WORD AND MUSIC / John Waters with
   Stewart D'Arrietta and Band
LUST c.1661- *Theatre Royal,Haymarket 19/7/93 - 06/11/93*
   DENIS LAWSON-SOPHIE ALDRED-MARK HADDIGAN & Company
MATADOR - *Queens (2 Apr 91 - 27 Jul 91)*
   JOHN BARROWMAN-STEPHANIE POWERS-NICKY HENSON & CO
ME AND MY GIRL - *Adelphi Theatre from 12/2/85-16/1/93*
   DAVID STEAMES-LOUISE ENGLISH-ALFRED MARKS & Comp
*MISS SAIGON - *Drury Lane Theatre from 20/9/89*
   LEA SALONGA-JONATHAN PRYCE-SIMON BOWMAN & Company
MOBY DICK - *Piccadilly from 11/3/92 - 4/7/92*
   TONY MONOPOLY-HOPE AUGUSTUS-THERESA KARTELL & Com
NOEL & GERTIE - *Duke Of York (Nov 91 -)*
   EDWARD PETHERBRIDGE-SUSAN HAMPSHIRE & COMPANY
*PHANTOM OF THE OPERA - *Her Majesty's from 9/10/86*
   PETER POLYCARPOU as the current Phantom
*PIAF - *Piccadilly from 8 Dec 1993*
   ELAINE PAIGE as Edith Piaf with full company
PICKWICK - *Sadlers Wells Theatre from 13 Oct- 20 Nov 93*
   HARRY SECOMBE-ALXEANDRA BASTEDO-ROY CASTLE & Comp

RADIO TIMES *Queen's Theatre from 15 Oct 92-9/1/93*
    TONY SLATTERY in NOEL GAY'S Musical
RE:JOYCE! - *Vaudeville* (1989 ended 25 Nov 89)
    MAUREEN LIPMAN as Joyce Grenfell
RETURN TO THE FORBIDDEN PLANET *Cambridge 18/9/89-9/1/93*
    BOB CARLTON'S 1950's Sci-Fi Musical (Var Arts)
ROBIN PRINCE OF SHERWOOD - *Piccadilly 3/2/93-2/5/93*
    MIKE HOLLOWAY-LIZ CURNICK & COMPANY
ROCKY HORROR PICTURE SHOW *Piccad.*(16 Jul 90- 22 Sep 91)
    TIM McINNERY-GINA BELLMAN-ADRIAN EDMONDSON & COMP
SHOWBOAT *London Palladium* (1 Aug 90 - 22 Sep 90)
    Opera North-Royal Shakespeare Company Cast
SIKULU *Queens from 7/4/92 - 4/7/92*
    JOSEPH MOTSAMAI-ANDY CHABELI-GEORGE MALULEKE & Co
SLICE OF SATURDAY NIGHT,A *Arts Theatre (27/9/89-May 91)*
    BINKY BAKER-DAVID EASTER-CLAIRE PARKER & COMPANY
SLICE OF SATURDAY NIGHT,A *Strand The. 6/9/93- 20/11/93*
    DENNIS WATERMAN-SONIA-DANNY McCALL and Company
SOME LIKE IT HOT *Prince Edward from 19/3/92 - 20/6/92*
    TOMMY STEELE-MANDY PERRYMENT-BILLY BOYLE and Co
SOMEONE LIKE YOU - *Strand* (15 Mar 90 - 26 Apr 90)
    PETULA CLARK-DAVE WILLETTS-JOANNE CAMPBELL & COMP
SONG AND DANCE - *Shaftesbury* (25 Apr 90 - 1 Sep 90)
    MARTI WEBB-WAYNE SLEEP AND COMPANY
SOPHISTICATED LADIES - *Globe from 6/1/92 - 4/92*
    JACQUELINE DANKWORTH & Co. (mus: Duke Ellington)
SOUND OF MUSIC The - *Sadler's Wells 22/6/92 - 5/9/92*
    LIZ ROBERTSON-CHRISTOPHER CAZENOVE-ROBIN NEDWELL
SPREAD A LITTLE HAPPINESS *Whitehall 23/6/92 - 18/7/92*
    Vivian Ellis music: THELMA RUBY-SIMON SHEPHERD
*STARLIGHT EXPRESS - *Apollo Victoria from 27/3/84 / New*
    Re-Vamped 1993 Show - LON SATTON-RAY SHELL & Co
STOP IN THE NAME OF LOVE *Comedy* (5 Jul 90 - 11 Aug 90)
    THE FABULOUS SINGLETTES 60's Revue
SUNDAY IN THE PARK WITH GEORGE *National Lytt.*(12/3/90)
    PHILIP QUAST-MARIA FRIEDHAM & COMPANY
*SUNSET BOULEVARD - *Adelphi Theatre from 12 July 1993*
    PATTI LuPONE in ANDREW LLOYD WEBBER'S New Musical
SWELL PARTY A-*Vaudeville 3/10/91 - 3/92* (m:Cole Porter)
    NICKOLAS GRACE-ANGELA RICHARDS-DAVID KERNAN & Co.
SWEENEY TODD - *National Theatre (Cottesloe) Summer 1993*
    ALUN ARMSTRONG-JULIA McKENZIE-DENNIS QUILLEY & Co
TANGO ARGENTINA - *Aldwych* (June 91 - 14 Jul 91)
    Soulful Show about Argentina's Famous Dance
TRIBUTE TO THE BLUES BROTHERS *Whitehall 6/8/91 - 6/6/92*
    CON O'NEILL-WARWICK EVANS and Company
70 GIRLS 70 - *Vaudeville Theatre from 17/6/91- 12/91)*
    DORA BRYAN and Company
WHICH WITCH -*Piccadilly from 22/10/92* THE OPERA Musical
    Closed 1/93

CHECK WITH THE THEATRE BOX OFFICE FOR LATEST DETAILS

B.A.F.T.A. 1992 AWARDS

The 24th BAFTA Awards Ceremony Held At London's Hilton Hotel Was Hosted By Griff Rhys Jones (London) Mel Smith (Los Angeles) and t/x live by BBC1 on 21 March 1993

FILM SECTION:
Best Film: HOWARDS END (James Ivory-Ismail Merchant)
Best Director: ROBERT ALTMAN (The Player)
Best Actor: ROBERT DOWNEY JUNIOR (Chaplin)
Best Actress: EMMA THOMPSON (Howards End)
Best Supp.Actor: GENE HACKMAN (The Unforgiven)
Best Supp.Actress: MIRANDA RICHARDSON (Damage)
Best O.F.Score: DAVID HIRSCHFIELDER (Strictly Ballroom)
Best Orig Screenplay: WOODY ALLEN (Husbands and Wives)
Best Adap.Screenplay: MICHAEL TOLKIN (The Player)
Best Foreign Language Film: RAISE THE RED LANTERN China
Best Animated Short: DAUMIER'S LAW (G.Gibbons-G.Dunbar)
Best Short Film: OMNIBUS (Anne Bennet-Sam Karmann)
TELEVISION SECTION:
Best Actor: JOHN THAW (Inspector Morse) (Central)
Best Actress: HELEN MIRREN (Prime Suspect 2)(Granada)
Best Comedy Series: ABSOLUTELY FABULOUS (BBC2)
Best L.Ent.Prog: NOEL'S HOUSE PARTY (BBC1)
Best L.Ent.Perf: JOANNA LUMLEY (Absolutely Fab.)(BBC2)
Best Single Drama: AN UNGENTLEMANLY ACT (BBC1)
Best Drama Serial: ANGLO-SAXON ATTITUDES (Thames)
Best Drama Series: INSPECTOR MORSE (Central)
Best Factual Series: ART ATTACK (Meridian)
Best News Coverage: SERBIAN PRISON CAMPS (ITN News)
Best TV Music: JEFF BECK-JED STOLLER (Frankie's House)
Best Animated Short: *not awarded this year*
Best Children's Drama: THE BORROWERS (BBC1)
Best Children's Educt: *not awarded this year*
Best Foreign TV Progr: TOSCA (Italy) (BBC2/C4)
OTHER BAFTA AWARDS:
Alexander Korda (Best Brit.F): NEIL JORDAN(Crying Game)
Flaherty Doc: MAN WHO LOVED GARY LINEKER(Video Diaries)
Alan Clarke: KENITH TRODD (Producer)
Huw Wheldon Arts: OMNIBUS (Angela Carters Curious Room)
Desmond Davis: *not awarded this year*
Michael Balcon: KENNETH BRANAGH (Director)
Richard Dimbleby: JOHN COLE (Political Editor) (BBC)
Writers Award: LAWRENCE MARKS-MAURICE GRAN (Various)
Academy Award Originality: *not awarded this year*
Academy Fellowship Award: SYDNEY W.SAMUELSON
BAFTA Special Award 1993:   MAGGIE SMITH

BRITISH COMEDY AWARDS 1992

Held At The London Television Centre Hosted By Jonathan Ross.Transmitted By London Weekend TV 5th December 1992

```
Top Comedy Film:                          HEAR MY SONG
Top Comedy Writer:   DAVID RENWICK (One Foot..) (BBC1)
Top USA Film Comedy Actor:                         n/a
Top TV Comedy:                                     n/a
Top Comedy TV Actor:  DAVID JASON (Darling Buds..)(YTV)
Top Comedy TV Actress:  STEPHANIE COLE (Waiting..)(BBC)
Top Comedy Newcomer:  ALAN CUMMING (Bernard And..)(BBC)
Top Comedy TV Personality:                 PAUL MERTON
Top Male Comedy Performer:               RORY BREMNER
Top Female Comedy Personality:              RUBY WAX
Top New TV Comedy:                      BOTTOM (BBC2)
Best TV Com.Drama:   MURDER MOST HORRID (Talkback BBC2)
Top Presenter (BBC):                    BRUCE FORSYTH
Top Presenter (ITV):                    DES O'CONNOR
Top Presenter (C4):                    CLIVE ANDERSON
Best Ent.Ser.:   HAVE I GOT NEWS FOR YOU (Hat Trick/BBC)
Best Sit-Com (BBC):      ONE FOOT IN THE GRAVE (BBC)
Best Sit-Com (ITV):     MEN BEHAVING BADLY (Thames)
Best Sit-Com (C4):                         DESMONDS
Best New Stage Comedian:                           n/a
Top British Stand-Up Stage Performance:            n/a
Top Comedy Club Performer:                  JO BRAND
Top Stage Variety Performer:             LES DAWSON
Top Radio Comedy:                        ONE THE HOUR
Lifetime Ach. (Comedy):                    ERIC SYKES
Lifetime Ach. (Int.Comedy):                        n/a
Lifetime Ach. (Film):                              n/a
Lifetime Ach. (Stage):                             n/a
Lifetime Ach. (Telev):                             n/a
```

EVENING STANDARD BRITISH FILM AWARDS 1992

Held At The Savoy Hotel London 31 January 1993 & Hosted By Clive Anderson

```
Best Film:                HOWARDS END (Dir: James Ivory)
Best Actor: DANIEL DAY-LEWIS (The Last Of The Mohicans)
Best Actress: EMMA THOMPSON Howards End/Peter's Friends
Peter Sellers Comedy:  PETER'S FRIENDS (Dir: K.Branagh)
Best Screenplay:   TERENCE DAVIES (The Long Day Closes)
Technical Ach: SUE GIBSON (Hear My Song/Secret Friends)
Most Promising Newcomer:   PETER CHELSOM (Hear My Song)
```

EVENING STANDARD DRAMA AWARDS 1993

Held At The Savoy Hotel London 29 November 1993

```
Categories Nominated:-
Best Actor / Best Actress / Best Comedy / Best Director
Best Musical / Best Play / Most Promising Playwright
```
results to be published at a later date

IVOR NOVELLO AWARDS 1992

The Ivor Novello Awards Are Administered By The British Academy Of Songwriters Composers And Authors And Are Sp onsored By The Performing Right Society. They Were Held At The Grosvenor House Hotel London During May 1993

```
Best Cont.Song: "WOULD I LIE TO YOU" (Peter Vale-Mick
                              Leeson) CHARLES & EDDIE
Best Film Theme: "TEARS IN HEAVEN" E.Clapton-W.Jennings
Best International Hit Of The Year "WOULD I LIE TO YOU"
Best Selling A-Side: "WOULD I LIE TO YOU" (Peter Vale-
                      Mick Leeson) CHARLES & EDDIE
Best Song Musically-Lyrically: "WHY" (Annie Lennox)
Best Theme (TV): "CIVVIES" (Michael Storey)
Most Performed Work: "DEEPLY DIPPY" (Fred and Richard
             Fairbrass-Rob Manzoli) (RIGHT SAID FRED)
Outstanding Contribution To British Music:  THE HOLLIES
O/S Contemporary Song Collection:SIOBHAN FAHEY-MARCELLA
    DETROIT-DAVID A.STEWART for SHAKESPEARE'S SISTER
Songwriters Of Year:  COLIN ANGUS-RICHARD WEST (SHAMEN)
Special Award: BRYAN ADAMS-MICHAEL KAMEN-ROBERT J.LANGE
                  (Everything I Do I Do It For You)
Special Award:Internat.Achievement: ROD TEMPERTON (USA)
Special Jimmy Kennedy Award:                  LES REED
Special Lifetime Achievement:          GEORGE SHEARING
```

THE   OSCARS   1993

The 65th Annual Academy Awards - THE OSCARS Held In Hollywood, California March 1993

```
Best Film: (Directed by CLINT EASTWOOD)- THE UNFORGIVEN
Best Director:       CLINT EASTWOOD - THE UNFORGIVEN
Best Actor:           AL PACINO - SCENT OF A WOMAN
Best Actress:         EMMA THOMPSON - HOWARDS END
Best Supp.Actor:      GENE HACKMAN - THE UNFORGIVEN
Best Supp.Actress:    MARISA TOMEI - MY COUSIN VINNY
Best Orig Music Score:        (Alan Menken) ALADDIN
Best Orig Song. (A.Menken-Tim Rice) "A Whole New World"
Best Orig Screenplay:     (Neil Jordan) THE CRYING GAME
Best Adap Screenplay:(Ruth Prawer Jhabvala) HOWARDS END
Best Animated Short: 'MONA LISA DESCENDING A STAIRCASE'
Best Art Direction:                       HOWARDS END
Best Cinematography:      A RIVER RUNS THROUGH IT
Best Costume Design:      BRAM STOKER'S DRACULA
Best Editing:                THE UNFORGIVEN
Best Foreign Film:           INDOCHINE (France)
Best Make Up:            BRAM STOKER'S DRACULA
Best Sound:              LAST OF THE MOHICANS
Best Sound Effects:      BRAM STOKER'S DRACULA
Best Special Effects:        DEATH BECOMES HER
```

LAURENCE OLIVIER AWARDS 1992

Presented by The Society Of West End Theatre. Held at
The Dominion Theatre London on 18 April 1993 and trans
mitted by BBC2. Hosted by Diana Rigg-Edward Fox

```
Best Actor:       ROBERT STEPHENS (Henry IV Parts 1 & 2)
Best Actress:ALISON STEADMAN Rise & Fall O.Little Voice
Best Actor (Musical):       HENRY GOODMAN (Assassins)
Best Actress (Musical):      JOANNA RIDING (Carousel)
Best Comedy Perfor: SIMON CADELL (Travels With My Aunt)
Best Direct.(Play): STEPHEN DALDRY (An Inspector Calls)
Best Director (Musical):                    (Carousel)
Best Musical:                        CRAZY FOR YOU
Best Supp Actor:                                  n/a
Best Supp Actress:                                n/a
Comedy Of The Year:      RISE AND FALL OF LITTLE VOICE
Observer (Kenneth Tynan) Award:                   n/a
O/S Achievement (Dance):  THE JUDAS TREE (Royal Ballet)
O/S Achievement (Opera):      STIFFELIO (Royal Opera)
O/S Ent.Of The Year:                              n/a
O/S Revival (Musical):                       CAROUSEL
O/S Revival (Play):  AN INSPECTOR CALLS (J.B.Priestley)
O/S Supp.Role In Musical:       CLIVE ROWE (CAROUSEL)
Play Of The Year:SIX DEGREES OF SEPARATION (John Guare)
Special Award: (Posthumously awarded) KENNETH MACMILLAN
```

SONG FOR EUROPE 1993 (BBC TV)
BBC Television Centre 9 April 1993 / Terry Wogan
Winning Order / Song Title / Performing Artist / Points

```
1 - BETTER THE DEVIL YOU KNOW         SONIA - 156955
2 - OUR WORLD                         SONIA -  77695
3 - SO MUCH OF YOUR LOVE              SONIA -  70454
4 - A LITTLE LOVE                     SONIA -  55053
5 - LIFE AFTER LOVE                   SONIA -  38308
6 - I'M GONNA PUT A SPELL ON YOU      SONIA -  27795
7 - TRUST                             SONIA -  26745
8 - IT'S JUST A MATTER OF TIME        SONIA -  18251
```

The Winning Song Of The Above Competition "Better The
Devil You Know" written by Dean Collinson and Red and
performed by Sonia, Then Went On To Represent The UK
in The...

EUROVISION SONG CONTEST 1993

1993 Eurovision Song Contest Held In Co.Cork,Ireland on
15th May 1993 Transmitted By BBC1 TV and BBC Radio 2

25 Countries Took Part In The 1993 Eurovision Song Cont
est...Results Over The Page

EUROVISION SONG CONTEST 1993

Final Order / Country / Song / Artist / Points Scored

```
1 -  IRELAND "In Your Eyes" (J.Walsh) NIAMH KAVANAGH 187
2 -  U.KINGDOM "Better The Devil You Know"      SONIA 164
3 -  SWITZERLAND "Quite Simply Me"       ANNIE COTTON 148
4 -  FRANCE "Mama Corsica"              PATRICK FLORI 121
5 -  NORWAY "All My Thoughts"             SILJE VIGE 120
6 -  HOLLAND "Einstein In Reverse"       RUTH JACOTT  92
7 -  SWEDEN "Eloise"                       ARVINGARNA  89
8 -  MALTA "This Time"             WILLIAM MANGION  69
9 -  GREECE "Greece Land Of Light"   KATERINA GARBI  64
10-  PORTUGAL "Nightfall In The City"       ANABELA  60
11-  SPAIN "Men"                   EVAN SANTAMARIA  58
12-  ITALY "The Sun Of Europe"     ENRICO RUGGERI  45
13-  ICELAND "You'll Know The Answer"         INGA  42
14-  AUSTRIA "Maria Magdalena"          TONY WEGAS  32
15-  CROATIA "Don't Ever Cry"                  PUT  31
16-  BOSNIA-HERZGOVINA"Pain Of The Whole World"FAZLA  27
17-  FINLAND "Come To Me"           KATRI-HELENA  20
18-  GERMANY "Far Away"      MUNCHENER FREIHEIT  18
19-  CYPRUS "Don't Stop"    KYRIAKOS ZYMBOULAKIS  17
20-  LUXEMBOURG "Heaven Only Knows"    MODERN TIMES  11
21-  TURKEY "My Brunette My Love"   BURAK AYDOS etc.  10
22-  DENMARK "Beneath T.Stars I.T.Sky" TOMMY SEEBACH   9
22-  SLOVENIA   "Quiet Rainy Day"         IX BAND   9
24-  ISRAEL "Sing A Song"            SHIRU GROUP   4
25-  BELGIUM "Somebody Like You"          BARBARA   3
```

*RECORDING DETAILS OF BOTH THE WINNING SONG AND UK ENTRY
SEE 'EUROVISION SONG CONTEST 1993' ON PAGE 76 (TV SECT)*

SEE 'EUROVISION SONG CONTEST 1993' ON PAGE 76 (TV SECT)

VARIETY CLUB OF GREAT BRITAIN AWARDS 1992

*Variety Club Awards Held At London Hilton On 3 February
1993. Hosted By Judi Spiers and Alan Titchmarsh / BBC1*

```
BBC Radio Personality: (BBC Radio 2)   GLORIA HUNNIFORD
BBC Television Personality:        PATRICIA ROUTLEDGE
Film Actor:                         DANIEL DAY-LEWIS
Film Actress:                          EMMA THOMPSON
Independent Radio Personality:     (LBC) MIKE DICKIN
ITV Personality:                   MICHAEL BARRYMORE
Outstanding New Talent:                LESLIE GARRETT
Recording Artist:                        ERIC CLAPTON
Show Business Personality:         PHILLIP SCHOFIELD
Stage Actor:                           PETER O'TOOLE
Stage Actress:                        MAUREEN LIPMAN
Variety Club Special Award:   SIR RICHARD ATTENBOROUGH
```

UPSTAIRS DOWNSTAIR	131	
URSUS	241	
US GIRLS	131	
USED PEOPLE	241	
UTU	241	
UTTERLY BRILLIANT	131	
V...The Series	131	
VAGRANT	241	
VALERIE	131	
VALMOUTH	241	
VALUED OPINION	131	
VAMP	242	
VAMPIRE CIRCUS	242,297	
VAMPIRE LOVERS	242	
VAMPYR: Soap Opera	131	
VAN DAMME, Jean Cl	297	
VAN DER VALK	131	
VANGELIS	298	
VANISH	49	
VANISHING The	242	
VANITY FAIR	131	
VANITY FAIR MAGAZI	49	
VANTAGE CHEMISTS	49	
VARIETY CLUB AWARD	314	
VAUXHALL	49	
VELVET CLAW The	131	
VENEZIA PERFUME	49	
VENOS	50	
VENTURERS The	131	
VERDICT IS YOURS	131	
VERONIKA VOSS	242	
VERTIGO	242	
VERY BRITISH COUP	131	
VERY GOOD EDDIE	242	
VERY JEAN MUIR	131	
VERY PECULIAR PRAC	131	
VERY POLISH PRACTI	131	
VET SCHOOL	131	
VET'S IN THE WILD	131	
VEUVE DU VERNAY PER	50	
VIC REEVES BIG NIG	131	
VICTOR AND HUGO	132	
VICTOR The	242	
VICTORIA WOOD AS S	132	
VICTORIAN KITCHEN	132	
VICTORY AT SEA	132,298	
VIDAL SASSOON	50	
VIDEO DIARIES	132	
VIDEO FANTASIES	132	
VIDEO VIEW	132	
VIETNAM	132	
VIEW The	132	
VIEW TO A KILL	242	
VILEDA	50	
VIMTO	50	
VIN DE PAYS	50	
VIOLENT STREETS	242	
VIRGINIAN The	132	
VIRTUAL MURDER	132	
VIRTUE IN DANGER	242	
VISION QUEST	242	
VISION THING The	132	
VISIONS	132	
VISIT The	132	
VISITOR The	242	
VITTEL	50	
VITALITE	50	
VIVA LAS VEGAS	242	
VIVE LA DIFFERENCE	132	
VODAPHONE	50	
VOLKSWAGEN	50	
VOYAGE OF TERROR	242	
VOYAGE OF T.DAMNED	242	
VOYAGE TO THE BOTT	132	
VOYAGER	242	
WAGES OF FEAR	242	
WAGON TRAIN	132	
WAGON WHEELS	50	
WAITING FOR GOD	132	
WALDEN	132	
WALDMAN'S	50	
WALK DON'T RUN	242	
WALK O.T.WILD	132,242	
WALK THE TALK	132	
WALKABOUT	242	
WALKERS SNACKS	50,51	
WALL OF SILENCE	133	
WALL The	133,242	
WALL STREET	242	
WALNUT WHIP	51	
WALLS ICE CREAM	51	
WALT DISNEY FILMS	304	
WALTONS The	133	
WANDERERS The	243	
WAR AND REMEMBRANC	133	
WAR OF THE WORLDS	133	
WAR REQUIEM	243	
WAR STORIES	133	
WARLOCK	243	
WARNING SIGN	243	
WARSAW CONCERTO	298	
WARTIME KITCHEN A	133	
WATCHING	133	
WATER UNDER THE BR	133	
WATER WARS	133	
WATERWAYS	133	
WATT ON EARTH	133	
WAX CRACKS HOLLYW	133	
WAXMAN, Franz	266,276,293	
WAY AHEAD The	133	
WAY WE WERE The	243	
WAYNE'S WORLD	243	
WE OF THE NEVER NE	243	
WE'LL MEET AGAIN	133	
WEB OF THE SPIDER	243	
WEBB, Marti	278,286	
WEDDING BANQUET	243	
WEDLOCK	243	
WEDNESDAY WEEPIE	133	
WEEK IN POLITICS	133	
WEEKEND WORLD	133	
WEETABIX	51	
WEIGHT WATCHERS	51	
WELCOME BACK KOTTE	133	
WELCOME HOME ROXY	243	
WENDERS, Wim	287	
WENDY CRACKED A WA	243	
WEST SIDE STORY	243	
WESTBEACH	133	
WETHERBY	244	
WETTER THE BETTER	133	
WEXFORD TRILOGY	133	
WHALES OF AUGUST	244	
WHAT A CRAZY WORLD	244	
WHAT ABOUT LUV	244	
WHAT SHALL WE TELL	133	
WHAT THE PAPERS SA	133	
WHAT YOU LOOKIN' A	133	
WHAT'S ON MAGAZINE	51	
WHAT'S UP DOC	133	
WHAT'S UP TIGER LI	244	
WHEN HARRY MEET SA	244	
WHEN IN GERMANY	133	
WHEN THE BOAT COME	134	
WHEN THE WHALES CA	244	
WHEN THE WIND BLOW	244	
WHERE IN THE WORLD	134	
WHERE THERE'S LIFE	134	
WHERE'S CHARLEY	244	
WHERE'S WALLY	134	
WHICH WITCH	244	
WHICKER'S WORLD	134	
WHILE I LIVE	244	
WHIPSNADE ZOO	51	
WHISKAS	51	
WHISPERS IN T.DARK	244	
WHISTLE BLOWER The	244	
WHISTLE DOWN T.WIN	244	
WHISTLE TEST	134	
WHITBREADS	51	
WHITE CHRISTMAS	244	
WHITE MEN CAN'T J	244	
WHITE MISCHIEF	244	
WHITE PALACE	244	
WHITE ROCK	244	
WHITE SANDS	245	
WHITE SHADOW	134	
WHITE TRIBE OF AFR	134	
WHO CARES	134	
WHO PAYS THE FERRY	134	
WHO PLAYS WINS	245	
WHO'S BLUFFING WHO	134	
WHO'S THAT GIRL	245	
WHO'S THE MAN	245	
WHOSE LINE IS IT A	134	
WHS	51	
WIDE AWAKE CLUB	134	
WIDE EYED & LEGLES	134	
WIDOWS	134	
WILD AT HEART	245	
WILD BUNCH The	299	
WILD DUCK	245	
WILD INDIA	134	
WILD IS THE WIND	245	
WILD ORCHID	245